**H. acids, $R-CO_2H$**

$C_6H_5CO_2H$ — benzoic acid

$CH_3CO_2H$ — acetic acid

**I. acid derivatives**

1. di-and substituted acids

$CH_2(CO_2H)_2$ — malonic acid

$CH_3CH(OH)CO_2H$ — lactic acid

2. acid chlorides, $R-COCl$

$CH_3COCl$ — acetyl chloride

$C_6H_5COBr$ — benzoyl bromide

3. esters, $RCO_2R'$

$CH_3CO_2CH_3$ — methyl acetate

$C_6H_5CO_2CH_2CH_3$ — ethyl benzoate

$CH_3O_2C-C\equiv C-CO_2CH_3$ — dimethyl acetylenedicarboxylate

4. amides, $RCONH_2$

$CH_3CONH_2$ — acetamide

5. anhydrides, $R-CO-O-CO-R'$

$CH_3CO-O-COCH_3$ — acetic anhydride

$CH_3CO-O-COC_6H_5$ — acetic benzoic anhydride

maleic anhydride

6. nitriles (cyanides), $R-CN$

$CH_3CN$ — acetonitrile (methyl cyanide)

**J. aromatic nitro compounds, $Ar-NO_2$**

$C_6H_5NO_2$ — nitrobenzene

**K. amines**

1. primary (1°), $R-\ddot{N}H_2$

$CH_3\ddot{N}H_2$ — methylamine

$C_6H_5\ddot{N}H_2$ — aniline

NMR Shifts
F - 3.2
Cl - 2.2
Br - 1.9
I - 1.5

2. secondary (2°), $R_2\ddot{N}H$

$C_6H_5\ddot{N}HCH_3$ — *N*-methylaniline

3. Tertiary (3°), $R_3\ddot{N}$

$(CH_3)_2\ddot{N}CH_2CH_3$ — dimethylethylamine

pyridine

4. quaternary ammonium salts (4° salts), $R_4N^+$

$(CH_3)_4\overset{+}{N}\overset{-}{O}H$ — tetramethylammonium hydroxide

**L. diazonium compounds (salts), $Ar-N_2^+$**

$C_6H_5N_2^+Cl^-$ — benzenediazonium

**M. amino acids, $R$**

$(NH_2)$

$CH_2(NH_2)CO_2H$ — glycine

$CH_3CH(NH_2)CO_2H$ — alanine

# MODERN ORGANIC CHEMISTRY

# Modern Organic Chemistry

**Rodger W. Griffin Jr.**
Professor of Chemistry
New College
Sarasota, Florida

**McGraw-Hill Book Company**
New York St. Louis San Francisco London Sydney Toronto Mexico Panama

**Modern Organic Chemistry**



*Library of Congress Catalog Card Number*
69-12260

24779

1 2 3 4 5 6 7 8 9 0 H D B P 7 6 5 4 3 2 1 0 6 9

# Preface

This text is the result of my teaching experience with premedical and other nonmajor students at Harvard and the University of California (Berkeley), with appropriate modifications of teaching techniques due to the unique nature of the curriculum at New College. Although this text is designed for the nonmajor, every effort has been made to discuss mechanistic and synthetic organic chemistry rather than simply to present material ''about'' chemistry. A good foundation in these principles of organic chemistry will provide today's student with the *understanding* needed in his future career. A few industrial and medical applications of organic reactions are presented in the problems; however, discussion of applications has been limited, and the teacher is encouraged to provide examples from his own teaching and research experiences.

Aliphatic and aromatic chemistry have been integrated; examples have also been drawn from heterocyclic and organometallic chemistry. The material selected will illustrate chemical principles, which are repeated, elaborated, and interwoven throughout the text. All who teach organic chemistry are familiar with the problems of presenting it as a coherent, whole body of knowledge, particularly during the early weeks of study, when many new terms and concepts must be introduced. This text encourages the student to review previous material continually and to place the earlier chapters in their proper context. The necessary chemical abbreviations are introduced and used from the outset.

The book is organized into three parts: Part One: Hydrocarbons and Halides (Chaps. 1 to 8), Part Two: Oxygen- and Nitrogen-containing Organic Compounds (Chaps. 9 to 16), Part Three: Organic Compounds of Biological Interest (Chaps. 17 to 21). Only the common functional groups have been included, although reference is made to some others, such as ketenes and isocyanates. Of the various special topics which might have been suitable for Part Three, those chosen reflect the interests of many nonmajor students of organic chemistry and those of the author.

My experience has been that beginning organic chemistry is difficult for many students, especially those for whom chemistry is of peripheral interest. The addition of spectroscopy would be a burden under which many might falter. Unless students have the opportunity to use spectroscopic techniques in the laboratory constantly, interpretation simply becomes a matter of searching through masses of empirical data in reference books. Consequently, I have chosen to omit spectroscopic methods, relying on the individual teacher to provide whatever details will be appropriate for his particular class.

Even with the moderate choice of material many teachers will find more than they wish to cover in the allotted time. The following chapters can be omitted or mentioned briefly without a loss in continuity: Chap. 6 (Dienes and Polymerization), Chap. 10 (Phenols), Chap. 11 (Ethers), Chap. 15 (Derivatives of Carboxylic Acids), and the sections on diazonium salts in Chap. 16. Additional omissions can be made within the chapters retained in order to allow time for the chapters in Part Three.

For all errors of omission and commission, I bear the sole responsibility. I wish to thank the many students, colleagues, reviewers, editors, and typists who have been so generous with their time and abilities. Many students at the University of California took hours out of an already busy schedule to form a book committee that provided valuable constructive criticism during the summer of 1965. I would like to thank Prof. J. Deyrup (University of Florida), Prof. R. Olafson (Pennsylvania State), and Dr. A. Rosowsky (Children's Cancer Hospital) for their respective reviews of Parts One to Three. I thank especially Dr. Graham Solomons, of the University of South Florida, who read the entire manuscript in detail. I am grateful to Mrs. Ruth Croci and her staff, at the University of California, and to Mrs. Nancy Hall, of New College, for their expertise in typing the manuscript in its various forms over the past four years, and to Mrs. Mary Gall, who typed the final manuscript copy.

*Rodger W. Griffin Jr.*

# To the Student

This book has been written for you. It has been written not only to impart knowledge of organic chemistry but also to help you make that knowledge yours. Unlike history or philosophy, chemistry cannot profitably be read chapter by chapter but must be vigorously attacked with a dozen sharp pencils and a ream of inexpensive paper close at hand. Included in the body of the text are many questions and problems. Some are answered immediately; others are signposts of later subject material. You should attempt to answer these questions when they appear, so that the subsequent material will be more meaningful. The problems at the end of each chapter are an integral part of the text. Solve them all; you will not need to resort to memorization. When information is used to solve problems, it rapidly becomes part of your knowledge. It is much easier and more profitable to spend time in *understanding* organic chemistry than to memorize a mass of uncorrelated facts.

Students who have used preliminary versions of the manuscript have repeatedly emphasized that molecular models, particularly the framework molecular-orbital models, are indispensable for acquiring an accurate picture of molecular geometry. Many students have commented that a thorough understanding of Chaps. 1 and 2 at the outset builds self-confidence and provides a sound basis for studying the remaining chapters.

Since this is *your* book, your criticisms, comments, and corrections will be welcomed so that any errors or misprints that may have slipped through can be corrected in succeeding printings.

*Rodger W. Griffin Jr.*

# Contents

## PART II OXYGEN- AND NITROGEN-CONTAINING ORGANIC COMPOUNDS

# Part One: Hydrocarbons and Halides

# Chapter One

You are embarking on a course of study which originated in man's curiosity about the constituents of natural materials around him, such as the coloring matter in leaves and flowers, plant and animal poisons, the components of coal and oil, and the chemicals of which man's body is composed and which are transformed by natural processes. Early workers not only isolated pure chemical substances from these natural sources but also determined their chemical composition, carried out reactions with them, and learned to synthesize them in the laboratory from nonliving materials. Many principles of chemistry have been elucidated in these studies. Today the field of organic chemistry, with its relationship to biology, agriculture, medicine, and other areas, provides a fascinating livelihood for thousands of persons throughout the world. The principles and experimental observations of organic chemistry do not change, although they are sometimes modified or reinterpreted, but specific applications of organic compounds change constantly. Therefore we shall emphasize principles rather than applications, although the latter will be used when appropriate in examples and problems.

## INORGANIC AND ORGANIC CHEMISTRY

Inorganic chemistry deals with all 103 elements, but the principles are often demonstrated with about the first 70. Organic chemistry focuses on the carbon atom and the compounds it forms with mainly the first 20 elements and especially hydrogen, oxygen, and nitrogen. *Organic chemistry* is not formally defined here. By the end of the course you will have arrived at your own definition of these words. Although frequently it has been defined as "the chemistry of carbon compounds," this rather vague, general phrase is better replaced later by one based on your own experience. Since there are more than a million com-

# Review and Background

pounds containing carbon, we cannot profitably spend time examining each separately; instead we shall study the correlations and generalizations made possible by such detailed studies. These correlations rest ultimately on experimental facts.

The main portion of this text discusses classes of organic compounds which are similar because a carbon atom is attached to a common group of atoms such as —OH, —Cl, —$NO_2$, etc. The questions we shall answer about these classes of compounds are: How are they named? What are their chemical and physical properties? How can they be synthesized? What reactions do they undergo? *How* do they undergo these reactions? By what properties or reactions can one class of organic molecules be distinguished from other classes? What are the sources of these compounds, and how are they used? The last five chapters discuss classes of compounds that are of special interest and biological significance.

As the body of scientific knowledge in chemistry, physics, and biology grows, rigid distinctions between the classical branches become more difficult to define. The older divisions of inorganic, analytical, organic, physical, and nuclear chemistry have given birth to interdisciplinary areas such as organometallic, physical organic, and bioorganic chemistry. These somewhat artificial divisions have also begun to weaken; the boundary between organic chemistry and biochemistry is often difficult to draw, if it even exists! You have already studied general inorganic chemistry and recognize many of the common chemical names and symbols. Since many elementary chemical terms will not be explained here, you should refer to your general chemistry text for any that are not familiar. The inorganic chemistry needed to understand organic reactions will be mentioned at the appropriate place in the text.

Most high-school and first-year college chemistry courses dwell on the principles of chemistry using examples from inorganic chemistry. For this reason, Table 1-1 compares some inorganic criteria with organic ones. **You must remember that there are exceptions to every entry** in Table 1-1. Organometallic compounds, which contain both metal and carbon atoms, do not necessarily have properties midway between those listed for inorganic and organic compounds. Of the criteria listed, the one of particular concern in this chapter is bonding; the others will be discussed later.

**Table 1-1**
**Comparison of inorganic and organic chemistry**[†]

| *Criterion* | *Inorganic* | *Organic* |
|---|---|---|
| elements involved | all 103 | relatively few (mainly C, H, O, N, S, P, F, Cl, Br, I) |
| bonding | ionic | covalent (shared electron pairs) |
| rates of reaction: | | |
| at room temperature | fast | slow |
| at higher temperatures | very fast | moderately fast to explosive |
| catalyst required? | no | yes, often |
| mechanism of reaction | usually ionic | ionic, free-radical, and others |
| side reactions | no, many are quantitative | yes, nearly always |
| physical properties: | | |
| conductivity of salts | electrolytes | nonelectrolytes |
| melting point | > 700° | < 300° |
| volatility | nonvolatile | readily distilled (often at low pressure) |
| solubility: | | |
| in water | yes | no |
| in nonaqueous organic solvents | no | yes |
| electrical conduction in solutions and melts | yes | no |

[†] There are exceptions to every entry in this table.

## ELECTRONIC STRUCTURE OF ATOMS

The periodic table classes the known elements in a systematic manner based on the increasing number of protons (and thus electrons) in the

**Table 1-2**
**A short periodic table**

| *Group* | 0 | I | II | III | IV | V | VI | VII |
|---|---|---|---|---|---|---|---|---|
| | | H | | | | | | |
| | He | Li | Be | B | C | N | O | (F) |
| | Ne | Na | Mg | Al | Si | P | S | Cl |
| | Ar | K | Ca | | | | Se | Br |
| | Kr | Rb | | | | | | I |
| | Xe | Cs | | | | | | |

neutral atom. Table 1-2 shows a small portion of the periodic table. Although only about one-quarter of the elements are listed, they will be of principal concern here. The group 0 elements are included only to show their relationship to the other elements. The symbols for carbon and hydrogen appear in color because these two elements form the backbone of organic chemistry. Fluorine has been placed in parentheses, even though it is a halogen, since fluorocarbon compounds and reactions differ from other halocarbon chemistry. **In this text, the term halogen will generally exclude fluorine.**

## 1-1 ELECTRONIC STRUCTURE

Starting with hydrogen and proceeding from left to right in the periodic table, each new element has one more electron and one more proton than the previous element, and sufficient neutrons to make up the appropriate atomic mass. Two or more atoms that contain the same number of protons but different numbers of neutrons are ***isotopes***.

In this text, we shall study the interactions of electrons binding carbon to other atoms. The electrons associated with an atom are found in shells designated 1, 2, 3, . . ., and these, in turn, are composed of ***orbitals***. Electrons do not move in fixed orbits but are expected to be found in a given volume. Although the Heisenberg uncertainty principle states that it is impossible to determine precisely both the position and momentum of a particle, we can consider volumes (orbitals) in which the probability of finding the electron is about 0.99. These orbitals are designated *s*, *p*, *d*, or *f*, according to the type of line (*s*harp, *p*rinciple, *d*iffuse, or *f*undamental) that they produce in an x-ray spectrum. Although each orbital can contain two electrons with opposite spins, they are very differently shaped. The *s* orbitals are spherically symmetric about the nucleus, whereas the *p* orbitals may be described as dumbbell-shaped. The *d* and *f* orbitals, which are unimportant for the first-row elements, have more complex geometries.

Each shell contains one more type of orbital than the preceding shell. The first shell (numbered 1) consists of a single *s* orbital, denoted 1*s*.

The second shell contains $s$ and $p$ orbitals, denoted $2s$ and $2p$; the third shell contains $3s$, $3p$, and $3d$ orbitals. For a given shell, there is only one $s$ orbital, but there are three $p$ orbitals, five $d$ orbitals, and seven $f$ orbitals in each shell having orbitals of these types.

| Type of atomic orbital: | $s$ | $p$ | $d$ | $f$ |
|---|---|---|---|---|
| Number of orbitals: | 1 | 3 | 5 | 7 |

The electronic structure of shells is summarized in Table 1-3. Recall that each orbital may contain two electrons. The so-called *magic numbers* of 2 electrons (first shell), 8 (second shell), and 18 (third shell) are derived from these orbital considerations.

**Table 1-3 Electronic shells and orbitals**

| *Shell* | | | *Orbitals* | | *Number of electrons* |
|---|---|---|---|---|---|
| 4 | — $4s$ | — — — $4p$ | — — — — — $4d$ | — — — — — — — $4f$ | 32 |
| 3 | — $3s$ | — — — $3p$ | — — — — — $3d$ | | 18 |
| 2 | — $2s$ | — — — $2p$ | | | 8 |
| 1 | — $1s$ | | | | 2 |

## 1-2 THE ATOMIC-ORBITAL REPRESENTATION OF THE FIRST TEN ELEMENTS

To show the electronic basis of the periodic table clearly, the atomic-orbital representation of the first 10 elements will be discussed in this section. Bear in mind that hydrogen, carbon, nitrogen, and oxygen are the atoms most often bound to carbon in organic molecules.

**Hydrogen, H:** The first element, hydrogen, has atomic number 1. An atom of hydrogen has only one electron, which may be represented as a sphere with the probability of finding the electron indicated by the density of shading (Fig. 1-1). For convenience the sphere can be projected into a circle that encloses the volume of highest probability. Note that the circle is *not* the path traveled by the electron but rather defines the area in which the electron is most likely to be found. The electron in the hydrogen atom is denoted $(1s)^1$, where the superscript

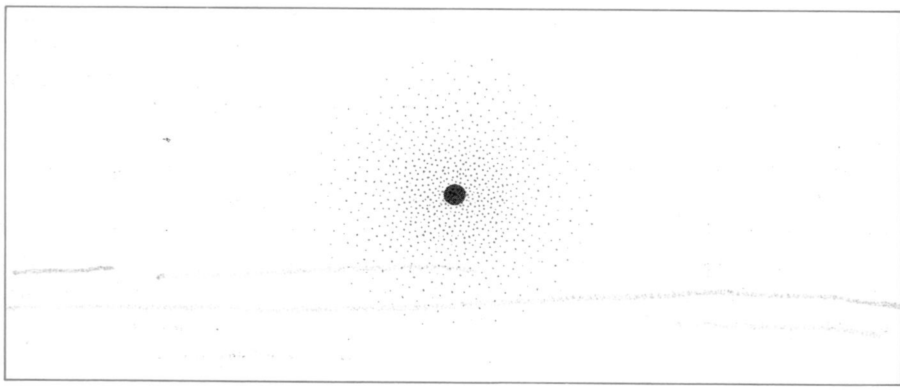

**Figure 1-1 Electron density of the hydrogen atom, the 1*s* orbital: the nucleus is represented by the dot at the center**

indicates that one electron is found in the 1*s* orbital. The hydrogen atom is sometimes represented as H·; removal of the single electron from the hydrogen atom leaves the hydrogen ion, or proton, $H^+$ (Fig. 1-2).

The geometry of molecular orbitals will be presented later, but to a first approximation one can draw a molecule of hydrogen, $H_2$, using what we shall call the *isolated-atom molecule*, as shown in Fig. 1-3.

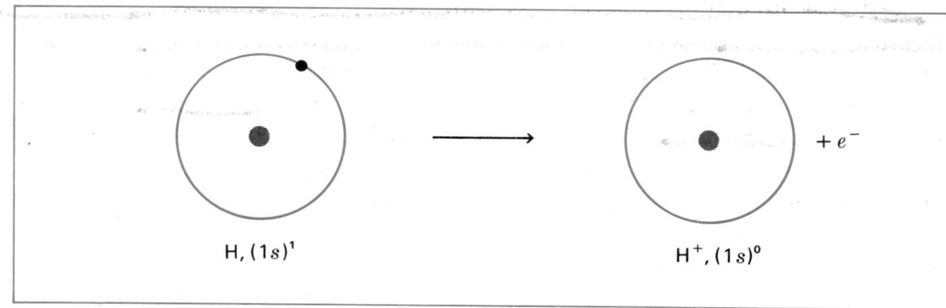


**Figure 1-2 Ionization of the hydrogen atom**

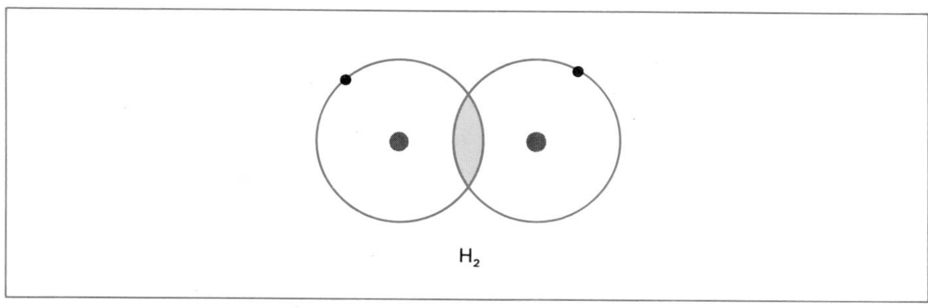


**Figure 1-3 Isolated-atom molecule of hydrogen**

The two simple hydrogen atoms are drawn together so that their orbitals overlap, but no further refinements are made. This model simply indicates the atomic orbitals involved, but it does not give an accurate picture of the newly formed orbitals of the hydrogen molecule.

**Helium, He:** Addition of an electron and proton (and the appropriate number of neutrons) to the hydrogen atom produces a picture of the helium atom. This process fills not only the first electron orbital (1*s*) but also the first shell, since the first shell *is* the 1*s* orbital. Total ionization of the helium atom gives the ion, $He^{++}$, also called an ***alpha particle*** (see Fig. 1-4).

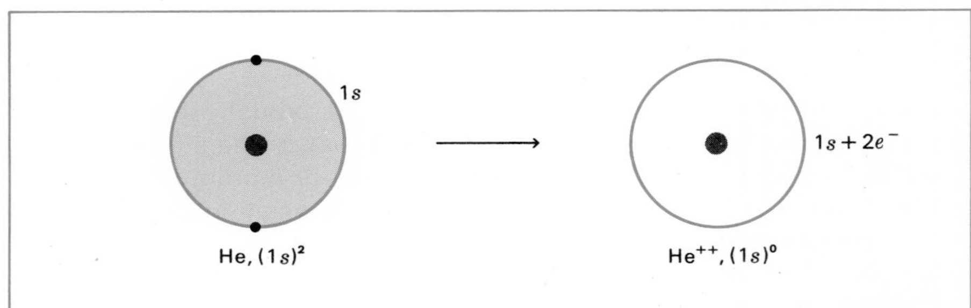


**Figure 1-4 Formation of $He^{++}$, an alpha particle**

Elements in which a shell (not just an orbital) is filled are found in group 0 of the periodic table and are called ***rare gases***. Energies higher than those encountered in common chemical reactions are required to remove electrons from a rare gas. The older term for these elements, inert gases, has been rendered obsolete by the discovery that under appropriate conditions relatively stable compounds of the higher members of this series can be formed. This is especially true of xenon, Xe, which forms fluorides such as $XeF_2$, $XeF_4$, and $XeF_6$ by direct combination with fluorine.

**Lithium, Li:** In lithium (atomic number 3) the 1*s* orbital is completely filled. Like the hydrogen atom, lithium contains one outer electron;

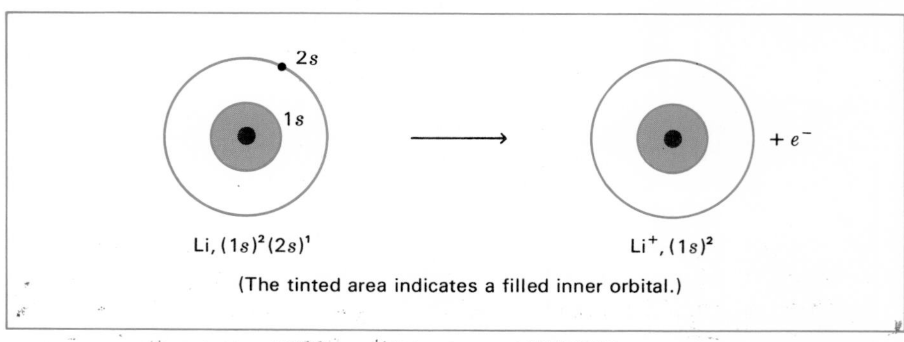


(The tinted area indicates a filled inner orbital.)

**Figure 1-5 Ionization of the lithium atom**

the $2s$ electron is readily lost to an electron acceptor, leaving a lithium ion with the same electronic configuration as helium: $Li^+$, $(1s)^2$ (see Fig. 1-5). Atoms or ions that have the same electronic configuration are termed isoelectronic. The lithium ion is isoelectronic with the helium atom and the hydride ion, $H^-$, $(1s)^2$.

**Beryllium, Be:** The $2s$ orbital is filled by the addition of another electron to the system to give the electronic configuration $(1s)^2(2s)^2$, but beryllium is not a rare gas because the second shell also contains $p$ orbitals that are vacant in the neutral beryllium atom (see Fig. 1-6).

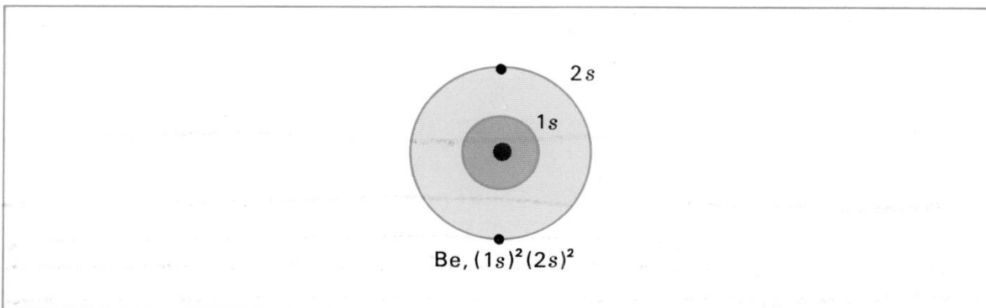


**Figure 1-6 Electronic configuration of the beryllium atom**

**Boron, B:** Although the $s$ orbitals are spherical, the three equivalent $p$ orbitals are dumbbell-shaped volumes directed at 90° to each other along the three axes of a cartesian coordinate system (Fig. 1-7). These

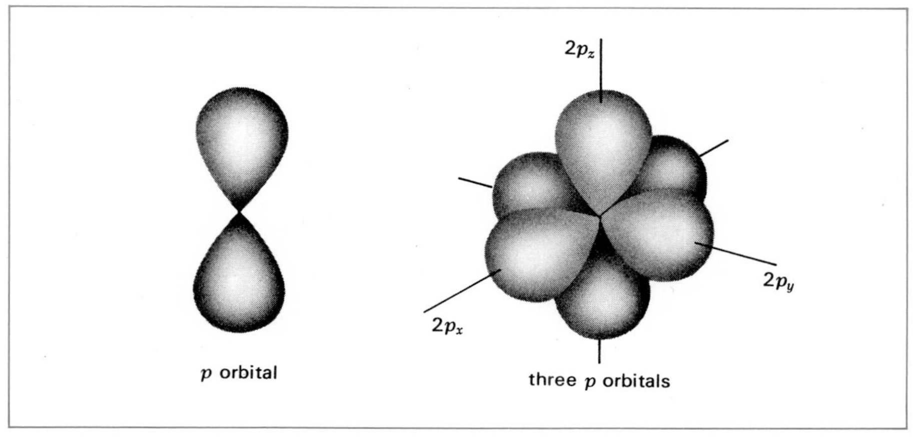


**Figure 1-7 Electron density of filled $p$ orbitals**

orbitals do not overlap. Again, a projection is more convenient than the three-dimensional representation. The $p$-orbital axes have been arbitrarily labeled $2p_x$, $2p_y$, and $2p_z$ (the $2p_z$ lies perpendicular to the plane of the page). The single $p$ electron of boron may be in either

Figure 1-8 Electronic configuration of the boron atom

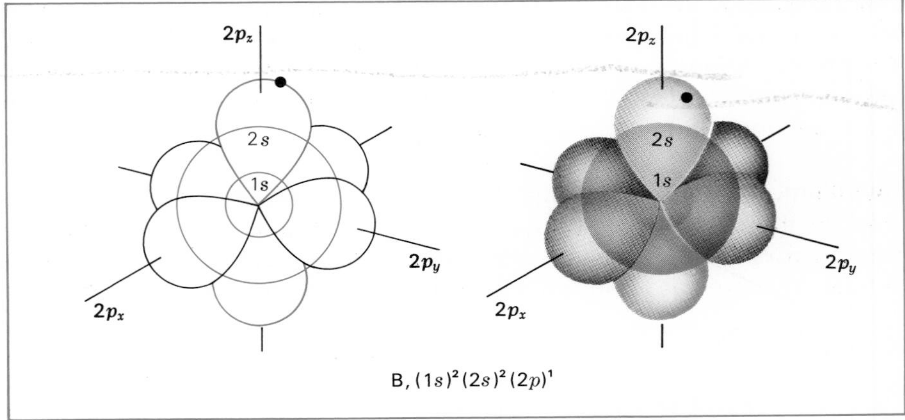


lobe of any of these equivalent orbitals; these lobes are equivalent (see Fig. 1-8).

The $p$ orbitals in a given shell are of slightly higher energy than the $s$ orbital. This is represented diagrammatically by extending the tip of the $2p$ orbital slightly beyond the radius of the $2s$ orbital. The difference in energy between the $1s$ and the $2s$ orbitals is much greater than that between the $2s$ and $2p$ orbitals because the energy difference between two shells is greater than that between two orbitals in the same shell.

**Carbon, C:** Because of the repulsion between electrons, the second $2p$ electron in the isolated carbon atom is found in an orbital (volume) different from the first $2p$ electron. Since a given $p$ orbital has two equivalent lobes, the two diagrammatic representations of the carbon atom in Fig. 1-9 are equivalent.

Figure 1-9 Electronic configuration of the carbon atom

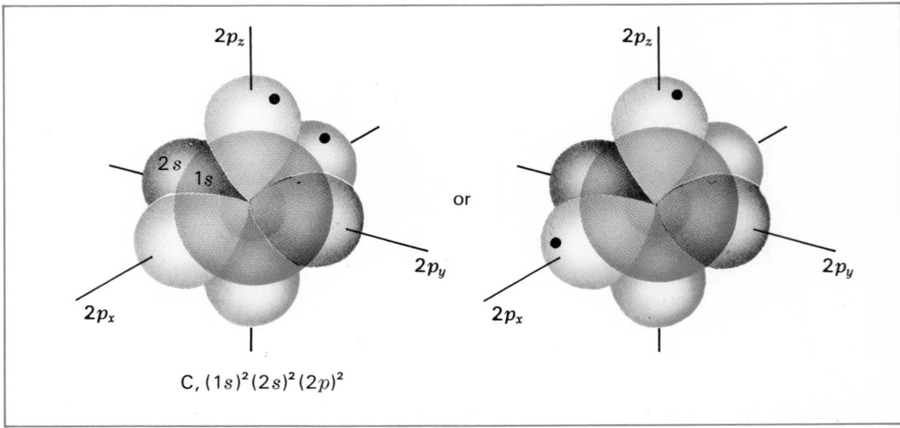


Because electrons act as rotating charges, they create a small magnetic field, the direction of which cannot be determined in the absence of an external magnetic field. However, when electrons are placed in such an external field $H_0$ these small electron magnetic components $H_e$ either add to the large field or subtract from it. Electron spins are *parallel* if they are in the same direction and *paired* if they are in opposite directions (see Fig. 1-10). For a given number of electrons in

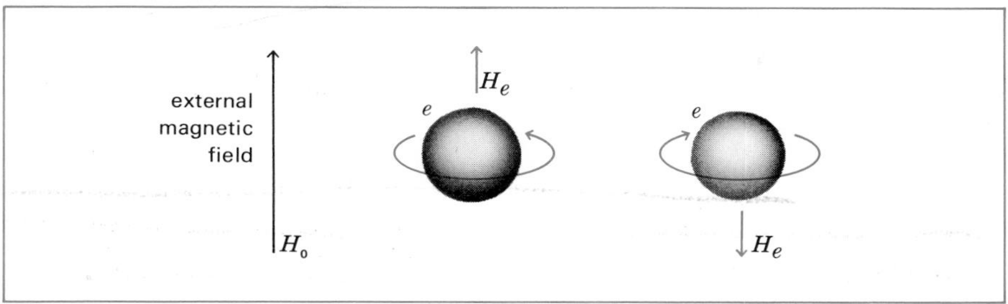


**Figure 1-10 Paired electrons in an external magnetic field**

orbitals of equivalent energy the lowest energy state is described by the electronic configuration in which all electron spins are parallel, if such a configuration is possible (***Hund's rule***). In the case of $s$ orbitals, two paired electrons fill the available orbital in a given shell. However, the three $p$ orbitals ($p_x$, $p_y$, $p_z$) must be filled as symmetrically as possible, with regard to electron spin. Therefore the electronic configuration of the isolated carbon atom is $(1s)^2$ $(2s)^2$ $(2p)^2$.

**Nitrogen N:** The electronic configuration of the nitrogen atom, $(1s)^2$, $(2s)^2$, $2p_x$, $2p_y$, $2p_z$, follows from what has been stated previously about the buildup of atoms (see Fig. 1-11).

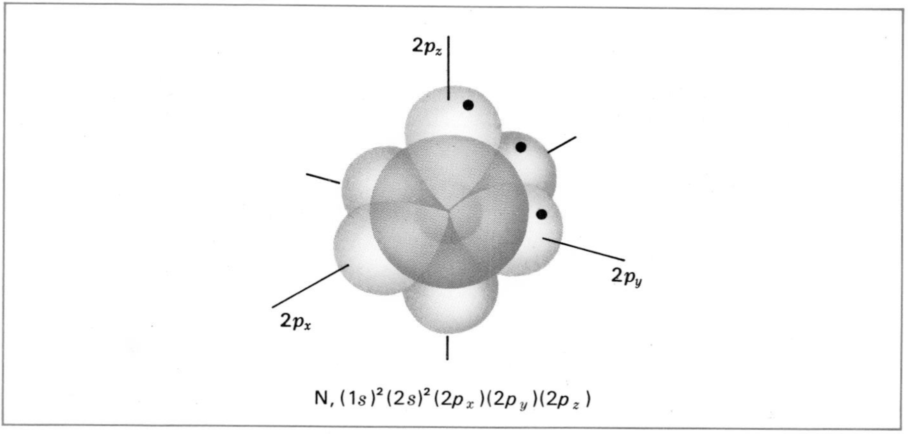


**Figure 1-11 Electronic configuration of the nitrogen atom**

Construct the ammonia molecule, $NH_3$, as the isolated-atom molecule (in the manner described for $H_2$). What is the predicted approximate H—N—H angle?

A reasonable prediction of the H—N—H bond angle in $NH_3$ from this simplified picture would be 90°. Or, taking into account the repulsion between hydrogen atoms, one might have predicted angles a little greater than 90°. Of course, the actual geometry of the ammonia molecule is not so simple as this crude picture predicts, because simple atomic orbitals undergo a change when forming chemical bonds. The value for the bond angles obtained from a detailed study of the molecular structure is 107° and reflects the orbital change that occurs when atoms form bonds.

**Oxygen, O:** In the oxygen atom two of the four $p$ electrons must occupy the same orbital and must have paired spins; this configuration can be drawn in three equivalent ways; one is shown in Fig. 1-12.

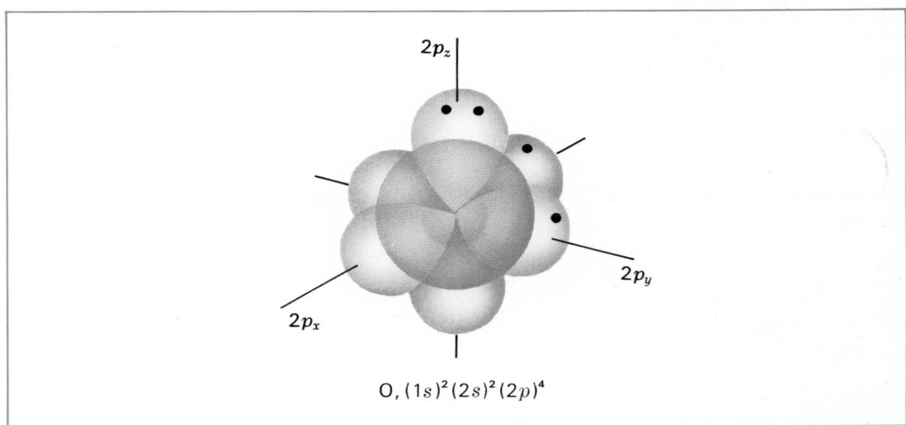


**Figure 1-12 Electronic configuration of the oxygen atom**

Draw the isolated-atom-molecule picture for water, $H_2O$.

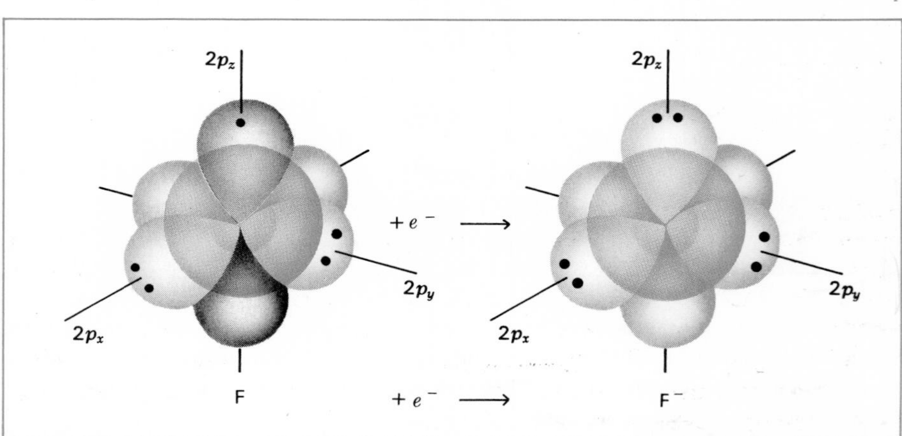


**Figure 1-13 Formation of the fluoride ion**

**Fluorine, F:** The fluorine atom, having seven electrons in the outer shell, needs only one additional electron to complete that shell and attain a rare-gas configuration. It therefore readily accepts an electron from another atom to become the fluoride ion, $F^-$. The fluoride ion and the neon atom are isoelectronic with the oxide ion, $O^{--}$ (see Fig. 1-13).

> **1.** Write the electronic configuration for the fluorine atom and the fluoride ion.
>
> **2.** Show the reaction between a lithium atom and a fluorine atom using these atomic-orbital diagrams.
>
> **3. Neon, Ne:** Draw the isolated-atom picture for neon, write its electronic configuration, and state why it is relatively unreactive in chemical transformations.

## BONDING IN MOLECULES

### 1-3 IONIC AND COVALENT BONDING

Because of their electronic configurations, atoms in groups I, II, and III of the periodic table tend to *lose* their valence electrons to form ions which are isoelectronic with the preceding rare gas, whereas atoms on the right-hand side of the table tend to *gain* electrons, to become isoelectronic with the next higher rare gas. Compounds containing only elements from the extreme ends of the short periods of the periodic table are usually ionic. Consider, for example, the alkali halides such as $Na^+Cl^-$ and $K^+Br^-$.

Elements in the center of the periodic table, and especially carbon, neither gain nor lose electrons readily to form ionic bonds. Instead they tend to *share* electron pairs to form *covalent bonds*. An electronic charge of +4 or −4 needed to form a completely full or empty outer shell would lead to a region of very high electron deficiency or electron density in a relatively small atom. Since carbon has four outer electrons and is in group IV, the result is a cardinal rule of organic chemistry. **The carbon atom in ordinary molecules has four bonds, or pairs of electrons, around it**; reactive intermediates often do not. Failure to observe this rule is one of the first errors committed by beginning students of organic chemistry. Table 1-4 lists a few examples, with the valence electrons of the atoms shown in the structures of the second column. These are called dot formulas or *Lewis structures*. In the third column the structures are written to show each bonding electron pair as a line; the nonbonding electrons have been omitted.

**Table 1-4**
**Some simple organic structures**

| *Molecular formula and name* | *Lewis structure* | *Open line structure* |
|---|---|---|
| $CH_4$<br>methane | H<br>H : C : H<br>H | H<br>\|<br>H—C—H<br>\|<br>H |
| $CH_3Cl$<br>methyl chloride | H<br>H : C : Cl :<br>H | H<br>\|<br>H—C—Cl<br>\|<br>H |
| $CH_2Cl_2$<br>methylene chloride | H<br>H : C : Cl :<br>: Cl : | H<br>\|<br>H—C—Cl<br>\|<br>Cl |
| $CHCl_3$<br>chloroform | : Cl :<br>H : C : Cl :<br>: Cl : | Cl<br>\|<br>H—C—Cl<br>\|<br>Cl |
| $CCl_4$<br>carbon tetrachloride | : Cl :<br>: Cl : C : Cl :<br>: Cl : | Cl<br>\|<br>Cl—C—Cl<br>\|<br>Cl |
| $CH_3OH$<br>methyl alcohol | H<br>H : C : O : H<br>H | H<br>\|<br>H—C—O<br>\| \\H<br>H |

Since carbon forms covalent bonds by sharing electrons, **carbon chains may be continued indefinitely or joined to form ring structures, and they may contain double and triple bonds** (see Table 1-5). Atoms other than carbon and hydrogen in organic compounds are known as *heteroatoms*. Common elements that may be involved in chain, ring, and multiple-bonded structures are oxygen, nitrogen, and sulfur. Because of these bonding possibilities, a fascinating array of chemical compounds is available to the organic chemist; unusual new molecules with interesting structures and reactivities are prepared every day.

Some of the common intermediates of carbon, illustrated by those derived from methane, are the *carbonium ion*, $CH_3^+$, the carbon *free radical*, $CH_3\cdot$, and the *carbanion*, $CH_3^-$. The carbonium ion and free radical are electron-seeking species and tend to form covalent bonds by attracting electron-rich species. The carbanion has a negative charge and tends to share these electrons with other more positive species.

**Table 1-5**
**Representative organic molecules**

| *Molecular formula and name* | *Open line structures* | *Condensed line structures* |
|---|---|---|
| $C_2H_6$<br>ethane | H H<br>H—C—C—H<br>H H | $CH_3—CH_3$ |
| $C_3H_6$<br>cyclopropane | 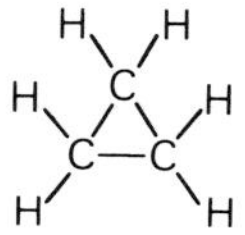 H H<br>H C H<br>C—C<br>H H | 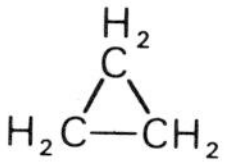 $H_2$<br>C<br>$H_2C—CH_2$ |
| $C_6H_{12}$<br>cyclohexane | 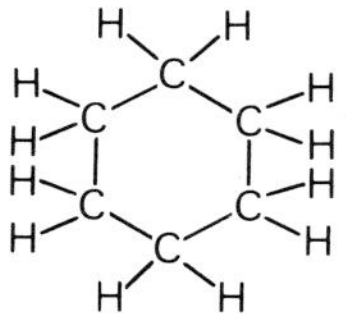 H H<br>H C H<br>H C C H<br>H C C H<br>H C H<br>H H | 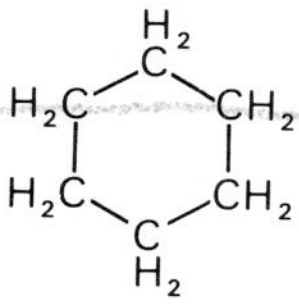 $H_2$<br>C<br>$H_2C$ $CH_2$<br>$H_2C$ $CH_2$<br>C<br>$H_2$ |
| $C_2H_4$<br>ethylene | 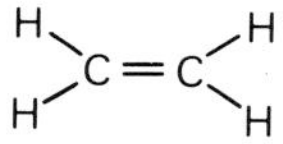 H H<br>C=C<br>H H | $CH_2=CH_2$ |
| $C_2H_2$<br>acetylene | H—C≡C—H | HC≡CH |
| $C_6H_6$<br>benzene | 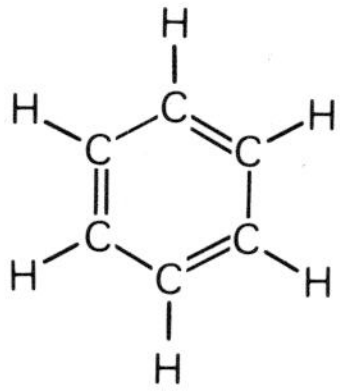 H<br>H C H<br>C C<br>C C<br>H C H<br>H | 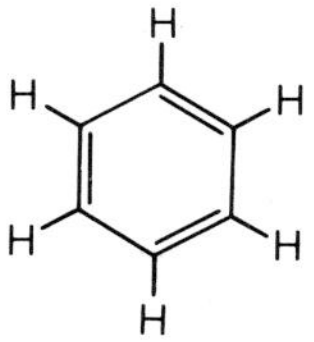 H<br>H H<br>H H<br>H |
| $C_5H_5N$<br>pyridine | 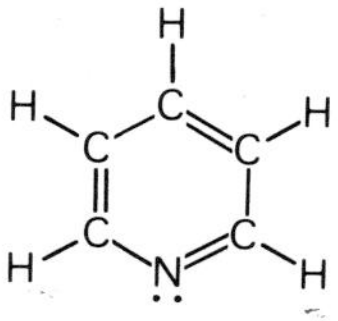 H<br>H C H<br>C C<br>C C<br>H N H<br>.. | 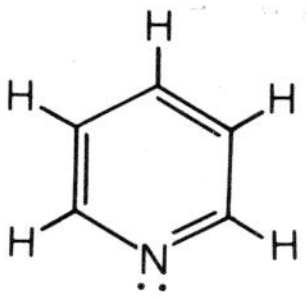 H<br>H H<br>H N H<br>.. |

## 1-4 ELECTRONEGATIVITY AND BOND POLARITY

*Electronegativity* is the tendency of an atom to attract bonding electrons. Qualitatively, if we start with fluorine as a reference, atoms further to the *left* in the periodic table become progressively *less* electronegative, since they achieve a lower energy by giving up electrons to revert to the preceding rare-gas configuration. Atoms *below* fluorine also become progressively *less* electronegative with increasing atomic number since the atoms become larger and the attraction of the positive nucleus is effectively screened by the greater number of electrons already present. You may ask: How can we express quantitatively the fact that some atoms tend to attract shared electrons more strongly than others? This is a difficult question to answer unequivocally. Several different electronegativity scales exist. Table 1-6 contains a self-consistent set of values in which the greater the numerical value for a given atom, the greater the tendency to gain electrons. We shall be concerned with the value of carbon relative to other elements commonly found in organic compounds. The decreasing order of electronegativity for these atoms is

F >> O > N > Cl > Br > C > I > H

**Table 1-6 Electronegativity values for selected atoms**

| *Group* 0 | I | II | III | IV | V | VI | VII |
|---|---|---|---|---|---|---|---|
| | H<br>2.1 | | | | | | |
| He | Li<br>0.97 | Be<br>1.47 | B<br>2.01 | C<br>2.50 | N<br>3.07 | O<br>3.50 | F<br>4.10 |
| Ne | Na<br>1.01 | Mg<br>1.23 | Al<br>1.47 | Si<br>1.74 | P<br>2.06 | S<br>2.44 | Cl<br>2.83 |
| Ar | K<br>0.91 | Ca<br>1.04 | | | | Se<br>2.48 | Br<br>2.74 |
| Kr | Rb<br>0.89 | | | | | | I<br>2.21 |
| Xe | Cs<br>0.86 | | | | | | |

In molecules such as $H_2$, $O_2$, and $Cl_2$, which consist of two identical atoms, the bonding electrons are shared equally between the two atoms; such bonds are said to be *nonpolar*. However, molecules composed of unlike atoms often contain bonds that are neither fully ionic nor covalent.

**Hydrogen chloride:** In the gaseous HCl molecule, the shared electrons form a region of high electron density closer to the chlorine atom than to the hydrogen, and the latter is partially positive with respect to the halogen.

$$\overset{\delta+}{H}-\overset{\delta-}{Cl}$$

Partial charges or charge separation are denoted by the small Greek letter δ, delta. This charge separation, or *bond polarity*, gives rise to a dipole moment in that bond along the line of centers of the two atoms, which is represented by an arrow pointing to the negative end of the bond.

$$\overset{\delta+}{H}-\overset{\delta-}{Cl}$$
$$+\!\!\longrightarrow$$

Note also that the line through the tail of the arrow makes a small plus sign. Molecules in which the centers of positive and negative charge do not coincide are said to have a net *dipole moment*.

**Water:** A water molecule has a V-shaped or bent structure. Since oxygen is more electronegative than hydrogen, the electron density is greater at the oxygen atom (Fig. 1-14). This gives rise to two equal bond polarities and a resultant dipole, which must be found by *vector* addition because bond polarities have both *magnitude* and *direction*.

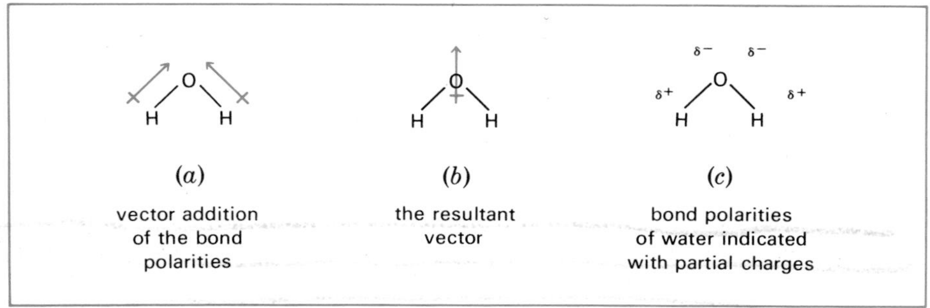


**Figure 1-14 Dipole moment of water**

In this text we shall not consider the numerical values of dipole moments but only whether individual bond polarities exist and whether the resultant is different from zero, i.e., whether it gives a net molecular dipole moment.

**Carbon tetrachloride:** A carbon atom to which four atoms are attached has a *tetrahedral* geometry; the angle between the individual bonds is 109°28'.

(a) (b) (c)

For convenience this three-dimensional structure (*a*) or (*b*) is generally reduced to a plane projection (*c*). Note that in (*b*) the wedges indicate atoms above the plane of the page; dotted lines indicate atoms below the plane of the page. Consider the bond polarities in carbon tetrachloride, $CCl_4$. Each C—Cl bond is polarized with the negative end of the dipole toward the chlorine. The four vectors sum to zero, and thus carbon tetrachloride has no net dipole moment.

**Methanol:** The simplest alcohol, methanol, $CH_3OH$, is a polar organic molecule (Fig. 1-15). The H—O—C angle (compare H—O—H)

**Figure 1-15 Dipole moment of methanol**

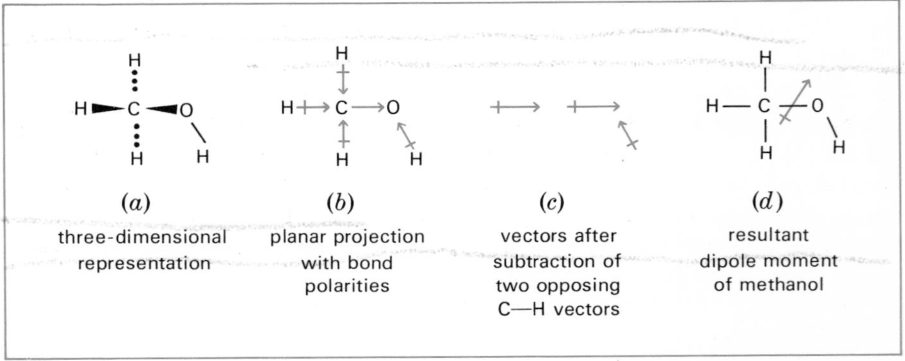

(*a*) three-dimensional representation (*b*) planar projection with bond polarities (*c*) vectors after subtraction of two opposing C—H vectors (*d*) resultant dipole moment of methanol

is 107 to 108°, and the oxygen is more electronegative than either the hydrogen or the carbon atom. The two vertical bond polarities in the second part of Fig. 1-15 cancel, and the resultant vector, which is clearly appreciable, is directed away from the oxygen atom.

In summary, the greater the difference in electronegativities between two bonded atoms, the greater the bond polarity. Note however, that even a molecule with polar bonds may have no net dipole moment.

## LEWIS STRUCTURES

Because chemical reactions involve a redistribution of electron density within and between molecules to form new bonds, knowledge of the electron density around the individual atoms of a molecule is necessary for a detailed study of reactions. To picture the electron distribution of atoms in a molecule, we can write *Lewis structures*, in which the chemical symbol represents the nucleus and inner electrons and dots represent the valence electrons, as was shown in Table 1-4. When only one reasonable electronic structure can be written for a molecule, application of electronegativities makes it possible to predict relative electron densities from the Lewis structure.

Lewis structures of simple molecules can usually be written by inspection; but more complex structures often require a lengthy trial-and-error procedure. An orderly approach will aid this process. The steps given below are only chemical common sense. Do not memorize them. Try to understand the reason for each one and its importance; practice in solving problems is the best way to become familiar with Lewis structures.

1. Arrange the atoms in the correct order and in the proper geometry. For simple inorganic molecules, consult a general chemistry text for any that are unfamiliar. The geometry of the molecules can often be deduced later in the process, but generally a carbon atom with four, three, or two atoms around it will have a tetrahedral, planar, or linear geometry, respectively.

2. Add the number of valence electrons of all the atoms involved. This is determined by the group of the periodic table to which *each* atom belongs. If the species is an ion, either add the number of negative charges or subtract the number of positive charges. This is a bookkeeping procedure, which makes it possible to check the final structure when it is drawn.

3. Arrange an octet of electrons around each atom, except for two around a hydrogen atom. An atom is usually at its lowest energy when it has a rare-gas configuration, attained by gaining, losing, or sharing electrons. An exception to this point occurs with atoms beyond the first row, especially sulfur and phosphorus, since they may use *d* orbitals to accommodate more than eight electrons. Consider $PCl_5$, $SO_3$, and $SF_6$.

4. Avoid formal charges if possible; otherwise place negative charges on the most electronegative atom(s) and separate like charges; avoid double charges on one atom. The formal charge on an atom is calculated by considering the number of electrons on a given atom in terms of its position in the periodic table, the number of unshared electrons, and the number which are shared.

$$\text{Formal charge} = (\text{valence electrons of isolated atom}) - \left(\text{unshared electrons} + \frac{\text{shared electrons}}{2}\right)$$

For example, in carbon monoxide :C:::O:, the carbon has a single negative formal charge:

$$4 \text{ valence electrons} - (2 \text{ unshared electrons} + \tfrac{1}{2} \times 6 \text{ shared electrons}) = -1$$

and the oxygen has a single positive formal charge

$$6 - (2 + \tfrac{6}{2}) = +1$$

Table 1-7 shows the application of this process to some ions and molecules. Not all chemical species can be expressed by good Lewis structures as outlined above, common exceptions being $AlCl_3$, $B_2H_6$, and $SO_3$. Try to write Lewis structures for these, but note that at least one of the above points is violated.

## RESONANCE

For many compounds two or more good Lewis structures can be written by the process described above. For example, the formate ion shown in Table 1-7 can be represented by two equivalent structures, (*a*) and (*b*).

H—C(=O)O⁻ ⟷ H—C(O⁻)=O    H—C⁺(O⁻)O⁻

(*a*) (*b*) (*c*)

equivalent resonance structures    high-energy resonance structure

A third one (*c*) can be written, but it is not nearly so important as the other two, since it involves unnecessary charge separation. These are called ***resonance structures***. None represents the true structure, which is actually a combination of both (*a*) and (*b*), called a ***hybrid***. Probably the best representation of the real electronic configuration is formulation (*d*), in which each oxygen atom carries one-half the negative charge and where the dotted line signifies one-half a bond.

H—C(⋯$O^{\frac{1}{2}-}$)⋯$O^{\frac{1}{2}-}$

(*d*)

It is not possible to represent this last structure unambiguously by a

**Table 1-7**
**Lewis structures and formal charge calculations**

| *Molecule or ion* | *Geometry* | *Total valence electrons* | *Lewis structure* | *Formal charge calculation* |
|---|---|---|---|---|
| $H_2O$<br>water | O<br>H H<br>bent or V-shaped | 1(O) = 6<br>2(H) = 2<br>8 | :Ö:<br>H H<br>(see Note 1) | H: $1 - 0 - \frac{2}{2} = 0$<br>O: $6 - 4 - \frac{4}{2} = 0$ |
| $CO_2$<br>carbon dioxide | O C O<br>linear | 2(O) = 12<br>1(C) = 4<br>16 | Ö::C::Ö | O: $6 - 4 - \frac{4}{2} = 0$<br>C: $4 - 0 - \frac{8}{2} = 0$ |
| $NO_2^+$<br>nitronium ion | O N O<br>linear | 2(O) = 12<br>1(N) = 5<br>17<br>−1<br>16<br>(see Note 2) | Ö::N⁺::Ö | O: $6 - 4 - \frac{4}{2} = 0$<br>N: $5 - 0 - \frac{8}{2} = +1$ |
| $HCO_2H$<br>formic acid | H—C(=O)OH | 2(H) = 2<br>2(O) = 12<br>1(C) = 4<br>18 | H:C(:Ö:)(:Ö:H) | H: by inspection = 0<br>C: $4 - 0 - \frac{8}{2} = 0$<br>C = O: $6 - 4 - \frac{4}{2} = 0$<br>O − H: $6 - 4 - \frac{4}{2} = 0$ |
| $HCO_2^-$<br>formate anion | H—C(=O)O⁻<br>or<br>H—C(O⁻)=O | 1(H) = 1<br>2(O) = 12<br>1(C) = 4<br>17<br>+1<br>18<br>(see Note 3) | H:C(:Ö:)(:Ö:⁻)<br>or<br>H:C(:Ö:⁻)(:Ö:) | H: by inspection = 0<br>C: as before = 0<br>C = O: as before = 0<br>C − O: $6 - 6 - \frac{2}{2} = -1$ |

Notes:

1. There are eight electrons around the oxygen but only two electrons around the hydrogen.
2. Subtract one electron, since the ion is positively charged.
3. Add one electron, since the ion is negatively charged.

single Lewis structure. A double-headed arrow is used throughout this text to represent resonance.

$$H-C{\overset{\displaystyle O}{\underset{\displaystyle O^-}{\lessgtr}}} \longleftrightarrow H-C{\overset{\displaystyle O^-}{\underset{\displaystyle O}{\lessgtr}}}$$

It must be emphasized that the formate anion *does not* vibrate or oscillate between the two structures; rather the anion is *always* a combination, or hybrid, in which a high electron density is found around the oxygen atoms. In the chemical sense, then, it is incorrect to say that a molecule or ion ''resonates.'' In chemistry, *resonance* is a noun, the name of a condition. It should not be used as a verb.

When several structures can be written, which will contribute significantly to the resonance hybrid? The quantitative answer lies in the realm of quantum mechanics, which shows that *every* structure which can be written may be taken into account and will somewhat lower the energy of the resultant hybrid. The energy of any one of several equivalent (or nearly equivalent) structures that can be written is *always* greater than the energy of the hybrid formed from them. The following three criteria result from quantum-mechanical considerations; only those structures which meet them contribute significantly to the resonance hybrid.

**1. The relative position of the atoms (nuclei) may not change between formal structures.** If there is a change in position, these are no longer resonance structures but different molecules and thus cannot contribute to a hybrid.

**2. Only structures with the same number of unpaired electrons may contribute.** If there are no unpaired electrons in the most feasible Lewis structures which can be written, then there can be none in any of the resonance structures. Most of the species encountered here, except free radicals, such as the methyl radical, $CH_3\cdot$, have no unpaired electrons. The oxygen molecule is an exception in that it contains two unpaired electrons,

$:\dot{\underset{\cdot\cdot}{O}}:\dot{\underset{\cdot\cdot}{O}}:$

**3. Only those structures having similar energies or stabilities will contribute appreciably to the resonance hybrid.** This rule may be the most difficult to apply to a particular problem because it involves a qualitative judgment in the absence of specific numerical values for the energy of each form. Generally, when two or more uncharged forms can be written, they will make the largest contribution; a smaller, but significant, contribution to the hybrid will be made by structures in which there is a single charge separation. If the structure already has a charge or a charge separation, then the next multiply charged structure will make only a small contribution as, for example, in the formate ion, structure (*c*). Structures in which like charges are separated as far as possible will be more significant than those in which they are placed on nearby atoms, because the electronic or nuclear repulsion will be lower. The total energy of a hybrid structure is lower than that of any given resonance structure which can be written; this difference is called the ***resonance energy***. The resonance energy can be measured by studying heats of hydrogenation (Sec. 7-3).

Two approaches have been used to represent the electronic structure of a molecule; the one under discussion is the ***valence-bond*** approach, in which formal atomic structures are combined. A second method is the ***molecular-orbital*** treatment, which is described in the next section. The valence-bond approach is applied below to resonance structures of some specific molecules and ions.

**Ethylene:** The ethylene molecule, $CH_2{=}CH_2$, may be written in at least five ways

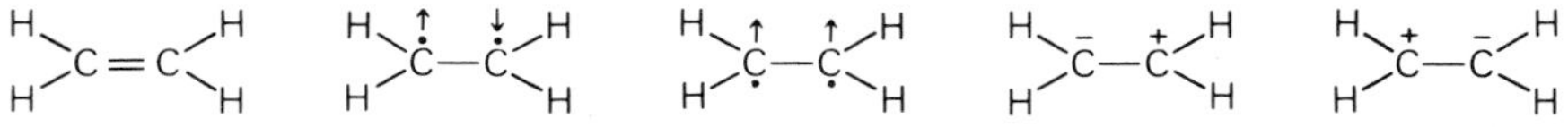

$$H_2C{=}CH_2 \qquad H_2\overset{\uparrow}{\dot{C}}{-}\overset{\downarrow}{\dot{C}}H_2 \qquad H_2\overset{\uparrow}{\dot{C}}{-}\overset{\uparrow}{\dot{C}}H_2 \qquad H_2\overset{-}{C}{-}\overset{+}{C}H_2 \qquad H_2\overset{+}{C}{-}\overset{-}{C}H_2$$

(*a*) (*b*) (*c*) (*d*) (*e*)

The arrows in (*b*) and (*c*) indicate the relative direction of electron spin on carbon atoms; in (*d*) and (*e*) the electrons are paired but are both on a single carbon atom. Ethylene is a fairly simple case, and it should be noted that (*a*) is the structure of lowest energy. Structure (*b*) represents the isolation of one electron on each carbon atom with the spins still paired. These two structures, therefore, are not of comparable stability, since it takes energy to accomplish this electron separation. Structure (*b*) does not contribute substantially to the resonance hybrid and may be omitted. Which of the above rules is violated by structure (*c*)? Since structures (*d*) and (*e*) are of higher energy than (*a*), as a result of the charge separation, they would be expected to contribute only slightly to the resonance hybrid. In summary, ethylene is best represented by structure (*a*); the singly charge-separated structures, (*d*) and (*e*), are next in importance.

**1,3-Butadiene:** As with ethylene, only one reasonable uncharged structure can be written for 1,3-butadiene, $CH_2{=}CH{-}CH{=}CH_2$, and this makes the major contribution to the resonance hybrid. A consideration of the singly charge-separated species leads to a number of other structures which, taken together, contribute somewhat to the overall structure.

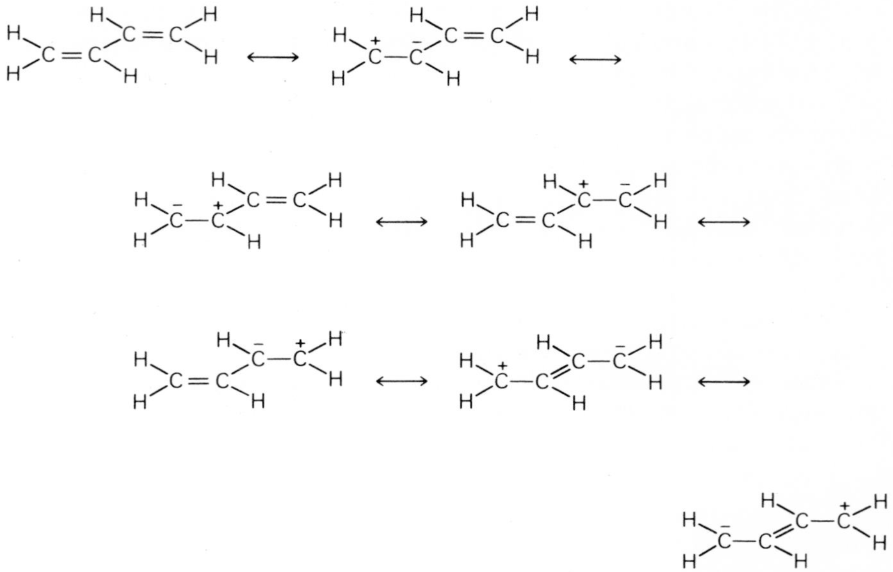

Note that the last two structures attribute some double-bond character to the bond between the second and third carbons. The reactions of 1,3-butadiene afford evidence of this partial double-bond character (Sec. 6-3).

**Benzene:** Benzene is one of the most frequently cited examples of the resonance phenomenon. It is possible to write many structures for benzene, some of which are shown below. Others can be written, but of them all only the uncharged ones contribute significantly, and of these the two ***Kekulé structures*** contribute principally to the hybrid.

Kekulé structures:

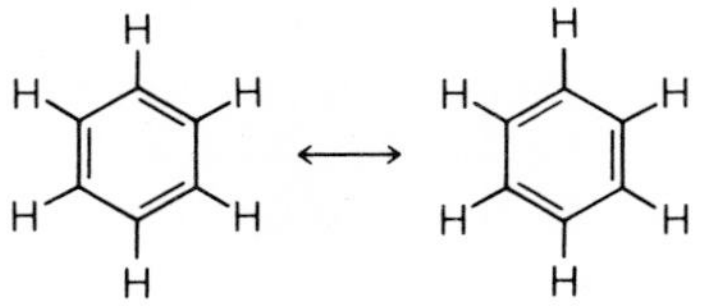

Dewar structures:

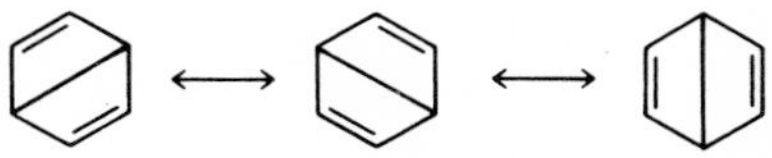

Singly charged structures:

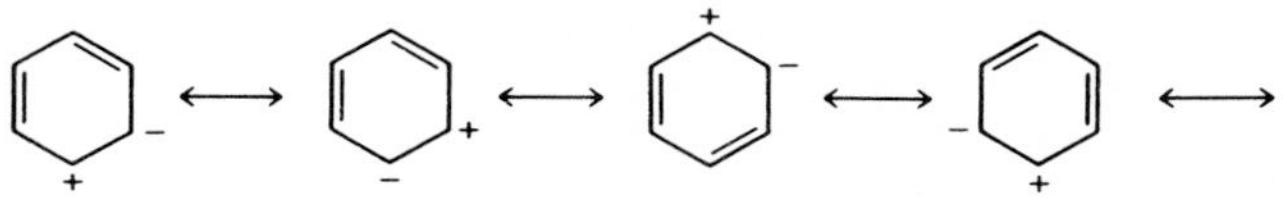

and others

A small contribution is made, in theory, by the three Dewar structures, in which there is one long bond in each representation. (Remember that the nuclei may not be moved.)

Perhaps a better representation for the benzene molecule is

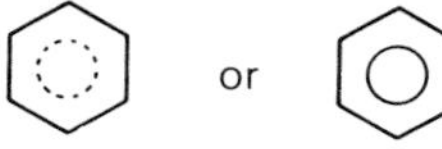

showing the electron density spread evenly over the six carbons. The latter symbol is gaining wider use, but we shall continue to employ Kekulé structures and realize that the resonance phenomenon is always implied by the Kekulé structure of benzene and its related compounds.

**Benzyl cation, anion, and radical:** One of the simple benzene derivatives is methylbenzene, or *toluene*.

$CH_3$

Removal of one of the methyl hydrogens as a hydride ion, proton, or hydrogen atom results in the formation of the benzyl cation, benzyl anion, or benzyl radical. Only two major contributing structures can be written for toluene, but there are several additional possibilities for the corresponding cation, anion, and radical. The resonance structures for the cation are

$\overset{+}{C}H_2$ ⟷ $\overset{+}{C}H_2$ ⟷ $CH_2$ ⟷ $CH_2$ ⟷ $CH_2$

These structures indicate that not only is the electron density lower in the benzene ring, but it is especially decreased at specific ring carbon atoms.

> The electronic distribution in methyl azide, $CH_3N_3$, is not immediately apparent, and we may begin by writing Lewis structures for all the forms that might contribute to the resonance hybrid. Several electronic configurations for this molecule are given below, in which the known N—N—N angle of 180° is given. Calculate the formal charge for each atom, state which structures are expected to contribute to the resonance hybrid, and show why others may be discarded.
>
> $CH_3$—N=N≡N  $CH_3$—N=N=N  $CH_3$—N—N≡N  $CH_3$—N≡N—N
>
> H:C:N::N:::N:  H:C:N::N::N:  H:C:N:N:::N:  H:C:N:::N:N:

## CARBON MOLECULAR ORBITALS IN ORGANIC COMPOUNDS

In previous sections we have considered the valence-bond description of molecules, where every reasonable structure is written and then weighted properly to yield a picture of the electronic distribution in a molecule. Here we shall discuss an alternative approach, *the molecular-orbital method*, in which an orbital framework is constructed about the nuclei and the electrons are subsequently assigned to the orbital system.

### 1-5 HYDROGEN MOLECULE

Consider again the hydrogen molecule, which is described in valence-bond terms by the structure H:H or H—H. Small contributions are also made by ionic structures $H^+H^-$ and $H^-H^+$.

In the molecular-orbital method, the two $1s$ atomic orbitals are brought together and give rise to two new molecular orbitals. This technique is a refinement of the previous isolated-atom-molecule picture (Fig. 1-16). It is called a *linear combination of atomic orbitals* (LCAO) and will be used throughout this text to depict molecular orbitals. The addition of atomic orbitals to obtain high electron density in

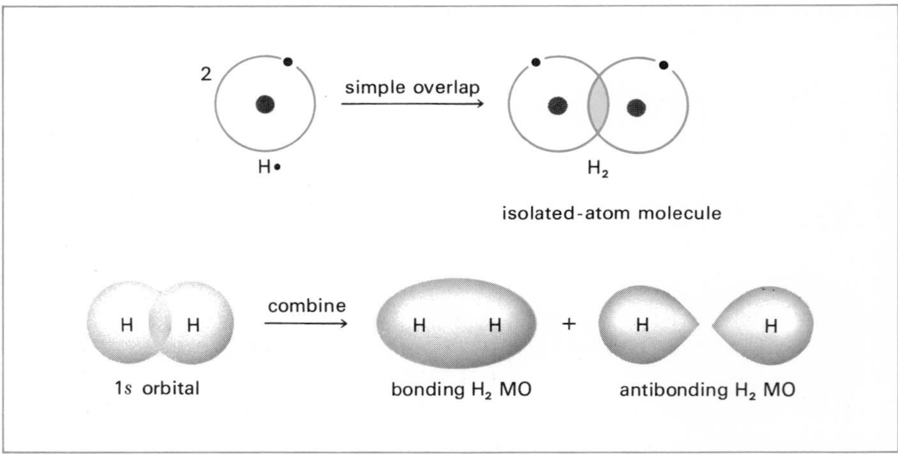


**Figure 1-16 Formation of the hydrogen molecule**

the regions of overlap between atoms gives bonding molecular orbitals; subtraction gives antibonding molecular orbitals. Thus, every combination of two atomic orbitals gives rise to two new molecular orbitals, one, bonding, of lower energy than the atomic orbitals, and one, antibonding, of higher energy. Hereafter, the higher-energy antibonding orbital will be disregarded; the bonding orbital is the more important one for discussing molecules in the bonding state. After the molecular-orbital framework has been constructed, the electrons are then added to the system.

## 1-6 CARBON ATOM IN ORGANIC COMPOUNDS

The electronic configuration of the isolated carbon atom is $(1s)^2\,(2s)^2\,(2p)^2$. Since only the valence electrons are involved in bonding, the nucleus and the 1$s$ electrons have been omitted for convenience from Fig. 1-17. This representation of an isolated (gaseous) carbon atom,

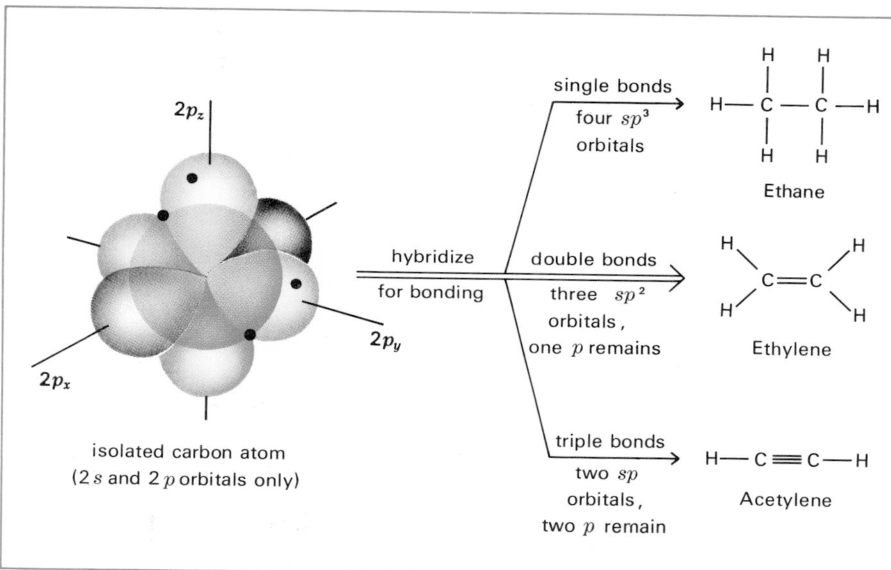


**Figure 1-17 Hybridization of carbon atomic orbitals for bonding in molecules**

which shows two unpaired $p$ electrons, might lead to the prediction that carbon is divalent. This is not the case, except for the special reactive intermediates. In bond formation in organic molecules the carbon atomic orbitals achieve a lower energy by mixing, or ***hybridizing***. The orbitals hybridize in various proportions, depending on the bonding involved, in order to attain a configuration of lower energy, and their geometry is changed in doing so. As shown in Fig. 1-17, there may be single, double, and triple carbon-carbon bonds in organic molecules.

## 1-7 CARBON SINGLE BONDS

In methane, $CH_4$, carbon is bonded to four hydrogen atoms. The known properties of methane indicate that the four bonds are equivalent; this requires four equivalent carbon atomic orbitals. If the one $s$ orbital and three $p$ orbitals from the second shell are "mixed," the hybrid obtained contains four new equivalent atomic orbitals, called $sp^3$ (Fig. 1-18) because they are formally one-fourth $s$ and three-fourths $p$ in character. Each $sp^3$ orbital has a large lobe and a smaller one. Recall that a $p$ orbital also has two lobes; however, in $p$ orbitals these lobes are the

**Figure 1-18** ***sp*³ Hybridization**

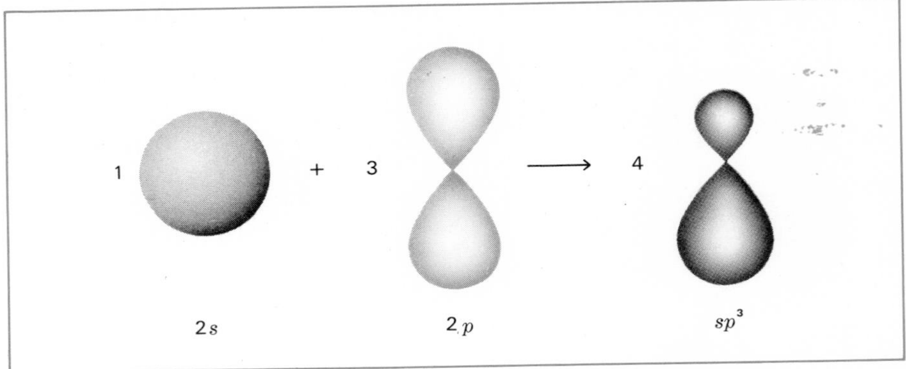


**Figure 1-19** ***sp*³ Hybridization of carbon atom**

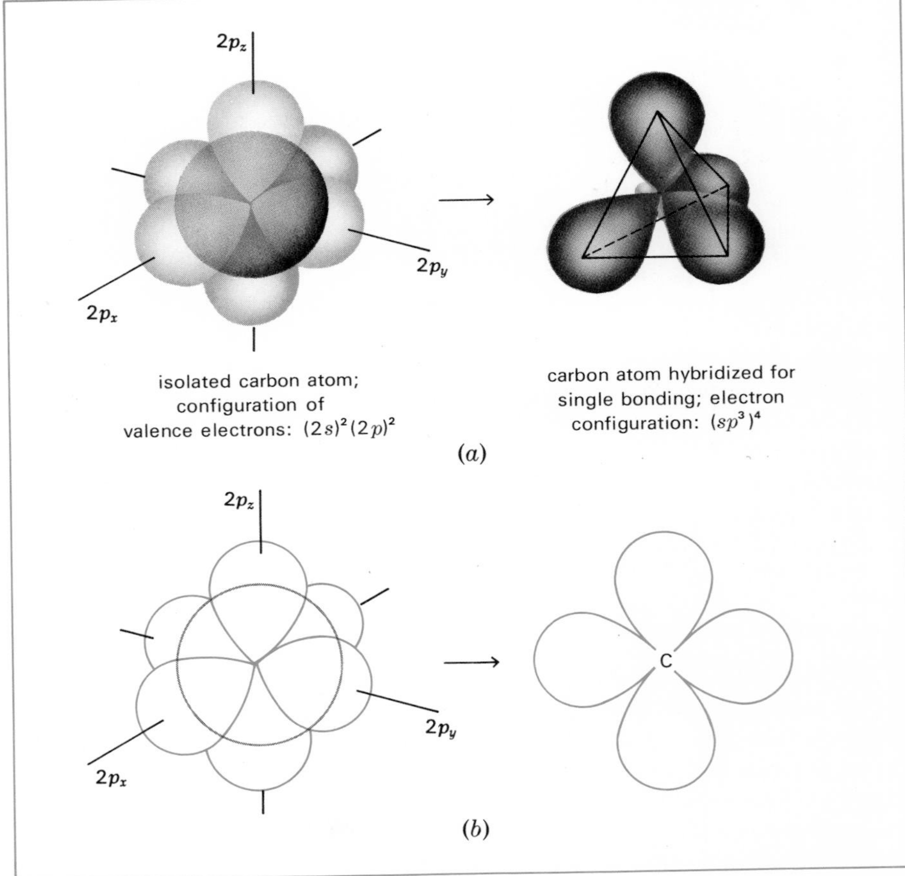

same size. Because they are not involved in bonding overlap, the smaller lobes will be omitted from most discussions and drawings.

The bonding configuration of lowest energy (corresponding to the maximum distance between bonds) is a tetrahedron with the four hydrogens at the corners and the carbon at the center; these new orbitals are directed from the carbon atom at angles of 109°28'. Generally, this tetrahedral geometry will be represented by a planar projection in two dimensions (Fig. 1-19*b*); the correct geometry is depicted in Fig. 1-19*a*.

How is this bonding representation applied to a specific molecule, such as methane? Four hydrogen atoms, each with one electron in a 1*s* orbital, are brought up to each of the four equivalent $sp^3$ orbitals, and the electrons are shared. Each bonding molecular orbital now contains two electrons, the maximum number it may contain, and the overlap is called a ***sigma*** **($\sigma$) *bond***. The LCAO picture of methane is shown in Fig. 1-20 and this linear-combination description will be used through-

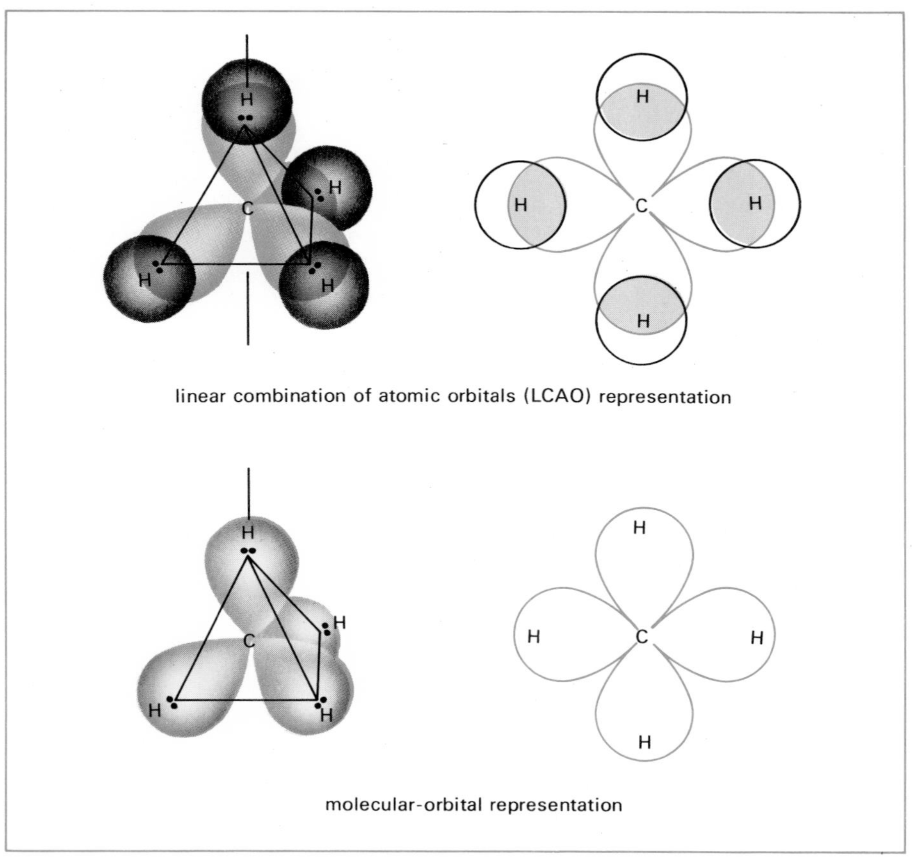


**Figure 1-20 Representations of methane**

out this text, although the molecular-orbital (MO) picture is implied by the LCAO one.

Ethane, $CH_3CH_3$, the next higher member of the alkane, or paraffin hydrocarbon, series, is represented below by the LCAO picture. Label all the orbitals and bonds. Draw the MO picture. Predict the H—C—H and H—C—C bond angles.

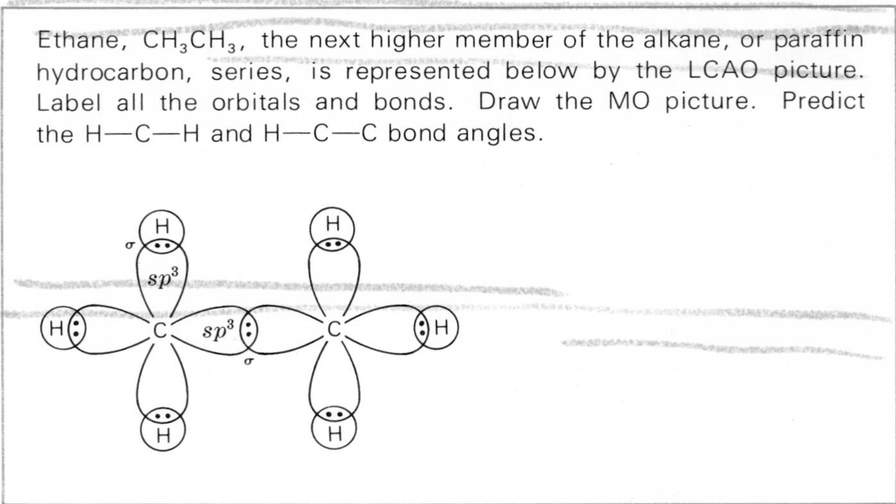


Note that the carbon-carbon single bond in ethane is a σ bond; it is axially symmetric about the line joining the center of each carbon atom. The carbon-carbon single bond is formed from two $sp^3$ hybridized carbon atomic orbitals, and there is free rotation about this bond. Note that a C—H bond is also axially symmetrical. When the geometry of the atomic orbitals involved is known, the approximate bond angles in molecules can be predicted. These representations do not show the geometrical distortion that occurs when the molecule is formed from the atomic orbitals; however, this angle is generally a good first approximation.

**Figure 1-21** ***sp*² Hybridization**

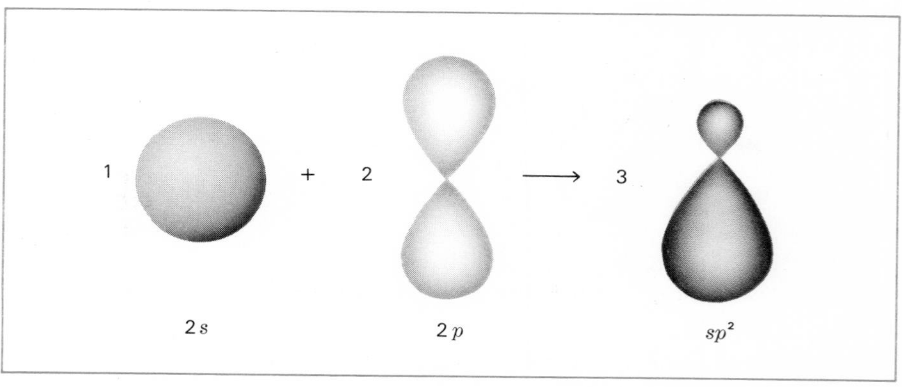

By an extension of these concepts, draw and completely label the LCAO picture of propane, $CH_3CH_2CH_3$.

## 1-8 CARBON DOUBLE BONDS

In ethylene, $CH_2{=}CH_2$, the simplest organic hydrocarbon with a carbon-carbon double bond, there are only three atoms around each carbon, although each carbon has the required four bonds or pairs of electrons. One *s* orbital is mixed with only two *p* orbitals to obtain three new $sp^2$ orbitals that have two lobes; one *p* orbital remains (Fig. 1-21). The three $sp^2$ hybrid carbon orbitals are evenly spaced at 120° in a plane, the configuration of lowest energy, and the remaining *p* orbital is perpendicular to that plane. Again, the smaller lobe of each $sp^2$ orbital has been omitted from Fig. 1-22*b*.

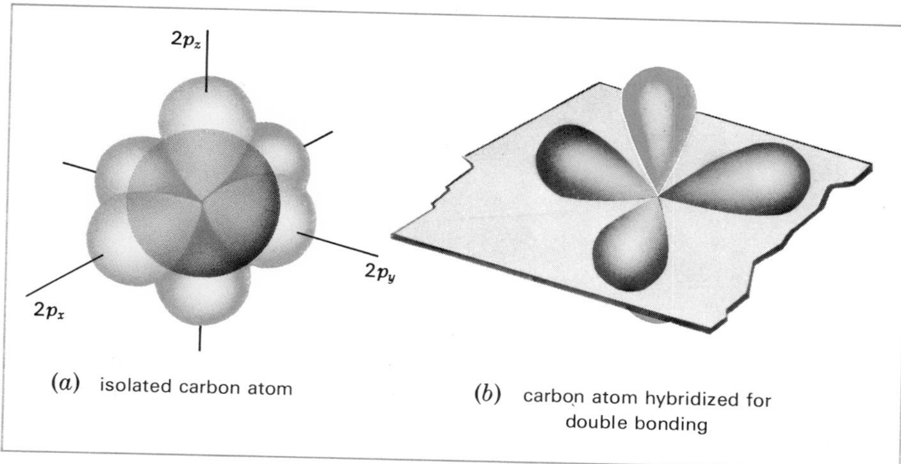


(*a*) isolated carbon atom

(*b*) carbon atom hybridized for double bonding

**Figure 1-22** $sp^2$ **Hybridization of the carbon atom**

The addition of two $sp^2$ hybridized carbon orbitals to form a $\sigma$ bond and a $\pi$ bond by $sp^2$-$sp^2$ and $2p$-$2p$ overlap forms the carbon skeleton for ethylene. Overlap of a hydrogen $1s$ orbital with each remaining $sp^2$ orbital completes the ethylene picture. All six atoms lie in one plane (see Fig. 1-23*a*).

The double bond is composed of two different bonds, one $\sigma$ and one $\pi$ bond. The *p* orbitals overlap because they have a favorable orientation (parallel), and this overlap is commonly represented by lines connecting the *p* orbitals. (If the drawing were made to scale, the *p* orbitals would actually overlap.) This *p*-*p* overlap is called a $\pi$ bond. It has no *s* character. Although there is only one $\pi$ bond in ethylene, it has two lobes, one above and one below the molecular plane. $\pi$ bonds are weaker than $\sigma$ bonds and are more exposed; these double bonds, or

**Figure 1-23 The ethylene molecule**

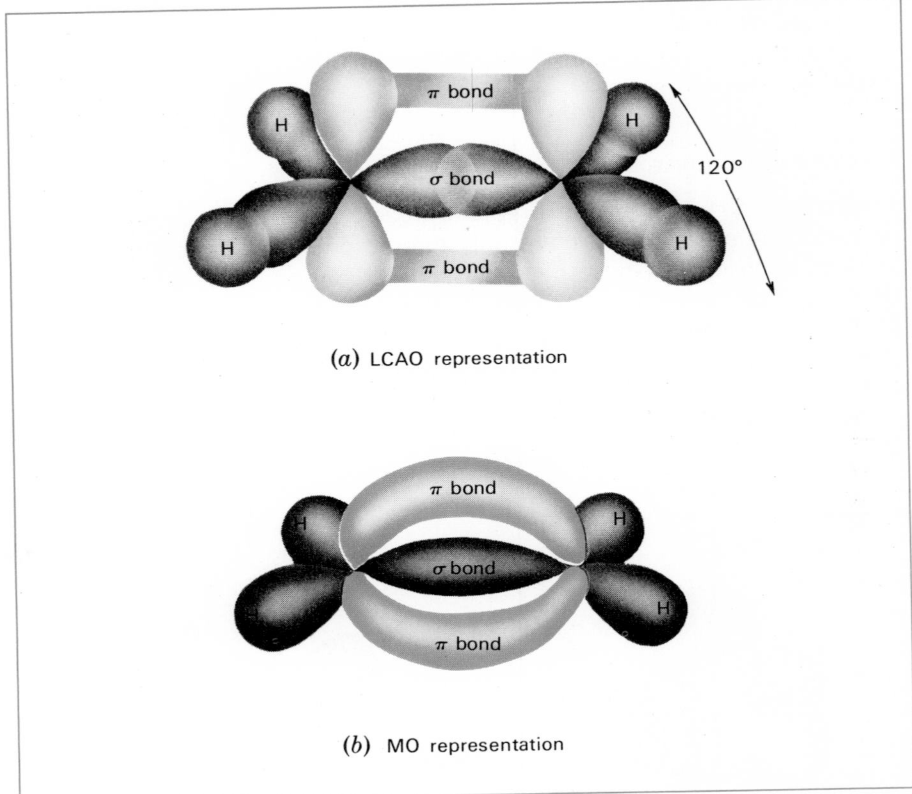


unsaturated centers, readily undergo addition reactions. Note that the molecule is not free to rotate about the double bond; the π bond does not have an axial symmetry between the atoms and holds the molecule in a planar configuration because the maximum overlap is achieved only when the *p*-orbital axes are parallel. The predicted H—C—H and H—C—C bond angles are about 120°. The molecular-orbital bonding picture is shown in Fig. 1-23*b*. Recall that the combination of two atomic orbitals gives rise to two molecular orbitals: only the ***bonding*** π molecular orbital is shown here; the antibonding one will be disregarded, as before.

### 1-9 CARBON TRIPLE BONDS

Acetylene, H—C≡C—H, contains a carbon-carbon triple bond. The carbon atoms are hybridized using one *s* orbital and only one *p* orbital, affording two new *sp* orbitals; two unchanged *p* orbitals, at 90° to each

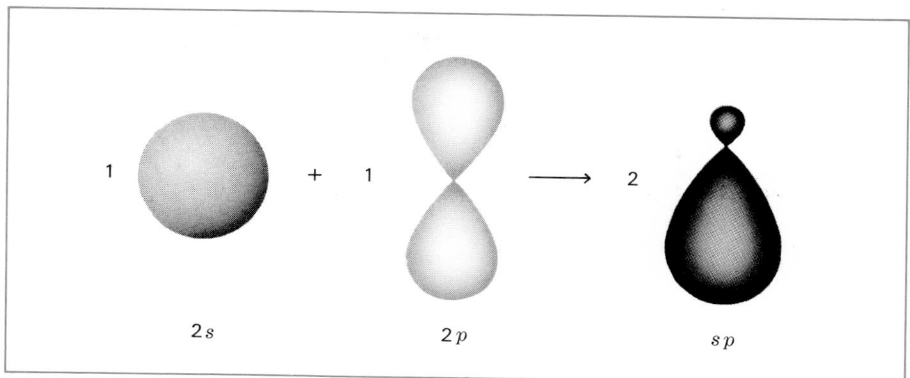


**Figure 1-24** ***sp*** **Hybridization**

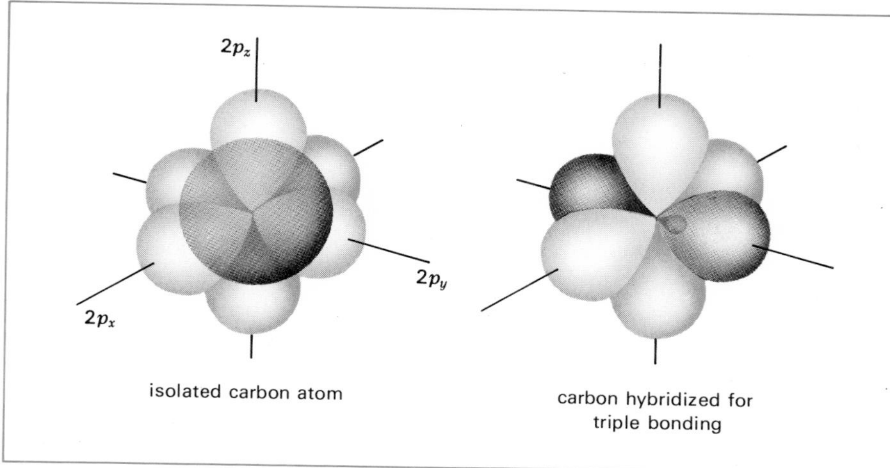


**Figure 1-25** ***sp*** **Hybridization of the carbon atom**

other, are available for $\pi$ bonding (Figs. 1-24 and 1-25). In acetylene two of these carbon fragments combine with two $1s$ orbitals of hydrogen. The electron cloud of the newly formed $\pi$ bonds is distributed with cylindrical symmetry about the carbon-carbon $\sigma$ bond (see Fig. 1-26). Note that a $p$ orbital can overlap effectively with the adjacent $p$ orbital only when their axes are parallel. Acetylene is a linear molecule; the H—C—C and C—C—H angles are 180°.

As mentioned before, atoms other than carbon and hydrogen, such as B, N, O, and S, are known in organic chemistry as heteroatoms. The bonds they form with carbon indicate that their orbitals are sometimes hybridized like those of the carbon to which they are attached. Other heteroatoms, such as halogens, can be depicted by the isolated-atom picture with the appropriate overlap.

For each of the following molecules draw the LCAO picture, showing the atomic orbitals and electrons. Label the orbital hybridization and the bonds (either $\sigma$ or $\pi$) and show the approximate bond angles formed by all sets of three adjacent atoms. The use of colored pencils will be a great help in clarifying your diagrams.

**1.** $CH_2{=}CH{-}CH{=}CH_2$

1,3-butadiene

Note the $p$-orbital overlap between $C_2$ and $C_3$.

**2.** (benzene ring: six C–H, with H on each carbon)

benzene

All adjacent $p$ orbitals overlap in this planar molecule. Is it reasonable that a benzene ring with an inscribed circle is a good representation? Note the similarity of the circle to the $\pi$ molecular orbital which is formed above and below the plane of the 12 atoms.

**3.** $CH_2{=}CH{-}C{\equiv}C{-}H$

vinylacetylene

Careful here! Remember that $p$ orbitals overlap only with others whose axes are parallel.

**4.** $CH_2{=}C{=}CH_2$

allene

Why is the central carbon $sp$ hybridized?

**5.** $CO_2$

carbon dioxide

To which of the above molecules is this similar?

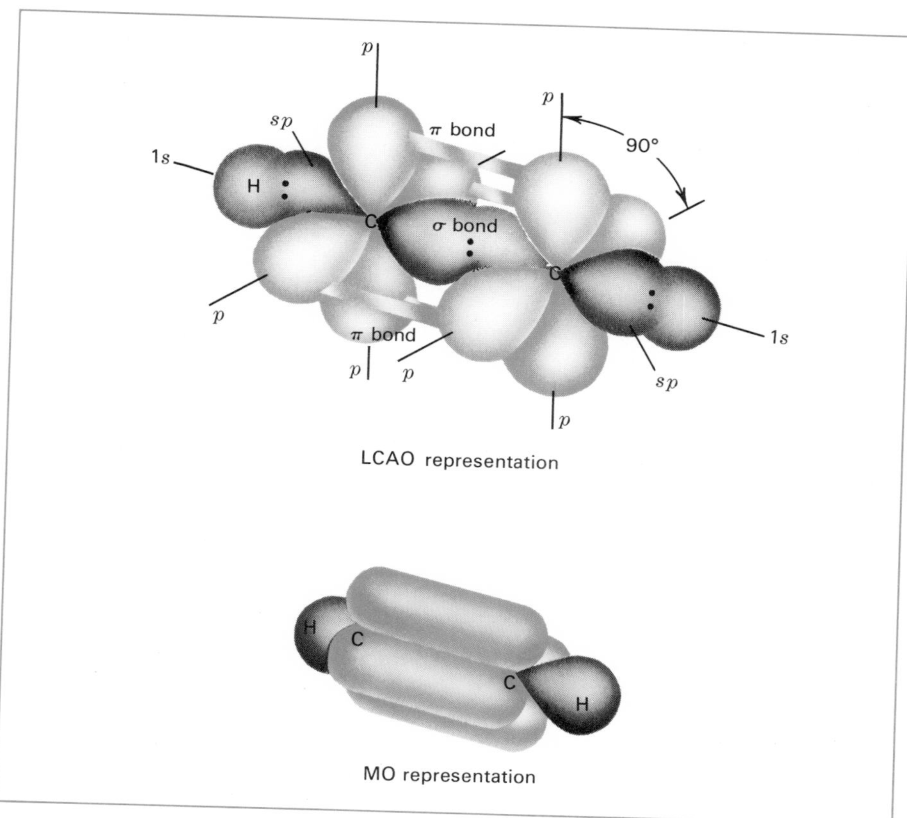


**Figure 1-26 The acetylene molecule**

## A GENERAL CLASSIFICATION OF ORGANIC COMPOUNDS

The study of organic chemistry is simplified by grouping the molecules according to the ***functional groups*** (or types of reactive sites) they contain. It is not possible to discuss one functional group without at least referring to others. The table inside the front cover is a ***reference list*** of representative structures and names of compounds in each group, which will be mentioned before they are studied in detail. Glance through the list and look for some similarities and familiar compounds; it is not meant to be studied now and **certainly not to be memorized!** In the listing, R— means any organic group and Ar— means one containing the benzene ring (or a similar ring such as naphthalene or phenanthrene) attached to the substituent. R—, R'—, and R''— indicate different organic groups.

## SUGGESTED READINGS


### Electronegativity and polarity

Benson, S.W.: Bond Energies, *J. Chem. Educ.*, **42**, 502 (1965). An excellent resource paper with discussion, tables of values, and many references.

Little, E.J., Jr., and M.M. Jones: A Complete Table of Electronegativities, *J. Chem. Educ.*, **37**, 231 (1960).

Thompson, H.B.: The Determination of Dipole Moments in Solution, *J. Chem. Educ.*, **43**, 66 (1966).

Wilmshurst, J. K.: Ionic Character, Polarity, and Electronegativity, *J. Chem. Educ.*, **39**, 132 (1962).

### Atomic and molecular orbitals

Bent, H.A.: Distribution of Atomic *s* Character in Molecules and Its Chemical Implications, *J. Chem. Educ.*, **37**, 616 (1960).

Berry, R. S.: Atomic Orbitals, *J. Chem. Educ.*, **43**, 283 (1966). An excellent resource paper giving equations, graphs, and references.

Cohen, I.: The Shape of the $2p$ and Related Orbitals, *J. Chem. Educ.*, **38**, 20 (1961).

Friedman, H.G., Jr., G.R. Choppin, and D.G. Feuerbacher: The Shapes of the *f*-orbitals, *J. Chem. Educ.*, **41**, 354 (1964).

Maybury, R.H.: The Language of Quantum Mechanics, *J. Chem. Educ.*, **39**, 367 (1962). An elementary discussion of quantum mechanics, explaining a variety of concepts.

Meislich, H.: Rules for Molecular Orbital Structures, *J. Chem. Educ.*, **40**, 401 (1963).

### Electronic structure and repulsion

Bent, H.A.: Isoelectronic Systems, *J. Chem. Educ.*, **43**, 170 (1966). An excellent resource paper discussing the concept with examples and references.

Goldwhite, H.: Elementary One-upmanship: H or C?, *J. Chem. Educ.*, **41**, 626 (1964). An interesting answer to the question: Are there more carbon-containing or hydrogen-containing compounds?

Panckhurst, M.H.: The Electronic Structures and Stereochemistry of $NO_2$, $NO_2^+$ and $NO_2^-$, *J. Chem. Educ.*, **39**, 270 (1962).

Sanderson, R.T.: Principles of Chemical Bonding, *J. Chem. Educ.*, **38**, 382 (1961).

Sanderson, R.T.: A Rational Periodic Table, *J. Chem. Educ.*, **41**, 187 (1964).

### Historical development of chemical structure

Brown, H.C.: Foundations of the Structural Theory, *J. Chem. Educ.*, **36**, 104 (1959). Reviews the background against which Kekulé and Couper advanced structural theory.

*Kekulé-Couper Centennial Symposium*

Campaigne, E.: The Contributions of Fritz Arndt to Resonance Theory, *J. Chem. Educ.*, **36**, 336 (1959). Gives a historical discussion of early chemists who contributed to the theory of structural organic chemistry.

Hiebert, E.N.: The Experimental Basis of Kekulé's Valence Theory, *J. Chem. Educ.*, **36**, 320 (1959).

Leicester, H.M.: Contributions of Butlerov to the Development of Structural Theory, *J. Chem. Educ.*, **36**, 328 (1959).

Strong, F.C., III: The Atomic Form Periodic Table, *J. Chem. Educ.*, **36**, 344 (1959).

## PROBLEMS†

**1**. For each of the following molecules, determine the direction of the polarity of each bond and state whether or not the molecule has a resulting dipole moment.

★(*a*) $C_6H_5Br$, bromobenzene

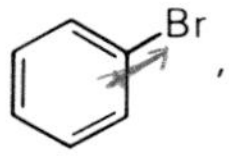

★(*b*) ICl, iodine monochloride

★(*c*)
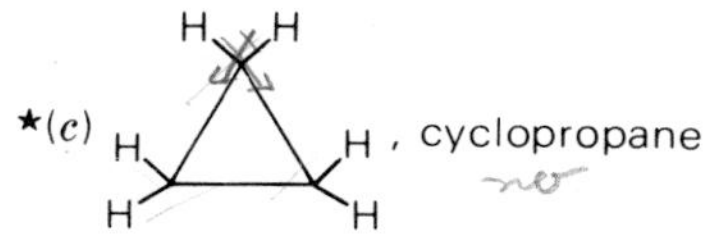

, cyclopropane

★(*d*) HCCH, acetylene

(*e*) $CH_2O$, formaldehyde

(*f*) $CHCl_3$, chloroform

★(*g*) $CH_2CH_2$, ethylene

★(*h*)

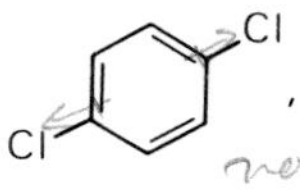

, *p*-dichlorobenzene

**2**. Write Lewis structures (dot formulas) for each of the following molecules. Show all valence electrons and indicate formal charges clearly if present.

(*a*) the compounds listed in Table 1-5

★(*b*) $CH_3CH_2OH$, ethyl alcohol

★(*c*) $CHCl_3$, chloroform

(*d*) $CH_3OCH_3$, dimethyl ether

(*e*) $C_6H_5Br$, bromobenzene

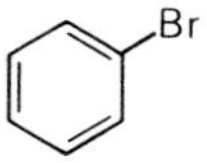

★(*f*) $CH_3F$, fluoromethane

★(*g*) $CH_3NH_2$, methylamine

★(*h*) HCCH, acetylene

(*i*) $CH_3ONa$, sodium methoxide (ionic)

★(*j*) $CH_3MgI$, methylmagnesium iodide (ionic $C^-Mg^+$ bond)

(*k*) $AlCl_3$, aluminum chloride

(*l*) $PCl_5$, phosphorus pentachloride

(*m*) $Cl_2$, chlorine

★(*n*) $CH_2O$, formaldehyde

(*o*) $CH_2CHCl$, vinyl chloride

★(*p*) $H_2NCN$, cyanamide

**3.** Using Lewis structures (dot formulas), give at least two reasonable structures which may contribute significantly to the resonance hybrid of ***each*** of the following molecules or ions. Show ***all*** valence electrons and indicate the formal charge(s) clearly if present.

†Answers to starred problems are given in the section immediately preceding the index.

★(*a*) $CH_2N_2$, diazomethane (***Hint***: Contains a nitrogen-nitrogen bond but is not cyclic.)

★(*b*) $CH_2{=}CH{-}C(=O)H$, acrolein, or propenal

(*c*) $CH_3{-}\overset{O}{\overset{\|}{C}}{-}CH{=}CH_2$, methyl vinyl ketone

★(*d*) $(CH_3)_3PO$, trimethylphosphine oxide

(*e*) $CH_3NO_2$, nitromethane (***Hint***: Contains a nitrogen-carbon bond.)

(*f*) $H_2SO_4$, sulfuric acid

★(*g*) $HNO_3$, nitric acid

★(*h*) $C_6H_5{-}\overset{+}{C}H_2$, the benzyl cation

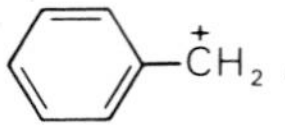

(*i*) $C_6H_5{-}\overset{-}{C}H_2$, the benzyl anion

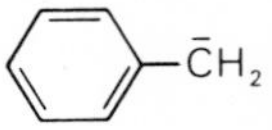

(*j*) $C_6H_5{-}\dot{C}H_2$, the benzyl radical

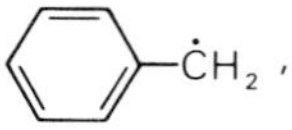

(*k*) $CH_2{=}CH{-}\overset{+}{C}H_2$, the allyl cation

(*l*) $CH_2{=}CH{-}\overset{-}{C}H_2$, the allyl anion

★(*m*) $CH_2{=}CH{-}\dot{C}H_2$, the allyl radical

(*n*) $SO_3$, sulfur trioxide

**4**. (*a*) Draw clearly and neatly the LCAO (molecular-orbital) picture for each of the following compounds. Label the hybridization of each orbital and label all bonds as either $\sigma$ or $\pi$, showing the orbital overlap with shading. Heteroatoms (except halogens) should be hybridized in a manner similar to the carbon to which they are attached.

(*b*) On a separate diagram containing only the atomic symbols and bonds (extended structural formulas) show the theoretical bond angles.

★(*i*) HCCCN, cyanoacetylene

★(*ii*) $C_3H_6$, propene, or vinylmethane

(*iii*) $CH_3CH{=}CO$, methylketene

(*iv*) HCCCCH, diacetylene

★(*v*) $CH_2CHCHO$, acrolein, or propenal

(*vi*) $CH_2CHCl$, vinyl chloride

★(*vii*) $CH_3CHCCH_2$, methylallene

(*viii*) $C_6H_5{-}CCH$, phenylacetylene

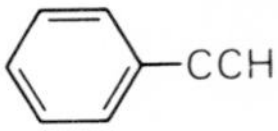

(*ix*) $CH_3CN$, acetonitrile, or methyl cyanide

★(*x*) $C_6H_5{-}CH{=}CH_2$, styrene, or vinylbenzene

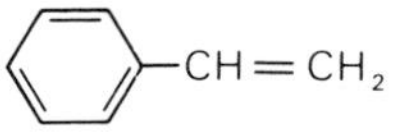

(*xi*) $H_2N{-}NH_2$, hydrazine

(*xii*) $CH_3{-}\underset{O}{\underset{\|}{C}}{-}CH_3$, acetone

★**5**. Refer to the table on the front endpaper and label the functional groups in these molecules. Each is a naturally occurring steroid with a cyclopentanoperhydrophenanthrene carbon skeleton.

(*a*) [cyclopentanoperhydrophenanthrene skeleton structure]

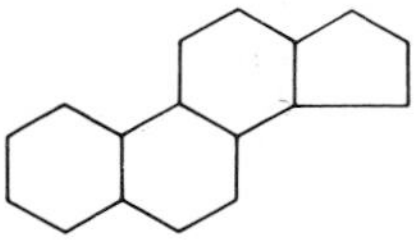

cyclopentanoperhydrophenanthrene
Show clearly all the hydrogen
atoms in this molecule.

(b) [structure: $H_3C(CH_2)_3-CH(CH_3)_2$ side chain, $H_3C$, $H_3C$, HO]

cholesterol
found in animal blood
and in gallstones

(c) [structure: $H_3C$ $CH_2CH_2CO_2H$, $H_3C$, HO, $H_3C$, HO, OH]

cholic acid
occurs in human
and in ox bile

(d) [structure: $H_3C$, OH, HO]

estradiol
female sex hormone,
produced in ovaries

(e) [structure: $H_3C$, OH, $H_3C$, O]

testosterone
male sex hormone,
produced in testes

(f) [structure: OHC, $COCH_2OH$, HO, $H_3C$, O]

aldosterone
produced in adrenals,
located in kidneys

(g) [structure: $H_3C$, OH, O, $COCH_2OH$, $H_3C$, O]

cortisone
used in treatment of
rheumatoid arthritis

# Chapter Two

The *alkanes*, or *paraffin hydrocarbons*, which are the simplest organic compounds, have no functional groups since all the carbon atoms are bonded either to other carbons by single bonds or to hydrogen atoms. These compounds are relatively unreactive under ordinary laboratory conditions, but they can be forced to undergo reactions by drastic treatment. Often these reactions are of limited importance to the research organic chemist, but the reactivity of alkanes is of considerable industrial interest since they are important as fuels. Natural gas and gasoline from petroleum are, for the most part, lower members of the alkane series. Although the reactions in this chapter are little used in the laboratory, they are a convenient starting point for the study of organic chemistry.

Of great importance is the section on nomenclature. This language is necessary for effective communication. It is readily learned by practice, but it is not an end in itself. After thorough drill in this chapter, you will find fewer nomenclature questions in successive chapters; you are expected to learn the language early in your study of organic chemistry.

The detailed pathway by which a chemical reaction takes place is called the *mechanism* of the reaction. It answers the question: ***How does the reaction take place?*** This concept is introduced later in the chapter, and mechanisms will be used throughout the text to explain the observed course of many organic chemical reactions.

## STRUCTURE

Since alkanes contain only carbon-carbon single bonds and carbon-hydrogen bonds, all carbon orbitals are $sp^3$ hybridized. In the preferred arrangement of the carbon skeleton, the carbon atoms of such molecules form a zigzag chain with C—C—C angles of about 109°, rather than the straight chain usually depicted in structural formulas. The rela-

# Alkanes (Paraffins)

tive position taken by singly bonded atoms in a molecule is called the *conformation*. There are an infinite number of conformations of the ethane molecule, resulting from free rotation about the carbon-carbon single bond. Two extreme ones are shown in Fig. 2-1 using "sawhorse" drawings and Newman projections. The latter are made by

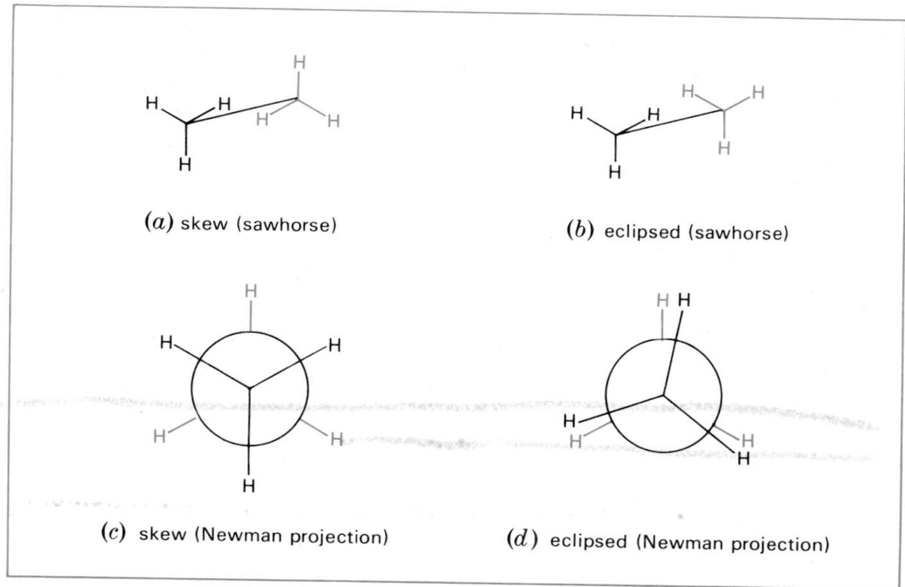


**Figure 2-1 Skew and eclipsed conformations of ethane**

sighting along the axis of the carbon-carbon bond; only the first carbon atom is seen. The lower-energy conformation, in which the nonbonded hydrogen atoms are as far apart as possible, is called the *skew conformation*. In the *eclipsed conformation* the hydrogen atoms actually are visually eclipsed if a model is examined along the carbon-carbon bond axis. These conformational descriptions are also applicable to higher alkanes and will be used later in predicting the course of certain chemical reactions.

# NOMENCLATURE

## 2-1 METHANE, ETHANE, AND PROPANE

Formulas for organic compounds may be written either in the line form or the condensed form, as illustrated with the first four members of the alkane series.

```
    H                         H   H
    |                         |   |
H—C—H        CH4          H—C—C—H        CH3—CH3 or C2H6
    |                         |   |
    H                         H   H
```

line — condensed: $CH_4$ — methane

line — condensed: $CH_3{-}CH_3$ or $C_2H_6$ — ethane

```
    H   H   H
    |   |   |
H—C—C—C—H       CH3CH2CH3 or C3H8
    |   |   |
    H   H   H
```

line — condensed: $CH_3CH_2CH_3$ or $C_3H_8$ — propane

```
    H   H   H   H
    |   |   |   |
H—C—C—C—C—H       CH3CH2CH2CH3 or CH3(CH2)2CH3
    |   |   |   |
    H   H   H   H
```

line — condensed: $CH_3CH_2CH_2CH_3$ or $CH_3(CH_2)_2CH_3$ — butane

Here we shall study the system of nomenclature based on rules formulated in 1930 and revised in 1949 by the International Union of Pure and Applied Chemistry, the *IUPAC system*. No system of nomenclature was formulated until long after the recognition and widespread study of many organic compounds, although early scientific meetings had established a less complete set of rules, on which many of the present ones are based. A number of organic compounds, particularly those which were early found in nature, are known by a common, or trivial, name. Study and learn the IUPAC system of nomenclature throughout the text. This name is always correct, although some trivial names have been incorporated into the IUPAC system because of common usage.

Methane, ethane, propane, and higher alkanes differ from each other by a $-CH_2-$ group. Their general formula can be written $C_nH_{2n+2}$. Such a series of compounds with the same functional group in which each higher member differs from the preceding one by a given unit is a *homologous series*. Members of the alkane homologous series are designated by the root name for the carbon chain plus the generic ending *-ane*.

| | |
|---|---|
| Methane: | $CH_4$ |
| Ethane: | $CH_3CH_3$ |
| Propane: | $CH_3CH_2CH_3$ |
| Butane: | $CH_3CH_2CH_2CH_3$ |
| Pentane: | $CH_3CH_2CH_2CH_2CH_3$ |
| Hexane: | $CH_3CH_2CH_2CH_2CH_2CH_3$ |

When alkanes undergo reactions which remove a hydrogen, the resulting ***alkyl group***, which is unstable and further reacts, may also be written in the line and condensed forms. There is only one possible methyl group and one ethyl group, but there are two propyl groups.

```
   H                     H  H
   |                     |  |
H—C—      CH3—       H—C—C—      CH3CH2—    or    C2H5—
   |                     |  |
   H                     H  H

methyl group                    ethyl group
```

```
   H  H  H                      H  H  H
   |  |  |                      |  |  |
H—C—C—C—   CH3CH2CH2—     H—C—C—C—H   CH3CHCH3   or   (CH3)2CH—
   |  |  |                      |  |  |         |
   H  H  H                      H     H

1-propyl group, IUPAC           2-propyl group, IUPAC
(n-propyl group, common)        (isopropyl group, common)
```

The $C_3H_7$— formulation is therefore ambiguous and should not be used. Straight-chain hydrocarbons are called ***normal*** alkanes, and ones with a terminal methyl group branch are the corresponding ***isoalkanes***. Instead of using $C_3H_7$—, write either $n$-$C_3H_7$— or $i$-$C_3H_7$—. These are the $n$-propyl and isopropyl groups. The IUPAC nomenclature requires the use of numbers to denote the position of each substituent. The first compound in the following problem is named either isopropyl bromide (trivial, two words) or 2-bromopropane (IUPAC, one word).

> Name the following compounds.
>
> ```
> CH3—CH—CH3        CH3
>      |               \
>      Br               CH—I      CH3CH2CH2Cl
>                      /
>                   CH3
> ```

A carbon atom is said to be *primary* (often denoted 1°); *secondary*, 2°; *tertiary*, 3°; or *quaternary*, 4°; according to the number of other carbons attached to it. Propane, $CH_3CH_2CH_3$, contains two primary carbon atoms (the terminal ones) and one secondary carbon. Note the use of parentheses in the problem below to indicate groups on a given atom when the chemical structure is written on one line.

> How many 1°, 2°, 3°, and 4° carbon atoms are found in the following compounds?
>
> 1. $(CH_3)_3C—CH_2—CH_2—CH(CH_3)—CH_2—C(CH_3)_3$
> 2. $(CH_3)_2CH—CH(CH_3)—C(CH_3)_2—CH_2—CH_2—CH_3$

Further, a functional group, such as the hydroxyl group, —OH of alcohols, is said to be primary, 1°, secondary, 2°, or tertiary, 3°, depending upon the description of the *carbon atom* to which it is attached.

> 1. Write structures for a primary, secondary, and tertiary alcohol, R—OH, and for the corresponding bromide, R—Br.
> 2. Why can there be no quaternary alcohols or bromides?

## 2-2 BUTANE

Two structures can be written for butane, $C_4H_{10}$, the fourth member of the $C_nH_{2n+2}$ series.

```
    H   H   H   H
    |   |   |   |
H—C—C—C—C—H      CH3—CH2—CH2—CH3      or      CH3(CH2)2CH3
    |   |   |   |
    H   H   H   H
```

*n*-butane, common (butane, IUPAC)

```
    H   H   H                 H
    |   |   |                 |
H—C—C—C—H         CH3—C—CH3      or      (CH3)3CH
    |   |   |                 |
    H   |   H                CH3
    H—C—H
        |
        H
```

isobutane, common (2-methylpropane, IUPAC)

**Compounds with the same molecular formula but different structural formulas are called structural isomers.** There are structural isomers of three types: (1) *skeletal isomers*, such as the butanes, in which the carbon skeletons differ; (2) *positional isomers*, such as the propyl bromides, in which the location of the substituent differs; and (3) *functional isomers*, illustrated by the formula $C_2H_6O$, which represents either dimethyl ether, $CH_3—O—CH_3$, or ethyl alcohol, $CH_3CH_2OH$. Other types of isomerism will be discussed in later chapters.

The alkyl groups derived from the butanes are shown in Table 2-1, using the bromides as examples. Note the abbreviations *sec-* or *s-* for secondary and *tert-* or *t-* for tertiary. Since the two $C_4H_{10}$ structures are not identical, the $C_4H_9—$ groups derived from them are different. To determine the number of isomers which correspond to a monosubstituted alkane, for example, $C_5H_{11}Cl$, *first* write all the alkane structures, $C_5H_{12}$, and proceed to determine the number of different alkyl groups derived from each.

**Table 2-1**
**Alkyl groups derived from the butanes**

From *n*-butane:

$CH_3CH_2CH_2CH_2—Br$

*n*-butyl bromide, trivial
(1-bromobutane, IUPAC)

$CH_3CH_2CH(Br)CH_3$

*sec*-butyl bromide, trivial
(2-bromobutane, IUPAC)

From isobutane:

$CH_3CH(CH_3)—CH_2—Br$

isobutyl bromide, trivial
(1-bromo-2-methylpropane, IUPAC)

$CH_3—C(CH_3)_2—Br$

*tert*-butyl bromide, trivial
(2-bromo-2-methylpropane, IUPAC)

The bromides derived from *n*-butane are *n*-butyl bromide (trivial, two words), or 1-bromobutane (IUPAC, one word), and *sec*-butyl bromide, or 2-bromobutane. Note that 1-bromobutane is a primary and 2-bromobutane is a secondary halide; the latter is a *sec*-alkyl halide. **Systems of nomenclature should not be mixed.** The following are incorrect: 1-butyl bromide and 2-propyl chloride. *tert*-Butyl bromide is also named 2-bromo-2-methylpropane, which is written as one word using hyphens to separate the numbers from the substituent name. Numbers are separated from each other by commas; for example, 2,2-dibromopropane, $CH_3CBr_2CH_3$.

## 2-3 IUPAC RULES OF NOMENCLATURE

Common, or trivial, naming becomes exceedingly complex when the organic structures contain more than five carbons; the IUPAC systematic nomenclature is therefore increasingly important for a consistent discussion. Nomenclature is meant to be simple, easily understood, and readily used. A word of caution. Do not be misled because a structure is not written the way you are accustomed to seeing it. The following representations of isobutyl bromide are all the same, although some are more convenient, more familiar, or more conventional than others.

$CH_3{-}\underset{\displaystyle CH_3}{\underset{|}{C}}H{-}CH_2{-}Br$ $\qquad (H_3C)(H_3C){>}CH{-}CH_2Br \qquad Br{-}CH_2CH(CH_3)_2$

$Br{-}CH_2{-}\overset{\displaystyle CH_3}{\overset{|}{C}}H{-}CH_3 \qquad CH_3{-}\overset{\displaystyle CH_3}{\overset{|}{C}}H{-}\underset{\displaystyle Br}{\underset{|}{C}}H{-}H \qquad Br(H)(H)C{-}\underset{\displaystyle H_3C}{\underset{|}{\overset{H}{\overset{|}{C}}}}{-}\underset{\displaystyle H}{\underset{|}{\overset{H}{\overset{|}{C}}}}{-}H$

$H{-}\underset{\displaystyle H}{\underset{|}{\overset{H}{\overset{|}{C}}}}{-}Br$ attached to $H_2{>}\underset{\displaystyle H}{\underset{|}{C}}{-}\underset{\displaystyle H}{\underset{|}{C}}{-}CH_3 \qquad Br(H)C{<}\dots$ (zigzag: $BrCH_2{-}CH(CH_3){-}CH_3$ with all H shown) $\qquad CH_3{-}CH(CH_3){-}CH_2Br$

Although the first four alkanes have common names, the names of the rest are usually based on Greek roots denoting the number of carbon atoms (Table 2-2). Other organic compounds have IUPAC names determined by the alkane of which they are nominally derivatives and by the nature and location of functional groups in the molecule. The organic functional group may be a multiple carbon-carbon bond, the point of attachment of a heteroatom, such as oxygen, nitrogen, or halogen, or of a group of atoms (see inside front cover). Most organic reactions take place at these reactive sites and involve change or loss of this functionality.

Some of the IUPAC rules of nomenclature are given below. A more complete set, with examples, can be found in the "Handbook of Chemistry and Physics."† $CH_3CH(CH_2CH_3)CH(Cl)CH_2CH(Br)CH_3$ is used as an example.

† R. C. Weast (ed.), "Handbook of Chemistry and Physics," 49th ed., pp. C1-C52, Chemical Rubber Publishing Company, Cleveland, Ohio, 1968.

**Table 2-2**
**The $C_nH_{2n+2}$ homologous series**

| | | | |
|---|---|---|---|
| $C_1$ | methane | $C_9$ | nonane |
| $C_2$ | ethane | $C_{10}$ | decane |
| $C_3$ | propane | $C_{11}$ | undecane (Latin)<br>hendecane (Greek) |
| $C_4$ | butane | $C_{12}$ | dodecane |
| $C_5$ | pentane | $C_{20}$ | eicosane |
| $C_6$ | hexane | $C_{30}$ | triacontane |
| $C_7$ | heptane | $C_{50}$ | pentacontane |
| $C_8$ | octane | | |

**1.** Find the longest continuous carbon chain, regardless of the direction of the chain, and write the parent name.

$$\overset{(6)}{}CH_3-\overset{5}{\underset{4... }{C}}H-\overset{4}{\underset{4}{C}}H(Cl)-\overset{3}{\underset{5}{C}}H_2-\overset{2}{\underset{6}{C}}H(Br)-\overset{1}{\underset{7}{C}}H_3$$

$$\begin{array}{l} \quad |^{3} \\ {}^{6}CH_2 \\ \quad |^{2} \\ {}^{7}\underset{1}{C}H_3 \end{array}$$

(choice of numbering depends on rule 3)

In this case the longest carbon chain contains seven carbons, and the compound is therefore a ***heptane***.

**2.** For compounds containing functional groups, the ***primary function***, such as

$-OH \qquad >C=O \qquad$ or $\qquad -CO_2H$

is given the lowest number. Next in order of numbering come double bonds, triple bonds, and finally substituents such as an alkyl group or halogen atom. Usually the longest chain including the maximum number of functional groups or substituents is chosen.

**3.** Number the carbon atoms in the chain given below so that the functional groups or substituents are given the ***lowest*** possible number.

$$\begin{array}{ccccccccc} & & & & Cl & & & & \\ & & | & & | & & | & & | \\ - & & C & - & C & - & C & - & C - Br \\ & & | & & | & & | & & | \\ & & & & Cl & & & & \end{array}$$

(Note that in the numbers 1,3,3 are lower than 2,2,4 as determined by the smallest *individual* number, that is, 1 vs. 2.) The numbering of the example is

```
      5      4          3      2          1
CH3—CH—CH(Cl)—CH2—CH(Br)—CH3
      |
     6CH2
      |
     7CH3
```

since 2,4,5 is lower than 3,4,6.

**4.** Give each substituent a name and a number, using prefixes di- (2), tri- (3), tetra- (4), penta- (5), hexa- (6), etc. If there is a choice, use either alphabetical (bromo before chloro) or size (methyl before ethyl) preference. The name of the compound used as an example is **2-bromo-4-chloro-5-methylheptane.**

**5.** Complex side chains are named by indicating the point of attachment to the main chain, denoting this carbon 1 of the side chain and enclosing the side-chain name in parentheses.

```
                                                  CH2—CH3
                9       8       7       6     5    4   3|   2     1
Examples:  CH3—CH2—CH2—CH2—CH—CH—C—CH2—CH3
                                          |     |    |
                                         1CH  CH3  CH2—CH3
                                         / \      3
                                      H3C  2CH2CH3
```

4-methyl-3,3-diethyl-5-(1-methylpropyl)nonane
(4-methyl-3,3-diethyl-5-*sec*-butylnonane)

```
         1
       H3C  CH3
        2|  3|
  CH3—C—C—CH2—CH3
         |   4|
       H3C  CH2
             5|
             CH
            /  \
         H3C   6CH3
```

2,2,3,5-tetramethyl-3-ethylhexane

(Any of the three terminal methyl groups could have been numbered 1, and either of the higher-end terminal ones could have been numbered 6.)

```
                              CH3
                               |
                   CH3        CH2
                   5|   4     3|
CH3—CH2—C—CH2—C—CH3
                    |          |
                  6CH2       2CH2
                    |          |
                  7CH2       1CH3
                    |
                  8CH3
```

3,5-dimethyl-3,5-diethyloctane

## PHYSICAL PROPERTIES

Although the first four hydrocarbons in the alkane series are gases at room temperature, the $C_5$ to $C_{18}$ normal alkanes are liquids. *n*-Pentane (b.p. 36°) and *n*-hexane (b.p. 68°) are often used as solvents because they are easily removed by distillation. Branching hydrocarbons generally have lower boiling points than the normal ones.

The specific gravity, which is the density of a compound *relative* to that of water at the same temperature, ranges from about 0.6 to 0.8 for alkanes. Since alkanes are immiscible with water, they float on the surface.

## REACTIONS

The alkanes are rather unreactive and generally insoluble not only in the common polar solvents such as water but also in cold (25°) concentrated sulfuric acid. Under specified conditions these hydrocarbons do undergo a few reactions, most of which are not good laboratory preparations; however, the industrial applications of these reactions are many and varied.

### 2-4 $O_2$: COMBUSTION ANALYSIS

The reaction of fuels (alkanes) with air (oxygen) releases energy which provides power for many uses in our industrial society. The complete combustion of organic compounds in the laboratory allows us to calculate the simplest, or *empirical, formula.* When the weight of the organic compound which is burned in excess oxygen and the weights of $CO_2$ and $H_2O$ produced are known, the empirical formula can be calculated.

*Example*: $C_3H_8 + 5O_2 \longrightarrow 3CO_2 + 4H_2O$

(If you are interested in more detailed numerical problems, consult a general chemistry text.) In order to determine the unique *molecular formula*, it is necessary to know also the molecular weight.

### 2-5 $Cl_2$, $Br_2$: PHOTOCHEMICAL HALOGENATION

Alkanes react with chlorine or bromine in the presence of light to give halogenated hydrocarbons. Elemental fluorine reacts with explosive violence, and the net result is usually the formation of carbon tetrafluoride, $CF_4$, by the rupture of all carbon-carbon bonds. In striking contrast, iodine, $I_2$, is unreactive toward alkanes even when an excess is employed at high temperatures. With $Cl_2$ and $Br_2$ the reaction usually does not give the monohalogenated product exclusively.

*General*: $R—H + Cl_2 \xrightarrow{h\nu} R—Cl + HCl$

*Specific*: $CH_4 + Cl_2 \xrightarrow{h\nu} CH_3Cl + HCl$

methyl chloride (chloromethane)

This may react further:

$CH_3Cl + Cl_2 \xrightarrow{h\nu} CH_2Cl_2 + HCl$

methylene chloride (dichloromethane)

The symbols $h\nu$ represent light energy of the appropriate frequency and come from the equation $E = h\nu$, where $E$ = energy, $h$ = Planck's constant and $\nu$ (Greek nu) = frequency.

$CH_3CH_3 + I_2(xs) \xrightarrow{h\nu}$ N.R.

If no reaction occurs in a reasonable time under the conditions normally employed for a given reaction, we shall write N.R. meaning *no reaction*. We shall abbreviate the word ''excess'' as xs.

Under photochemical halogenation conditions an aromatic ring containing a methyl group will be halogenated preferentially at the methyl group; further halogenation occurs at a second methyl group, if possible.

*Examples*: toluene $\xrightarrow[h\nu]{Br_2}$ benzyl bromide

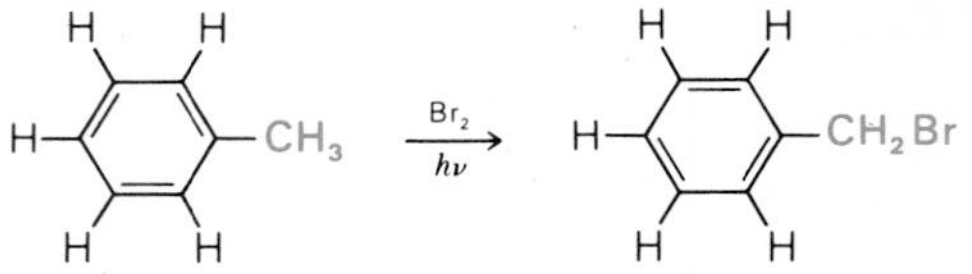

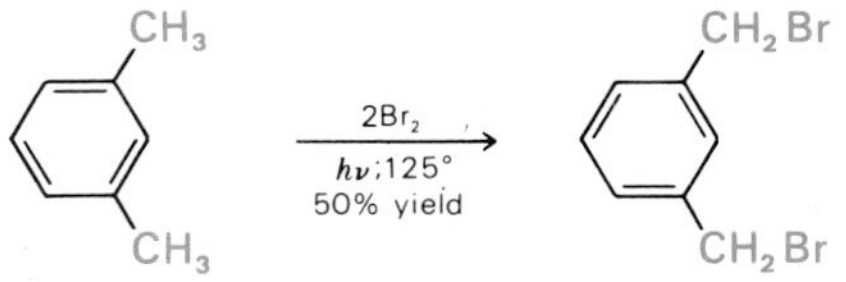

o-xylene $\xrightarrow[h\nu; 125°, 50\% \text{ yield}]{2Br_2}$ (bis(bromomethyl)benzene, $CH_2Br$ / $CH_2Br$)

## 2-6 THE FREE-RADICAL MECHANISM OF PHOTOCHEMICAL HALOGENATION

In the previous section the general and specific reactions for photochemical halogenation were illustrated, but we have not yet shown *how* the reaction takes place. Here we wish to describe formally the electrons and their approximate position *during* the course of the reaction.

The Heisenberg uncertainty principle states that the position and the momentum (hence, energy) of a particle can be determined only to a given approximation. Thus, any mechanism we write will be an approximation of the relative values of time and energy.

Although many organic reactions occur via ionic species, i.e., by an *ionic mechanism*, photochemical halogenation and others we shall study later occur by way of *free-radical* pathways. A free radical is an uncharged atom or group of bound atoms one of which has an unpaired electron and needs an additional electron to complete its octet. Examples are:

Bromine atom: $:\ddot{\underset{..}{Br}}\cdot$

Methyl radical: $H:\overset{H}{\underset{H}{\ddot{\underset{..}{C}}}}\cdot$

Often only the unpaired electron is represented, as follows: Br · or $CH_3\cdot$. Ionic mechanisms are the favored pathways of reactions which take place in polar solution and between reactants which contain easily polarized bonds, because the formation of ions is facilitated by polarized bonds and the charges can be dispersed by polar solvents. Free-radical mechanisms are the favored pathways of reactions in the gas phase or in nonpolar solvents because radicals are uncharged but very reactive species which tend to gain electrons. Free-radical reactions are often aided by light or high temperatures in the formation of the initial radicals. Peroxides, compounds containing the weak —O—O— bond, are also good radical sources since gentle heating often serves to break the —O—O— bond.

$$H—O—O—H \xrightarrow{\Delta} 2HO\cdot$$

Photochemical halogenation is also a ***chain reaction***, one in which only a few initiating radicals are sufficient to produce many times their number of products. The steps of a chain reaction may be labeled initiation, propagation, and termination.

*Mechanism*

Initiation: $Cl_2 \xrightarrow{h\nu} 2Cl\cdot$

Propagation: $Cl\cdot + CH_4 \longrightarrow CH_3\cdot + HCl$

$CH_3\cdot + Cl_2 \longrightarrow CH_3Cl + Cl\cdot$

These two steps are repeated many times

Termination: $Cl\cdot + Cl\cdot \longrightarrow Cl_2$ reverse of initiation

$Cl\cdot + CH_3\cdot \longrightarrow CH_3Cl$ *minor* source of product

$CH_3\cdot + CH_3\cdot \longrightarrow CH_3CH_3$

The *initiation* step produces the first radicals, which serve to initiate the chain process. The *propagation* steps involve no *net* destruction of radicals, and the Cl· formed in the second propagation step may then react further with $CH_4$ and continue, at least theoretically, indefinitely. However, the *termination* steps do result in the *net loss* of radical species, which, by combining with each other, interrupt the chain process. Often the initial radical allows several thousand propagation reactions to take place before a termination step occurs. Because they are high-energy species, radicals often combine on or with the walls of the reaction vessel.

The first-formed product, $CH_3Cl$ in this case, may react further, and usually all possible substitution products are observed, at least in trace quantities. The reaction conditions and relative proportions of reagents determine the main product.

$$Cl_2 + CH_4(xs) \xrightarrow{h\nu} CH_3Cl + HCl$$

$$Cl_2(xs) + CH_4 \xrightarrow{h\nu} CCl_4 + HCl$$

| $CH_4$ | $\longrightarrow$ $CH_3Cl$ | $\longrightarrow$ $CH_2Cl_2$ | $\longrightarrow$ $CHCl_3$ | $\longrightarrow$ $CCl_4$ |
|---|---|---|---|---|
| | methyl chloride | methylene chloride | chloroform | carbon tetrachloride, trivial |
| methane | (chloromethane) | (dichloromethane) | (trichloromethane) | (tetrachloromethane, IUPAC) |

In the first propagation step the Cl· attacks the $CH_4$ molecule. In this book reactive unisolated intermediates (such as Cl·) and transition states will be enclosed in brackets; dotted lines will be used to represent bonds being formed or broken in the transition state between starting materials and products.

$$[Cl\cdot] + H{-}\underset{H}{\overset{H}{\underset{|}{\overset{|}{C}}}}{-}H \longrightarrow \left[ Cl\cdots H\cdots \underset{H}{\overset{H}{\underset{|}{\overset{|}{C}}}}{-}H \right]^{\bullet} \longrightarrow Cl{-}H + [CH_3\cdot]$$

transition state

Like carbonium ions, free radicals seek electrons to complete their octet. They are therefore attracted to centers of high electron density and are said to be *electrophilic*. The ease of removal of hydrogen atoms from an alkane is in the order 3° > 2° > 1°, since the order of stability of the resulting carbon radicals is 3° > 2° > 1°. A tertiary (or secondary) radical is stabilized, in part, by the resonance contributions of the following type, in which the hydrogens on the adjacent carbons release electrons to the carbon atom bearing the electron:

$$\mathrm{H_3C{-}\dot{C}H{-}CH_3}\ (\text{with } \mathrm{CH_3}) \longleftrightarrow \mathrm{H_3C{-}C(=CH_2)\,{\cdot}H{-}CH_3} \longleftrightarrow \mathrm{H_3C{-}C(=CH_2){-}CH_3\ \dot{H}}$$

$\updownarrow$

and others

This contribution is small, but it is sufficient to increase the stabilization of the secondary or tertiary radical or carbonium ion. It is in this context that a methyl group (or other alkyl group to a lesser extent) is said to donate electrons.

*Example*:

$$\underset{\text{isobutane}}{\mathrm{CH_3{-}C(CH_3)_2{-}H}} \xrightarrow[h\nu]{Br_2} \underset{\substack{t\text{-butyl bromide}\\ \text{major}}}{\mathrm{CH_3{-}C(CH_3)_2{-}Br}} + \underset{\substack{\text{isobutyl bromide}\\ \text{minor}}}{\mathrm{CH_3{-}CH(CH_3){-}CH_2Br}}$$

> How many monochlorohexanes can be formed from *n*-hexane? How many dichloro isomers can be formed from each of the monochloro compounds? Name all of the compounds.

## PREPARATION

The ***synthesis*** of both known compounds and new compounds plays an important role in organic chemistry. Since a variety of methods is usually available for the preparation of any given molecule, the method of choice is based on several factors: purity (how difficult is the separation of side products from the desired material?), yield (which method will give the greatest amount of desired product in the highest purity?), ease of operation (can the reaction be readily carried out in the ***laboratory*** in a reasonable length of time using available equipment?), and, finally, cost and availability of starting material. Cost is not usually an important factor in research work if the compound is needed in only small amounts. Often there is more than one feasible laboratory sequence starting with available chemicals and using common reactions.

When preparations and reactions are discussed, you should ask: Where does the starting material come from? Is it commercially available? How can it be synthesized? Many of the starting materials in this chapter are alkyl halides, which can usually be prepared from the corresponding alcohol and hydrogen halide. Most simple alcohols are commercially available.

## 2-7 THE GRIGNARD REACTION

The Grignard reagent, RMgX or ArMgX, prepared from an alkyl halide and magnesium, is one of the most important and versatile reactants in organic chemistry; it will be discussed in detail in Chap. 9. Hydrocarbons can be synthesized by treating a Grignard reagent with a compound containing a weakly acidic hydrogen.

*General*: $$\text{R—X} \xrightarrow[\text{dry ether}]{\text{Mg in}} [\text{R—MgX}] \xrightarrow{\text{H—OH}} \text{R—H} + \text{Mg(OH)X}$$

Hydrogen atoms bonded to an acetylene, —C≡C—H, or to such heteroatoms as O, N, and S are commonly acidic enough to react with the Grignard reagent and are therefore said to be ***active hydrogens***. Alcohols, R—O—H, phenols, Ar—O—H, and acids, —COOH, all react to yield hydrocarbons with the Grignard reagent.

The organometallic reagent is prepared by the direct action of magnesium metal on an alkyl or aromatic halide (not fluoride) in a ***dry*** solvent, such as:

Ether: $CH_3CH_2—\ddot{\underset{..}{O}}—CH_2CH_3$ or Tetrahydrofuran (THF): [five-membered ring with :Ö:]

The actual structure of the Grignard reagent has been the subject of much recent research, which has shown that the detailed structural description varies with the particular Grignard reagent and solvent under consideration. Here we shall use RMgX for an alkylmagnesium halide and ArMgX for an arylmagnesium halide, with the realization that this is an oversimplified notation which explains the chemical results only in the simplest terms. The bond polarization of the C—Mg bond indicates the anion character of the alkyl or aryl group $\overset{\delta-}{\text{R}}—\overset{\delta+}{\text{MgX}}$.

*Specific*:

$$CH_3CH_2CH_2I \xrightarrow[\text{dry ether}]{\text{Mg in}} \underset{\substack{n\text{-propylmagnesium iodide} \\ \text{(not isolated)}}}{[CH_3CH_2CH_2MgI]} \xrightarrow{H_2O} CH_3CH_2CH_3 + \text{Mg(OH)I}$$

$$C_6H_5\text{—Br} \xrightarrow[\text{2. } D_2O \text{ (water-}d_2\text{)}]{\text{1. Mg in dry ether}} C_6H_5\text{—D}$$

(Note the use of "heavy water," deuterium oxide, to introduce an isotope.) The last equation shows the successive steps of the reaction in abbreviated form. The reagents are enumerated over the arrow in the order in which they are used.

## 2-8 REDUCTION OF ALKYL HALIDES

**Lithium aluminum hydride**: An excellent reducing agent, lithium aluminum hydride, $LiAlH_4$, is formally a source of hydride ion, $H^-$, in preparing hydrocarbons from halogen derivatives. It will reduce many multiply bonded functional groups except isolated carbon-carbon double or triple bonds. Dry ether and THF are the commonly used solvents. For isotopic preparations, $LiAlD_4$ is available for use as a solvent.

$$CH_2{=}CH{-}CH_2Cl \xrightarrow[\text{85\% yield}]{LiAlH_4} CH_2{=}CH{-}CH_3 + LiCl + AlCl_3$$

allyl chloride (3-chloropropene) → propene

$$CH_3(CH_2)_8CH_2Br \xrightarrow[\text{70\% yield}]{LiAlH_4} CH_3(CH_2)_8CH_3$$

1-bromodecane → *n*-decane

**Hydrogenolysis**: The breaking of a carbon-heteroatom bond, such as C—X, with hydrogen and a catalyst is called ***hydrogenolysis***. Such metals as platinum, Pt, palladium, Pd, ruthenium, Ru, rhodium, Rh, and nickel, Ni, have been used as catalysts for the reaction. The hydrogen molecule is dissociated into hydrogen atoms on the metal surface, where the hydrogenolysis takes place.

$$CH_3CH_2CH_2Cl \xrightarrow{H_2/Pt} CH_3CH_2CH_3 + HCl$$

**Hydriodic acid and phosphorus**: A reducing system of hydriodic acid, HI, containing red phosphorus as a catalyst is sufficient to convert an alkyl halide to the corresponding hydrocarbon.

$$(CH_3)_2CHI \xrightarrow[\Delta]{HI/\text{red P}} CH_3CH_2CH_3 + I_2$$

## 2-9 HYDROGENATION OF ALKENES AND ALKYNES

*Unsaturated* hydrocarbons are those containing carbon-carbon double or triple bonds. Although the following chapters consider alkenes and alkynes in greater detail, it should be noted that catalytic hydrogenation or deuteration (addition of $H_2$ or $D_2$ to the unsaturated bond) leads to alkanes in nearly 100% yields.

*General*: $R_2C{=}CR_2 \xrightarrow{H_2/Pt \text{ or } Pd} R{-}CHR{-}CHR{-}R$

an alkene → an alkane

$R{-}C{\equiv}C{-}R \xrightarrow{H_2/Pt \text{ or } Pd} R{-}CH_2{-}CH_2{-}R$

an alkyne → an alkane

In these equations R = —H, alkyl, and aryl groups, which may all be the same (R) or different (R, R', R'', etc.).

*Specific*: $CH_2{=}CH{-}CH_3 \xrightarrow{H_2/Pt} CH_3CH_2CH_3$

propene → propane

$CH_2{=}CH_2 \xrightarrow{D_2/Pd} CH_2D{-}CH_2D$

ethylene → ethane-1,2-$d_2$

$C_6H_5{-}CH{=}CH_2 \xrightarrow{H_2/Pd} C_6H_5{-}CH_2CH_3$

styrene → ethylbenzene

$C_6H_5{-}C{\equiv}C{-}H \xrightarrow{2H_2/Pd} C_6H_5{-}CH_2CH_3$

phenylacetylene

The aromatic system of a benzene ring is preserved under the usual conditions of reduction (30°, 1 atm of hydrogen). Under more strenuous conditions or with the use of very active catalysts, the ring itself may be reduced.

Catalytic hydrogenation is a facile means of determining the degree of unsaturation *quantitatively*.

*Example*: Suppose that 1 mole of compound A, $C_4H_6$, takes up 2 moles of hydrogen. This tells us that the product, $C_4H_{10}$, is saturated and contains no rings (cycloalkanes are of the $C_nH_{2n}$ series) and that A must contain either two double bonds or one triple bond. A unique structure cannot be determined; compound A may be any one of the following:

$CH_2{=}CH{-}CH{=}CH_2$ (1,3-butadiene) $CH_3{-}CH{=}C{=}CH_2$ (1,2-butadiene) $CH_3{-}C{\equiv}C{-}CH_3$ (dimethylacetylene) $CH_3CH_2C{\equiv}CH$ (ethylacetylene)

## 2-10 THE WURTZ REACTION

Symmetrical paraffin hydrocarbons can be prepared by treating a single alkyl halide with sodium (the Wurtz reaction). The result is the joining of two alkyl groups with loss of the halogens. The synthesized hydrocarbon, therefore, contains an even number of carbon atoms. Generally it is a poor synthetic method, but it does have limited use. The main difficulty is the formation of many side products resulting from breaking of the carbon-carbon bond and rearrangement of the carbon skeleton of the alkyl groups.

*General*: $2RX \xrightarrow{2Na} R{-}R + 2NaX$

*Specific*: $2CH_3CH_2CH_2CH_2Br \xrightarrow{2Na} CH_3(CH_2)_6CH_3 + 2NaBr$

1-bromobutane → octane

The reaction is usually carried out by heating the alkyl halide with sodium in a solvent that does not react with these reagents, such as diethyl ether (called simply ether) or 1,4-dioxane, an example of a heterocycle.

$CH_3CH_2{-}\ddot{\underset{\cdot\cdot}{O}}{-}CH_2CH_3$

ether

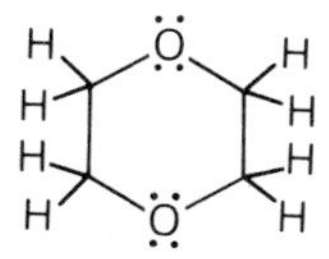

1,4-dioxane

The reaction may afford fair yields of hydrocarbons *symmetrical* about a carbon-carbon bond, but it can seldom be used with two different halides to prepare an unsymmetrical compound or one with an odd number of carbons. The desired reaction *does* take place, but the products may be difficult to separate, and others (not shown) which may be formed by rearrangement reactions can complicate the purification procedure. Finally, most organic reactions do not give a 100% yield, and it is always necessary to consider the removal of unreacted starting material.

Name these compounds.

$$CH_3-\underset{\underset{I}{|}}{CH}-CH_3 + CH_3CH_2CH_2I \xrightarrow{Na} (H_3C)_2CH-CH(CH_3)_2 + CH_3(CH_2)_4CH_3 + CH_3\underset{\underset{CH_3}{|}}{CH}CH_2CH_2CH_3$$

b.p. 90° | 102° | 58° | 69° | 60°

## 2-11 WURTZ-FITTIG REACTION

The synthesis of an alkylaryl hydrocarbon can be accomplished by heating an aliphatic and an aromatic halide with sodium in an inert solvent. This *is* a mixed, or crossed, reaction of two halides and is known as the Wurtz-Fittig reaction. There are usually better methods of synthesizing the desired hydrocarbon; however, the products are often separable because of the vast differences in molecular weight and thus in physical properties.

*General*: $$Ar-X + R-X \xrightarrow[\Delta]{Na} Ar-R + R-R + Ar-Ar$$

*Specific*: $$C_6H_5-Br + CH_3Br \xrightarrow[\Delta]{Na} C_6H_5-CH_3 + CH_3CH_3 + C_6H_5-C_6H_5$$

toluene, a liquid, b.p. 110° | ethane, a gas, b.p. −88° | biphenyl, a solid, m.p. 70°

$$C_6H_5-Br + CH_3CH_2CH_2CH_2Br \xrightarrow[\text{dry ether, 65\% yield}]{\text{Na in}} C_6H_5-CH_2CH_2CH_2CH_3$$

*n*-butylbenzene

## 2-12 DECARBOXYLATION OF ACIDS AND THEIR SALTS

Treatment of a carboxylic acid, R—COOH, with a base such as NaOH gives the corresponding sodium salt. If this salt is then heated strongly with soda lime (a mixture of CaO and NaOH), the products are the ***next lower hydrocarbon*** and carbon dioxide; one carbon is lost from the organic compound. The new hydrogen atom in the product is derived from the soda lime.

*General*: $$\text{R—COOH} \xrightarrow{\text{base}} \text{RCO}_2^-\text{Na}^+ \xrightarrow[\text{CaO-NaOH}]{\Delta} \text{R—H} + \text{CO}_2\uparrow$$

*Specific*: $$\underset{\text{acetic acid}}{\text{CH}_3\text{COOH}} \xrightarrow[\text{2. }\Delta;\text{ CaO-NaOH}]{\text{1. NaOH}} \underset{\text{methane}}{\text{CH}_4} + \text{CO}_2\uparrow$$

Although methane is obtained from acetic acid, $CH_3COOH$, in good yields, many other acids afford only 10 to 20% of the corresponding hydrocarbon. Decarboxylation of the acid itself, rather than the salt, is often more satisfactory. The direct decarboxylation of an acid can be effected by heating it in an organic base, such as pyridine, with a catalytic amount of copper chromite, $CuO \cdot Cr_2O_3$.

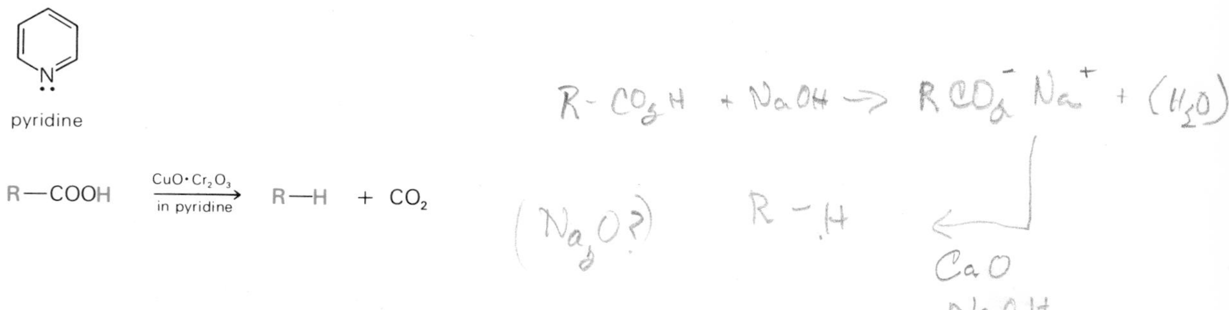

pyridine

$$\text{R—COOH} \xrightarrow[\text{in pyridine}]{\text{CuO}\cdot\text{Cr}_2\text{O}_3} \text{R—H} + \text{CO}_2$$

### QUALITATIVE ANALYSIS

Because alkanes have no functional groups, they are usually identified on the basis of their nonreactivity rather than by their transformations to other molecules. Alkanes are often identified by simple physical means such as melting point, boiling point, density, and refractive index. They are insoluble in the common solvents of qualitative organic analysis, namely, water, dilute NaOH, dilute HCl, and concentrated $H_2SO_4$.

## SUGGESTED READINGS


### Occurrence and reactions

March, J.: The Decarboxylation of Organic Acids, *J. Chem. Educ.*, **40**, 212 (1963).

Mason, B.: Organic Matter from Space, *Sci. Am.*, **208** (3), 43 (1963). Reviews findings that meteorites contain a number of known hydrocarbons.

Pinkerton, R. C.: Electrochemistry and the Alkyl Free Radicals, *J. Chem. Educ.*, **39**, 554 (1962).

Rossini, F. D.: Hydrocarbons in Petroleum, *J. Chem. Educ.*, **37**, 554 (1960).

Russell, G. A.: Fundamental Processes of Autoxidation, *J. Chem. Educ.*, **36**, 111 (1959). Discusses the mechanism of oxidations of organic compounds with molecular oxygen.

### Nomenclature

Hurd, C. D.: The General Philosophy of Organic Nomenclature, *J. Chem. Educ.*, **38**, 43 (1961).

Soloveichik, S., and H. Krakauer: Oxidation Stages of Organic Aliphatic Compounds, *J. Chem. Educ.*, **43**, 532 (1966). Assigns an oxidation stage to organic molecules on the basis of the oxidation stage of the carbon atom bearing the functional group.

### Conformational analysis

Eyring, H., D. M. Grant, and H. Hecht: The Rotational Barrier in Ethane, *J. Chem. Educ.*, **39**, 466 (1962).

Miller, S. I.: Rotational and Pseudorotational Barriers in Simple Molecules, *J. Chem. Educ.*, **41**, 421 (1964).


## PROBLEMS

**1.** In addition to cyclic compounds, the following paraffins have been isolated in 0.05 to 1.1% by volume from a distilled sample of gasoline from a well in Ponca City, Oklahoma. Write the structure for each of these compounds and label each carbon atom as primary (1°), secondary (2°), tertiary (3°), or quaternary (4°).

★(*a*) 2,3-dimethylbutane
★(*b*) 2-methylpentane
(*c*) *n*-hexane
(*d*) 2-methylhexane
(*e*) *n*-heptane
(*f*) *n*-octane
★(*g*) 2,3-dimethylheptane
(*h*) 4-methyloctane
(*i*) *n*-nonane
(*j*) 2-methylbutane
★(*k*) 2,2-dimethylpentane
(*l*) 3-methylhexane
(*m*) 2-methylheptane
(*n*) 2,6-dimethylheptane
(*o*) 4-methyloctane
(*p*) 3-methyloctane
(*q*) *n*-decane

**2**. Name each of the following compounds.

★(*a*) $CH_3—CHBr—CHBr—CHBr—CH_3$

★(*b*) $CH_3—C(CH_3)_2—C(CH_3)_2—C(CH_3)_3$

★(*c*) $CH_2Cl—CHBr—CH_3$

(*d*) $CH_3CH_2CH_2CH(CH_3)CH(F)CH_3$

(*e*) $CH_3(CH_2)_8CH_2Br$

★(*f*) $CH_3—CH_2—CH—CH_2—CH_3$ (with a benzene ring on the CH)

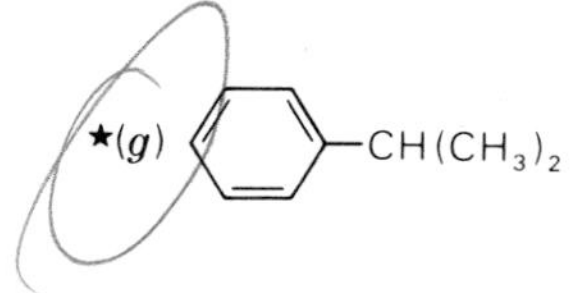

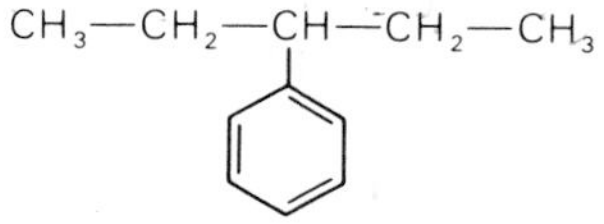

★(*g*) $C_6H_5—CH(CH_3)_2$

(*h*)

$$\begin{array}{c} CH_2—CH_2—CH_3 \\ | \\ CH_3CH_2—C—CH_2—CH_2—CH_2—CH_2—Cl \\ | \\ CH_3 \end{array}$$

**3**. Write the structure of:

(*a*) all the octanes, $C_8H_{18}$, and name them (***Hint***: There are 18.)

(*b*) the octanes which could be prepared by treating a halide with sodium (Wurtz reaction)

(*c*) all the $C_8H_{18}O$ alcohols. Name each and label it as a primary (1°), secondary (2°), or tertiary (3°) alcohol. The —OH group is considered a principal function, and $CH_3CH_2CH_2CH_2OH$ is named 1-butanol rather than 1-hydroxybutane.

*Example*:

$$\begin{array}{c} \qquad\qquad\qquad CH_3 \\ \qquad\qquad\qquad | \\ CH_3—CH—CH_2—C—CH_3 \\ \quad | \qquad\qquad | \\ \quad CH_3 \qquad\quad CH_3 \end{array}$$

2,2,4-trimethylpentane (cannot be prepared by the Wurtz reaction)

$$\begin{array}{l} CH_2—CH—CH_2—C(CH_3)_3 \\ | \qquad | \\ OH \quad CH_3 \end{array}$$

1° alcohol
2,4,4-trimethyl-1-pentanol

$$\begin{array}{l} \qquad\quad OH \\ \qquad\quad | \\ CH_3—C—CH_2—C(CH_3)_3 \\ \qquad\quad | \\ \qquad\quad CH_3 \end{array}$$

3°
2,4,4-trimethyl-2-pentanol

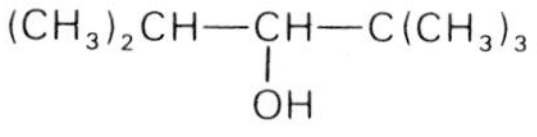

$$\begin{array}{l} (CH_3)_2CH—CH—C(CH_3)_3 \\ \qquad\qquad\quad | \\ \qquad\qquad\quad OH \end{array}$$

2°
2,2,4-trimethyl-3-pentanol

$$\begin{array}{l} \qquad\qquad\qquad\qquad CH_3 \\ \qquad\qquad\qquad\qquad | \\ (CH_3)_2CH—CH_2—C—CH_2OH \\ \qquad\qquad\qquad\qquad | \\ \qquad\qquad\qquad\qquad CH_3 \end{array}$$

1°
2,2,4-trimethyl-1-pentanol

Note that the —OH, a functional group, is given the lowest number.

★**4**. Compound A, $C_{14}H_{30}$, was prepared by treating compound **B**, $C_7H_{15}I$, with sodium in ether. Treatment of **B** with $LiAlH_4$ yielded compound **C**. Although **A** gave two monobromo compounds (**D**, **E**) on photochemical bromination, **C** gave three monobromo compounds (**F**, **G**, **H**) of which compound **F** predominated. Give structures and names for each of the lettered compounds.

**5**. Name the starting material and give the structural formula and name of the product(s). If no reaction occurs, write N.R.

★(*a*) $CH_3CH_2I$ + chlorocyclohexane $\xrightarrow{Na}$

★(*b*) $CH_3CH_2CH_3$ $\xrightarrow{LiAlH_4}$

★(*c*) iodocyclopentane $\xrightarrow[\text{dry ether}]{\text{Mg in}}$

★(*d*) product in (*c*) $\xrightarrow{CH_3CH_2OH}$

(*e*) $CH_3{-}CH{=}CH{-}CH_2Cl$ $\xrightarrow[\Delta]{H_2/Pt}$

★(*f*) cyclopentene $\xrightarrow{D_2/Pt}$

(*g*) $C_6H_5{-}OH$ + $[CH_3CH_2MgBr]$ $\longrightarrow$

★(*h*) biphenyl $\xrightarrow[25°]{H_2/Pt}$

(*i*) $CH_3CO_2H$ $\xrightarrow[\text{2. soda lime; }\Delta]{\text{1. KOH}}$

(*j*) methylcyclohexane $\xrightarrow[h\nu]{Cl_2}$

(*k*) $CH_3CH_2CH_3$ $\xrightarrow{F_2}$

**6**. Write a reasonable mechanism for the photochemical bromination of ethane. Label the initiation, propagation, and termination steps.

★**7**. Indicate syntheses of the following compounds from these organic starting materials:

$CH_2{=}CH{-}CH_2{-}Br$ $\qquad$ p-iodotoluene ($H_3C{-}C_6H_4{-}I$) $\qquad$ $(CH_3)_3C{-}Cl$

(*a*) $CH_3—C(CH_3)(H)—CH_3$

(*b*) $H_3C—C_6H_4—D$ (para)

(*c*) $CH_2D—CHD—CH_2—CH_2—CHD—CH_2D$

(*d*) $H_3C—C_6H_4—CH_2CH_2CH_3$ (para)

(*e*) $CH_3—C(CH_3)_2—C(CH_3)(CH_2Cl)—CH_3$

# Chapter Three

The relationship between *cycloalkanes* and alkanes can be visualized as the result of removing two nonadjacent hydrogen atoms from the latter and joining the carbon atoms to form a ring. Of course, they are not actually prepared in this way. Cycloalkanes, or *alicyclics* as they are sometimes called, belong to the $C_nH_{2n}$ homologous series. The chemistry of these compounds, except for cyclopropanes and cyclobutanes, is like that of the alkanes; i.e., cycloalkanes do not dissolve in concentrated sulfuric acid but do undergo some free-radical substitution reactions of limited laboratory value.

This chapter is confined to a discussion of the lower members of the series and the geometry of cyclohexanes.

## NOMENCLATURE

The parent cycloalkanes are named by adding the prefix *cyclo-* to the alkane name. The carbon atoms of the rings are numbered so that substituents are given the lowest possible numbers. Substituents on the *same* side of the ring are denoted *cis* and those *across* from each other, with respect to the ring, are labeled ***trans***. A similar nomenclature is followed for substituents on a double bond, in which such geometrical isomerism (isomerism based on configuration rather than order of linkage) is also possible.

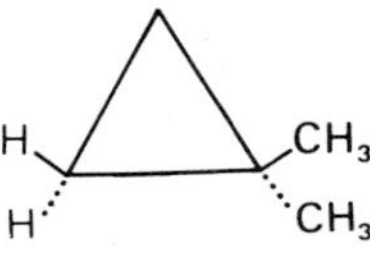


1,1-dimethyl-
cyclopropane

H₃C CH₃
H H

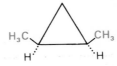

*cis*-1,2-dimethyl-
cyclopropane

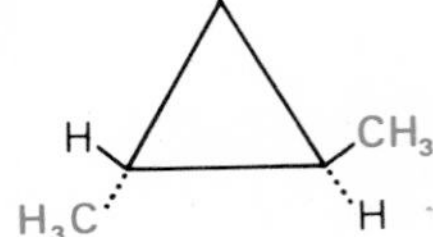


*trans*-1,2-dimethyl-
cyclopropane

# Cycloalkanes

Table 3-1 gives representative examples of simple and substituted cycloalkanes.

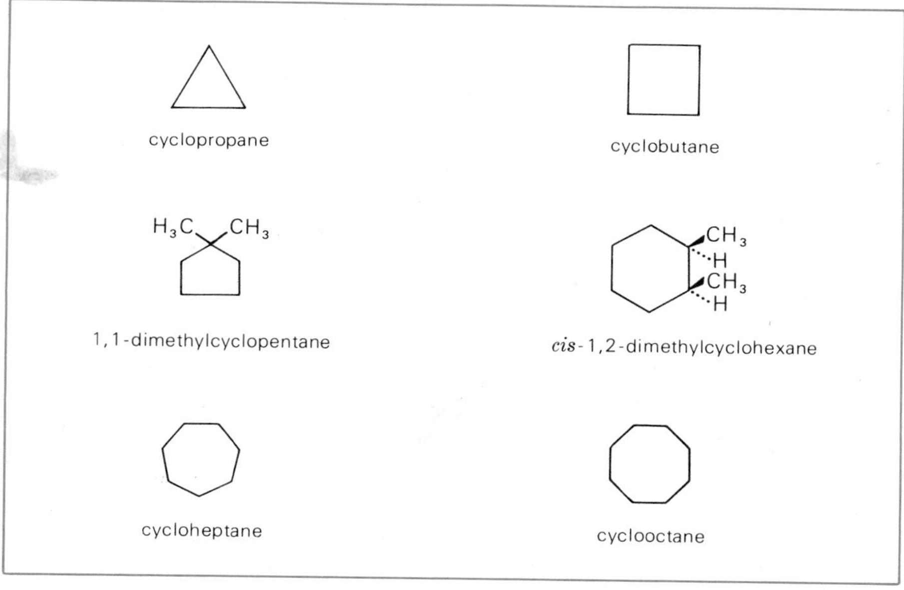


**Table 3-1**
**Representative cycloalkanes**

## CONFORMATIONAL STRUCTURES

### 3-1 CYCLOPROPANE, CYCLOBUTANE, AND CYCLOPENTANE

The molecular geometry of a given chemical structure is called its *conformation*. The three carbon atoms of cyclopropane define a plane, and the six hydrogen atoms are located in two parallel planes above and below it. The cyclobutane carbon skeleton, which deviates slightly from planarity might be described as a "butterfly-wings" conformation. Four of the carbon atoms in cyclopentane are nearly planar, but the fifth is puckered out of the plane, in what has been described as an "envelope" conformation (see Fig. 3-1). Each of these conformations represents a state of minimum energy among the various possibilities available to the molecule.

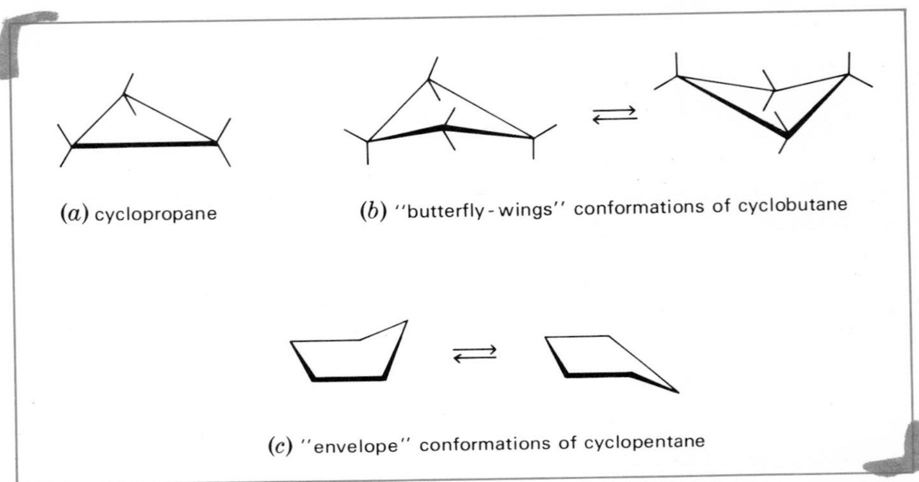

**Figure 3-1 Conformations of $C_3$—$C_5$ cycloalkanes**

(*a*) cyclopropane (*b*) "butterfly-wings" conformations of cyclobutane (*c*) "envelope" conformations of cyclopentane

### 3-2 CYCLOHEXANE CONFORMATIONAL ANALYSIS

Cyclohexane is not planar but may oscillate (or flip) between two preferred chair forms of low energy via a high-energy conformation which somewhat resembles a boat or twisted boat (see Fig. 3-2). Although

**Figure 3-2 Chair and boat conformations of cyclohexane**

chair boat chair

the normal tetrahedral angle is 109°28′, the carbon-carbon bond angles in cyclopropane are 60°, and those in cyclobutane are 90°; thus cyclopropanes and cyclobutanes are highly strained. Cyclopentanes and cyclohexanes relieve the strain which would be present if they were planar by adopting these lower-energy conformations, which allow the carbon-carbon bond angles to become very close to the tetrahedral 109°.

The boat form of cyclohexane is of considerably higher energy than the chair forms as a result of ***steric repulsion*** or ***nonbonded interactions*** of $H_1$ and $H_4$ and of the eclipsed $H_2$ and $H_3$ atoms. Atoms which are not bonded to one another but which are very close because of the molecular conformation may exert either attractive or repulsive forces. These forces are called steric attractions or repulsions or, more generally, nonbonded interactions (see Fig. 3-3*a*). Since the boat form is unstable relative to the possible chair conformations, it is omitted in the following discussion.

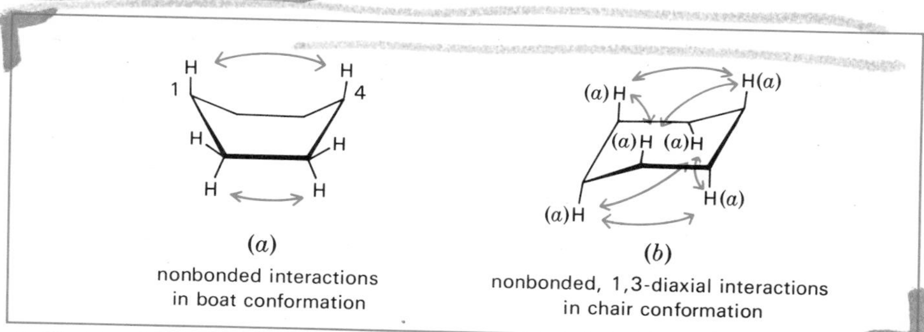


(*a*)
nonbonded interactions in boat conformation

(*b*)
nonbonded, 1,3-diaxial interactions in chair conformation

**Figure 3-3**

The carbon atoms $C_2$, $C_3$, $C_5$, and $C_6$ of cyclohexane lie nearly in one plane, and ***relative to this plane*** all hydrogen atoms may be labeled as either ***equatorial*** (bonds lying more or less in this plane) or ***axial*** (bonds lying more or less perpendicular to this plane). When one form flips, all those substituents which were axial (*a*) become equatorial (*e*) and vice versa (see Fig. 3-4).

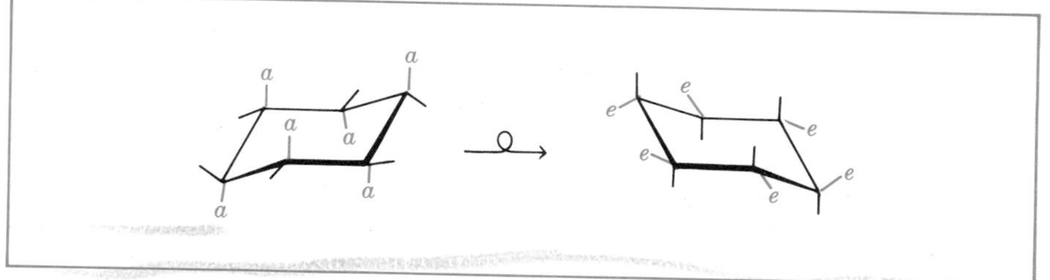


**Figure 3-4 Chair-chair interconversion**

A model reveals that the most severe nonbonded interactions in the chair conformation are those in the 1,3 diaxial relationship, and the analyses in the following sections are based on this premise (see Fig. 3-3*b*). Large, bulky substituents are more stable in the equatorial position, where steric repulsions are minimized. For instance, methylcyclohexane exists predominantly in the chair form having the methyl group in the equatorial conformation.

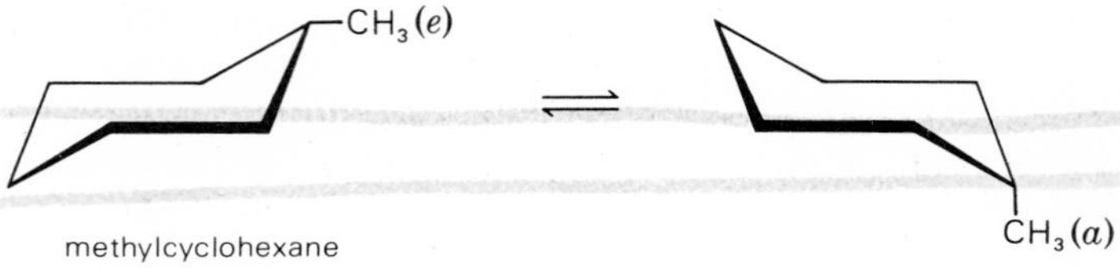

$CH_3(e)$ ⇌ $CH_3(a)$

methylcyclohexane preferred conformation

This is generally the case with monosubstituted cyclohexanes. At room temperature the flip between the two ring conformations is usually very rapid, and *on the time average* the carbon skeleton is nearly planar. It is necessary to cool the sample well below 0° in order to observe the conformational preference of simple cyclohexanes.

### 3-3 CONFORMATIONAL ANALYSIS OF DISUBSTITUTED CYCLOHEXANES

For the disubstituted cyclohexanes there are only three structural isomers, namely, 1,2-, 1,3-, and 1,4-dimethylcyclohexane, but for each structural isomer there are two geometrical isomers, the cis and trans forms, and each geometrical isomer can exist in two chair conformations. We have 12 structures to consider in order to predict the more stable conformer in each pair of dimethylcyclohexanes. Two groups on adjacent carbon atoms are closer to each other, that is cis, if one occupies an axial position and the other an adjacent equatorial position.

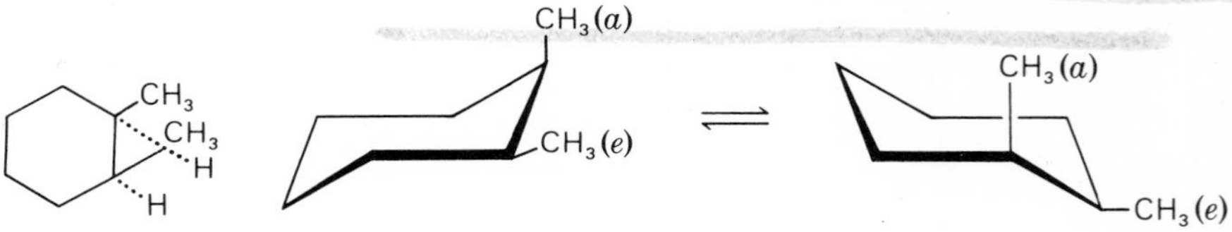

$CH_3$, $CH_3$, H, H — $CH_3(a)$, $CH_3(e)$ ⇌ $CH_3(a)$, $CH_3(e)$

*cis*-1,2-dimethylcyclohexane

equivalent conformations

With two methyl groups the conformations here are identical, but they are *not* the same if the two groups are different. The more stable conformation has the larger of two different substituents in the equatorial position.

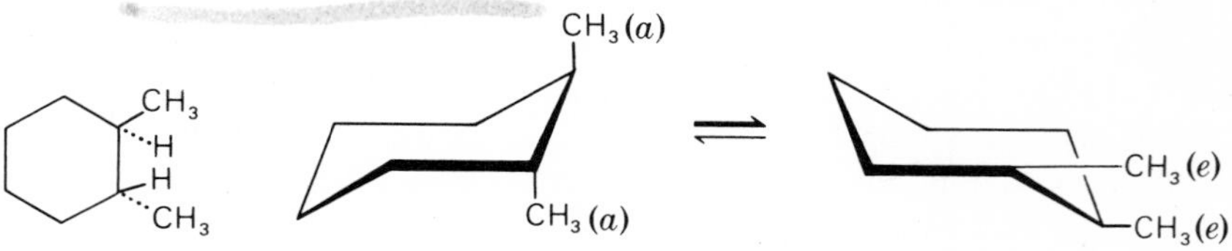

$CH_3$, H, H, $CH_3$ — $CH_3(a)$, $CH_3(a)$ ⇌ $CH_3(e)$, $CH_3(e)$

*trans*-1,2-dimethylcyclohexane

preferred

1,2 Diaxial substituents are as far from each other as possible, that is trans, but after a ring flip, they are diequatorial, (*e*), (*e*), which is the preferred conformation because they then encounter fewer 1,3 diaxial repulsions. Regardless of which groups are present, trans 1,2-disubstituted cyclohexanes are expected to prefer the diequatorial conformation.

Cis 1,3 substituents are closer when both are in the diaxial arrangement; however, the 1,3 nonbonded interactions are relieved by a ring flip to the preferred conformation (*e*), (*e*). Again, this is true regardless of which two substituents are chosen.

$H_3C$, H, $CH_3$, H

*cis*-1,3-dimethylcyclohexane

$CH_3(a)$ $CH_3(a)$ ⇌ $CH_3(e)$ $CH_3(e)$

preferred

$H_3C$, H, H, $CH_3$

*trans*-1,3-dimethylcyclohexane

$CH_3(a)$ $CH_3(e)$ ⇌ $CH_3(a)$ $CH_3(e)$

equivalent, here

The analysis of the 1,4 isomers follows directly from that given above for the cis 1,2-disubstituted cyclohexanes, which are analogous in conformation to the 1,2-disubstituted compounds.

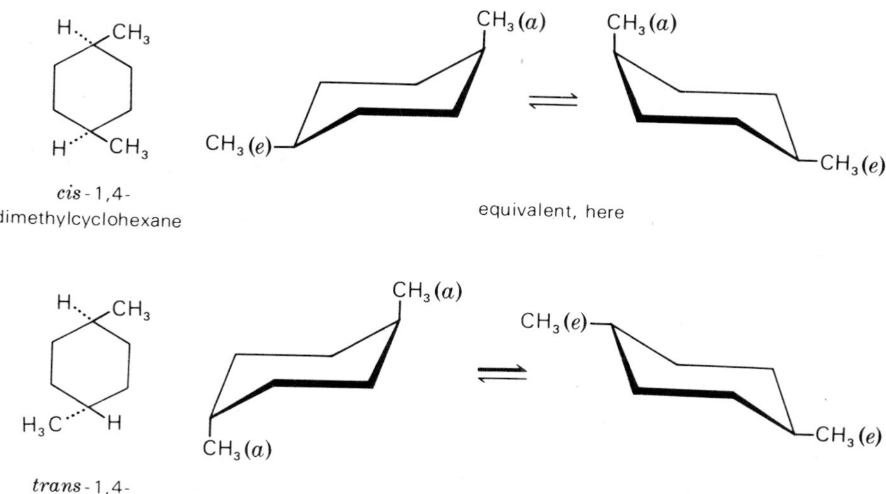


*cis*-1,4-dimethylcyclohexane

equivalent, here

*trans*-1,4-dimethylcyclohexane

preferred

### 3-4 TRI- AND HIGHER-SUBSTITUTED CYCLOHEXANES

Polysubstituted cyclohexanes can be analyzed in the same manner as the less substituted ones; the largest substituents prefer the equatorial positions, thereby minimizing the 1,3 diaxial repulsions. The more stable conformer of a given geometrical isomer can be determined by placing the first substituent in, for example, the axial position, then placing the others cis or trans relative to it. Finally, a ring flip, if necessary, will give the more stable conformation, i.e., the one with fewer 1,3 diaxial repulsions.

## REACTIONS

In a given homologous series the first member often differs from the rest in its reactions, as is true of the first element in any group of the periodic table. Although the reactions of cycloalkanes resemble those of alkanes, cyclopropane and cyclobutane are highly strained as a result of the large deviation of the C—C—C and H—C—H angles from the 109°28' between carbon-carbon single bonds. Models of these compounds show the bonds as bent, in contrast to the relatively unstrained rings of higher cycloalkanes. Thus, these rings are opened fairly readily with reagents such as hydrogen and bromine.

$$\triangle \xrightarrow{H_2/Pt} CH_3CH_2CH_3$$

$$\triangle \xrightarrow{Br_2} \underset{Br}{CH_2}—CH_2—\underset{Br}{CH_2} \quad + \text{ others from substitution}$$

1,3-dibromopropane
(from ring opening)

We have already seen that cyclopentanes and cyclohexanes tend to adopt nonplanar stable conformations. Since they are less strained than the lower members, they generally do not undergo ring-opening reactions.

## PREPARATION OF CYCLOPROPANES: THE SIMMONS-SMITH REACTION

Because of the highly strained character of cyclopropanes and because several unusual cyclopropane compounds have been found in nature

(Table 3-2), only a newer (1960) synthesis of these compounds will be discussed here.

**Table 3-2**
**Natural products containing the cyclopropane ring**

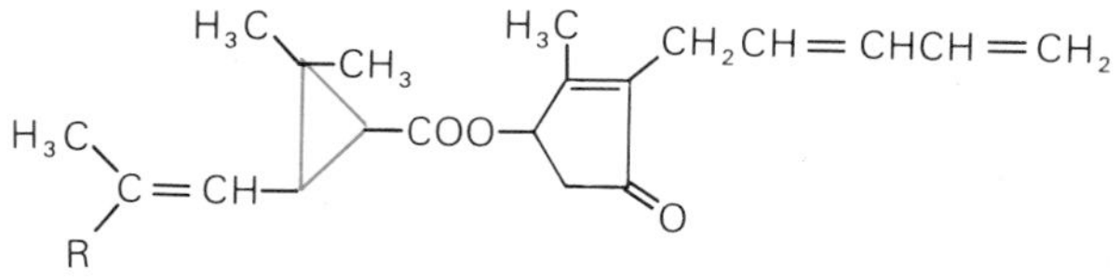

two insecticide compounds isolated from pyrethrum flowers

R = $-CH_3$, pyrethrin I
R = $-CO_2CH_3$, pyrethrin II

$CH_3(CH_2)_7$–(cyclopropene)–$(CH_2)_7CO_2H$

Sterculic acid
principal compound in oil of a tropical tree, *Sterculia foetida*

Named for its codiscoverers, the Simmons-Smith reaction consists of the addition of methylene iodide (diiodomethane), $CH_2I_2$, to an alkene in the presence of a zinc-copper couple.† The addition reaction takes place under mild conditions, about 40° in refluxing ether and leads to a high preponderance of a single isomer; for instance, starting with the trans olefin, one obtains the corresponding trans cyclopropane almost exclusively. Reactions which produce primarily a single predictable isomer are called *stereospecific*. This stereospecific reaction leads to products which would be difficult to synthesize by other means.

General: RHC=CHR (*cis*) $\xrightarrow[\text{Zn-Cu couple in ether; }\Delta]{CH_2I_2}$ *cis* cyclopropane

RHC=CHR (*trans*) ⟶ *trans* cyclopropane

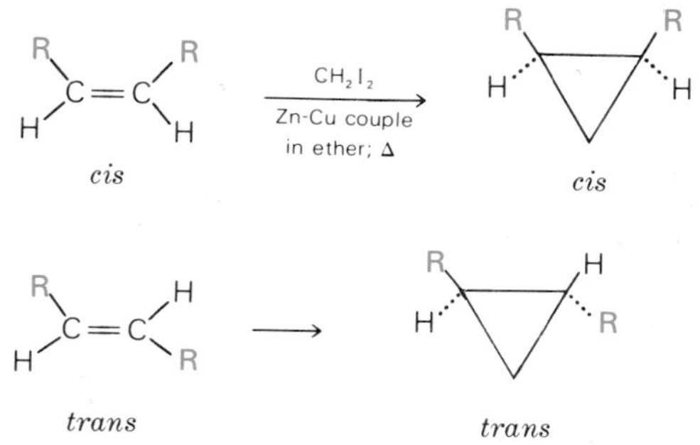

†Treatment of metallic zinc with a solution containing cupric ion, $Cu^{++}$, causes the copper to be reduced and plate out on the zinc surface.

*Specific*: $CH_3—CH=CH_2$ $\xrightarrow[\text{Zn-Cu couple}]{CH_2I_2}$ methylcyclopropane

propene

cis-2-butene $\xrightarrow[\text{Zn-Cu couple}]{CH_2I_2}$ *cis*-1,2-dimethylcyclopropane

*trans*-3-hexene $\xrightarrow[\text{Zn-Cu couple}]{CH_2I_2}$ *trans*-1,2-diethylcyclopropane

cyclohexene $\xrightarrow[\text{Zn-Cu couple}]{CH_2I_2}$ norcarane

## SUGGESTED READINGS

### Synthesis and reactions

Finley, K. T.: The Synthesis of Carbocyclic Compounds, *J. Chem. Educ.*, **42**, 536 (1965). A historical survey of the synthesis of small- and large-ring compounds.

Gordon, A. J.: Halogenation and Olefinic Nature of Cyclopropane, *J. Chem. Educ.*, **44**, 461 (1967). Cites conditions under which cyclopropane reacts with halogens and names the products obtained.

Schreck, J. O.: Chemistry of Methylenes, *J. Chem. Educ.*, **42**, 261 (1965).

Wasserman, E.: Chemical Topology, *Sci. Am.*, **207** (5), 94 (1962). Shows the synthesis of a compound containing two linked rings and suggests other interesting organic isomers which may be synthesized.

Wilson, A., and D. Goldhamer: Cyclobutane Chemistry, I. Structure and Strain Energy; II. Reactions and Mechanisms, *J. Chem. Educ.*, **40**, 504, 599 (1963).

### Bonding

Bernett, W. A: A Unified Theory of Bonding for Cyclopropanes, *J. Chem. Educ.*, **44**, 17 (1967). A discussion of various models used to explain the bonding in cyclopropanes.

Goldish, E.: Strain and Interatomic Distances in Small-ring Molecules, *J. Chem. Educ.*, **36**, 408 (1959). Presents structural data (bond lengths and bond angles) for small-ring organic compounds and discusses briefly how they are determined.

### Conformational analysis

Allinger, N. L.: Conformational Analysis in the Elementary Organic Course, *J. Chem. Educ.*, **41**, 70 (1964).

Eliel, E. L.: Conformational Analysis in Mobile Systems, *J. Chem. Educ.*, **37**, 126 (1960).

Vogel, G.: An Aid to Visualizing Fused Ring Systems, *J. Chem. Educ.*, **42**, 278 (1965). Describes a pencil-and-paper method for drawing conformational representations of reduced systems such as perhydroanthracenes and perhydrophenanthrenes.

## PROBLEMS

**1**. Name the following compounds by any consistent system of nomenclature.

★(*a*)

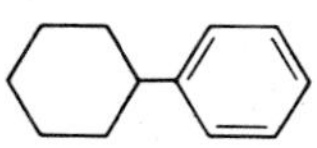

★(*b*) $H_3C$ $CH_3$ Cl

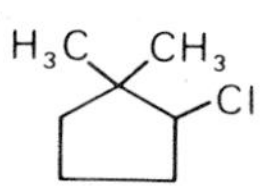

★(*c*) $CH_3$ $CH_3$ H H

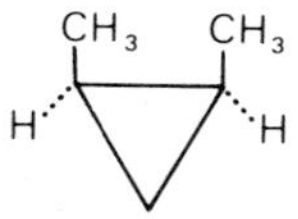

★(*d*) OH $CH_3$ H H

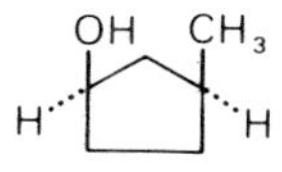

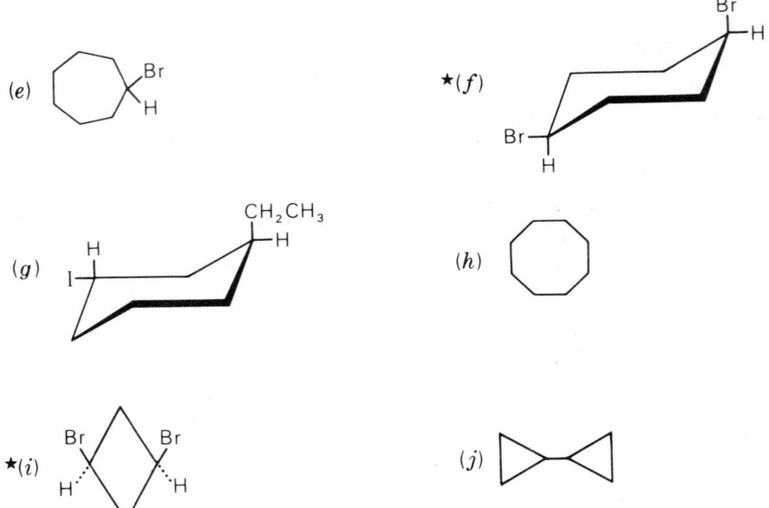


**2.** Draw the structures that correspond to each geometrical isomer of the following compounds:

★(*a*) 1,2,3-tribromocyclopropane

★(*b*) 1,3-dichloro-2,4-cyclobutanedicarboxylic acid

(*c*) 1,2,4-triphenylcyclopentane

(*d*) 1,2,3,4,5,6-hexahydroxycyclohexane (Show the preferred conformation of each geometrical isomer which can be drawn.)

★**3.** (*a*) Draw the preferred conformation of the two geometrical isomers of decalin.

(*b*) On the basis of 1,3 diaxial interactions, which of the two isomers would be expected to be the more stable?

★**4.** Draw the preferred conformation of all of the tertiary butylcyclohexanols. Note that the bulky alkyl group will prefer the equatorial position.

**5.** Draw the preferred conformation of all the geometrical isomers of the following molecules (the wavy line indicates an unspecified axial or equatorial geometry):

(*a*) $C(CH_3)_3$, D, $CH_3$

(*b*) $CH_3$

(*c*) I, $H_3C$, D

★**6**. Many mono, di, tri, and higher cyclopropane derivatives have been prepared via the Simmons-Smith reaction and investigated as potential fuels. For the following, draw the structures of the cyclopropane derivatives which would be obtained by treating the olefin with Zn(Cu)-$CH_2I_2$ in ether, assuming that all double bonds are reactive:

(*a*) [3-methylenecyclohexene: cyclohexene ring bearing $=CH_2$]

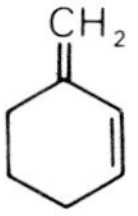

(*b*) [1,4-cyclohexadiene]

(*c*) [cyclohexylidenecyclohexane]

(*d*) [3-methylenecyclopentene: cyclopentene ring bearing $=CH_2$]

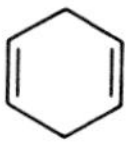

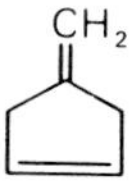

(*e*) $CH_2{=}CH{-}CH{=}CH_2$

# Chapter Four

The simplest hydrocarbons that contain a functional group are the *alkenes*, also called *olefins*, which are formally related to the alkanes by the removal of two adjacent hydrogen atoms with the creation of a carbon-carbon double bond $>C=C<$. They are reduced to alkanes by hydrogen in the presence of a metal catalyst. Since they have one double bond, they belong to the $C_nH_{2n}$ homologous series. Unlike the alkanes, alkenes dissolve in concentrated sulfuric acid and readily *add* chlorine and bromine to the double bond.

The concept and use of reaction mechanisms, especially those of *elimination*, to form a carbon-carbon double bond, and of *addition* to the carbon-carbon double bond, are important parts of this chapter. Many reactions of olefins are stereospecific, and they can be understood in terms of the mechanism of the reaction.

## NOMENCLATURE

The -*ane* ending for an alkane is replaced by -*ene* for an alkene. Again, functional groups, including the double bond, are given the lowest possible number in the longest chain. This chain also determines the cis or trans designation for the olefin.

$$\overset{1}{C}H_3\overset{2}{C}H_2(H)\overset{3}{C}=\overset{4}{C}(CH_3)\overset{5}{C}H_2\overset{6}{C}H_2\overset{7}{C}H_3$$

*cis*-4-methyl-3-heptene

The first two members of this series are often called *ethylene* and *propylene* rather than *ethene* and *propene*.

# Alkenes (Olefins)

$$\mathrm{H_2C{=}CH_2}$$

ethylene
(ethene)

$$\mathrm{H_2C{=}CH{-}CH_3}$$

propylene
(propene)

There are four $C_4$ alkenes, of which only one is also known by a common or trivial name:

$CH_2{=}CH{-}CH_2CH_3$ — 1-butene, b.p. −5°

$H_3C(H)C{=}C(H)CH_3$ — *cis*-2-butene, 1°

$H_3C(H)C{=}C(CH_3)H$ — *trans*-2-butene, 2.5°

$(H_3C)_2C{=}CH_2$ — 2-methylpropene (isobutylene) −6°

Recall that the molecular-orbital picture for a double bond shows that the $\pi$ bond (maximum $p$-orbital overlap) prevents rotation about the carbon-carbon $\sigma$ bond. Therefore, there are two possible arrangements of substituents about a double bond, and *geometrical isomers* exist. Given the double bond, as in 2-butene, the two methyl groups can be placed on different carbon atoms either on the *same* side of the bond (*cis*-2-butene) or *across* from each other (*trans*-2-butene). The cis and trans isomers are two distinct compounds with different, but similar, chemical and physical properties.

| | *cis*-1,2-dichloroethylene ($ClHC{=}CHCl$, Cl on same side) | *trans*-1,2-dichloroethylene ($ClHC{=}CHCl$, Cl across) |
|---|---|---|
| m.p. | −80° | −50° |
| b.p. | 60° | 48° |
| density | 1.29 | 1.27 |

A similar situation was encountered in the stereochemistry of substituted ring structures (Chap. 3).

A few alkenyl groups derived from the alkene series have common names, shown in Table 4-1, which also gives additional examples of alkene nomenclature.

**Table 4-1 Nomenclature examples**

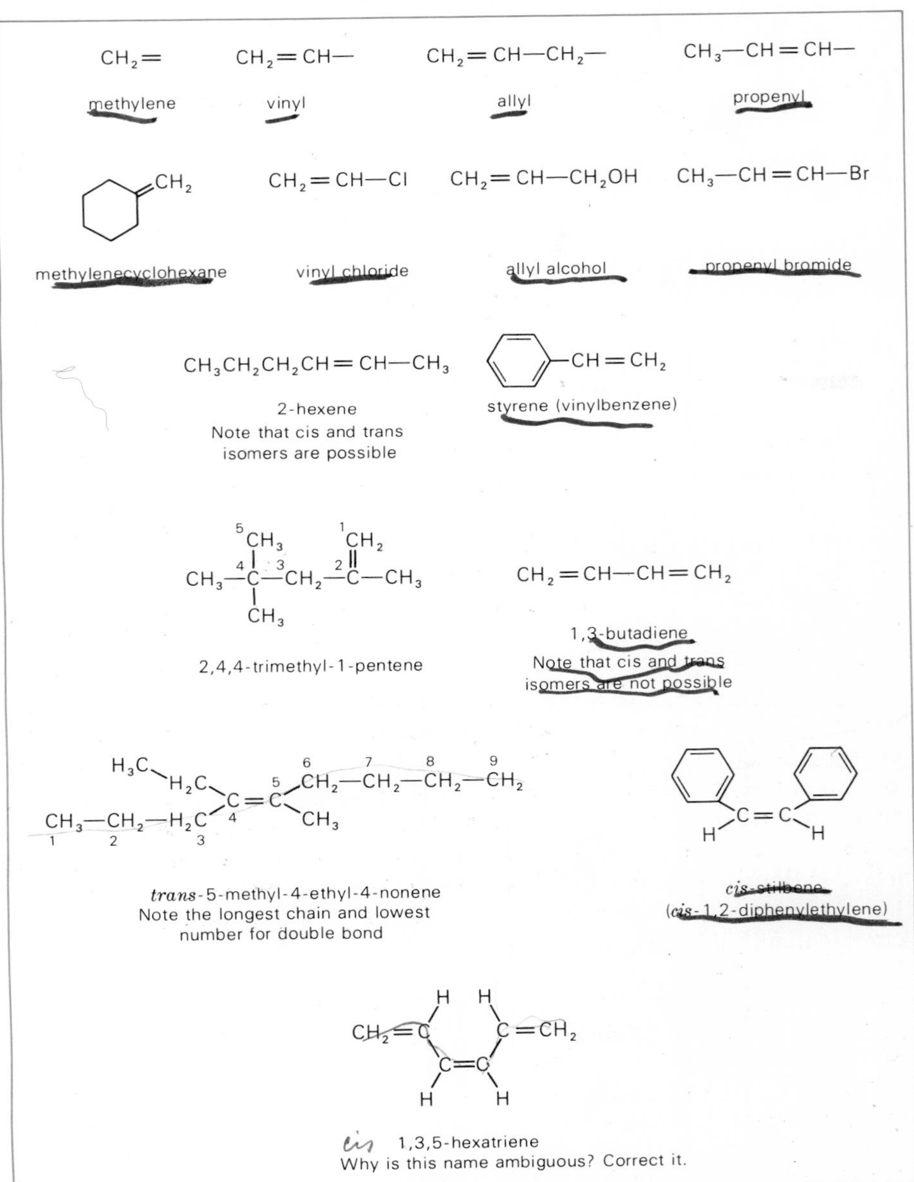

## PREPARATION

### 4-1 DEHYDRATION OF ALCOHOLS AND CARBONIUM ION STABILITY

Alkenes can be formed by dehydrating alcohols either by heating with an acid catalyst or by passing the alcohol vapor or liquid over heated alumina, $Al_2O_3$. The mechanism of the former is discussed below; the mechanism of the latter is not clearly understood.

*General*: $R{-}CH_2{-}CH_2OH \longrightarrow R{-}CH{=}CH_2 + H_2O$

*Specific*: $CH_3{-}C(CH_3)_2{-}OH \xrightarrow[\text{or } Al_2O_3;\ \Delta]{H_2SO_4;\ \Delta} (H_3C)_2C{=}CH_2 + H_2O$

*t*-butyl alcohol → isobutylene

*Mechanism of acid-catalyzed reaction*

Step 1: $(CH_3)_3C{-}\ddot{O}H + H^+ \overset{\text{fast}}{\rightleftharpoons} [(CH_3)_3C{-}\overset{H}{\ddot{O}^+}{-}H]$

oxonium ion intermediate

Step 2: $[(CH_3)_3C{-}\overset{+}{O}H_2] \overset{\text{slow}}{\rightleftharpoons} [(CH_3)_3C^+] + H_2O$

carbonium ion intermediate

Step 3: $[CH_3{-}\overset{+}{C}(CH_2{-}H)(CH_3)] \rightleftharpoons (H_3C)_2C{=}CH_2 + H^+$

**Step 1:** This is a reversible formation of an oxonium ion or oxonium salt intermediate by protonation of the oxygen atom. Compare the term *oxonium* with *carbonium*, which means a positively charged carbon atom.

**Step 2:** As the slowest one in the sequence, this is called the *rate-determining step* since the slowest step determines the rate at which the *product* will be formed. In this case, it is the loss of a water molecule from the intermediate oxonium ion to form a tertiary carbonium ion intermediate. Curved arrows are used in writing mechanisms to denote the incipient motion of *electrons and of atoms*.

Some analogies may clarify the concept of a rate-determining step. Suppose we have a large single line of cars moving at different speeds. Eventually the slowest one will set the pace for all those behind it, although the cars in front may be miles ahead and thus out of the picture. Another analogy is a funnel filled with sand. The rate at which the sand will empty from a filled funnel is governed essentially by the size of the opening and not by the amount of sand in the funnel.

**Step 3:** This is the product-forming step, in which a proton is lost and the $H^+$, truly a catalyst, is regenerated. Since positive charges represent the ***absence*** of electrons, we shall never "move a positive charge" with arrows, only electrons and atoms.

This mechanism is an elimination ($E$) in which only one molecular species (***unimolecular***) is involved in the slow, rate-determining step. It is characterized as an ***$E_1$ mechanism***. Since the oxonium ion is formed in a rapidly reversible reaction, it can be shown that as long as both alcohol and acid are present, some oxonium salt will always be present to react. Since the rate is a function only of the alcohol when small amounts of acid are used, it is a ***first-order*** reaction rate.† The rate of the reaction may be expressed as

$$\text{Rate of alkene formation} = k_1' \text{[oxonium ion]}$$

where $k_1'$ is a proportionality constant and the brackets refer to the concentration of the oxonium ion. Since the oxonium ion concentration is given by the equilibrium expression for step 1,

$$K_{eq} = \frac{\text{[oxonium ion]}}{[H^+]\text{[alcohol]}}$$

$$\text{[Oxonium ion]} = K_{eq}[H^+]\text{ [alcohol]}$$

Recall that the acid is a catalyst and is regenerated; hence it is a constant which can be combined with $K_{eq}$, the equilibrium constant for step 1. Thus,

$$\text{Rate of alkene formation} = k_1 \text{ [alcohol]}$$

where $k_1$ incorporates both the hydrogen ion concentration and $K_{eq}$. An example of an $E_2$ mechanism is given in Sec. 4-2.

In the dehydration cited above, isobutylene was the only possible product from the simple dehydration of ***tert***-butyl alcohol. Since many alcohols, such as $CH_3CH_2CH(OH)CH_3$, present a choice of possible products, we need to be able to predict the major product. This prediction is based on a consideration of the relative stability of the newly

†Since the rate will be affected by high acid concentration, this apparent dependence on only the alcohol is called a ***pseudo first-order*** reaction rate.

formed olefins. Since alkyl groups are electron-donating and stabilize the double bond, the more highly substituted olefin is usually the major product from acid-catalyzed alcohol dehydration.

$$\underset{\text{2-butanol}}{CH_3CH_2\underset{\large OH}{\underset{|}{C}}HCH_3} \xrightarrow[\Delta]{H_2SO_4} \underset{\substack{\text{2-butene}\\ \text{major}}}{CH_3{-}CH{=}CH{-}CH_3} + \underset{\substack{\text{1-butene}\\ \text{minor}}}{CH_3CH_2CH{=}CH_2}$$

$$\left[CH_3CH_2\underset{^+OH_2}{\underset{|}{C}}HCH_3\right] \xrightarrow{-H_2O} \left[CH_3{-}\overset{H}{\underset{H}{C}}{-}\overset{+}{C}H{-}CH_3\right] + \left[CH_3{-}\overset{H}{\underset{H}{C}}{-}\overset{+}{C}H{-}CH_3\right]$$

(2-butanol $\rightleftharpoons$ with $+H^+$; each carbonium ion loses $-H^+$ to give 2-butene and 1-butene respectively)

Once the secondary carbonium ion intermediate, $CH_3CH_2C^+HCH_3$, is formed from 2-butanol, there are two possible pathways for the reaction. The major product is the *internal* olefin, 2-butene; the *terminal* olefin, 1-butene, is formed in smaller amounts. It is generally true that although one product can be made to predominate, others will also be formed, at least in trace quantities.

The fact that alkyl groups are electron-releasing and tend to spread the charge over additional atoms accounts for the order of stability of carbonium ions: 3° > 2° > 1°. This is also the order of the ease of acid-catalyzed alcohol dehydration. The order of stability for olefins is based on the electron-releasing effect of alkyl groups; data from heats of hydrogenation (Sec. 7-3) provide evidence compatible with this order: tetrasubstituted olefins > tri > di > mono > ethylene.

*Example*: $R_2C{=}CR_2 > R_2C{=}CHR > R_2C{=}CH_2 > \textit{trans}\text{-}RCH{=}CHR >$

$$\textit{cis}\text{-}RHC{=}CHR > R{-}CH{=}CH_2 > CH_2{=}CH_2$$

In contrast to the structure of olefins formed by passing alcohol vapor over aluminum oxide, the use of thorium oxide (thoria) gives terminal olefins from 2-alkanols. The yields are generally 90 to 95%, and the olefins obtained are nearly pure.

$$R{-}CH_2{-}\underset{OH}{\underset{|}{C}H}{-}CH_3 \xrightarrow[Al_2O_3]{\Delta} R{-}CH{=}CH{-}CH_3 + H_2O$$

$$R{-}CH_2{-}\underset{OH}{\underset{|}{C}H}{-}CH_3 \xrightarrow[ThO_2]{\Delta} R{-}CH_2{-}CH{=}CH_2 + H_2O$$

The adsorption of the 2-alkanols on the thorium oxide surface probably occurs in the conformation which minimizes eclipsing interactions (Fig. 4-1). The cyclic six-membered transition state is relatively unstrained. Examples of five- and six-membered cyclic transition states and intermediates will be encountered later in the text.

> The reaction with thoria has been used to dehydrate the following compounds. Formulate these reactions and name the product from each:
>
> **1.** 4-methyl-2-pentanol
>
> **2.** 2,3-butanediol
>
> **3.** 1-cyclohexylethanol

### 4-2 DEHYDROHALOGENATION OF ALKYL HALIDES

Although the reaction of alkyl halides with ***dilute base*** leads to the formation of the corresponding alcohol ($R—CH_2—X + OH^- \longrightarrow R—CH_2OH + X^-$), treatment of an alkyl halide with a concentrated ***strong base***, such as solid KOH dissolved in ethanol, leads to the elimination of HX and formation of an alkene by an $E_2$ mechanism.

*General*: $R—CH_2—CH_2Br \xrightarrow{\text{strong base}} RCH{=}CH_2 + HBr$

*Overall*: $CH_3CH_2CH_2Br \xrightarrow[\text{KOH}]{\text{alc.}} CH_3—CH{=}CH_2 + HBr \xrightarrow{\text{KOH}} K^+Br^- + H_2O$

*Mechanism*: $CH_3—CH_2—CH_2Br + H\bar{O} \xrightarrow{\text{slow}} \left[ HO\cdots H\cdots CH(CH_3)\text{⋯}CH_2\cdots Br \right]^- \longrightarrow H_3C(H)C{=}CH_2 + Br^- + H_2O$

transition state

The slow step in this elimination involves two species, the hydroxide ion and the alkyl halide; that is, it is ***bimolecular***. When the concentration of either the halide or the base is doubled, the rate is doubled. This is thus a ***second-order reaction*** rate (first order in $OH^-$ and first order in alkyl halide); the rate depends on the concentration of both species. Reactions in which bonds are being made and broken at about the same time are said to proceed by a ***concerted mechanism***. In this case the $OH^-$ removes the proton and the double bond is created ***at the same time*** the bromide ion is leaving. Or, to say it another way, the O—H bond and the C═C bonds are forming ***while*** the C—Br bond is being broken. Thus, there is no distinct intermediate in this case but

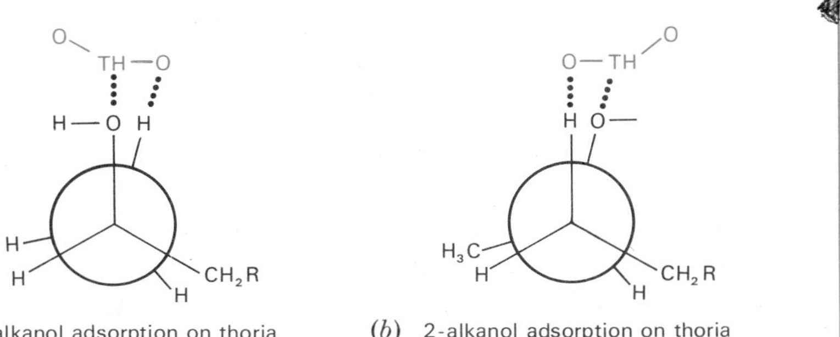


(*a*) 2-alkanol adsorption on thoria surface leading to 1-alkene: minimum eclipsing interaction

(*b*) 2-alkanol adsorption on thoria surface leading to *trans*-2-alkene

**Figure 4-1 Interaction of alcohols with thoria**

only negatively charged transition states. The transition state represented in most reactions in this text is the one about halfway between reactants and products. All chemical reactions involve transition states, but not all have discrete intermediates.

The dehydrohalogenation reaction, like the acid-catalyzed dehydration of alcohols, gives the more highly substituted olefin as the major

## 4-3 DEHALOGENATION WITH ZINC OR IODIDE ION

Dehalogenations with Zn or $I^-$ take place under relatively mild conditions and lead to very few side reactions.

$$\underset{\text{Br}}{CH_2}—\underset{\text{Br}}{CH_2} \xrightarrow{Zn} CH_2{=}CH_2 + ZnBr_2$$

$$CH_3—\underset{\text{Br}}{CH}—\underset{\text{Br}}{CH_2} \xrightarrow{2I^-} CH_3—CH{=}CH_2 + I_2 + Br^-$$

Since 1,2-dihalides are usually prepared by treating an olefin with halogen,

$$CH_2{=}CH_2 + Br_2 \longrightarrow \underset{\text{Br}}{CH_2}\underset{\text{Br}}{CH_2}$$

these reactions are not applicable as synthetic procedures, but they can be used as a means of purification. Suppose, for example, we wish to separate a mixture containing cyclohexane (b.p. 80°) and cyclohexene (b.p. 84°) into its pure constituents. The boiling points are so close that distillation is not feasible. However, the 1,2-dibromocyclohexane boils at 145° (100 mm), can readily be separated from cyclohexane, and can be converted back to the olefin by treatment with Zn or $I^-$.

The mechanisms of many reactions will not be given or will be mentioned only briefly, because of time and space limitations or because they are not of sufficient interest. The mechanisms which *are* presented should not be memorized. For a given reaction a reasonable mechanism can often be written from a consideration of the general principles presented in Chap. 1, by knowing the structure of the starting materials and products, and by knowing the reaction conditions. The *best* mechanism, that which agrees with all known data, is found by determining the kinetic order of the reaction experimentally, by examining all the products formed in the reaction, and by instrumental methods which are available for probing molecules.

## REACTIONS

### 4-4 $H_2$: CATALYTIC HYDROGENATION

Simple alkenes react with hydrogen in the presence of a metal catalyst to yield the saturated or reduced alkane.

$$CH_3{-}CH{=}CH_2 \xrightarrow[\text{Pt or Pd}]{H_2} CH_3CH_2CH_3$$

The organic molecule is adsorbed on the metallic surface, on which the hydrogen has already been adsorbed and dissociated. Both hydrogen atoms then enter the same side of the molecule. The result is a stereospecific cis addition (Fig. 4-2) since the geometry (stereochemistry) of

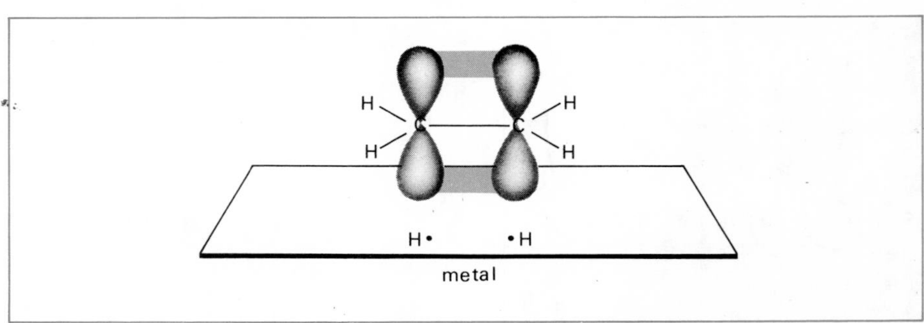


**Figure 4-2 Schematic representation of catalytic hydrogenation**

the product is a result of the method of synthesis. Although the cis nature of hydrogenation cannot be demonstrated with ethylene, two of the many possible reactions in which this cis addition can be shown are the deuteration of cyclohexene and the hydrogenation of 1,2-dimethylcyclohexene. The first is an example of the use of isotopes to help determine the stereochemistry and the mechanism.

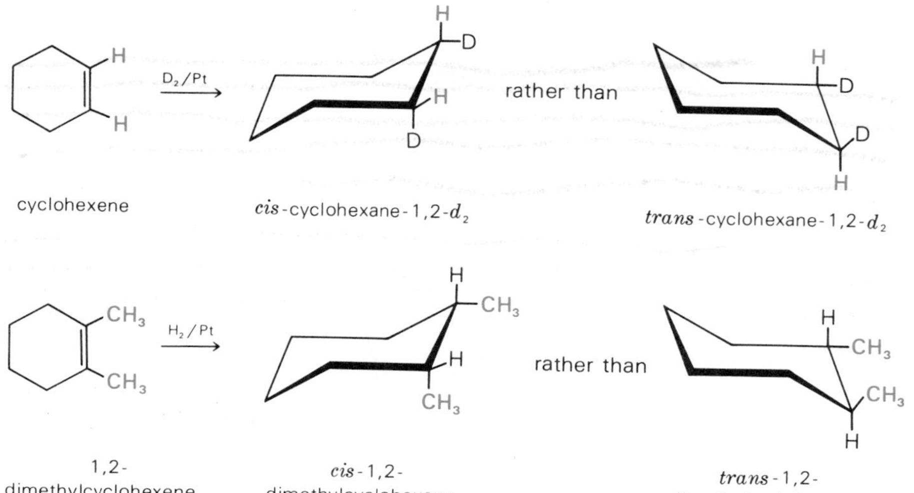


## 4-5 $Cl_2$, $Br_2$: ELECTROPHILIC TRANS ADDITION OF HALOGEN

1,2-Dihalides are formed by the stereospecific (trans) addition of chlorine or bromine to olefins.

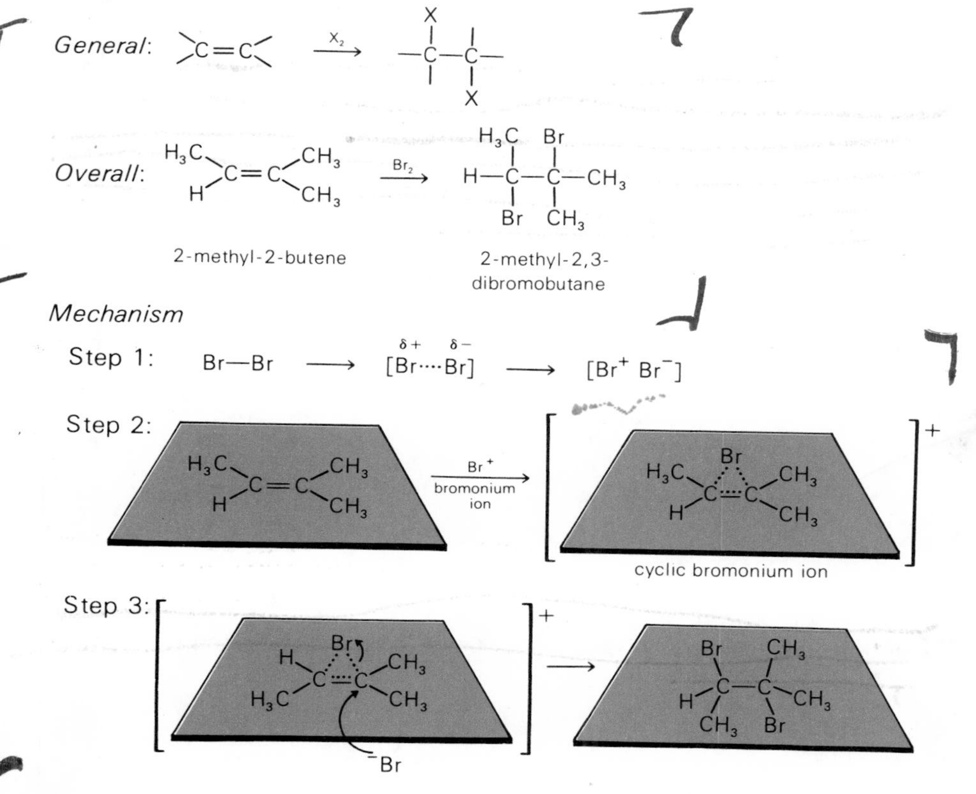

**Step 1**: The nonpolar halogen molecule may be considered to become partially polarized as the halogen, $X_2$, approaches the double bond, a region of high electron density. There may also be some polarization of the halogen molecule if the reaction is carried out in a polar solvent such as water or methyl alcohol, $CH_3OH$.

**Step 2**: The bromonium ion, $Br^+$, or the polarized bromine molecule is then attacked by the electrons of the double bond, forming a *cyclic bromonium ion* intermediate, which may be considered a resonance-stabilized hybrid:

$$\left[ CH_3{-}CH{-}\overset{+}{C}(CH_3)_2 \text{ (Br bridged to CH)} \longleftrightarrow CH_3{-}\overset{+}{C}H{-}C(CH_3)_2 \text{ (Br bridged to C)} \right]$$

3° carbonium ion structure — 2° carbonium ion structure

These two structures are of comparable but slightly different energy. Why is the tertiary carbonium ion expected to be the greater contributor to the hybrid? In the secondary carbonium ion only one methyl group is releasing electrons to the positive center, whereas two methyl groups are contributing to the tertiary carbonium ion.

**Step 3**: In the final step the bromide ion, $Br^-$, attacks the tertiary carbon, which has the lowest electron density, from the side opposite the first bromine, and the trans product is formed. This "backside" attack mechanism predicts that the bromination of an alkene, say ethylene, in the presence of $Na^+Cl^-$ should lead to the formation of some 1-bromo-2-chloroethane; this is observed.

We may consider the reaction of halogen with cyclohexene, among others, in order to establish the trans addition nature of the mechanism.

$$\text{cyclohexene} \xrightarrow{Br_2} \textit{trans}\text{-1,2-dibromocyclohexane} \quad \text{rather than} \quad \textit{cis}\text{-1,2-dibromocyclohexane}$$

*trans*-1,2-dibromocyclohexane — *cis*-1,2-dibromocyclohexane

### 4-6 $KMnO_4$: OXIDATION OF ALKENES

Under *mild conditions*, usually at 0 to 5° in dilute buffered alkaline solution, potassium permanganate, $KMnO_4$, reacts with double bonds to yield the 1,2-diol.

$$CH_3CH{=}CH_2 \xrightarrow[0°]{\text{dil. KMnO}_4} \underset{\text{OH}}{CH_3CH}{-}\underset{\text{OH}}{CH_2} + \text{further oxidation products}$$

1,2-propanediol

Diols are also called *glycols*, and those in which the hydroxyl groups are situated on adjacent carbons are known as *vicinal* diols or *vicinal* glycols. Stereochemically, the reaction is a cis addition which probably proceeds through a cyclic intermediate, which is then hydrolyzed to the diol.

$$\left[\begin{array}{l} CH_3 \\ | \\ CH{-}O \\ | \qquad\quad \rangle Mn\langle^{=O}_{O^-} \; K^+ \\ CH_2{-}O \end{array}\right]$$

Generally the formation of diols by this route is not the method of choice because the intermediate diol and dialdehyde are oxidized at the same rate or faster than the starting olefin. Unless special precautions are taken to remove the alcohol as it is formed or to control the oxidation by using base at room temperature (or lower), a complex product mixture results.

$$\text{cyclohexene} \xrightarrow{KMnO_4} \text{cis-1,2-cyclohexanediol} \xrightarrow[\text{fast}]{\text{moderately}} \text{adipaldehyde} \xrightarrow{\text{fast}} HOOC(CH_2)_4COOH$$

*cis*-1,2-cyclohexanediol, a *vicinal* glycol; adipaldehyde, a dialdehyde; adipic acid, a diacid

The main uses of permanganate oxidation are in the synthetic preparation of acids and ketones and to help in determining structure. The products formed from alkenes and $KMnO_4$ under *forcing conditions* (hot, concentrated permanganate) depend on the original structure of the olefin: terminal olefinic carbons, $=CH_2$, are oxidized to carbon dioxide; monosubstituted alkene carbons, $=CHR$, give acids, $RCO_2H$, as their salts; and disubstituted ones, $=CR_2$, give ketones, $R_2C{=}O$ (see Table 4-2). Cyclic monoolefins retain all the original carbon atoms in the appropriate product. Oxalic acid, HOOC—COOH, if initially formed, is oxidized under these conditions to 2 moles of $CO_2$; formic acid, H—COOH, is similarly oxidized. Alkyl groups (especially methyl groups) attached to an aromatic system such as the benzene ring are oxidized to the corresponding aromatic acid. This stability of the aromatic ring system is similar to its stability under reducing condtions (Sec. 7-4).

**Table 4-2**
**Examples of $KMnO_4$ oxidation**

| | Comments |
|---|---|
| $CH_3-CH=CH_2 \xrightarrow[\Delta]{KMnO_4} CH_3CO_2H + CO_2\uparrow$ | this carbon is not found in the isolable products |
| $H_3C(H)C=C(H)CH_3 \longrightarrow CH_3CO_2H$ (cis) or $H_3C(H)C=C(H)CH_3$ (trans) | only one product formed; but two moles of acid for every mole of starting olefin. |
| $CH_3CH=C(CH_3)_2 \longrightarrow CH_3CO_2H + O=C(CH_3)_2$<br>acetic acid, acetone | |
| cyclopentene $\longrightarrow H_2C(CH_2-CO_2H)_2$<br>glutaric acid | only one product, which retains all the original carbon atoms |
| $CH_2=CH-CH=CH_2 \longrightarrow$ only $CO_2\uparrow$ | why? |
| $(H_3C)_2C=C(CH_3)-CH_2-CH_2-CH=CH_2 \xrightarrow[\Delta]{KMnO_4}$<br>5,6-dimethyl-1,5-heptadiene<br>$(H_3C)_2C=O + CH_3-\overset{O}{\overset{\Vert}{C}}-CH_2-CH_2-COOH + CO_2\uparrow$<br>acetone, 4-ketopentanoic acid | |
| toluene $\xrightarrow[\Delta]{KMnO_4}$ benzoic acid ($C_6H_5CO_2H$) | note the stability of aromatic systems |
| indane $\xrightarrow[\Delta]{KMnO_4}$ phthalic acid ($C_6H_4(COOH)_2$) $+ CO_2\uparrow$ | |

## 4-7 $O_3$: OZONOLYSIS

Ozone, $O_3$, which is produced from oxygen,

$$3O_2 \xrightarrow[\text{discharge; 4-6\% yield}]{\text{silent elec.}} 2O_3$$

is also particularly useful for structural determinations. Alkenes react rapidly and quantitatively with ozone, giving a colorless intermediate ozonide. The intermediate ozonides produced from alkenes and this strong oxidizing agent are often explosive and therefore not isolated but decomposed directly in solution. Under reducing conditions ($Zn/H_2O$) the ozonide gives aldehydes, and under oxidizing conditions ($H_2O_2$) it gives the corresponding acids. Disubstituted olefinic carbons give ketones.

$$CH_3CH{=}CH_2 \xrightarrow{O_3} \text{an ozonide} \xrightarrow[Zn/H_2O]{\text{reductive conditions}} CH_3CHO \text{ (acetaldehyde)} + O{=}CH_2 \text{ (formaldehyde)}$$

$$\text{an ozonide} \xrightarrow[\text{oxidative conditions}]{H_2O_2} CH_3COOH \text{ (acetic acid)} + HCOOH \text{ (formic acid)}$$

Data from hydrogenations (Sec. 2-9) can be used to supplement that obtained from $KMnO_4$ and $O_3$ oxidation in structural investigations.

Compound **X**, $C_6H_{10}$, yielded formaldehyde and biacetyl after ozonolysis and reductive work-up. What can you deduce about its structure?

$$\underset{C_6H_{10}}{X} \xrightarrow[2.\ H_2O/Zn]{1.\ O_3} CH_2O + CH_3{-}\overset{O}{\overset{\|}{C}}{-}\overset{O}{\overset{\|}{C}}{-}CH_3$$

The products, as written, account for only five of the six carbons originally present. Thus, 2 moles of $CH_2O$ must be formed for every mole of biacetyl. Further, starting with six carbons, the alkane homologous series is $C_6H_{14}$. Since the corresponding alkene homologous series is $C_6H_{12}$, $C_6H_{10}$ must have one of the following gross structures:

1. two double bonds
2. one double bond and one ring
3. two rings
4. a triple bond

Now we can write

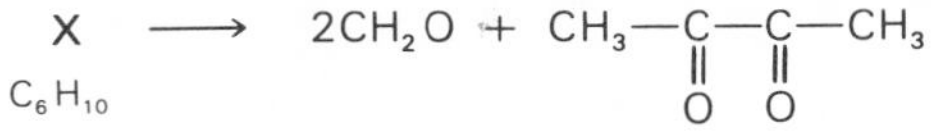

$$\underset{C_6H_{10}}{X} \longrightarrow 2CH_2O + CH_3—\underset{\underset{O}{\|}}{C}—\underset{\underset{O}{\|}}{C}—CH_3$$

Thus,

$$CH_3—\underset{\underset{O}{\|}}{C}—\underset{\underset{O}{\|}}{C}—CH_3 + \underset{H_2C}{\overset{O}{\|}}\ \underset{CH_2}{\overset{O}{\|}} \longleftarrow CH_3—\underset{\underset{H_2C}{\|}}{C}—\underset{\underset{CH_2}{\|}}{C}—CH_3$$

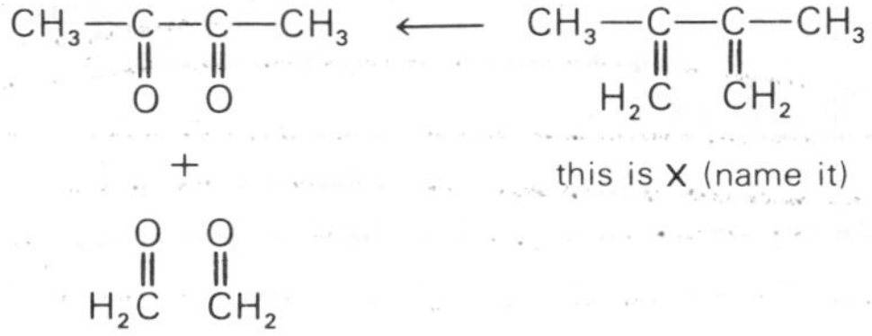

this is X (name it)

Compound **Y**, $C_7H_{10}$, gave OHC—CHO and $(CH_3)_2C(CHO)_2$ after ozonolysis and reductive work-up. It readily absorbed 2 moles of hydrogen. Propose a structure for **Y**.

## 4-8 ADDITION OF HYDROGEN HALIDES: THE MARKOWNIKOFF RULE

The addition of halogen halides to a double bond takes place by electrophilic addition of a proton followed by backside attack of the halide ion. The mechanism is like that of halogenation (Sec. 4-5).

*Examples*: cyclohexene $\xrightarrow[\text{(KI + } H_3PO_4\text{) 90\% yield}]{HI}$ iodocyclohexane

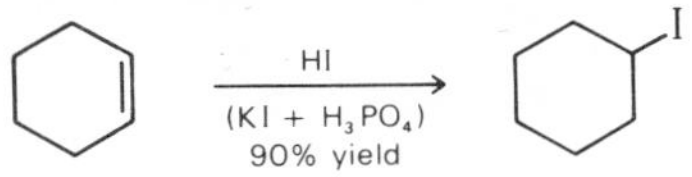

$$(CH_3)_2C{=}CH_2 \xrightarrow{HCl} (CH_3)_2\underset{\underset{Cl}{|}}{C}—CH_3 + (CH_3)_2\underset{\underset{H}{|}}{C}—CH_2Cl$$

major product — minor product

*Overall*: $CH_3—CH{=}CH_2 \xrightarrow{HBr} CH_3—\underset{\underset{Br}{|}}{CH}—CH_3 + CH_3—CH_2—CH_2Br$

2-bromopropane major — 1-bromopropane minor

*Mechanism*: $CH_3—CH{=}CH_2 \longrightarrow \left[CH_3—\overset{+}{C}H—CH_2(H) \longleftrightarrow CH_3—CH(H)—\overset{+}{C}H_2\right]$

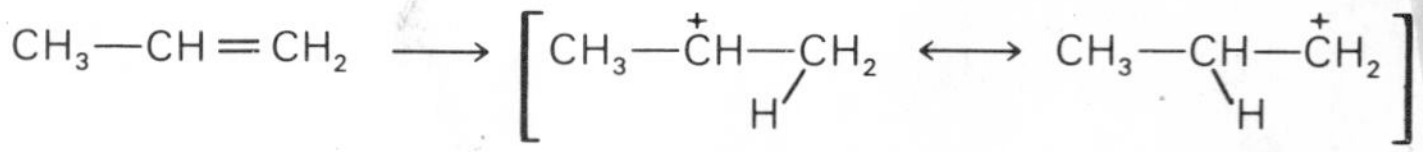

$$\left[ CH_3-\overset{+}{C}H-CH_2(H) \quad Br^- \right] \longrightarrow CH_3-\underset{Br}{CH}-CH_3$$

It is necessary to decide *how* the addition will take place when two possible products may be formed. This dilemma can be resolved by considering the ionic resonance structures which contribute to the intermediate. Of the two which can be written

$$\underset{\text{I}}{CH_3-CH(H)-\overset{+}{C}H_2} \longleftrightarrow \underset{\text{II}}{CH_3-\overset{+}{C}H-CH_2(H)}$$

structure II makes a larger contribution because of the increased stability of secondary carbonium ions as compared with primary ones. The attack of $Br^-$ is predominantly at $C_2$. This line of reasoning, based on the electron release of alkyl groups, is known as the Markownikoff rule. **The relatively positive portion of any unsymmetrical addend goes to that carbon in the alkene which already bears the greater number of hydrogen atoms (and hence has the lesser number of alkyl groups to stabilize the carbonium ion intermediate)**. Do not simply memorize the rule. Be sure you understand the underlying reasons for its validity.

Although hydrohalogenation of 1-methylcyclohexene would not establish the stereochemistry, use of 1-methylcyclohexene-2-*d* serves to illustrate the point.

1-methylcyclohexene-2-*d* $\xrightarrow{HBr}$ (CH₃, Br, H, D) or (CH₃, Br, H, D)

major product

## 4-9 HOCl, HOBr: ELECTROPHILIC TRANS ADDITION OF HYPOHALOUS ACIDS

The reaction of hypohalous acids, HOX, with olefins leads to products derived from breaking the O—X bond, rather than the H—O bond, even though these compounds are weak acids; i.e., in water $HOX \rightleftharpoons H^+ + OX^-$. The polarization, $\overset{\delta-}{HO}-\overset{\delta+}{X}$, indicates that the $X^+$, or some similar halogen species which has positive character, first attacks the double bond. Note also that the halogen atom has an oxidation state of +1 in hypohalous acids.

*Examples*: $\underset{\text{propene}}{CH_3-CH=CH_2} \xrightarrow{HOBr} CH_3-\underset{OH}{CH}-\underset{Br}{CH_2}$

1-bromo-2-propanol
a bromohydrin

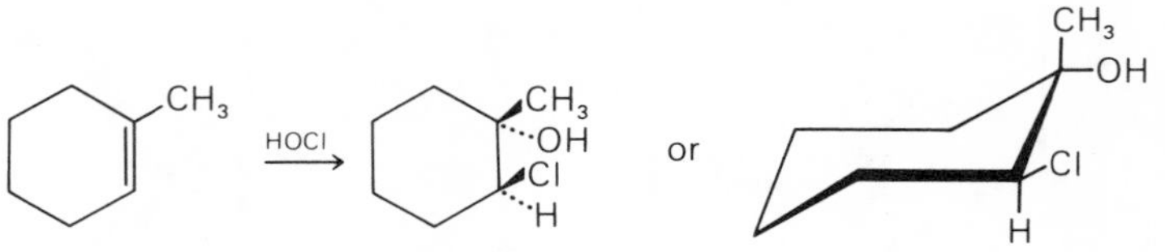

$$\text{methylcyclohexene} \xrightarrow{HOCl} \text{1-methyl-}trans\text{-2-chlorocyclohexanol (a chlorohydrin)}$$

methylcyclohexene

1-methyl-*trans*-2-chlorocyclohexanol
a chlorohydrin

$$\text{cyclopentene} \xrightarrow[\text{55\% yield}]{HOCl} trans\text{-2-chlorocyclopentanol}$$

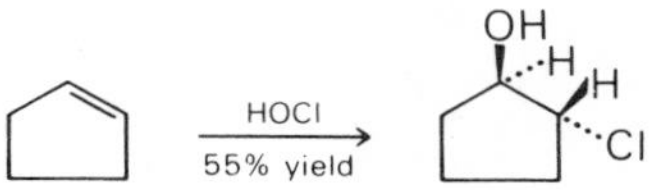

cyclopentene

*trans*-2-chlorocyclopentanol

| Formulate clearly the mechanism for each of the above examples. |
|---|

### 4-10 ADDITION OF $H_2SO_4$: COMMERCIAL ETHANOL PRODUCTION

Sulfuric acid also adds to olefinic linkages. This particular reaction of ethylene is the basis of an important industrial process for the preparation of synthetic ethyl alcohol. Isopropyl alcohol can be prepared in a similar manner from propene.

$$CH_2{=}CH_2 \xrightarrow{H_2SO_4} CH_3{-}CH_2OSO_2OH \xrightarrow[\Delta]{H_2O} CH_3CH_2OH + H_2SO_4$$

Whereas water does not readily add directly to an olefin, the highly polar intermediate (monoethyl sulfate) from the addition of $H_2SO_4$ can be hydrolyzed to the corresponding alcohol. Thus, olefins "dissolve" in concentrated sulfuric acid by reacting with it; the carbonium ion intermediate or sulfate is soluble in $H_2SO_4$.

### 4-11 ADDITION OF HBr: THE PEROXIDE EFFECT

In the presence of air or peroxides, the addition of HBr to olefins takes place by a ***free-radical mechanism***, rather than an ionic one.

*Ionic mechanism*: $CH_3{-}CH{=}CH_2 \xrightarrow[\text{no } O_2 \text{ (air)}]{HBr} CH_3{-}CH(Br){-}CH_3$

*Radical mechanism*: $CH_3{-}CH{=}CH_2 \xrightarrow[O_2 \text{ or peroxides}]{HBr} CH_3{-}CH_2{-}CH_2Br$

Since the major product is not the one expected from Markownikoff addition, this radical reaction is known as an ***anti-Markownikoff addition***. Since it takes place only in the presence of peroxides or some other free-radical source, this phenomenon is termed the *peroxide effect*. Hydrogen peroxide, HOOH, oxygen (and thus, air), peracids,

$$R{-}\overset{\overset{O}{\|}}{C}{-}O{-}O{-}H$$

and many other compounds containing an —O—O— bond are commonly used to initiate the radical reaction. Hydrogen bromide is the only common addend discussed in this chapter which behaves in this manner.

Since only traces of the free-radical reagent are necessary to produce the main product, the mechanism can be written as a chain reaction similar to that for alkane photochemical halogenation (Sec. 2-6).

Initiation: $HO{-}OH \xrightarrow[h\nu]{\Delta \text{ or}} 2HO\cdot$ (hydroxyl radicals)

$$HO\cdot + HBr \longrightarrow H_2O + Br\cdot$$

Propagation: $Br\cdot + CH_3{-}CH{=}CH_2 \longrightarrow [CH_3{-}\dot{C}H{-}CH_2Br]$

$$[CH_3{-}\dot{C}H{-}CH_2Br] + HBr \longrightarrow CH_3CH_2CH_2Br + Br\cdot$$

Why is this organic radical more stable than the alternative one? These two steps are repeated many times.

Termination: $2HO\cdot \longrightarrow H_2O_2$

$$HO\cdot + Br\cdot \longrightarrow HOBr$$

$$2CH_3{-}\dot{C}H{-}CH_2Br \longrightarrow \underset{H_3C}{\overset{BrH_2C}{>}}CH{-}CH\underset{CH_3}{\overset{CH_2Br}{<}}$$

Write as many other termination reactions as you can.

## 4-12 HYDROBORATION

Anti-Markownikoff cis hydration produces alcohols. For convenience we represent aluminum chloride, $Al_2Cl_6$, by its empirical formula, $AlCl_3$, and designate diborane, $B_2H_6$, as simply $BH_3$. Diborane can be prepared in a number of ways, two of which are

$$NaBH_4 + AlCl_3 \longrightarrow BH_3$$

sodium borohydride

$$NaBH_4 + F_3B{:}O\underset{CH_2CH_3}{\overset{CH_2CH_3}{<}} \longrightarrow BH_3$$

boron trifluoride etherate

Both sodium borohydride and boron trifluoride are commercially available.

The boron-hydrogen bonds of diborane add to carbon-carbon double bonds affording an intermediate alkylborane which can be readily oxidized by hydrogen peroxide and base to an alcohol.

$$>C=C< \xrightarrow{BH_3} >\underset{H}{C}-\underset{B}{C}< \xrightarrow{[O]} >\underset{H}{C}-\underset{OH}{C}<$$

In the first step of the reaction $BH_3$ reacts at room temperature with the alkene to give the alkylborane; simple mono- and disubstituted olefins give a trialkylborane, $R_3B$; trisubstituted olefins give the dialkylborane, $R_2BH$, but only one of the hydrogens is replaced with a tetrasubstituted olefin, $RBH_2$.

*General*: $CH_2=CHR \xrightarrow{BH_3} B(CH_2CH_2R)_3$

*Specific*: $CH_2=CH(CH_2)_3CH_3 \xrightarrow{BH_3} B(CH_2CH_2CH_2CH_2CH_2CH_3)_3$

1-hexene — tri-*n*-hexylborane

This is a cis addition in which a four-center transition state appears to be a reasonable mechanism

*Mechanism*: Note the electron-donating effect of alkyl groups.

$$CH_3-\overset{\delta+}{C}H=\overset{\delta-}{C}H_2 \xrightarrow{BH_3} \left[ CH_3-\overset{\delta+}{C}H\cdots\overset{\delta-}{C}H_2 \;\; \overset{\delta-}{H}\cdots\overset{\delta+}{B}< \right] \longrightarrow CH_3-\underset{H}{C}H-\underset{BH_2}{C}H_2$$

may react further with two moles of olefin

The cis stereochemistry and mode of addition can be illustrated with 1-methylcyclopentene or 1-methylcyclohexene.

*Example*: 1-methylcyclopentene $\xrightarrow{BH_3}$ [alkylborane: $H_3C$, H, H, B<] $\xrightarrow[H_2O_2/OH^-]{oxidation}$ *trans*-2-methylcyclohexanol

The second step in the reaction, the oxidation of the alkylborane with 30% $H_2O_2$ in base, is usually accomplished in almost quantitative yield with no rearrangement; the stereochemistry of the alcohol is the same as that of the alkylborane. The alkylborane need not be isolated for the subsequent oxidation, and both steps can be carried out in one flask.

The product distribution depends primarily not on the size of the alkyl groups present but on their electron-donating ability. With a trisubstituted olefin, however, the alcohol function appears predominantly on the less substituted carbon atom (see Table 4-3).

These two reactions provide a powerful and selective method for the addition of $H_2O$ to a double bond in a cis anti-Markownikoff fashion.

**Table 4-3**
**Examples of hydroboration of alkenes**

Terminal olefins: primary alcohols

$$CH_2{=}CHCH_2CH_2CH_2CH_3 \xrightarrow[2.\ H_2O_2/OH^-]{1.\ BH_3} CH_2(OH)CH_2CH_2CH_2CH_2CH_3 + CH_3CH(OH)CH_2CH_2CH_2CH_3$$

1-hexene → 1-hexanol 94% + 2-hexanol 6%

$$CH_3CH_2C(CH_3){=}CH_2 \xrightarrow[2.\ H_2O_2/OH^-]{1.\ BH_3} CH_3CH_2CH(CH_3){-}CH_2OH + CH_3CH_2C(OH)(CH_3){-}CH_3$$

2-methyl-1-butene → 2-methyl-1-butanol 99% + 2-methyl-2-butanol 1%

Disubstituted olefins: both alcohols in about equal amounts

$$H_3C{-}H_2C(H)C{=}C(H)CH_3 \longrightarrow CH_3CH_2CH_2CH(OH){-}CH_3 + CH_3CH_2CH(OH){-}CH_2CH_3$$

*trans*-2-pentene → 2-pentanol 51% + 3-pentanol 49%

Trisubstituted olefins: alcohol at less substituted carbon

$$CH_3{-}C(CH_3)_2{-}CH{=}C(CH_3){-}CH_3 \longrightarrow CH_3{-}C(CH_3)(H_3C){-}CH(OH){-}CH(CH_3){-}CH_3 + CH_3{-}C(CH_3)_2{-}CH_2{-}C(CH_3)(OH){-}CH_3$$

98% 2%

(Name these compounds.)

Tetrasubstituted olefins: similar to disubstituted ones

## QUALITATIVE TESTS

Because of the formation of alkyl sulfates (Sec. 4-10) alkenes are soluble in cold concentrated $H_2SO_4$; alkanes are not.

Solutions of potassium permanganate, $KMnO_4$, are so highly colored that even concentrations of 1 to 2% are pink. A rapid test for unsaturation is the decolorization of such a dilute solution.

$KMnO_4$ solutions $\xrightarrow{\text{olefin}}$ colorless solution of product + $MnO_2\downarrow$ 

pink to violet color — finely divided brown precipitate

Similarly, dilute solutions of bromine in carbon tetrachloride are red to red-brown and are rapidly decolorized as the bromine adds to olefins.

$Br_2$ (in $CCl_4$) $\xrightarrow{\text{olefin}}$ colorless solution of bromine-addition product

red-brown color

All the above tests are *negative* for benzene and other simple aromatic hydrocarbons, although some of these dissolve slowly in sulfuric acid.

## SUGGESTED READINGS

Diaper, D. G. M.: Ozonolysis, *J. Chem. Educ.*, **44**, 354 (1967).

Ihde, A.: The Unraveling of Geometric Isomerism and Tautomerism, *J. Chem. Educ.*, **36**, 330 (1959).

Jones, G.: The Markovnikov Rule, *J. Chem. Educ.*, **38**, 297 (1961).

Snyder, C. H.: Permanganate Hydroxylation of Alkenes, *J. Chem. Educ.*, **43**, 141 (1966).

Traynham, J. G.: The Bromonium Ion, *J. Chem. Educ.*, **40**, 392 (1963).

Walters, E. A.: Models for the Double Bond, *J. Chem. Educ.*, **43**, 134 (1966). Discussion of the bent-bond picture for double bonds.

## PROBLEMS

**1**. Name the following compounds and state the number of geometrical isomers which can exist.

★(*a*) $CH_3CH_2CH_2CH{=}CHCH_2CH_3$

(*b*) $CH_3CH{=}CH{-}CH_2CH_2CH(CH_3)CH{=}CH_2$

★(*c*) $CH_3CH_2C({=}CH_2)CH_2CH(CH_3)CH_2C({=}CH_2)CH_3$

(*d*) $CH_3$ $CH_3$

★(*e*) $H_5C_6$ $C_6H_5$ $H_5C_6$ $C_6H_5$ $H_5C_6$ $C_6H_5$

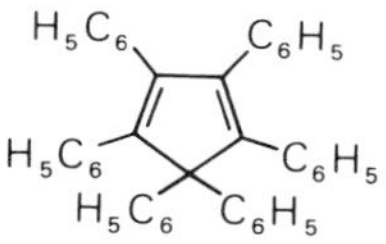

(*f*)

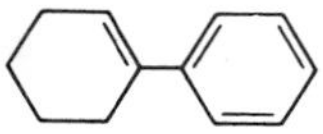

★(*g*)

★(*h*) Cl

★(*i*) $CH{=}CH_2$ $CH{=}CH_2$

(*j*) $H_2C{=}$

(*k*) Br— —$CH{=}CH_2$

(*l*) $H_3C$— —$CH{=}CH$— —$CH_3$

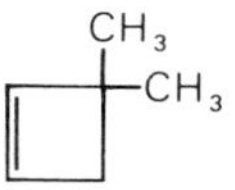

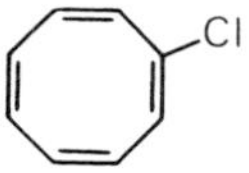

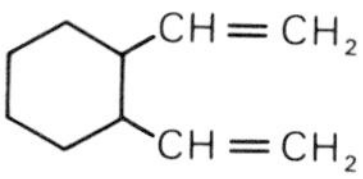

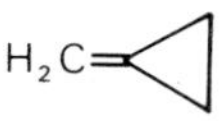

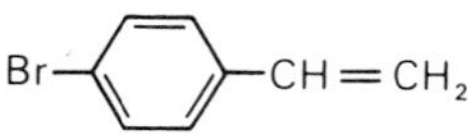

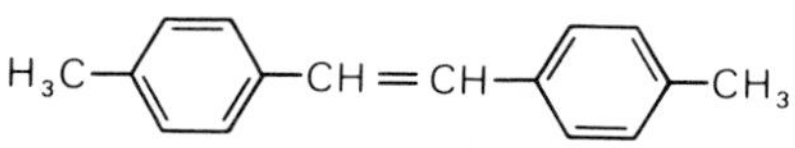

**2**. Draw the structures of the following compounds.

(*a*) *trans*-3-nonene

★(*b*) 1,9-decadiene

★(*c*) cyclobutadiene

(*d*) cyclopentadiene

(*e*) cycloheptatriene

★(*f*) 2,3-diethylcyclohexene

★(*g*) allyl bromide

★(*h*) vinyl chloride

(*i*) hexavinylbenzene

★(*j*) cyclohexylcyclohexene

**3**. Suppose that each of the following compounds is subjected to acid-catalyzed dehydration.

★(*a*) Predict the major product and give your reasons for the choice.

(*b*) Calculate the percent of each olefin which would be formed *on a statistical basis*.

★(*c*) Predict the major product formed by dehydration over thorium oxide.

(*d*) Name the starting alcohols and the olefins obtained in (*a*) and (*c*).

(*i*) $C_6H_5-CH(OH)-CH_2CH_3$

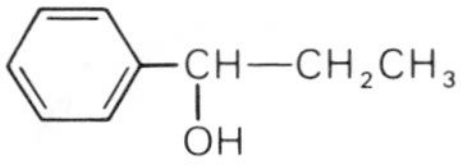

★(*ii*) $C_6H_5-CH_2-CH(OH)-CH_3$

(*iii*) $C_6H_5-CH_2-C(CH_3)(OH)-CH_3$

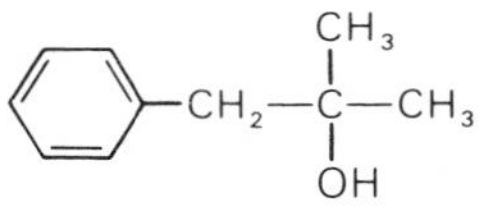

★(*iv*) $CH_2=CH-CH_2-CH(OH)-CH_3$

(*v*) $CH_2=CH-CH_2-C(CH_3)(OH)-CH_3$

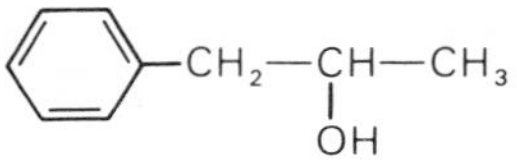

★(*vi*) 1-methylcyclohexanol (cyclohexane ring bearing $CH_3$ and OH on the same carbon)

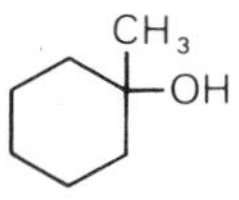

**4.** Explain in detail how dehalogenation with zinc could be used to separate a mixture of octane (b.p. 126°) and 1-octene (b.p. 123°) in order to obtain pure 1-octene. How would you purify the mixture in order to obtain pure octane?

★**5**. Name the starting material and give the name and show clearly the preferred conformation of the product:

(*a*) 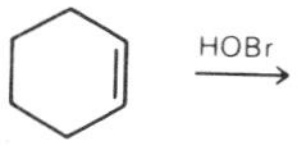 [cyclohexene] $\xrightarrow{HOBr}$

(*b*) [cyclohexene with $CH(CH_3)_2$ and $CH_3$ on the double-bond carbons] $\xrightarrow[\text{pressure}]{H_2/Pd}$

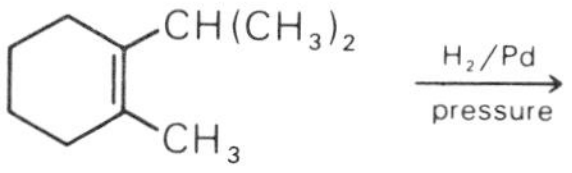

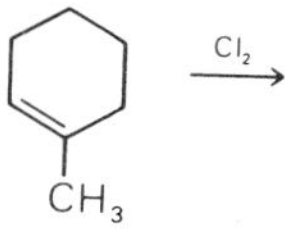

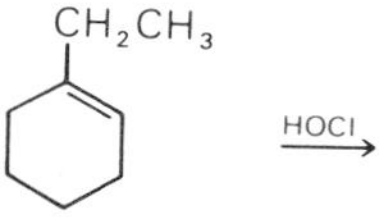

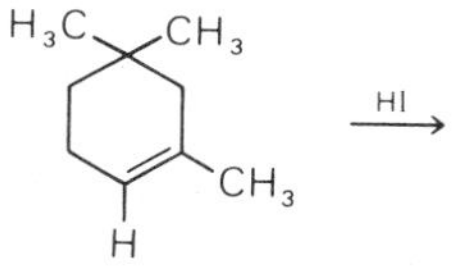

(*c*) [1-methylcyclohexene, $CH_3$] $\xrightarrow{Cl_2}$

(*d*) [cyclohexene with $CH_2CH_3$] $\xrightarrow{HOCl}$

(*e*) [cyclohexene with $H_3C$, $CH_3$, $CH_3$, H] $\xrightarrow{HI}$

(*f*) [cyclohexene with $H_3C$, $H_3C$] $\xrightarrow{Br_2}$

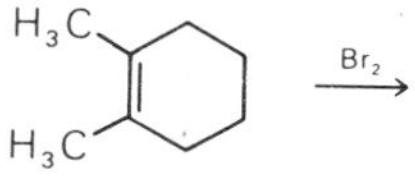

**6**. Predict the product distribution of alcohols expected from total hydroboration (followed by $H_2O_2$ oxidation) of the olefins in Prob. 6 of Chap. 3. Assume the reaction occurs separately at each double bond in polyolefins and note cis-trans isomers.

★**7**. An olefin, $C_6H_{12}$, capable of existing in cis and trans forms, gives $C_6H_{12}Br_2$ on treatment with $Br_2$ in $CCl_4$. This dibromide, on treatment with alcoholic KOH, yields a diene that is oxidized by $KMnO_4$ to propanoic acid, $CH_3CH_2COOH$, and $CO_2$. Write a structure for the starting olefin. Can only one structure be written which is consistent with these chemical observations?

★**8**. It has been found that ethylene stimulates the ripening process in many fruits. This is attributed to the ability of ethylene to bind to a metal receptor site in the vegetative tissue. How might such a binding take place?

# Chapter Five

## NOMENCLATURE

Compounds which contain a carbon-carbon triple bond are called *alkynes* or *acetylenes*. Acetylene is also the name of the first member of this $C_nH_{2n-2}$ homologous series. Alk*ynes* (compare with alk*ane* and alk*ene*) are unsaturated and undergo addition reactions. Although small-ring compounds may contain a cis double bond, the eight-membered ring is the smallest ring which can contain a stable trans carbon-carbon double bond. Similarly, an eight-membered ring is the smallest which can form a stable cyclic acetylene.

In addition to the IUPAC nomenclature, a substitutional system is also used which is based upon the parent compound, acetylene. Table 5-1 gives some examples. Recall that double bonds take precedence over triple bonds in numbering a carbon chain.

The only common acetylenic groups are ethynyl, H—C≡C—, and propargyl, H—C≡C—$CH_2$—.

**Table 5-1 Structures and names (IUPAC and substitutional) of representative acetylenes**

| | | |
|---|---|---|
| H—C≡C—H<br>(ethyne)<br>acetylene | $CH_3$—C≡C—H<br>propyne<br>methylacetylene | $CH_3$—C≡C—$CH_3$<br>2-butyne<br>dimethylacetylene |
| $CH_3$—$CH_2$—C≡C—H<br>1-butyne<br>ethylacetylene | $CH_2$=CH—C≡C—H<br>1-buten-3-yne<br>vinylacetylene | H—C≡C—C≡C—H<br>1,3-butadiyne<br>diacetylene |
| $C_6H_5$—C≡C—H<br>(phenylethyne)<br>phenylacetylene | $C_6H_5$—C≡C—$C_6H_5$<br>(diphenylethyne)<br>diphenylacetylene | |

# Alkynes (Acetylenes)

## ACIDS AND BASES

The Arrhenius concept of acids and bases is an exceedingly simple but limiting one. An acid is a proton donor or a substance whose aqueous solution contains $H^+$; a base is an hydroxide ion, $OH^-$, or a substance whose aqueous solution contains $OH^-$. Common examples of acids are HCl, $HNO_3$, $H_2SO_4$ and acetic acid $CH_3COOH$; examples of bases are NaOH, KOH, $NH_4OH$, and tetramethylammonium hydroxide $(CH_3)_4N^+OH^-$. The reaction of one equivalent of acid with one equivalent of base is called *neutralization*. Using the simple Arrhenius concept, all neutralizations are expressed by the equation

$$H^+ + OH^- \rightleftharpoons H_2O$$

Brönsted and Lowry considered acids and bases in terms of the proton. In this system an acid is defined as any substance which can donate a proton and a base as any substance which can accept a proton. This led to the concept of a *conjugate acid-base* pair: a conjugate acid is converted to a conjugate base by donation of a proton, and, similarly, a conjugate base is converted to a conjugate acid by accepting a proton.

$$\underset{\text{acid}}{HA} \underset{+H^+}{\overset{-H^+}{\rightleftharpoons}} \underset{\text{conjugate base}}{A^-}$$

$$\underset{\text{base}}{B:} \underset{-H^+}{\overset{+H^+}{\rightleftharpoons}} \underset{\text{conjugate acid}}{HB^+}$$

Since the strength of an acid is a measure of its tendency to donate a proton and the strength of a base is a measure of its tendency to accept a proton, the stronger an acid, the weaker its conjugate base, and the stronger a base, the weaker its conjugate acid. This shows that the equilibrium in any neutralization reaction will lie on the side of the weaker acid and base.

Strong acids include mineral acids, such as $HClO_4$, HCl, and $HNO_3$, and organic acids, Ar—COOH and R—COOH. Phenols, Ar—OH, are only moderately strong acids. Water and alcohols, R—O—H, are weak acids, whereas hydrogen, $H_2$, and hydrocarbons, Ar—H and R—H, are extremely weak acids. Very strong bases include the hydride ion, $H^-$, as well as most carbanions, $Ar^-$ and $R^-$. Hydroxide and alkoxide ions, $R—O^-$ are strong bases. Then, in order of decreasing base strength are phenoxide ions, $Ar—O^-$, carboxylate anions, $R—COO^-$, nitrate, chloride, and perchlorate ions.

A broader concept of acids and bases was put forward by G. N. Lewis. **Lewis acids are substances which can accept an electron pair, and Lewis bases are substances which can donate an electron pair.** In this sense, a neutralization reaction is one in which a covalent bond is formed from an acid and a base. The product is often referred to as an adduct or *coordinated complex*. Thus, Lewis acids include all cations, atoms without an octet of electrons (such as B in $BF_3$, Al in $AlCl_3$, and Fe in $FeBr_3$), and atoms which have vacant *d* orbitals available and can thus expand their octet (such as Si in $SiF_4$ and Sn in $SnCl_4$). Lewis bases include anions, atoms with unshared pairs of electrons, such as: $:NH_3$ and $H_2\ddot{O}:$, and multiply bonded atoms, such as $>C=C<$ and $—C\equiv C—$.

It should be clear from the foregoing paragraph that it is important to state or understand the context of a statement like "compound **Z** is an acid." There are many examples in which a compound might be considered either an acid or a base, depending on the acid-base system or reaction under discussion.

## 5-1 ACIDITY OF TERMINAL ACETYLENIC PROTONS

Recall that the atomic-orbital picture for the shells beyond the first one indicates that the *s* electrons are on the average closer to the nucleus than the *p* electrons. Thus, the *s* orbitals are the more electronegative and an *sp* hybrid, which contains a relatively large amount of *s* character, should be more electronegative than the $sp^2$ and $sp^3$ hybrids. Carbon atoms with *sp* hybridization can readily stabilize a negative charge. The terminal protons of acetylene and monosubstituted acetylenes are bonded to carbon by an *sp-s* bond, and consequently are slightly acidic. Acetylenic protons react not only with very strong bases such as alcoholic KOH and $NaNH_2$ but also give precipitates with heavy-metal cations such as $Ag^+$ and $Cu^+$. Compare the structure and weak acidity of these protons with those of hydrogen cyanide: $H—C\equiv N$, $H—C\equiv C—H$, and

$H—C≡C—CH_3$. The protons of terminal acetylenes also release methane (or other hydrocarbons) from Grignard reagents and form a new, acetylenic Grignard reagent, which may be used in other reactions (Sec. 9-10).

$$CH_3—C≡C—H + [CH_3CH_2MgBr] \longrightarrow [CH_3—C≡C—MgBr] + CH_3—CH_3\uparrow$$

## PREPARATION

### 5-2 ACETYLENE FROM NATURE'S RAW MATERIALS

Coke, C, limestone, $CaCO_3$, and water, $H_2O$, are among the most abundant natural raw materials. From them acetylene can be prepared industrially. By a series of reactions, although the routes are often tedious, nearly all organic compounds can be prepared, at least with a pencil on paper, from coke, limestone, water, and air; fire is also necessary!

Industrial:
$$CaCO_3 \xrightarrow{\Delta} CaO + CO_2$$
$$3C + CaO \xrightarrow[\text{elec. furnace}]{2000° \text{ in}} CaC_2 + CO\uparrow$$

Laboratory:
$$\underset{\text{calcium carbide}}{CaC_2} + 2H_2O \longrightarrow \underset{\text{acetylene}}{H—C≡C—H} + Ca(OH)_2$$

From acetylene various chemical intermediates and commercial products can be prepared.

### 5-3 DEHYDROHALOGENATION OF VICINAL DIHALIDES

Acetylenes can be prepared by treating dihalides with strong base. The mechanism of this dehydrohalogenation is similar to that discussed for the preparation of olefins from alkyl halides (see Sec. 4-2). Sodium amide, $NaNH_2$, prepared from sodium and liquid ammonia in the presence of a trace of $Fe^{3+}$ salts, is commonly employed as the strong base.

*Examples*:
$$Na + NH_3 \xrightarrow[\text{trace}]{Fe^{3+}} NaNH_2 + \tfrac{1}{2}H_2\uparrow$$

$$\underset{\text{styrene dibromide}}{C_6H_5—\underset{Br}{CH}—\underset{Br}{CH_2}} \xrightarrow[\text{liquid } NH_3,\ 50\%\text{ yield}]{NaNH_2 \text{ in}} \underset{\text{phenylacetylene}}{C_6H_5—C≡C—H}$$

$$CH_3(CH_2)_7CH{=}CH(CH_2)_7CO_2H \xrightarrow{Br_2} CH_3(CH_2)_7\underset{Br}{CH}{-}\underset{Br}{CH}(CH_2)_7CO_2H$$

oleic acid — 9,10-dibromostearic acid

$$\xrightarrow[\text{in liquid } NH_3]{NaNH_2} \quad 60\% \text{ yield}$$

$$CH_3(CH_2)_7{-}C{\equiv}C{-}(CH_2)_7CO_2H$$

stearolic acid

*Overall*: $CH_3{-}\underset{Br}{CH}{-}\underset{Br}{CH_2} \xrightarrow[\text{KOH or } NaNH_2]{\text{strong base alc.}} CH_3{-}C{\equiv}C{-}H$

*Mechanism*: $E_2$, *trans* elimination

$$CH_3{-}\underset{Br}{\overset{H}{C}}{-}\underset{Br}{\overset{H}{C}}{-}H + \bar{N}H_2 \longrightarrow [\text{transition state: } H\cdots NH_2,\ CH_3,\ H,\ Br,\ Br]^- $$

$$\downarrow$$

$$H_3C(H)C{=}C(H)Br + NH_3 + Br^-$$

*trans*-1-bromopropene

Although the reaction can be stopped at the olefin stage, it is usually allowed to proceed until none of the organic halide remains.

$$[CH_3{-}CH{=}CH{-}Br] + NH_2^- \longrightarrow CH_3{-}C{\equiv}C{-}H + NH_3 + Br^-$$

*Important side reaction*

$$H{-}\underset{H}{\overset{H}{C}}{-}\underset{Br}{\overset{H}{C}}{-}\underset{Br}{\overset{H}{C}}{-}H \quad \bar{N}H_2 \longrightarrow [H_2C{=}C(Br){-}\ ...]\ \ [CH_2(H)\text{–}C(Br){=}CH_2] + NH_3 + Br^-$$

2-bromopropene

$$[H_2C(H){-}C(Br){=}CH_2 \quad \bar{N}H_2] \longrightarrow CH_2{=}C{=}CH_2 + NH_3 + Br^-$$

allene

If the amide ion first attacks the hydrogen on the secondary carbon atom, the resulting intermediate then contains allylic primary hydrogen atoms that are subsequently attacked by a second amide ion. The product formed is an allene, a compound with two double bonds on one carbon atom. Allenes may be obtained as the major product. Allenes and acetylenes are equilibrated under these basic reaction conditions, and the major product depends on the specific reaction conditions of time, temperature, solvent, the base used, and its concentration.

## 5-4 DEHYDROHALOGENATION OF GEMINAL DIHALIDES

Two like substituents on a given carbon atom are known as *geminal* substituents (from *gemini*, twins). Geminal-dihalides can be prepared from aldehydes or ketones by treatment with $PCl_5$ or $PBr_5$.

$$R{-}C(=O){-}H \qquad \text{or} \qquad R{-}\underset{\|}{\overset{}{C}}{-}R \;(C{=}O)$$

aldehydes ketones

The $E_2$ elimination with strong base proceeds readily, to give acetylenes; allenes are also major by-products here.

$$CH_3{-}\overset{O}{\overset{\|}{C}}{-}C(CH_3)_3 \xrightarrow[\approx 100\%\text{ yield}]{PCl_5;\ 0°} CH_3{-}\underset{Cl}{\overset{Cl}{C}}{-}C(CH_3)_3 \xrightarrow[65\%\text{ yield}]{NaNH_2} H{-}C{\equiv}C{-}C(CH_3)_3$$

*tert*-butylacetylene

## 5-5 REACTION OF PRIMARY ALKYL HALIDES WITH METAL ACETYLIDES

Acetylene, H—C≡C—H, and terminal acetylenes, R—C≡C—H, can be converted to the corresponding salts by treatment with strong base, usually sodium or sodium amide.

$$CH_3{-}C{\equiv}C{-}H + Na \rightarrow CH_3{-}C{\equiv}C^-\ Na^+ + \tfrac{1}{2}H_2\uparrow$$

$$CH_3{-}C{\equiv}C{-}H + NaNH_2 \xrightarrow[NH_3]{\text{in liquid}} CH_3{-}C{\equiv}C^-\ Na^+ + NH_3$$

In the second step, almost any primary alkyl halide can be added, and displacement of the halogen leads to the formation of a new carbon-carbon bond.

*Examples:*

$$CH_3{-}C{\equiv}C^-\ Na^+ + CH_3I \rightarrow CH_3{-}C{\equiv}C{-}CH_3$$

$$H{-}C{\equiv}C^-\ Na^+ + CH_3I \xrightarrow[\text{yield}]{85\%} H{-}C{\equiv}C{-}CH_3$$

$$H{-}C{\equiv}C^-\ Na^+ + (CH_3)_2CH{-}CH_2{-}CH_2Br \xrightarrow[\text{yield}]{70\%} H{-}C{\equiv}C(CH_2)_2CH(CH_3)_2$$

isopentyl bromide 5-methyl-1-hexyne

Secondary and tertiary alkyl halides undergo a very ready elimination with strong bases such as Na, $NaNH_2$, and the metal acetylides. Aromatic halides are generally unreactive toward displacement reactions.

$$CH_3{-}C{\equiv}C^- + H{-}\underset{H}{\overset{H}{C}}{-}\underset{CH_3}{\overset{CH_3}{C}}{-}Br \rightarrow CH_3{-}C{\equiv}C{-}H + CH_2{=}C(CH_3)_2 + Br^-$$

methylacetylide — *tert*-butyl bromide — isobutylene

## REACTIONS

The reactions of acetylenes are due mainly to the unsaturation of the triple bond and to the weak acidity of terminal acetylenic protons.

### 5-6 REACTIONS WITH $H_2$, $X_2$, HX, $O_3$, AND $KMnO_4$

These reagents react with acetylenes in a manner similar to the reactions with alkenes except that 2 equiv are involved; usually the reactions occur more slowly and stepwise. When reactions have been stopped at an intermediate stage, they have been found to proceed stereospecifically, as expected. For instance, reduction of an acetylene with 1 equiv of hydrogen using a special catalyst, palladium-on-calcium carbonate deactivated with lead acetate, leads to the cis olefin. Bromination of a triple bond gives the trans dibromo compound and then the tetrabromide (see Table 5-2).

### 5-7 REACTIONS WITH HCN AND $H_2O$; TAUTOMERISM

Several simple molecules, such as HCN, that do not readily add to olefins can be added to acetylenic triple bonds.

$$H{-}C{\equiv}C{-}H \xrightarrow[Ba(CN)_2]{HCN} CH_2{=}CHCN$$

acrylonitrile
(vinyl cyanide)
(cyanoethylene)

Since acetylene is available in large quantities from cheap starting materials, these addition compounds are important industrial chemical intermediates. Of special interest is acetaldehyde, which can be prepared by adding water to the triple bond in the presence of a $HgSO_4$-$H_2SO_4$ catalytic system.

$$H{-}C{\equiv}C{-}H \xrightarrow[Hg^{++}\,SO_4^{--}]{H_2O;\ H^+} CH_3{-}C\begin{matrix}{=}O\\ \diagdown H\end{matrix}$$

**Table 5-2**
**Some examples of acetylene reactions**

Hydrogenation:

$$CH_3—C\equiv C—CH_3 \xrightarrow[\text{[Pb(OAc)}_2\text{]}]{H_2,\ \text{Pd-CaCO}_3} \underset{H}{\overset{H_3C}{>}}C=C\underset{H}{\overset{CH_3}{<}} \xrightarrow[\text{reduction}]{\text{further}} CH_3CH_2CH_2CH_3$$

Bromination:

$$C_6H_5—C\equiv C—H \xrightarrow{Br_2} \underset{Br}{\overset{C_6H_5}{>}}C=C\underset{H}{\overset{Br}{<}} \xrightarrow{Br_2} C_6H_5—CBr_2—CHBr_2$$

Oxidation:

$$\underset{\text{2-butyne}}{CH_3—C\equiv C—CH_3} \xrightarrow[\Delta]{KMnO_4} \underset{\text{acetic acid}}{2CH_3CO_2H}$$

Addition of HCl:

$$\underset{\text{acetylene}}{H—C\equiv C—H} \xrightarrow{HCl} \underset{\text{vinyl chloride}}{CH_2=CHCl} \xrightarrow{HCl} \underset{\text{1,1-dichloroethane}}{CH_3CHCl_2}$$

Ozonolysis:

$$CH_3—C\equiv C—CH_2CH_3 \xrightarrow[H_2O]{O_3} CH_3COOH + CH_3CH_2COOH$$

The mercuric ion, $Hg^{++}$, coordinates with the triple bond, thereby facilitating addition of the water molecule. The intermediate vinyl alcohol, $CH_2=CH—OH$, is not stable and rearranges to the more stable acetaldehyde.

$$H—C\equiv C—H \xrightarrow{H_2O} \left[\underset{H}{\overset{H}{>}}C=C\underset{O—H}{\overset{H}{<}}\right]$$

vinyl alcohol (unstable)

$$\left[\underset{H}{\overset{H}{>}}C=C\underset{O—H}{\overset{H}{<}}\right] \rightleftharpoons H—\underset{H}{\overset{H}{|}}{C}—C\underset{H}{\overset{O}{\lessgtr}}$$

enol form — keto form acetaldehyde

**Tautomerism**: These two forms, vinyl alcohol and acetaldehyde, are known as *tautomers* and differ in the position of the double bond ($>C=C<$ vs. $>C=O$) and of the proton (—O—H vs. $\geq$C—H). The unsaturated (*-ene* ending) vinyl alcohol (*-ol* ending) is known as the *enol* form, and acetaldehyde is the *keto* form (compare *keto*ne, $R{-}C({=}O){-}R'$). The keto and enol forms are in equilibrium, although the keto form predominates here. Cases are known (phenols, for example) in which the enol form is the major one. These forms are two different chemical compounds and under favorable circumstances can be separated.

$$\text{C}_6\text{H}_{10}(\text{OH})\text{C}{\equiv}\text{C}{-}\text{H} \xrightarrow[\text{65\% yield}]{\text{H}_2\text{O};\ \text{Hg}^{++};\ \text{H}_2\text{SO}_4} \text{C}_6\text{H}_{10}(\text{OH})\text{C}({=}\text{O}){-}\text{CH}_3$$

1-ethynylcyclohexanol → 1-acetylcyclohexanol

> Predict the product of the following reaction and clearly show its mode of formation.
>
> $$CH_3{-}C{\equiv}C{-}H \xrightarrow[Hg^{++};\ H_2SO_4]{H_2O}$$

## 5-8 HYDROBORATION OF ACETYLENES

In the same way that olefins react with diborane to give *alkyl*boranes (Sec. 4-12), acetylenes give *vinyl*boranes. Subsequent oxidation of this intermediate gives rise to an intermediate vinyl alcohol, which tautomerizes to the carbonyl compound.

$$CH_3CH_2{-}C{\equiv}C{-}CH_2CH_3 \xrightarrow{BH_3} (CH_3CH_2{-}C(H){=}C(B{<}){-}CH_2CH_3)_3$$

3-hexyne

$$\downarrow H_2O_2$$

$$CH_3CH_2CH_2{-}C({=}O){-}CH_2CH_3 \leftrightharpoons [CH_3CH_2CH{=}C(OH)CH_2CH_3]$$

3-hexanone — a vinyl alcohol

## 5-9 SELF-ADDITION OF ACETYLENE

Acetylene can be added to itself to form unsaturated compounds. The reaction may be stopped after 1 equiv of acetylene is added.

$$2H{-}C{\equiv}C{-}H \xrightarrow[\text{cat.}]{CuCl_2} H{-}C{\equiv}C{-}CH{=}CH_2$$

vinylacetylene (1-buten-3-yne)

$$\downarrow C_2H_2,\ CuCl_2$$

$$CH_2{=}CH{-}C{\equiv}C{-}CH{=}CH_2$$

divinylacetylene

The addition of HCl to the triple bond of vinylacetylene gives chloroprene, which is the building block of a synthetic rubberlike material, neoprene.

$$H{-}C{\equiv}C{-}CH{=}CH_2 \xrightarrow{HCl} H_2C{=}\underset{\displaystyle Cl}{\underset{|}{C}}{-}CH{=}CH_2$$

chloroprene

## QUALITATIVE TESTS

Both dilute $Br_2$ and $KMnO_4$ are decolorized by acetylenes. Terminal acetylenes, however, give precipitates with both $Ag(NH_3)_2^+$ and $Cu(NH_3)_2^+$. The reagents for these tests are prepared by dissolving the appropriate metal salt in concentrated ammonium hydroxide, a source of $NH_3$.

$$M^+ + 2NH_3 \longrightarrow M(NH_3)_2^+ \qquad M = Ag^+ \text{ or } Cu^+$$

$$R{-}C{\equiv}C{-}H \underset{\text{dil. } H^+}{\overset{M(NH_3)_2^+}{\rightleftharpoons}} R{-}C{\equiv}C{-}M\downarrow$$

The lower terminal acetylenes give solid salts, acetylides, which are explosive when dry; they can be isolated and decomposed in the moist state, yielding the original organic compound. Again, the metal salt formation is due to the weakly acidic terminal proton.

> How can 1-butyne and 2-butyne be separated using this reagent?

## SUGGESTED READINGS

Roderick, W. R.: Structural Variety of Natural Products, *J. Chem. Educ.*, **39**, 2 (1962). Lists, among others, some alkynes and ring compounds found in nature.

Rose, N. C.: Hydration of an Alkyne, *J. Chem. Educ.*, **43**, 324 (1966).

## PROBLEMS

**1**. Name the following compounds by any consistent system of nomenclature:

★(*a*) $CH_3{-}C{\equiv}C{-}$(cyclopropyl)

★(*b*) $H{-}C{\equiv}C{-}CH{=}CH_2$

(*c*) $H{-}C{\equiv}C{-}C{\equiv}C{-}H$

★(*d*) $C_6H_5{-}C{\equiv}C^-\ Na^+$

(*e*) $H{-}C{\equiv}C{-}MgBr$

★(*f*) $H{-}C{\equiv}C{-}C(OH)(CH_2CH_3){-}CH_2{-}CH_3$

(*g*) $CH_2{=}CH{-}CH_2{-}C{\equiv}C{-}CH_2CH_3$

**2**. Each of the following dehydrohalogenations has been accomplished in mineral oil at 100 to 150° using sodium amide. Formulate the reactions, using structural formulas, or name the compounds where the structures are given.

| *Halide* | *Acetylene* | *Yield, %* |
|---|---|---|
| 2,2-dichlorobutane | 1-butyne | 40% |
| 1-chloro-1-heptene | 1-heptyne | 60% |
| 2-bromo-4,4-dimethyl-1-pentene | 4,4-dimethyl-1-pentyne | 37% |
| $C_6H_{11}{-}CH_2{-}CBr{=}CH_2$ | $C_6H_{11}{-}CH_2{-}C{\equiv}C{-}H$ | 66% |
| $C_6H_{11}{-}CH_2{-}CH_2{-}CHBr{-}CH_2Br$ | $C_6H_{11}{-}CH_2{-}CH_2{-}C{\equiv}C{-}H$ | 65% |
| $CH_2{=}CBr{-}(CH_2)_7CH_3$ | $H{-}C{\equiv}C(CH_2)_7CH_3$ | 68% |

**3**. Name the starting material(s) and give the structural formula *and* name of the product(s). If no reaction occurs, write N.R.

★(*a*) $C_6H_5{-}C{\equiv}C{-}H \xrightarrow[2.\ C_6H_5CH_2Br]{1.\ NaNH_2}$

★(*b*) $CH_3CH_2CH{=}CH_2 \xrightarrow[2.\ \text{alc. KOH}]{1.\ Br_2}$

★(*c*) $D{-}C{\equiv}C{-}D \xrightarrow[D_2SO_4]{D_2O;\ Hg^{++}SO_4^{--}}$

(*d*) $CH_3{-}C{\equiv}C{-}H \xrightarrow[2.\ CH_3(CH_2)_4CH_2I]{1.\ NaNH_2}$

★(*e*) cyclobutyl—C≡C—cyclopentyl $\xrightarrow[25°]{H_2/Pt}$

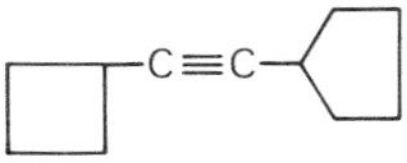

★(*f*) $CH_3CH_2Br \xrightarrow[\text{2. } C_6H_5—C≡C—H \text{; 3. } D_2O]{\text{1. Mg in dry ether}}$

(*g*) $C_6H_5—CH(I)—CH(CH_3)_2 \xrightarrow{H—C≡C^-Na^+}$

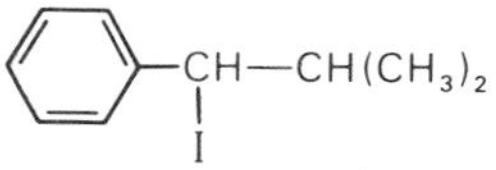

(*h*) $C_6H_5—C≡C—C_6H_5 \xrightarrow{Ag(NH_3)_2^+}$

★(*i*) $CH_3—C(CH_3)_2—CBr_2—CH_2—C(CH_3)_2—CH_3 \xrightarrow{\text{alc. KOH}}$

(*j*) $CH_3—C≡C—H \xrightarrow[\text{2. } H_2O_2]{\text{1. } BH_3/OH^-}$

★**4**. Propose a synthesis of the following compounds from coke, C, limestone, $CaCO_3$, and any necessary solvents and inorganic reagents. State all reactants and conditions.

(*a*) $CH_3—C(=O)—CH=CH_2$
methyl vinyl ketone

(*b*) $CH_2(Br)—C(Cl)=CH—CH_2(Br)$

★**5**. Compound **A**, $C_{10}H_{11}Br$, on treatment with $NaNH_2$ gives compound **C**, $C_{10}H_{10}$, in 63% yield. Compound **B**, $C_{10}H_{12}Br_2$, under similar conditions gives compound **C** in 55% yield. On ozonolysis compound **A** gives formaldehyde (and other products), but compound **B** is not readily ozonized.

Compound **C** gives a precipitate with $Cu(NH_3)_2^+$ and readily takes up 2 moles of hydrogen; 3 additional moles are taken up only under forcing conditions. Oxidation of compound **A**, **B**, or **C** with $KMnO_4$ yields benzoic acid, $C_6H_5COOH$. Write structures for compounds **A**, **B**, and **C**.

**6**. Compound **A**, $C_{15}H_{18}$, does not react with $Ag(NH_3)_2^+$ but readily absorbs hydrogen, to give compound **B**, $C_{15}H_{22}$. Oxidation of compound **A** with hot $KMnO_4$ yields benzoic acid and cyclohexanone (cyclohexane ring with =O) as the only isolable products. Write structures for compounds **A** and **B**.

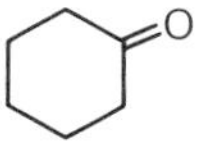

★**7**. Compound **X**, $C_{15}H_{16}$, gives a precipitate with $Ag(NH_3)_2^+$, decolorizes bromine, and yields cyclohexanone and benzoic acid on oxidation with hot $KMnO_4$. Catalytic hydrogenation of compound **X** gives $C_{15}H_{22}$; further hydrogenation is difficult, but leads to $C_{15}H_{28}$. Write a structure for compound **X**.

# Chapter Six

Three general types of carbon-carbon double bonds can occur in organic compounds. Any two double bonds may be characterized as *isolated*, *cumulated*, or *conjugated*.

$CH_2{=}CHCH_2CH_2CH{=}CH_2$ — 1,5-hexadiene (isolated)

$CH_2{=}C{=}CHCH_2CH_2CH_3$ — 1,2-hexadiene (cumulated)

$CH_2{=}CH{-}CH{=}CH{-}CH_2CH_3$ — 1,3-hexadiene (conjugated)

## 6-1 ISOLATED DOUBLE BONDS

Isolated dienes have double bonds separated by one or more saturated carbon atoms, which act as electronic insulators. These double bonds react independently; e.g., bromine adds first to one and then the other. There is essentially no influence of one double bond on another. Note that in 1,4-pentadiene (Fig. 6-1) there is no significant interaction between $C_2$ and $C_4$; $C_3$ acts as an insulator, thereby preventing *p-p* overlap.

## 6-2 ALLENES, CUMULATED DOUBLE BONDS

This general class of compounds is also known as the *cumulenes* because the double bonds are cumulated at a given carbon or carbons. The simplest compound of the series is *allene*, $CH_2{=}C{=}CH_2$.

In the atomic-orbital picture of Fig. 6-2, note that $HHC_1$ and $HHC_3$ define planes which are perpendicular and intersect at $C_2$. Since *p* orbitals may overlap effectively only with adjacent ones having their axes parallel, the two double bonds do not overlap.

# Dienes and Polymerization

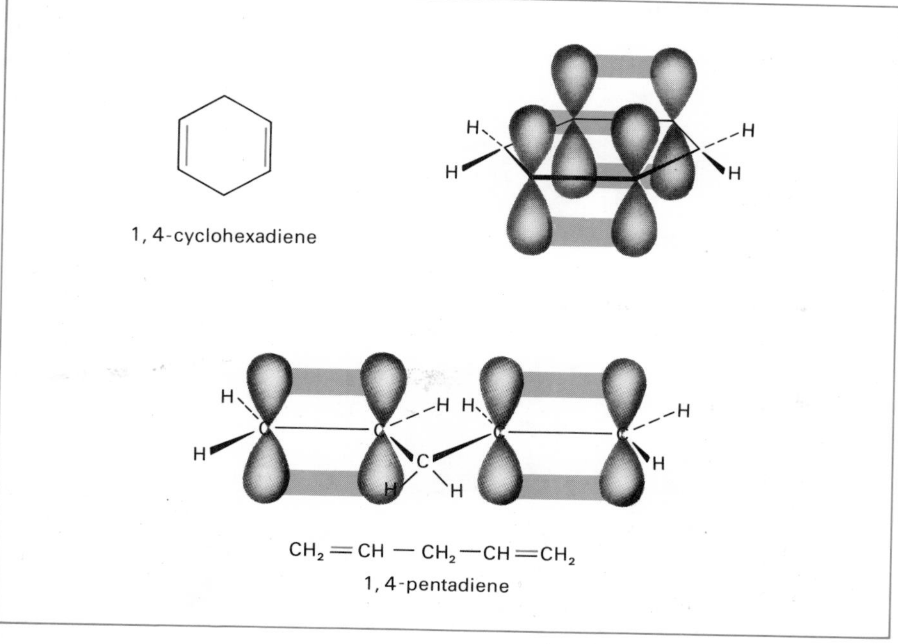


**Figure 6-1 Atomic orbitals of 1,4-cyclohexadiene and 1,4-pentadiene**

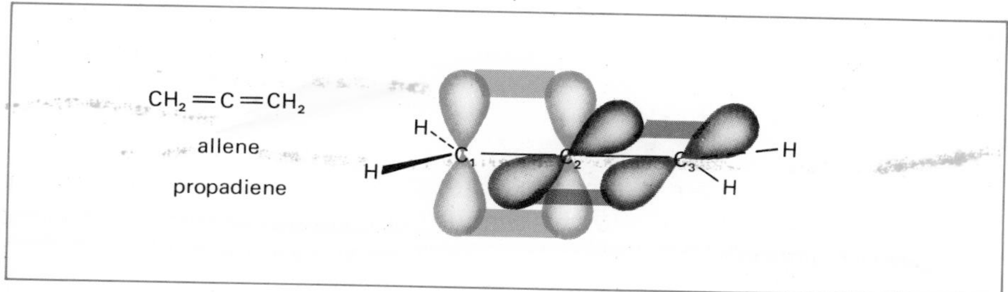


**Figure 6-2 Atomic orbitals of allene**

> Draw the next higher homolog of the cumulene series, butatriene, and note the number of ways in which two methyl groups may be attached to the compound. Why is cis-trans isomerism possible in disubstituted butatriene but not in 2,3-pentadiene?

### 6-3 CONJUGATED DOUBLE BONDS

Dienes containing alternating double and single bonds are called *conjugated* dienes. An overlap of the two $\pi$-electron systems is possible (Fig. 6-3). The molecular-orbital description of 1,3-butadiene shows that the two double bonds are not independent, and resonance forms can be written which also show this relationship.

$$CH_2{=}CH{-}CH{=}CH_2 \longleftrightarrow \bar{C}H_2{-}\overset{+}{C}H{-}CH{=}CH_2 \longleftrightarrow \bar{C}H_2{-}CH{=}CH{-}\overset{+}{C}H_2$$

$$\updownarrow$$

$$\overset{+}{C}H_2{-}CH{=}CH{-}\bar{C}H_2 \longleftrightarrow CH_2{=}CH{-}\overset{+}{C}H{-}\bar{C}H_2$$

Figure 6-3 Orbitals of conjugated dienes

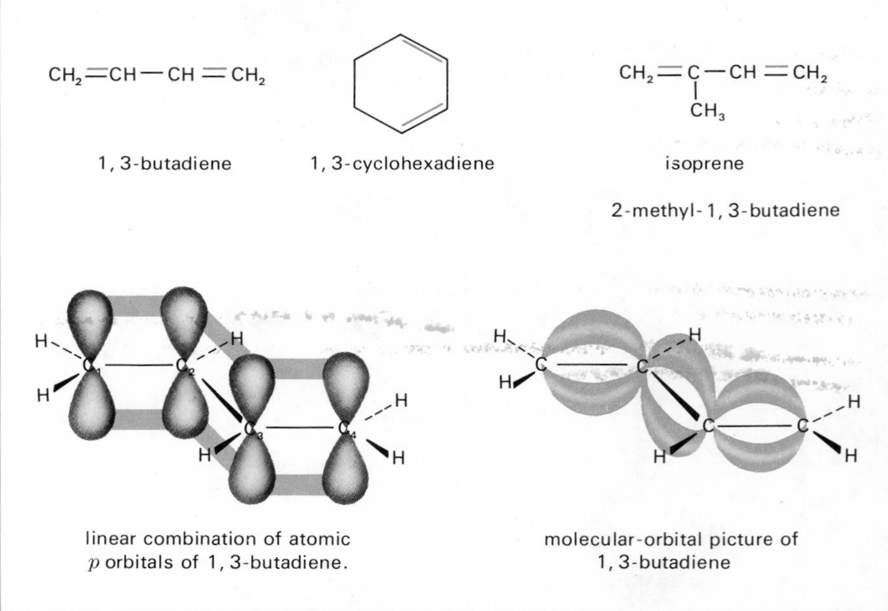


These charge-separated forms indicate that the $C_2$—$C_3$ bond contains some double-bond character. As might be expected, this conjugation of the double bonds leads to a lowering of the energy of the system (relative to two isolated ethylenic double bonds).

**1,4 Addition:** Ionic additions to a conjugated system generally lead to products resulting from a 1,4 addition.

$$CH_2{=}CH{-}CH{=}CH_2 \xrightarrow{Br_2} \underset{\displaystyle Br}{CH_2}{-}CH{=}CH{-}\underset{\displaystyle Br}{CH_2}$$

Consider the difference in ring size and strain of the cyclic bromonium ions derived from 1,2 and 1,4 addition.

$$\left[\underset{\displaystyle \;\;Br}{H_2C{\cdots}CH}{-}CH{=}CH_2\right]^+ \quad \text{vs.} \quad \left[\begin{array}{c} HC{=}CH \\ H_2C \qquad CH_2 \\ Br \end{array}\right]^+$$

1,2-addition — 1,4-addition

3,4-Dibromo-1-butene and 1,2,3,4-tetrabromobutane are also obtained as side products from the bromination of 1,3-butadiene.

## POLYMERIZATION

A ***polymer*** is a high-molecular-weight compound composed of many repeating units of a simpler molecule, called a ***monomer***. If only two units are joined, the resulting substance is a ***dimer***. Three constitute a ***trimer***; four constitute a ***tetramer***; and so on.

### 6-4 POLYMERIZATION OF OLEFINS

One of the simplest and most useful polymers is that derived from ethylene known as *polyethylene*. The polymerization reaction is usually initiated with a trace of a cation, radical, or anion; the reaction then proceeds by self-addition. In the example given, acid is used but radical sources such as oxygen (air) and anion sources such as organometallic reagents ($TiCl_2 \cdot R_3Al$) can also be used.

*Overall*:

$$\underset{\text{ethylene}}{xCH_2{=}CH_2} \xrightarrow{\text{cat.}} \underset{\text{polyethylene}}{{-}(CH_2{-}CH_2)_x{-}}$$

*Mechanism*:

$$CH_2{=}CH_2 \xrightarrow{H^+} CH_3{-}\overset{+}{C}H_2 \xrightarrow{CH_2=CH_2} CH_3{-}CH_2{-}CH_2{-}\overset{+}{C}H_2$$

$$CH_3{-}CH_2{-}CH_2{-}\overset{+}{C}H_2 \xrightarrow{CH_2=CH_2} CH_3CH_2CH_2CH_2CH_2\overset{+}{C}H_2$$

$$\downarrow$$

etc.

The polymerization process, once begun, continues until a termination step occurs, such as loss of a proton or the transfer of a proton from another polymer molecule.

Termination:

$$\sim CH_2-\overset{+}{C}H_2 \longrightarrow \sim CH=CH_2 + H^+$$

or

$$\sim \underset{\displaystyle H}{\underset{|}{C}}H-CH_2\sim + \sim CH_2-\overset{+}{C}H_2 \longrightarrow \sim\overset{+}{C}H-CH_2\sim + \sim CH_2-CH_3$$

Of course, trace impurities may also terminate the process by chemical reactions, e.g., a constituent from the glass or metal wall of the vessel.

Many other olefins, particularly terminal ones, are excellent monomers and provide useful, well-known polymers (see Table 6-1).

**Table 6-1**
**Examples of the polymerization reaction**

$$x\,C_6H_5-CH=CH_2 \xrightarrow{\text{init.}} \text{init}-CH_2-\underset{C_6H_5}{CH}-\left(CH_2-\underset{C_6H_5}{CH}\right)_{x-1}-$$

styrene — polystyrene

$$xCH_2=\overset{CH_3}{\overset{|}{C}}-CO_2CH_3 \xrightarrow[\text{radical init.}]{\text{source of free}} \text{init}-CH_2-\underset{H_3CO_2C}{\overset{H_3C}{C}}-\left(CH_2-\underset{CO_2CH_3}{\overset{CH_3}{C}}\right)_{x-1}-$$

methyl methacrylate — polymer plexiglas

$$xCF_2=CF_2 \xrightarrow{O_2} O_2-CF_2-CF_2-\left(CF_2-CF_2\right)_{x-1}-$$

tetrafluoroethylene — Teflon

## 6-5 POLYMERIZATION OF CONJUGATED DIENES

When conjugated dienes undergo 1,4 polymerization, the products are important plastics and rubbers. Chloroprene, derived from vinylacetylene, undergoes polymerization and gives neoprene. This reaction is illustrated with an anionic initiator.

*Overall*:

$$xCH_2=\underset{\displaystyle Cl}{\underset{|}{C}}-CH=CH_2 \xrightarrow{\text{init.}^-} \text{init}-(-CH_2-\underset{\displaystyle Cl}{\underset{|}{C}}=CH-CH_2-)_x-$$

chloroprene — neoprene

*Mechanism*

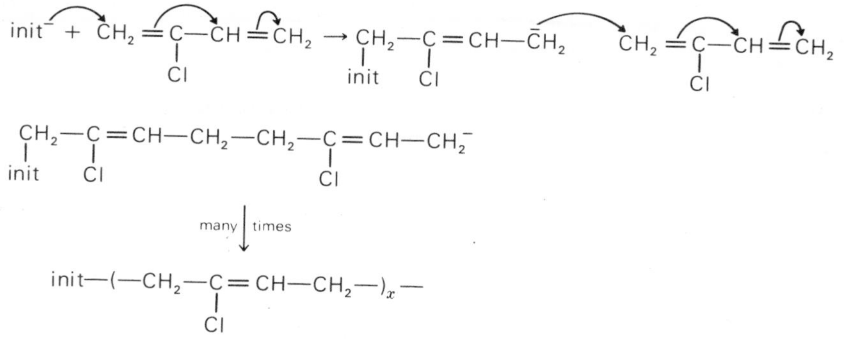


The chloro-substituted end of the molecule may be called the ***head*** and the other the ***tail***. The product is the result of joining the head of the monomer to the tail of the growing polymer in a regular fashion.

> In a similar way, isoprene (2-methyl-1,3-butadiene) is converted to natural rubber. Formulate this reaction with a radical initiator, R•.

## THE DIELS-ALDER REACTION

Olefins (and acetylenes) can react with ***conjugated dienes*** to form six-membered rings containing one (or two) double bonds. The product is known as a ***Diels-Alder adduct***, named for its codiscoverers. The olefin or acetylene is also known as a ***dienophile*** (diene loving).

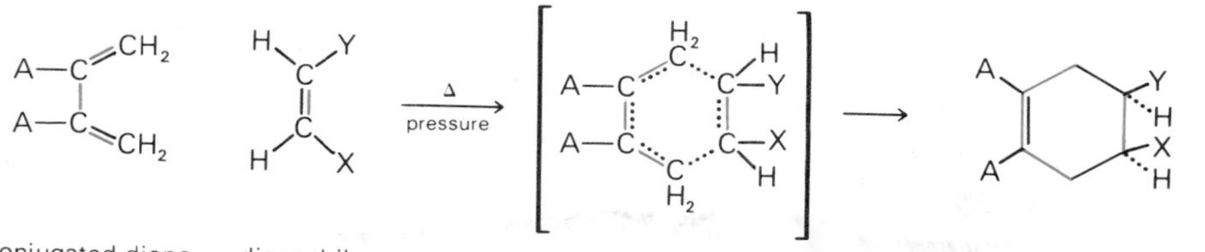


conjugated diene dienophile cyclic transition state Diels-Alder adduct

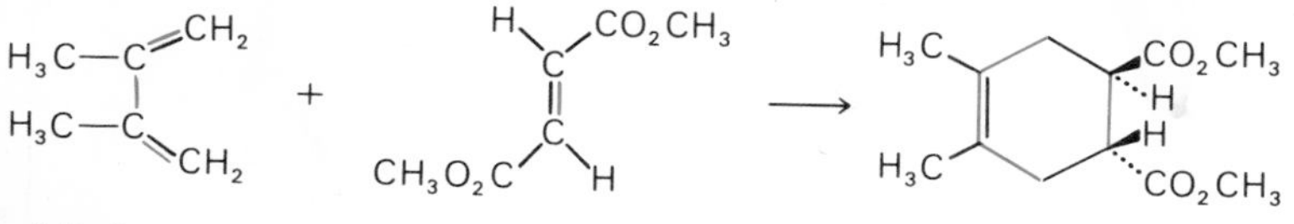

2,3-dimethyl-1,3-butadiene

dimethyl fumarate

Electron-donating substituents on the diene and electron-withdrawing ones on the dienophile considerably enhance the reactivity toward cycloaddition. At least some substituent activation is usually desirable. Alkyl groups, particularly the methyl group, and alkoxyl groups, —Ö—R, are good electron-releasing or electron-donating substituents for the diene. Examples of electron-withdrawing ones are

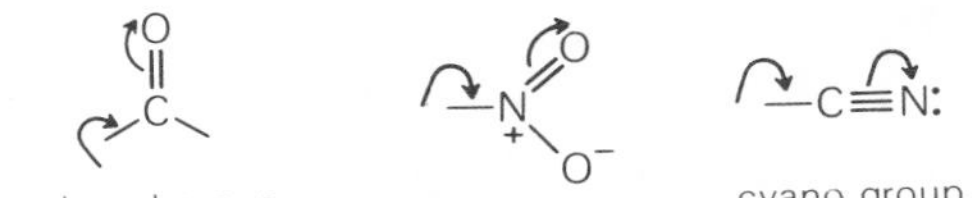

carbonyl group

nitro group

cyano group

Note that the stereochemistry of the olefin is preserved in the product; this is a cis cycloaddition. The reaction is usually carried out by heating the components in a high-boiling hydrocarbon solvent. With unreactive or low-boiling compounds the reaction must be carried out in a reinforced metal container (*bomb*) at high pressure. Lewis acids, such as $AlCl_3$, greatly accelerate the reaction at lower temperatures.

Dienes commonly used are alkyl- and aryl-substituted 1, 3-dienes, cyclic, and bicyclic ones; even some reactive aromatic and heterocyclic systems can be used. The dienophiles are usually substituted olefins or acetylenes; dienes themselves can sometimes act also as the dienophile, as in the case of cyclopentadiene.

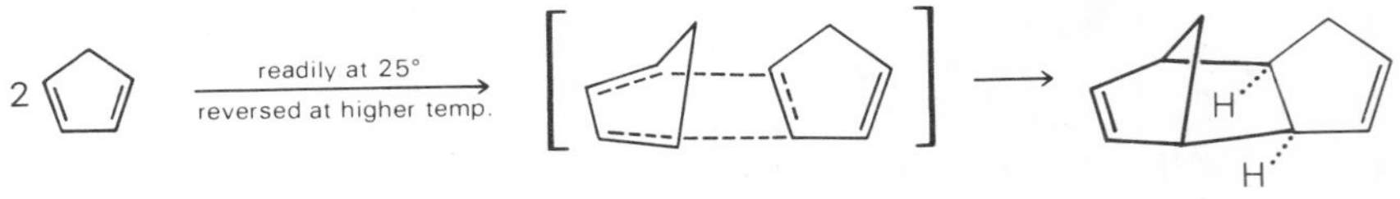

2 cyclopentadiene —readily at 25° / reversed at higher temp.→ [ ] → dicyclopentadiene

Often, as in the case of dicyclopentadiene, the Diels-Alder reaction can be reversed simply by heating the adduct and collecting the product(s). This technique can be used, for example, in the purification of anthracene via the maleic anhydride adduct.

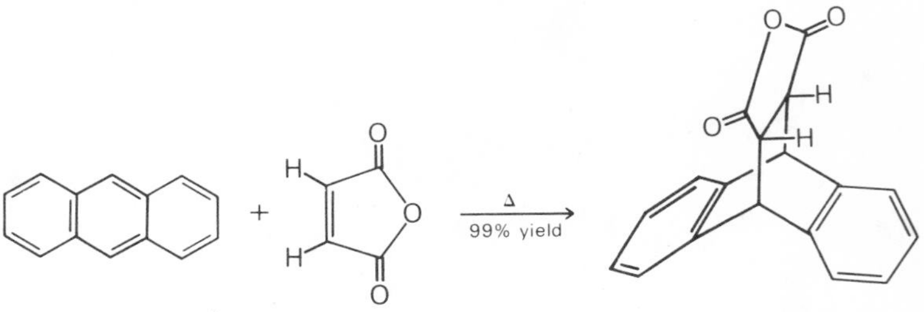

anthracene + maleic anydride —Δ, 99% yield→ recrystallize to purify and then heat to decompose

Six-membered rings containing three double bonds are extremely stable, as we shall study in detail in the next chapter, and the compounds formed in the Diels-Alder reaction can often be converted to these aromatic systems with ease. Often the hydrogen atoms can be removed simply by heating Diels-Alder adducts with palladium-on-carbon.

$H_3C-C(=CH_2)-C(=CH_2)-CH_3$ + $CH_3O_2C-C\equiv C-CO_2CH_3$ ⟶ (4,5-dimethyl-cyclohexa-1,4-diene-1,2-dicarboxylate, dimethyl ester) $\xrightarrow[-H_2]{\Delta/Pd}$ (4,5-dimethylphthalate, dimethyl ester)

dimethyl acetylenedicarboxylate

The benzene aromatic systems themselves are relatively unreactive in Diels-Alder reactions, but there are some exceptions. Even in such cases, the rearrangement to a new aromatic system is often facile.

*p*-methoxystyrene + maleic anhydride $\xrightarrow{\Delta}$ (adduct) $\xrightarrow[\text{rearrangement}]{\text{ready}}$ (aromatic product)

The usefulness of the Diels-Alder reaction is not limited to preparation of ***simple*** six-membered ring compounds but may be extended to form a variety of bridged compounds by the use of cyclic dienes and dienophiles.

anthracene + TCNE $\xrightarrow[\text{at } 25°]{\text{easily}}$ Diels-Alder adduct

Because of the strong electron-withdrawing nature of the four cyano groups, ***t***etra***cyan***oethylene (TCNE) is one of the most powerful dienophiles which has been prepared.

## SUGGESTED READINGS


Charlesby, A.: Ionizing Radiation and Organic Chemistry, *Sci. Am.*, **201** (3), 180 (1959). Effects of radiation on polymers such as Teflon and polyethylene.

Fisher, H. L.: New Horizons in Elastic Polymers, *J. Chem. Educ.*, **37**, 369 (1960).

Wunderlich, B.: The Solid State of Polyethylene, *Sci. Am.*, **211** (5), 80 (1964). Compares crystalline and noncrystalline polyethylene.

**A symposium on polymer chemistry**

Ferington, T. E.: Kinetics of Polymer Formation by Free Radical Mechanism, *J. Chem. Educ.*, **36**, 174 (1959).

Mayo, F. R.: Contributions of Vinyl Polymerization to Organic Chemistry, *J. Chem. Educ.*, **36**, 157 (1959).

Price, C. C.: The Geometry of Giant Molecules, *J. Chem. Educ.*, **36**, 160 (1959).

Slichter, W. P.: Molecular Characteristics of Rubber-like Materials, *J. Chem. Educ.*, **36**, 185 (1959).

**Polymer chemistry symposium**

MacKnight, W. J., G. E. Leroi, and A. V. Tobolsky: Physical Chemistry of Cross-linked Polysulfide Elastomers, *J. Chem. Educ.*, **42**, 4 (1965).

Marvel, C. S.: The Place of Polymers in Beginning Organic Chemistry, *J. Chem. Educ.*, **42**, 3 (1965).

Sorenson, W. R.: Polymer Synthesis in the Undergraduate Organic Laboratory, *J. Chem. Educ.*, **42**, 8 (1965).

Sorenson, W. R.: The Effect of Structure on Chemical and Physical Properties of Polymers, *J. Chem. Educ.*, **42**, 13 (1965).


## PROBLEMS

★**1**. A common preparation of 1,3-cyclohexadiene calls for high-temperature dehydrohalogenation with strong base of the product derived from the bromination of cyclohexene. The yield is not high, even though the diene is removed as it is formed, and the cooled flask must usually be discarded because of the large amount of "tar." Suggest a structure for the tar and show how it might readily be formed under these conditions.

**2**. Formulate the products from the following reactions.

★(*a*) isoprene + maleic anhydride $\xrightarrow[\text{at } 100°\text{; bomb}]{\text{in benzene}}$ ≈100% yield

★(*b*) 1-vinylcyclohexene + maleic anhydride $\xrightarrow[\text{at } 25°]{\text{in xylene}}$ 63% yield

(*c*) 1,3-cyclohexadiene + TCNE $\longrightarrow$

★(*d*) [1,1'-bicyclopentenyl structure] + maleic anhydride $\longrightarrow$

(*e*) 1,3-butadiene + [p-benzoquinone structure: six-membered ring with two C=O groups at opposite positions and two C=C double bonds] $\xrightarrow{\text{90\% yield}}$

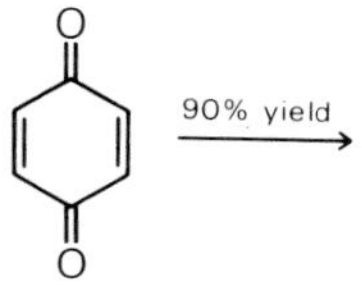

**3.** Using various combinations of dienes and dienophiles mentioned in the section on the Diels-Alder reaction, formulate 10 more plausible Diels-Alder adducts.

# Chapter Seven

The previous chapters have been concerned mainly with aliphatic hydrocarbons; we now turn to the aromatic and heterocyclic ones. In future chapters the chemistry of the functional groups attached to these three broad classes will be discussed together. Heterocyclic molecules are ring compounds containing atoms other than carbon, commonly nitrogen, oxygen, and sulfur. Organometallics will be used throughout this text as reagents, e.g., the Grignard reagent. See Table 7-1.

## STRUCTURE AND NOMENCLATURE

### 7-1 MOLECULAR-ORBITAL AND VALENCE-BOND DESCRIPTIONS OF BENZENE

Recall the differences between the molecular-orbital pictures for an isolated diene and a conjugated diene (Secs. 6-1 and 6-3). In the former,

**Table 7-1 Representative organic molecules**

| *Aliphatic* | *Aromatic* | *Heterocyclic* | *Organometallic* |
|---|---|---|---|
| $CH_3CH_2CH_2CH_3$ | [structure] | [structure] | $[CH_3MgI]$ |
| butane | benzene | pyridine | methylmagnesium iodide |
| [structure] | [structure] | [structure] | [structure] |
| cyclohexane | naphthalene | thiophene | phenyllithium |

# Aromatic Hydrocarbons and Electrophilic Aromatic Substitution

the two $\pi$ bonds are separated by at least one —$CH_2$— insulator, but in the latter, one molecular orbital extends over the four carbon atoms. In benzene, all adjacent $p$ orbitals overlap, and thus there is one molecular orbital which completely circles the molecule with lobes above and below the plane. This orbital has been described as doughnut-shaped (Fig. 7-1). The $\pi$ bond system in benzene has properties of unsaturation different from those found in ordinary double-bonded systems. Further, reactions in which an aromatic system is formed are generally facile ones.

The valence-bond approach predicts two equivalent structures for benzene. We shall continue to represent benzene with only a single Kekulé structure, but it should always be remembered that this is only one of two equivalent resonance structures.

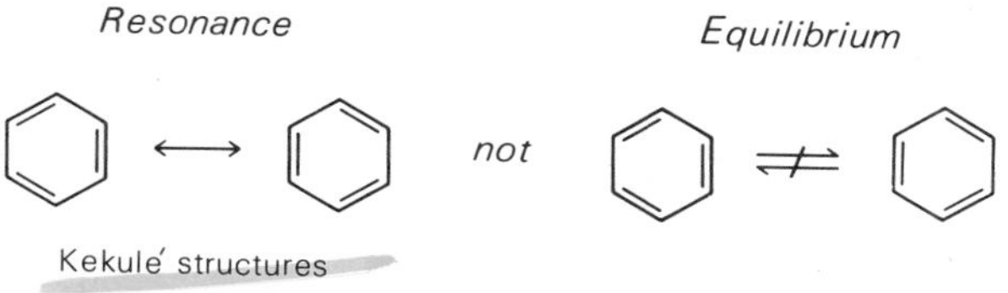

*Resonance* *Equilibrium*

⬡ ⟷ ⬡ *not* ⬡ $\rightleftarrows\!\!\!\!\!/$ ⬡

Kekulé structures

In fact, the $\pi$ system in benzene is often represented by a full circle:

The following symbols are used interchangeably to represent the phenyl group:

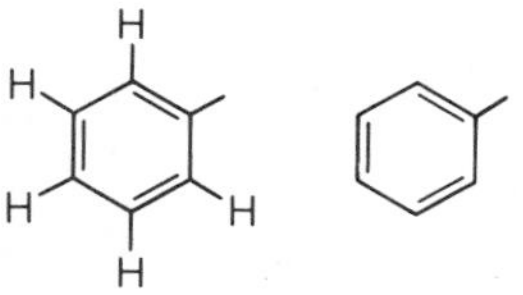

$C_6H_5$— ∅—

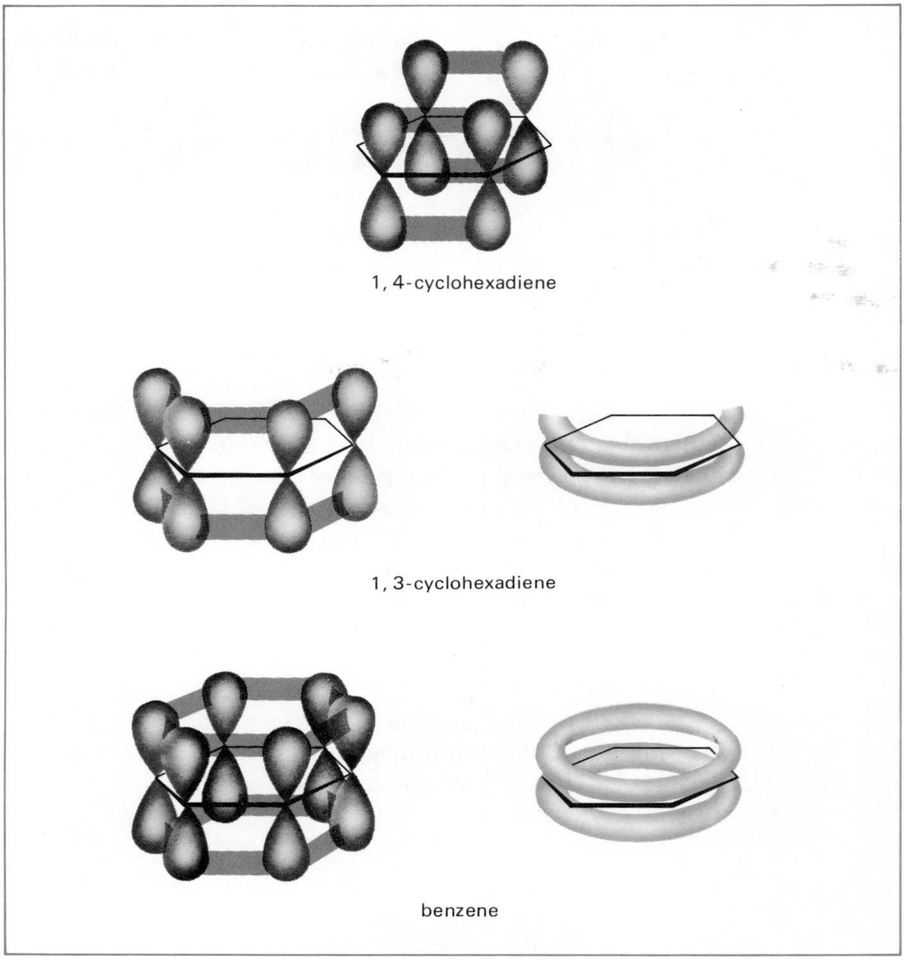

**Figure 7-1 Orbitals of 1,3- and 1,4-cyclohexadiene and benzene**

1, 4-cyclohexadiene

1, 3-cyclohexadiene

benzene

The symbol Ar- denotes any aromatic group. Another common aromatic group is derived from toluene and called the ***benzyl group***.

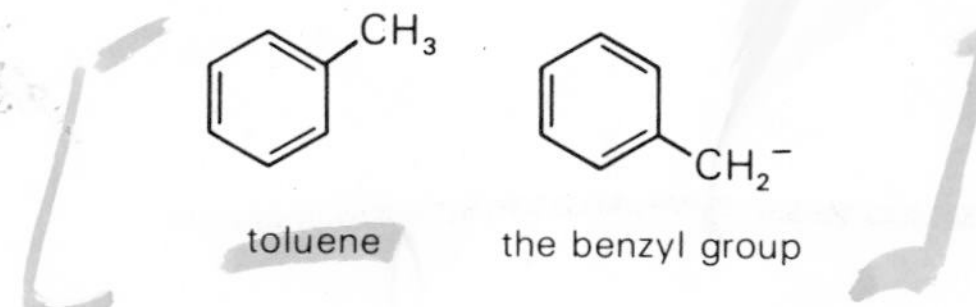


### 7-2 NOMENCLATURE

Benzene is the IUPAC name for the parent aromatic compound, $C_6H_6$, and monosubstituted compounds are usually named as derivatives of benzene.

bromobenzene nitrobenzene

The prefix number 1 is not required, since there can be only a single monobromobenzene. Another system employed for simple compounds utilizes the common group name, *phenyl*, and one sometimes sees the names phenyl bromide or phenyl fluoride for bromobenzene or fluorobenzene.

There are three different dibromobenzenes. They are designated *ortho* (1,2-disubstituted), *meta* (1,3), and *para* (1,4).

*ortho*-dibromobenzene
*o*-dibromobenzene
1,2-dibromobenzene

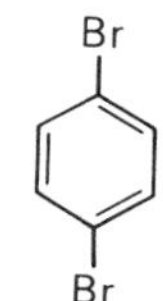

*meta*-dibromobenzene
*m*-dibromobenzene
1,3-dibromobenzene

*para*-dibromobenzene
*p*-dibromobenzene
1,4-dibromobenzene

These common designations (*o*-, *m*-, *p*-) are employed for disubstituted benzenes, but higher-substituted ones are generally numbered, giving the principal function the number 1.

*o*-bromofluorobenzene 1-bromo-2-chloro-3-fluorobenzene 3,5-dichloronitrobenzene

Although a consistent IUPAC system of nomenclature is available, many of the simple derivatives of benzene were isolated from natural products years ago and were assigned names appropriate to their source or properties. Many of these trivial names are in common use, and some of them are given in Table 7-2 for reference. By using them and by hearing others use them, they will become a part of your organic chemical vocabulary.

Higher aromatic systems, known as *polycyclic aromatic hydrocarbons*, are similar to benzene and its derivatives, and the carbons in these molecules are numbered in a regular fashion. Two systems are in common use for naming naphthalene compounds. In one the Greek letters $\alpha$ and $\beta$ denote the two different kinds of positions in the mole-

**Table 7-2**
**Trivial names of some aromatic molecules**

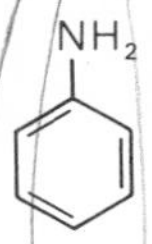
aniline

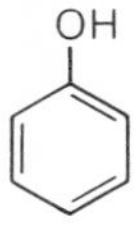
phenol

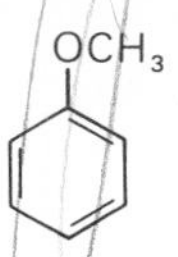
anisole

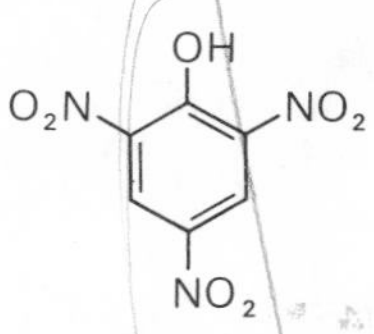
picric acid

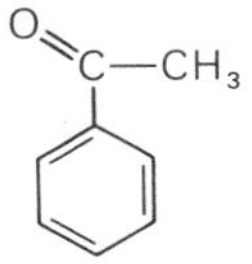
acetophenone

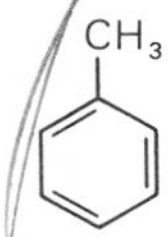
toluene

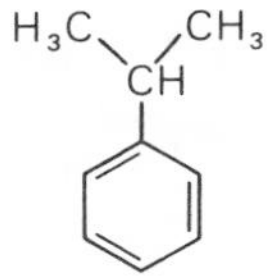
cumene

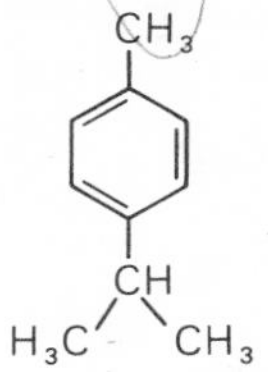
*p*-cymene

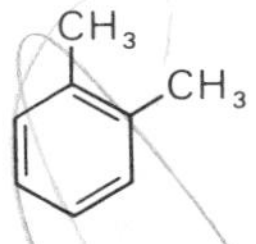
*o*-xylene

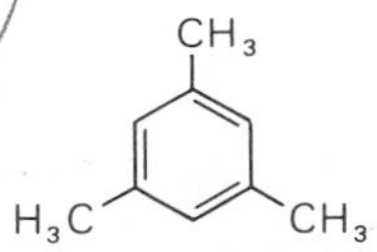
mesitylene

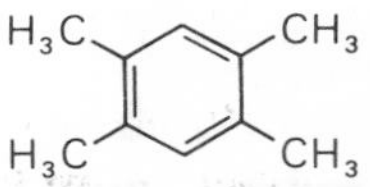
durene

cule. In the other, the IUPAC system, numbers are used, always beginning with 1 on an $\alpha$ position:

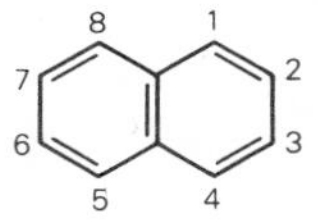

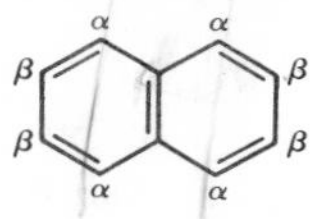

With anthracene, the number 1 always begins on a pseudo-alpha position ($\alpha$ and $\beta$ are generally reserved for naphthalene). Although there are four 1-positions in naphthalene or anthracene, there are only two in phenanthrene.

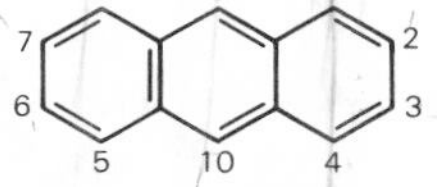
anthracene

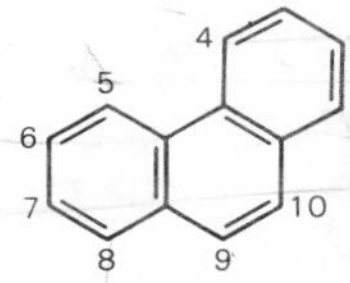
phenanthrene

Examples of substituted higher aromatics are shown in Table 7-3.

> Write the structure of 2,6-dimethylnaphthalene. Why is the name $\beta,\beta$-dimethylnaphthalene incorrect?

Heterocycles are numbered such that the heteroatom (or one of several such atoms) is given the number 1.

pyrrole    furan    thiophene    tetrahydrofuran (THF)

pyridine    $\alpha$-pyran    $\gamma$-pyran    pyrimidine

The numbering proceeds in the direction which will give other heteroatoms (or substituents) the lowest numbers. Since the heteroatom is the center of attention in these molecules, Greek letters are sometimes used to denote adjacent and subsequent positions.

**Table 7-3**
**Substituted higher aromatics**

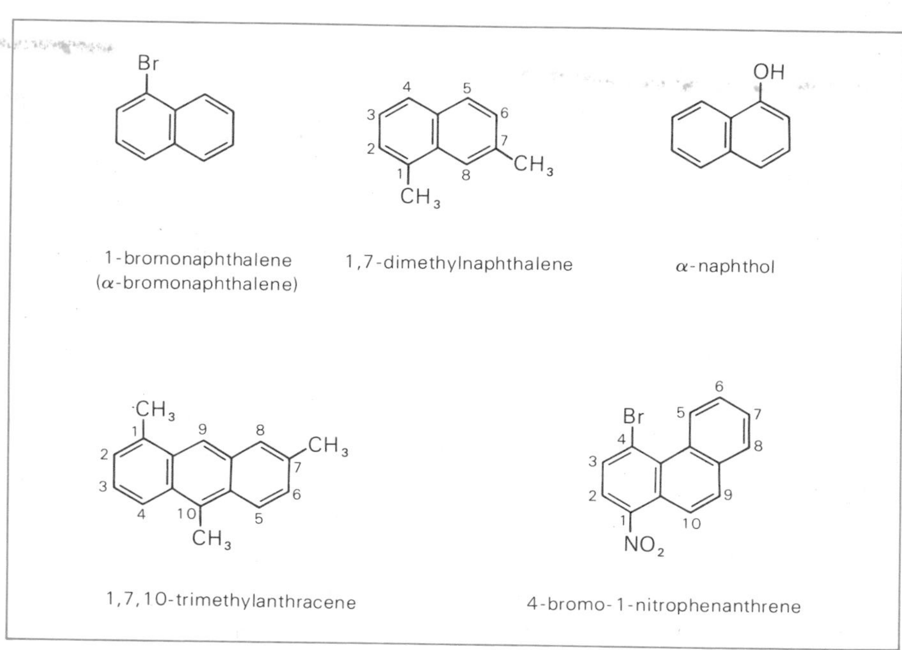


1-bromonaphthalene ($\alpha$-bromonaphthalene)

1,7-dimethylnaphthalene

$\alpha$-naphthol

1,7,10-trimethylanthracene

4-bromo-1-nitrophenanthrene

### 7-3 STABILITY AND RESONANCE ENERGIES FROM HEATS OF HYDROGENATION

Several quantitatively unsupported statements concerning unsaturated compounds were made earlier; four of these will be considered now.

**1.** The more highly alkylated olefin is the more stable.

**2.** Generally, trans compounds are more stable than the cis isomers.

**3.** Conjugated dienes are more stable than isolated dienes.

**4.** Aromatic compounds, such as benzene, are very much less reactive than ordinary conjugated olefins toward addition reactions and show "less unsaturation" than olefins.

In each case the compounds that are said to be more stable are the ones with lower energy.

Two general methods are available for determining relative energies: heats of combustion (burning the hydrocarbon with oxygen to form water and carbon dioxide) and heats of hydrogenation. The latter method is the more accurate (although fewer data on heats of hydrogenation are available). The critical requirement here is to choose the "correct" compounds for comparison.

**1.** It can be shown that increased alkylation on a carbon-carbon double bond gives rise to a more stable compound by considering a series of compounds with an increasing number of, say, methyl groups. Catalytic hydrogenation of ethylene is an exothermic reaction

$$CH_2{=}CH_2 \xrightarrow[\text{cat.}]{H_2} CH_3CH_3 + 32.8\ \text{kcal/mole}^{\dagger}$$

When a methyl group is substituted for one of the hydrogen atoms, it is found experimentally that only 30.1 kcal/mole is evolved

$$\underset{\text{propene}}{CH_3{-}CH{=}CH_2} \xrightarrow[\text{cat.}]{H_2} \underset{\text{propane}}{CH_3CH_2CH_3} + 30.1\ \text{kcal/mole}$$

Further substitution on the same carbon atom shows an additional lowering of the heat evolved

$$\underset{\text{isobutylene}}{(CH_3)_2C{=}CH_2} \xrightarrow[\text{cat.}]{H_2} \underset{\text{isobutane}}{(CH_3)_2CH{-}CH_3} + 28.4\ \text{kcal/mole}$$

In each case the addition of a methyl group decreases the amount of energy released in hydrogenation of the alkene. The methyl group (and other alkyl groups) are electron-donating substituents, and here we see evidence (*not proof*) of increased stability of the olefin due to the effect of alkyl groups. One methyl group lowers the energy about 2.7 kcal/mole; a second one lowers it an additional 1.7 kcal/mole. Ethylene

† This means that $\Delta H = -32.8$ kcal/mole; however, in this text we shall adopt the notation using the heat evolved.

was chosen as the best available model or reference compound for this series.

**2.** The effect of cis-trans isomerism can be illustrated with the 2-butenes

$$\text{H}_3\text{C}(\text{H})\text{C}{=}\text{C}(\text{H})\text{CH}_3 \xrightarrow[\text{cat.}]{\text{H}_2} \text{CH}_3\text{CH}_2\text{CH}_2\text{CH}_3 + 28.6\ \text{kcal/mole}$$

*cis*-2-butene

$$\text{H}_3\text{C}(\text{H})\text{C}{=}\text{C}(\text{H})\text{CH}_3 \xrightarrow[\text{cat.}]{\text{H}_2} \text{CH}_3\text{CH}_2\text{CH}_2\text{CH}_3 + 27.6\ \text{kcal/mole}$$

*trans*-2-butene

One must accept the magnitude of the 1 kcal/mole difference with caution since the individual measurements are probably accurate to only 0.1 to 0.2 kcal/mole. Nevertheless, the size of this difference is significant. These results can be displayed on a diagram, as in Fig. 7-2.

Since the product is the same in both reductions, this system of comparison is on firmer ground than the previous calculation of olefin stability.

**3.** The effect of conjugation as a stabilizing factor has been shown before by considering the maximum $p$-orbital overlap in 1,3-dienes. The magnitude of this effect can be determined experimentally from heats of hydrogenation.

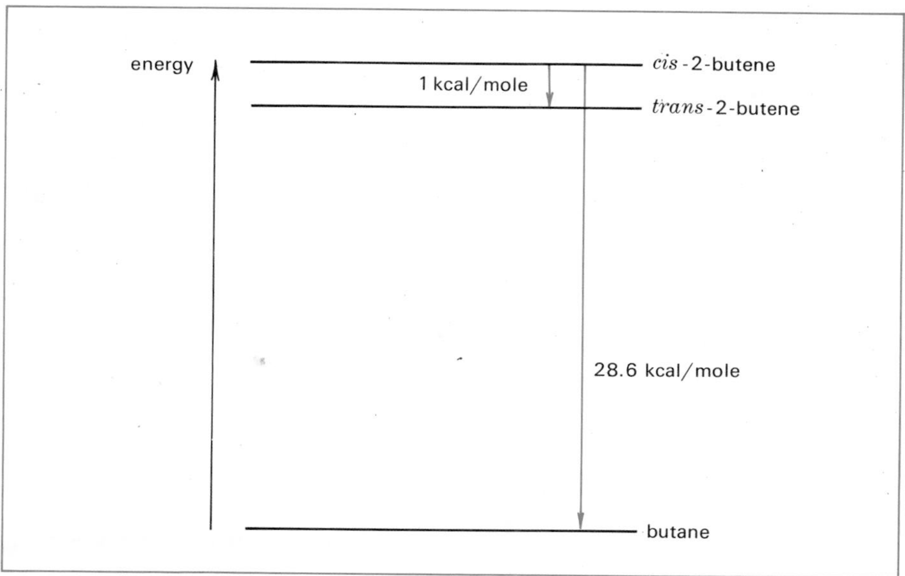


**Figure 7-2 Relative energies of butane and the 2-butenes**

Consider 1,3-butadiene. Here we must choose the best model compound, which, in general, should lead to the same reduction product as the molecule in question. Thus, ethylene would be a poor choice; 1-butene is a good one.

$$CH_3{-}CH_2{-}CH{=}CH_2 \xrightarrow[\text{cat.}]{H_2} CH_3CH_2CH_2CH_3 + 30.3 \text{ kcal/mole}$$

1-butene

$$CH_2{=}CH{-}CH{=}CH_2 \xrightarrow[\text{cat.}]{H_2} CH_3CH_2CH_2CH_3 + 57.1 \text{ kcal/mole}$$

1,3-butadiene

Using a simple additivity argument, 1,3-butadiene might be expected to evolve twice the heat of 1-butene (2 × 30.3 kcal/mole) or 60.6 kcal/mole. Experimentally, however, only 57.1 kcal/mole is observed. This difference, 3.5 kcal/mole, is attributed to the extra stability gained by the resonance situation in 1,3-butadiene due to the $C_2$—$C_3$ orbital overlap. This stabilization is called the ***resonance energy***.

**1.** What difficulties are encountered in choosing 2-butene as a model for the 1,3-butadiene calculations?

**2.** Given that the heat of hydrogenation of 1,3-cyclohexadiene is 55.4 kcal/mole, which of the following compounds (heats of hydrogenation are shown below each) would provide the best model?

| $CH_2{=}CH_2$ | (cyclohexene) | $CH_2{=}CH{-}CH{=}CH_2$ | (1,4-cyclohexadiene) |
|---|---|---|---|
| 32.8 kcal/mole | 28.6 | 57.1 | 59.3 |

**3.** Calculate the resonance energy of 1,3-cyclohexadiene.

**4.** The resonance energy of aromatic compounds can be determined experimentally by the method used above for conjugated dienes. For example, cyclohexene is used as the best model for benzene.

$$\text{cyclohexene} \xrightarrow[\text{cat.}]{H_2} \text{cyclohexane} + 28.6 \text{ kcal/mole}$$

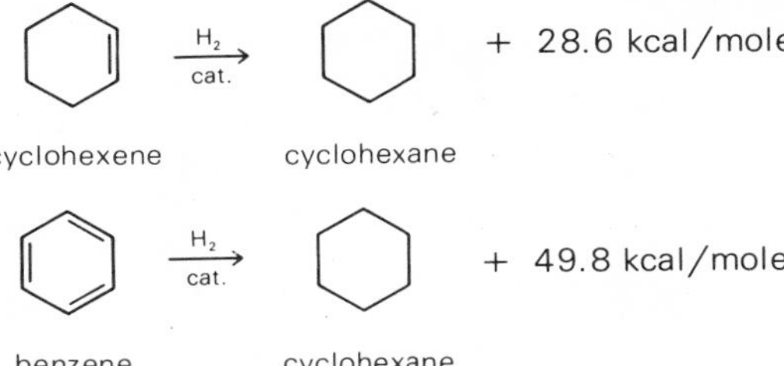


The resonance energy of benzene determined by this method is 36.0

kcal/mole [(3 × 28.6) − 49.8 = 36.0]. We are not dealing with 1,3,5-cyclohexatriene, whose name implies an alkatriene, but with *benzene*. It is a *new system*, which is characterized by an enhanced stability, a measure of which may be gained from heats of hydrogenation. Further, these systems tend to undergo substitution reactions instead of the addition reactions associated with alkenes; *substitution* reactions preserve this stable aromatic system.

> Why would the heats of hydrogenation of 1,3-cyclohexadiene plus ethylene *not* provide a suitable system for calculating the resonance energy of benzene?

## 7-4 AROMATIC ADDITION AND SUBSTITUTION REACTIONS

Although ordinary alkenes and dienes are readily reduced with hydrogen in the presence of a catalyst, benzene and other aromatic compounds usually undergo this reaction with greater difficulty. The addition reactions that do occur with aromatic compounds usually cannot be stopped short of total reaction, i.e., reduction in the case cited above.

benzene $\xrightarrow[\text{slow}]{H_2/\text{cat.}}$ 1,3-cyclohexadiene $\xrightarrow[\text{fast}]{H_2/\text{cat.}}$ cyclohexene $\xrightarrow[\text{very fast}]{H_2/\text{cat.}}$ cyclohexane

The various nonaromatic intermediates react much faster than the original aromatic molecule.

Chlorination of cyclohexene gives rise mainly to *trans*-1,2-dichlorocyclohexane.

cyclohexene $\xrightarrow[\text{addition}]{Cl_2}$ *trans*-1,2-dichlorocyclohexane (Cl, H, H, Cl)

In contrast the *addition* to benzene takes place with some difficulty and produces several isomers of 1,2,3,4,5,6-hexachlorocyclohexane.

Addition: benzene $\xrightarrow[\text{usually } \Delta \text{ or } h\nu]{3Cl_2\text{; no cat.}}$ 1,2,3,4,5,6-hexachlorocyclohexane (each carbon bearing H and Cl)

These addition isomers were originally denoted by Greek letters ($\alpha$, $\beta$, $\gamma$, $\delta$, etc.). The $\gamma$ isomer is sold as an insecticide under various trade names, such as Gammexane.

On the other hand, chlorine *substitution* on benzene occurs readily, to give mainly chlorobenzene. A Lewis acid catalyst, such as $FeCl_3$, is commonly required.

Substitution: 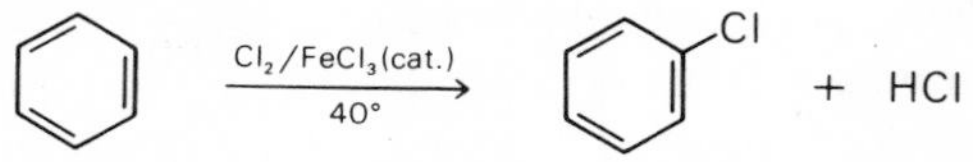 benzene $\xrightarrow[40°]{Cl_2/FeCl_3(\text{cat.})}$ chlorobenzene + HCl

Unlike alkenes or alkynes, benzene does not decolorize dilute solutions of bromine or potassium permanganate, is not readily reduced with hydrogen (catalyst), and does not give a precipitate with ammoniacal silver or copper solutions.

> Write other isomers of $C_6H_6$ which contain centers of unsaturation and show why these structures cannot correctly represent the benzene molecule on the basis of the qualitative tests for benzene.

The term aromatic originally denoted the pleasant aroma of compounds from natural sources containing this cyclic six-$\pi$-electron system. Today, aromatic indicates a ***stable system*** (with a reasonable resonance energy) which undergoes ***substitution*** rather than addition, retaining the "closed" $\pi$-electron system. Many such systems contain

**Table 7-4**
**Examples of $4n + 2$ $\pi$-electron systems**[†]

| | | | |
|---|---|---|---|
| $n = 1$ | benzene | cyclopentadienyl anion | cycloheptatrienyl cation |
| $n = 2$ | naphthalene | cyclooctatetraenyl dianion | |
| $n = 3$ | anthracene | phenanthrene | |

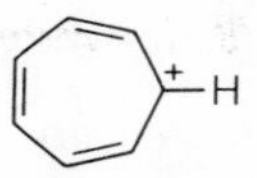

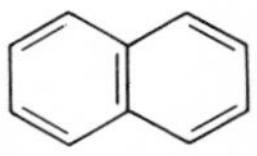

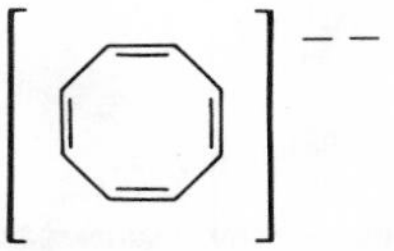

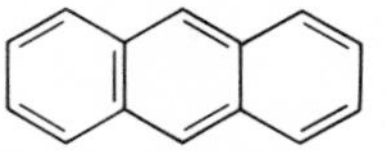

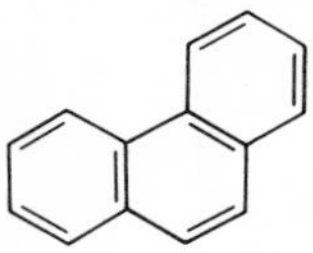

[†] Strictly speaking, the $4n + 2$ rule applies only to monocyclic systems; however, it can be applied to some planar, conjugated polycyclic systems.

only six $\pi$ electrons, but generally they contain $(4n + 2)$ $\pi$ electrons, where $n$ is an integer. For benzene, $n = 1$ (see Table 7-4).

In general, higher polycyclic aromatic compounds are somewhat less stable than benzene. Recall, for instance, the reactivity of anthracene in the Diels-Alder reaction with dienophiles such as tetracyanoethylene (TCNE) and maleic anhydride. The 9,10-positions of phenanthrene are similarly more reactive than other positions in the molecule when the reaction leads to disruption of the original aromatic system; note that the biphenyl aromatic system is present in the product.

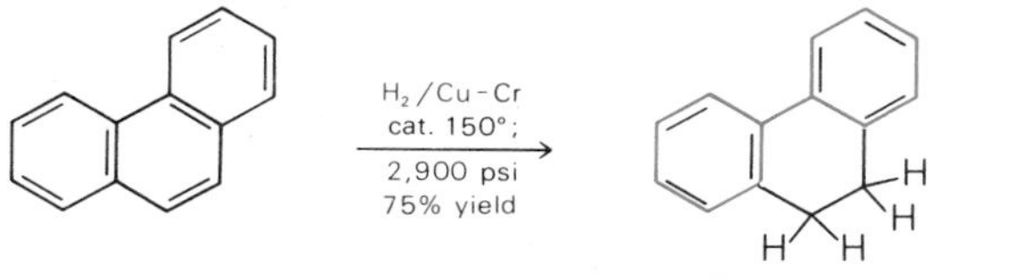

phenanthrene $\xrightarrow[\text{2,900 psi; 75\% yield}]{H_2/\text{Cu-Cr cat. } 150^\circ}$ 9,10-dihydrophenanthrene

## ELECTROPHILIC AROMATIC SUBSTITUTION

Benzene and other aromatic systems are centers of high electron density and are readily attacked by positive species, *electrophiles*, and generally not by negative ones, nucleophiles. Using a general electrophile, $E^+$, the overall reaction can be formulated as

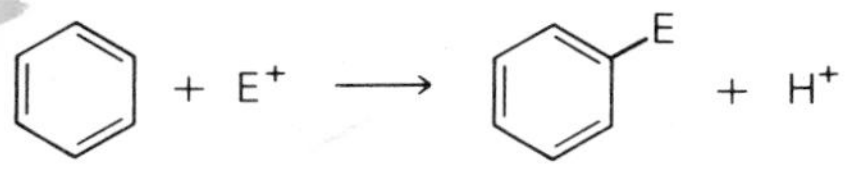

$$C_6H_6 + E^+ \longrightarrow C_6H_5E + H^+$$

Five common electrophilic aromatic substitution reactions are discussed in detail in the following sections. The mechanisms of these reactions are similar in many respects.

### 7-5 CHLORINATION AND BROMINATION

The halogenation reaction generally requires a Lewis acid catalyst such as $AlX_3$, $SnX_2$, or $FeX_3$. $FeX_3$ can be made by direct combination of the elements, so that it is sufficient, for instance, to add iron tacks to a mixture of bromine and the substrate.

*Overall*: benzene $+ Br_2 \xrightarrow{FeBr_3}$ bromobenzene $+ HBr$

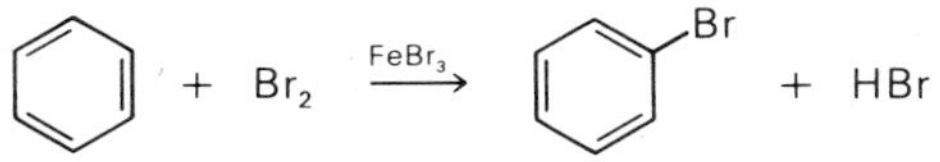

*Mechanism*: Since both bromine and benzene are nonpolar molecules, the function of the catalyst is to cause a polarization of bromine.

$$\mathrm{Br{-}Br + FeBr_3 \longrightarrow \overset{\delta+}{[Br}\cdots Br\cdots \overset{\delta-}{FeBr_3]} \longrightarrow \underset{\text{bromonium ion}}{[Br^+} + FeBr_4^-]}$$

The bromonium ion (or a similar species) then is attacked by the $\pi$ electrons of the aromatic system. Several resonance structures can be written for this intermediate

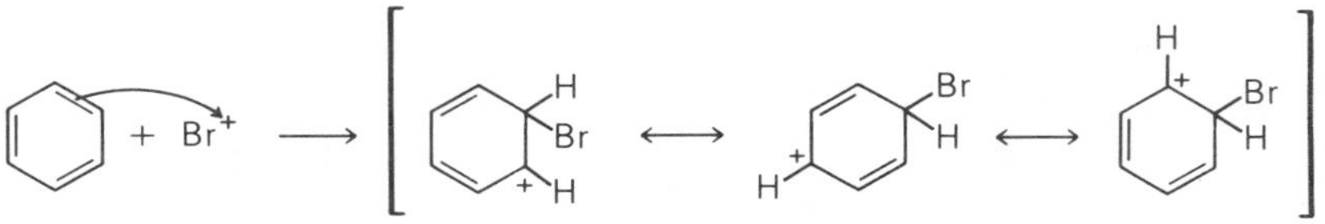

This intermediate *aronium ion* may be represented as 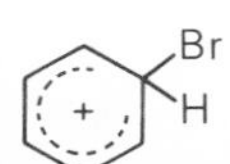


a composite which indicates that the positive charge is spread (unequally) over the remaining five carbon atoms. In the final step a proton is removed (assisted by $FeBr_4^-$) with aromatization.

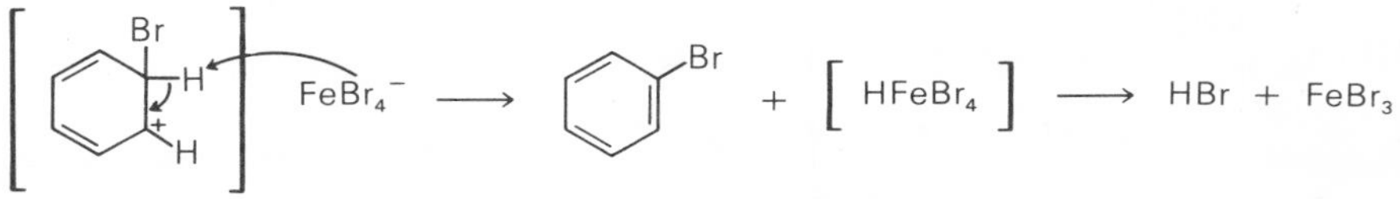

$$\mathrm{FeBr_4^- \longrightarrow C_6H_5Br + [HFeBr_4] \longrightarrow HBr + FeBr_3}$$

(The regenerated $FeBr_3$ is a true catalyst.) The intermediate aronium ion does not add further molecules of bromine nor does it add a bromide ion, $Br^-$. Again, the driving force for the aromatization is the stabilization that results from formation of the closed six-$\pi$-electron system.

## 7-6 NITRATION

Nitration is an important substitution reaction in the aromatic series. Subsequent reduction of the nitro group to the amino function, $—NH_2$, can be readily carried out, and other functional groups can be derived from this versatile amino group. Nearly all aromatic compounds undergo nitration, although the conditions required depend on the reactivity of the substrate.

The most common conditions are those employing *mixed acid*, a combination of concentrated nitric and sulfuric acids.

*Overall*: $$\underset{\text{benzene}}{C_6H_6} \xrightarrow{HNO_3/(H_2SO_4)} \underset{\text{nitrobenzene}}{C_6H_5NO_2} + H_2O$$

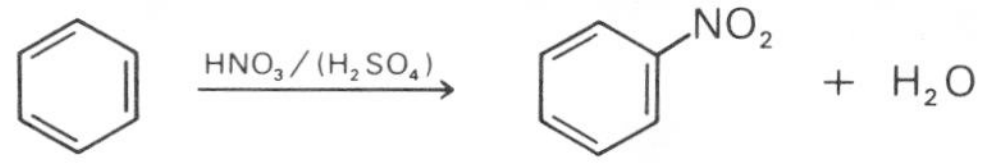

*Mechanism*: The nitronium ion, $NO_2^+$, is generated according to the following equation:

$$HNO_3 + 2H_2SO_4 \rightleftharpoons H_3O^+ + 2HSO_4^- + NO_2^+$$

hydronium ion      nitronium ion

The function of the sulfuric acid is twofold: (1) it dilutes the water formed in the overall reaction, and (2) it reacts with $HNO_3$ to produce a reasonable concentration of $NO_2^+$.

[benzene + $\overset{+}{N}O_2$ ⟶ [cyclohexadienyl cation bearing $NO_2$ and H on the same carbon, + on ring ⟷ write other resonance forms]]

[cyclohexadienyl cation with $NO_2$ and H] + $\bar{H}SO_4$ ⟶ nitrobenzene + $H_2SO_4$

Whereas halogenation and nitration are *irreversible* reactions, sulfonation and the Friedel-Crafts reactions, discussed below, are *reversible* ones.

chlorobenzene + HCl $\xrightarrow{FeCl_3}$ (not reversible, crossed arrow) benzene + $Cl_2$

nitrobenzene + $H_2O$ $\xrightarrow{H_2SO_4}$ (not reversible, crossed arrow) benzene + $HNO_3$

### 7-7 SULFONATION

The reagent employed for sulfonation is a source of $SO_3$, such as concentrated $H_2SO_4$, or fuming $H_2SO_4$, also known as *oleum*. Oleum is $H_2SO_4$ which contains additional quantities of dissolved $SO_3$. Usually the attacking species is $SO_3$

[$SO_3$ structure: O=$\overset{+}{S}$(=O)–$O^-$]

although in certain cases the protonated form, $HSO_3^+$, may be involved. The sulfur atom becomes attached to the carbon.

*Overall*: benzene + $H_2SO_4$ $\rightleftharpoons$ benzenesulfonic acid ($C_6H_5SO_3H$) + $H_2O$

benzene      benzenesulfonic acid

*Mechanism*: The $SO_3$ concentration in sulfuric acid may be considered to be a result of the self-reaction of $H_2SO_4$:

$$2H_2SO_4 \rightleftharpoons H_3O^+ + HSO_4^- + SO_3$$

The attack of the electrons in the aromatic system occurs on the sulfur atom of $SO_3$.

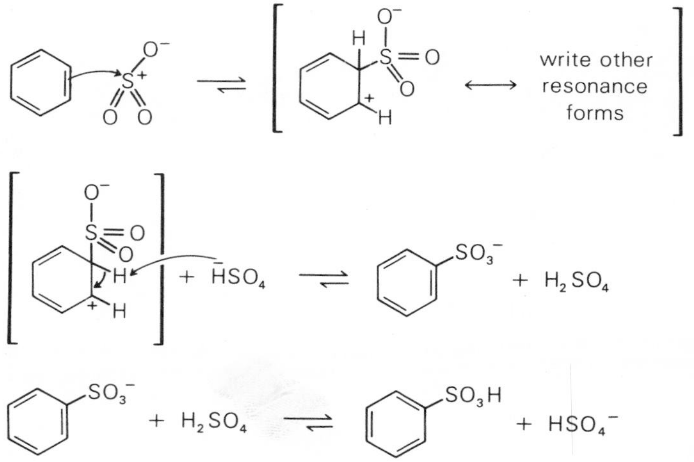

write other resonance forms

$$+ \ HSO_4 \rightleftharpoons \ \ + H_2SO_4$$

$$+ H_2SO_4 \rightleftharpoons \ \ + HSO_4^-$$

Note that in this example of aromatic substitution the electrophile, $SO_3$, does not carry a net positive charge, and therefore the intermediate does not have a net formal charge. This intermediate may be represented in composite form as

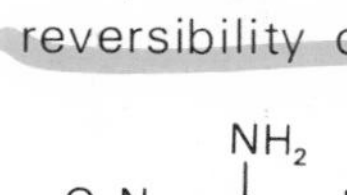

Contrast the difference in reaction conditions shown in Table 7-5 in terms of the acid used and the temperature at which sulfonation is effected. The reaction conditions are dictated by the ***reactivity*** (structure) of the molecule and will be discussed later in this chapter. The reversibility of sulfonation can be illustrated by the following example:

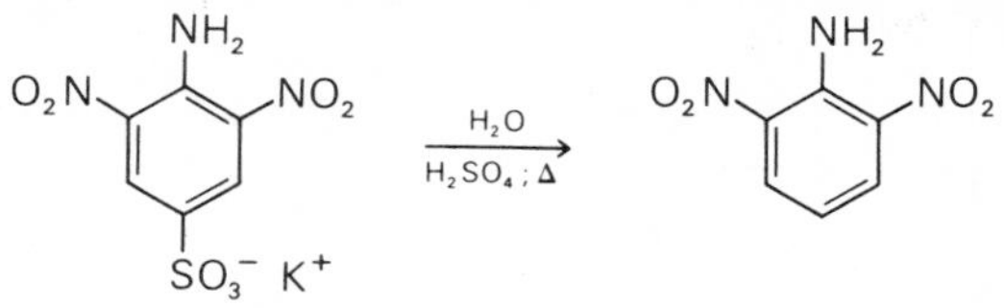

$$\xrightarrow[H_2SO_4;\ \Delta]{H_2O}$$

potassium 4-amino-3, 5-dinitrobenzenesulfonate

2,6-dinitroaniline

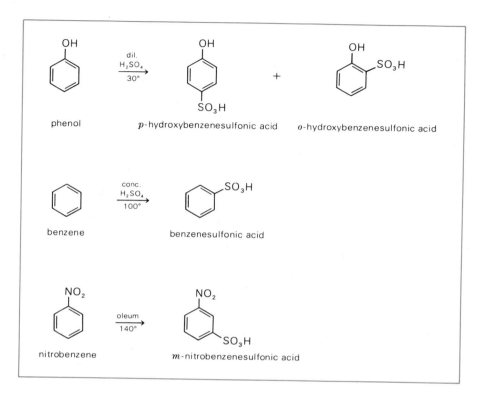

**Table 7-5**
**Aromatic sulfonation reactions**

| Reactant | Conditions | Product(s) |
|---|---|---|
| phenol | dil. $H_2SO_4$, 30° | *p*-hydroxybenzenesulfonic acid + *o*-hydroxybenzenesulfonic acid |
| benzene | conc. $H_2SO_4$, 100° | benzenesulfonic acid |
| nitrobenzene | oleum, 140° | *m*-nitrobenzenesulfonic acid |

## 7-8 FRIEDEL-CRAFTS ALKYLATION

As the name implies, the alkylation reaction affords a method of preparing alkyl-substituted aromatic compounds.

*General*: $C_6H_6 + R{-}X \xrightarrow[\text{trace}]{AlCl_3} C_6H_5R + HX$

It employs a trace of a Lewis acid catalyst, which interacts with the alkyl halide, alcohol, or olefin used as the alkylating agent. The activity of the catalyst required depends on the reactivity (structure) of the alkylating agent and the aromatic hydrocarbon. Reactive alkylating agents are those which readily form carbonium ions. Hydrocarbons with electron-donating substituents facilitate the Friedel-Crafts alkylation. Some of the more active Lewis acid catalysts are $AlCl_3$, $SbCl_3$, and $FeCl_3$; milder ones ($ZnCl_2$, $BiCl_3$) have been used with extremely reactive alkylating agents or substrates. Simple inorganic acids, such as $H_2SO_4$, $H_3PO_4$, and HF, are useful when alcohols or olefins are the alkylating agents. Examples are shown in Table 7-6.

Name the reagents and products shown in Table 7-6.

**Table 7-6**
**Friedel-Crafts alkylation reactions**

1. benzene + $C_6H_5CH_2Cl$ $\xrightarrow[\text{80\% yield}]{AlCl_3}$ $C_6H_5-CH_2-C_6H_5$

2. $CH_3C_6H_5$ + $(CH_3)_3CCl$ $\xrightarrow[\text{50\% yield}]{FeCl_3}$ $H_3C-C_6H_4-C(CH_3)_3$

3. benzene + $CH_3CH_2CH_2Cl$ $\xrightarrow[\text{50\% yield}]{AlCl_3}$ $C_6H_5CH_2CH_2CH_3$ (40%) + $C_6H_5CH(CH_3)_2$ (60%)

4. benzene + $CH_3(CH_2)_2CH_2Cl$ $\xrightarrow[80°]{AlCl_3}$ $C_6H_5(CH_2)_3CH_3$ (20%) + $C_6H_5CH_2CH(CH_3)_2$ (20%) + $C_6H_5CH(CH_3)CH_2CH_3$ ($CH_3CHCH_2CH_3$) (60%)

*Overall*: benzene $\xrightarrow[C_6H_5CH_2Cl]{AlCl_3}$ $C_6H_5-CH_2-C_6H_5$ + HCl

benzene — diphenylmethane

benzene $\xrightarrow[CH_3-CH=CH_2]{AlCl_3 \text{ or } H^+}$ $C_6H_5CH(CH_3)_2$

benzene — cumene (isopropylbenzene)

*Mechanism*: Whether an alkyl halide, olefin, or alcohol is used, the reactive species has some carbonium ion character even if it is not a full, free carbonium ion.

$$\underset{\text{alkyl halide}}{R{-}X} + AlX_3 \longrightarrow [\overset{\delta+}{R}\cdots X\cdots \overset{\delta-}{AlX_3}] \longrightarrow [\overset{+}{R}\quad \overset{-}{AlX_4}]$$

$$\underset{\text{olefin}}{R{-}CH{=}CH_2} + H^+ \rightleftharpoons [R{-}\underset{+}{C}H{-}CH_3]$$

$$\underset{\text{alcohol}}{R{-}CH_2{-}CH_2OH} + H^+ \rightleftharpoons [R{-}CH_2{-}CH_2\overset{+}{O}H_2] \rightleftharpoons [R{-}CH_2\overset{+}{C}H_2] + H_2O$$

Recall from previous discussions that the order of stability of carbonium ions is tertiary > secondary > primary. Often rearrangements are observed in which some of the product is derived from a more stable carbonium ion, rather than from the first one generated. For example, note in Table 7-6 the reaction of benzene with 1-chloropropane (and $AlCl_3$). In the final step of the mechanism, the $AlCl_4^-$ may act as a base to assist in the removal of a proton.

**Simple monoalkyl benzenes such as toluene cannot be prepared by Friedel-Crafts alkylation.** Since alkyl groups donate electrons to the aromatic system, the newly formed compound, e.g., toluene, would react much *faster* than the starting material (benzene), and the reaction would lead to polymethylated benzenes rather than mainly toluene. If a bulky halide is used, such as *tert*-butyl chloride, the reaction will give rise to a simpler mixture of products since it is unlikely, on steric grounds, that one will obtain an *o*-di-*tert*-butylbenzene by this method.

Write a reasonable mechanism for the following reactions:

1. Benzene + $CH_3CHClCH_3$ $\xrightarrow[AlCl_3]{\text{trace}}$ $C_6H_5{-}CH(CH_3)_2$

2. Benzene + $CH_3{-}CH{=}CH_2$ $\xrightarrow[AlCl_3]{\text{trace}}$ $C_6H_5{-}CH(CH_3)_2$

## 7-9 FRIEDEL-CRAFTS ACYLATION

The acylation reaction is similar to the Friedel-Crafts alkylation in that it employs a Lewis acid catalyst, usually anhydrous $AlCl_3$, and an aromatic substrate. However, the organic reagents are usually acid chlorides or anhydrides

$$R{-}C(=O){-}Cl \qquad R{-}C(=O){-}O{-}C(=O){-}R$$

acid chlorides anhydrides

which give rise to ketones, Ar—CO—R. If the anhydride is cyclic,

$$(CH_2)_n \text{ ring: } {-}C(=O){-}O{-}C(=O){-}$$

the product is a ketoacid

$$Ar{-}C(=O){-}(CH_2)_n{-}C(=O){-}OH$$

*Overall*:

$$C_6H_6 + CH_3C(=O)Cl \xrightarrow[\text{2. } H_3O^+ \text{ (hydrolysis)}]{\text{1. 1.1 equiv } AlCl_3 \text{ in dry solvent}} C_6H_5{-}C(=O){-}CH_3 + HCl + Al^{3+} + 3Cl^-$$

benzene acetyl chloride acetophenone

*Mechanism*: Since the carbonyl group contains unshared electrons, it is a Lewis base, and thus **every carbonyl group present is complexed with $AlCl_3$**, and a slight excess of $AlCl_3$ must be used for catalysis. Further, the $AlCl_3$ renders the carbonyl carbon more electrophilic, thus contributing to the ease of the reaction. In the formulas that follow, the complexed $AlCl_3$ is connected by a dotted line to the oxygen atoms.

$$CH_3{-}\overset{\delta+}{C}(={:}\overset{\delta-}{O}{:}){-}Cl + \xrightarrow[\text{1 equiv}]{AlCl_3} \left[ CH_3{-}\overset{\delta+}{C}(={:}O{:}\cdots\overset{\delta-}{AlCl_3}){-}Cl \longleftrightarrow CH_3{-}C^+(Cl){-}O{-}\bar{A}lCl_3 \right]$$

$$\xrightarrow[\text{cat. amount}]{AlCl_3} \left[ CH_3{-}\overset{\delta+}{C}(=O\cdots\overset{\delta-}{AlCl_3}){-}\overset{\delta+}{Cl}\cdots\overset{\delta-}{AlCl_3} \longleftrightarrow CH_3{-}\overset{\delta+}{C^+}(=O\cdots\overset{\delta-}{AlCl_3}) \quad \bar{A}lCl_4 \right]$$

The species is electrophilic, and the mechanism can be formulated as follows:

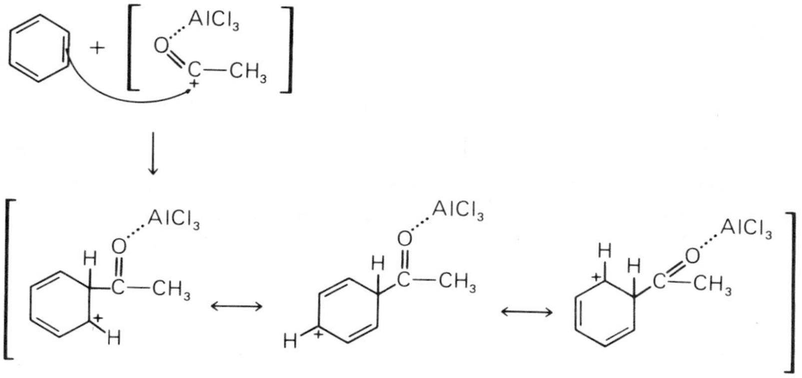

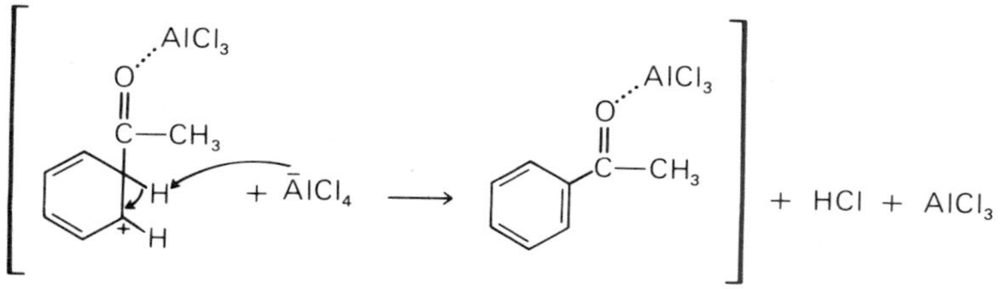

At this point, the carbonyl group in the product is still complexed with $AlCl_3$, and a ***separate hydrolysis step***, necessary for liberation of the ketone, is carried out with ice and dilute hydrochloric acid.

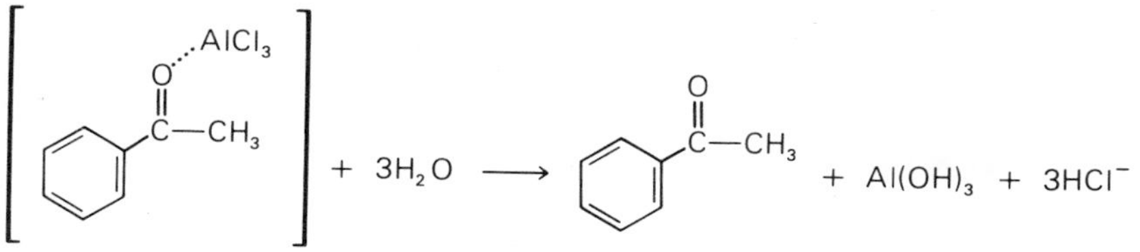

$$Al(OH)_3 + 3HCl \longrightarrow Al^{3+} + 3H_2O + 3Cl^-$$

The mechanism is similar for anhydrides, the initial step being the formation of an electrophilic reagent. Here 2.1 equiv of $AlCl_3$ is required. Succinic anhydride provides a method for adding four carbon atoms to an aromatic compound. This is the first step in the synthesis of naphthalene compounds from benzene and its derivatives (see Sec. 15-22).

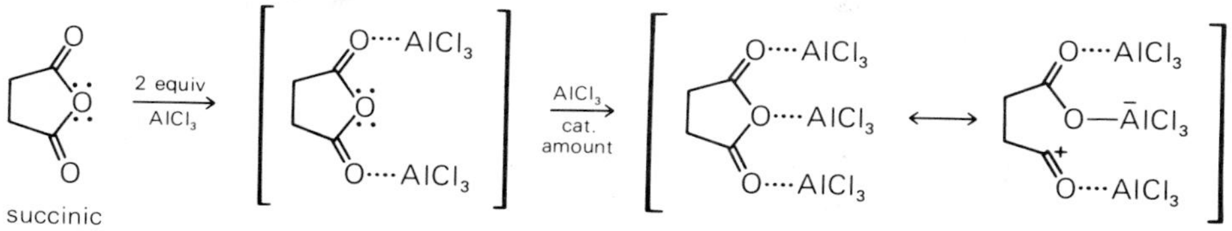

succinic anhydride

*Example*: $C_6H_6$ + succinic anhydride $\xrightarrow[\text{2. } H_3O^+\text{; 90\% yield}]{\text{1. 2.1 equiv } AlCl_3 \text{ in } CS_2}$ $C_6H_5\text{—}\overset{O}{\overset{\|}{C}}\text{—}\overset{\beta}{C}H_2\overset{\alpha}{C}H_2CO_2H$

*β*-benzoylpropionic acid

One comment about reactivity: Either a nitro group, $\text{—}NO_2$, or a carbonyl group, $\text{>}C\text{=}O$, adjacent to an aromatic ring will deactivate the ring with respect to the Friedel-Crafts acylation reaction. Nitrobenzene, in fact, is an excellent solvent for the reaction and does not undergo Friedel-Crafts reactions. The product formed by monoacylation of a hydrocarbon has a double bond adjacent to the ring and is generally not reactive to further substitution; contrast this with the Friedel-Crafts alkylation.

## 7-10 PREPARATION OF ACID CHLORIDES AND ANHYDRIDES

Earlier in the text it was suggested that when a reaction or preparation is given, you should ask where the starting material comes from. Since a complete discussion of organic acids and their derivatives is deferred until much later in the text, this section is a digression to answer that question for acid chlorides and anhydrides.

### *Acid chlorides*

$$R\text{—}\overset{O}{\overset{\|}{C}}\text{—}O\text{—}H + \underset{\substack{\text{thionyl chloride}\\ \text{b.p. } 77^\circ}}{SOCl_2} \rightarrow R\text{—}\overset{O}{\overset{\|}{C}}\text{—}Cl + HCl\uparrow + SO_2\uparrow$$

or

$$3R\text{—}\underset{O}{\underset{\|}{C}}\text{—}O\text{—}H + \underset{\substack{\text{phosphorous}\\ \text{trichloride}\\ \text{b.p. } 76^\circ}}{PCl_3} \rightarrow 3R\text{—}\underset{O}{\underset{\|}{C}}\text{—}Cl + \underset{\substack{\text{phosphorous}\\ \text{acid}}}{H_3PO_3}$$

Heating an acid with either $SOCl_2$ or $PCl_3$ provides satisfactory yields of the acid chloride, although the $SOCl_2$ usually gives a purer product in higher yield with greater ease. In that case the two by-products are evolved gases, and after the reaction has reached completion, the excess thionyl chloride is readily removed by distillation. With $PCl_3$ the acid chloride must be separated from the phosphorous acid by a more tedious route.

*Anhydrides*

$$2R{-}\overset{\overset{\large O}{\|}}{C}{-}OH + CH_3{-}\overset{\overset{\large O}{\|}}{C}{-}O{-}\overset{\overset{\large O}{\|}}{C}{-}CH_3 \xrightarrow{\Delta} R{-}\overset{\overset{\large O}{\|}}{C}{-}O{-}\overset{\overset{\large O}{\|}}{C}{-}R + 2CH_3CO_2H\uparrow \qquad (a)$$

acetic anhydride; acetic acid

$$(CH_2)_n(CO_2H)_2 + CH_3{-}\underset{\underset{\large O}{\|}}{C}{-}O{-}\underset{\underset{\large O}{\|}}{C}{-}CH_3 \xrightarrow{\Delta} (CH_2)_n(C{=}O)_2O + 2CH_3CO_2H\uparrow \qquad (b)$$

Anhydrides, except acetic anhydride itself, can be prepared according to Eq. (*a*) by heating the acid with acetic anhydride. The equilibrium is shifted to the right by the continuous removal of the lower-boiling acetic acid. Cyclic anhydrides [Eq. (*b*)] can also be prepared in this manner, although in certain cases simple heating of the diacid will cause a dehydration with the formation of the anhydride.

$$\begin{matrix} CH_2{-}COOH \\ | \\ CH_2{-}COOH \end{matrix} \xrightarrow{\Delta} \text{succinic anhydride} + H_2O$$

succinic acid — succinic anhydride

## DIRECTION AND EASE OF AROMATIC SUBSTITUTION

### 7-11 CORRELATION OF AROMATIC SUBSTITUTION REACTIONS

Using the data in Table 7-7 and those from the sulfonation experiments shown in Table 7-5, note that the benzene derivative which reacts under the milder conditions (phenol vs. nitrobenzene in sulfonation and acetanilide vs. nitrobenzene in nitration) is the compound which gives both ortho and para isomers, whereas the other gives almost exclusively the meta isomer. While it is dangerous to draw a general correlation from so few examples, nevertheless it is true that compounds containing ortho-para-directing substituents are more readily substituted than those having meta directors. Functional groups on an aromatic system may be arranged according to their ***directive*** power and whether they cause the aromatic compound to react faster or slower than benzene, which is taken as the standard for comparison.

**Table 7-7**
**Electrophilic aromatic substitution reactions**

Chlorination and nitration of acetanilide:

acetanilide $\xrightarrow[FeCl_3]{Cl_2}$ *o*-chloroacetanilide + *p*-chloroacetanilide + very little meta isomer

(NH—C(=O)—$CH_3$ on benzene; products carry Cl ortho and para)

acetanilide $\xrightarrow[40°]{HNO_3;\ H_2SO_4}$ *o*-nitroacetanilide 33% + *p*-nitroacetanilide 67% + very little meta isomer

(NH—CH(=O)—$CH_3$ on benzene as printed; products carry $NO_2$ ortho and para)

Chlorination and nitration of nitrobenzene:

nitrobenzene $\xrightarrow[FeCl_3]{Cl_2}$ *m*-chloronitrobenzene + very little ortho or para isomer

nitrobenzene $\xrightarrow[HNO_3\ 100°]{H_2SO_4\ /fuming}$ *m*-dinitrobenzene 93% + *o*-dinitrobenzene 6% + *p*-dinitrobenzene 1%

The position taken by an incoming group depends primarily on the substituent already present and only secondarily on the type of incoming group itself. For instance, recall that sulfonation of phenol affords the ortho and para isomers, whereas nitrobenzene gives almost exclusively the meta isomer.

There are at least two ways to analyze and predict the products of electrophilic aromatic substitution: (1) from a consideration of the ground state of the aromatic molecule (Secs. 7-12 and 7-13) and (2) from a consideration of the stability of the various possible intermediates (Sec. 7-14). As will be seen in the following sections the methods lead to somewhat different results; using the stability of the aronium ion intermediate is perhaps the more satisfying method.

## 7-12 RESONANCE AND INDUCTIVE EFFECTS

Three major factors must be considered in understanding directive and activating effects: resonance, inductive, and steric effects. The first two are generally the most helpful and are discussed first. Sometimes these two effects are additive, and sometimes they oppose each other; it is necessary to examine each in detail before the net result can be predicted. Resonance is generally the more important in determining the position of attack and often outweighs the weaker inductive effect.

Since the attacking species is an electrophile, $E^+$, electron-donating substituents are activators because they increase the electron density in the ring (relative to benzene). They also direct new substituents to the ortho and para positions.

### The $-NH_2$ group (aniline): an ortho-para director and activator

*Resonance*: Because aniline has an unshared pair of electrons on nitrogen, the following charge-separated resonance forms can be written:

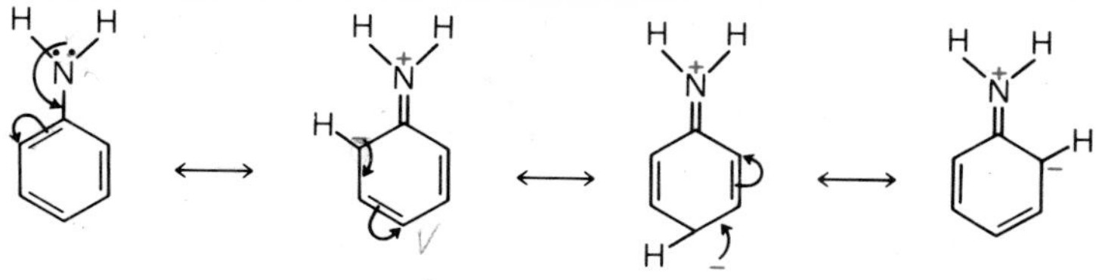

The composite form

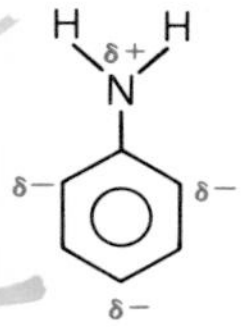

shows clearly that not only is the ring electron density increased, but it is specifically increased at the ortho and para positions.

*Inductive*: Consider only the carbon-nitrogen bond. Since a nitrogen atom is more electronegative than a carbon atom, it will be the minus end of the bond dipole. (Of course, this is not strictly correct, because we should consider not the electronegativity of the isolated atoms but the difference between the $sp^2$ aromatic carbon atom and the hybridized nitrogen.)

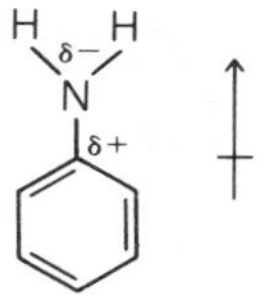

In this case, the resonance and inductive effects are in opposition. Experimentally, resonance predominates, and as a result the amino group is an ***activator*** and an ***ortho-para director***. Generally functional groups with unshared electrons on atoms next to the ring are ortho-para directors and activators since they can be written in resonance forms analogous to those for aniline.

| Carry through the analysis for anisole, $C_6H_5OCH_3$, similar to that given above for aniline. |
|---|

**The —$NO_2$ group (nitrobenzene): a meta director and deactivator**

*Resonance*: The following structures represent the resonance hybrid of nitrobenzene:

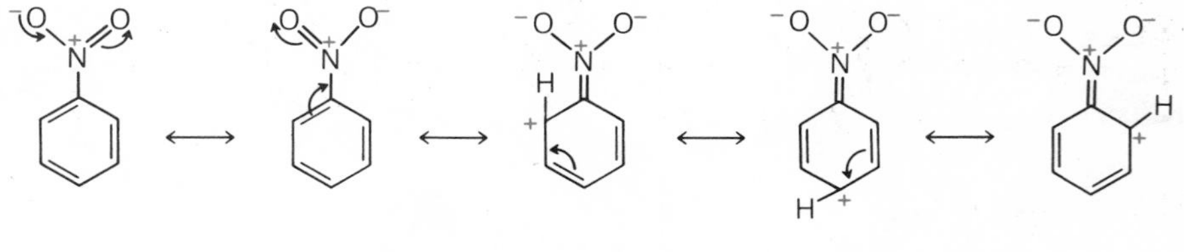

The composite representation shows that the electron density of the ring is decreased and specifically at the ortho and para positions.

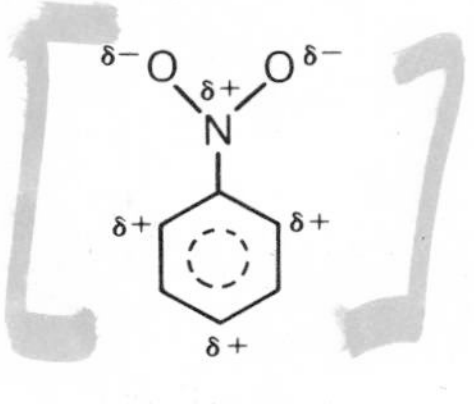

If an electrophile becomes attached to nitrobenzene, which is less reactive than benzene, it will enter the meta position by default. The

—$NO_2$ group, strictly speaking, does not "direct" to the meta position; rather, the meta position is simply the best of three poor choices.

*Inductive*: Because the resonance forms of the —$NO_2$ group show a positive charge on nitrogen, the bond dipole is best represented as

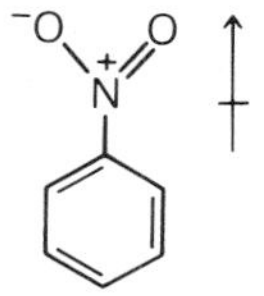

In this case the resonance and inductive effects are in the same direction, and the —$NO_2$ group is a deactivator and meta director. Functional groups with multiple bonds next to the ring are generally meta directors and deactivators.

| Carry out a similar analysis for benzaldehyde, $C_6H_5CHO$. |
|---|

**The halogens: ortho-para directors but deactivators.** It is an experimental fact that halobenzenes react less readily than benzene but yield ortho and para products. How are we to rationalize these facts?

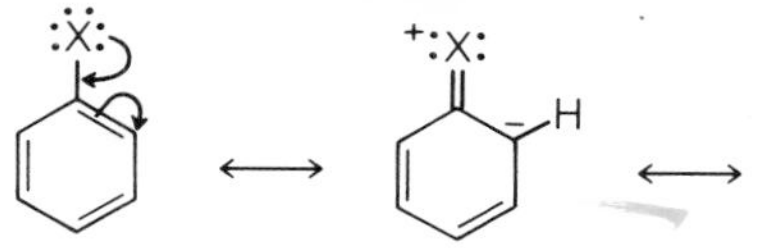

⟷ ⟷ and others

The resonance argument predicts that the halogens will be ortho-para directors and activators, whereas the inductive argument suggests that because of their high electronegativities the halogens will be deactivators.

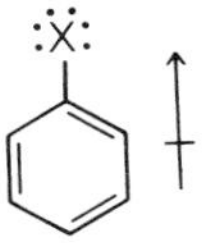

This dilemma is resolved by suggesting that for the halogens (as for most other substituents) the resonance effect predicts the position of substitution, whereas the rate is determined here by the inductive effect.

**The $CH_3$— group (toluene): ortho-para director and activator:** Although toluene undergoes substitution more readily than benzene and gives ortho and para substitution products, the usual resonance argument is difficult to apply. Since alkyl groups are electron-releasing by the inductive effect, toluene is more reactive than benzene. The separate consideration of resonance and inductive effects is not necessary if an analysis of the stability of various possible aronium ion intermediates is undertaken (see Sec. 7-14). In this type of analysis, the directive effects of halogen and alkyl substituents are more easily explained.

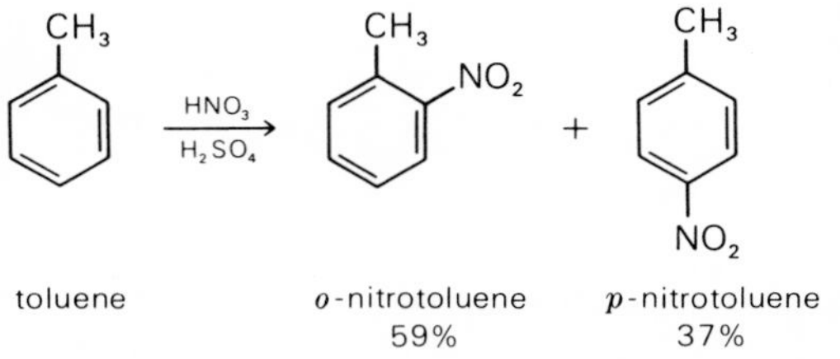

toluene $\xrightarrow[H_2SO_4]{HNO_3}$ *o*-nitrotoluene 59% + *p*-nitrotoluene 37%

## 7-13 STERIC EFFECTS

The nitration of *tert*-butylbenzene is a good example of steric influence. The product of electrophilic substitution is almost exclusively the para isomer because of the difficulty in approaching the ortho positions.

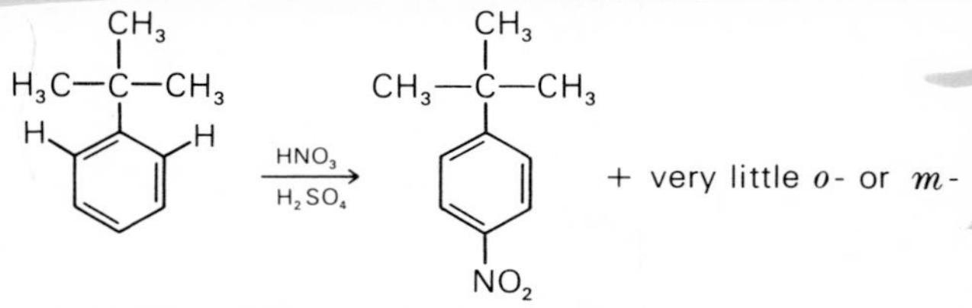

$$C_6H_5C(CH_3)_3 \xrightarrow[H_2SO_4]{HNO_3} p\text{-}O_2NC_6H_4C(CH_3)_3$$

+ very little *o*- or *m*-

Every substituent on a benzene ring offers some steric interference to an incoming group.

Steric effects are important in organic chemistry but especially so in biological systems, where the precise molecular geometry (in addition to all the other basic facts of organic chemistry) determines the course of human (and nonhuman) events.

## 7-14 STABILITY OF THE ARONIUM INTERMEDIATE

Another approach that can be used to predict the position taken by an incoming group in electrophilic aromatic substitution reactions consists of examining all possible resonance forms of the intermediate for the reaction at each position. By choosing those intermediates for which the greatest number of ***good*** resonance forms can be written, one may arrive at a reasonable prediction.

From nitrobenzene there are three good resonance forms for the intermediate leading to the meta isomer but only two for each of the ortho and para intermediates.

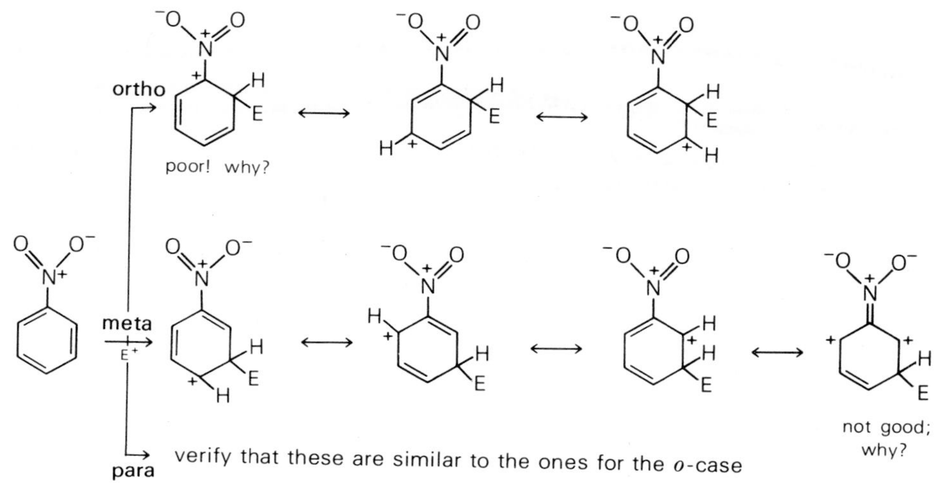

ortho

poor! why?

meta

$E^+$

not good; why?

para verify that these are similar to the ones for the *o*-case

Does this prediction agree with the previous one based on resonance and inductive effects?

With aniline there are four forms for each of the ortho and para intermediates but only three for the meta isomer.

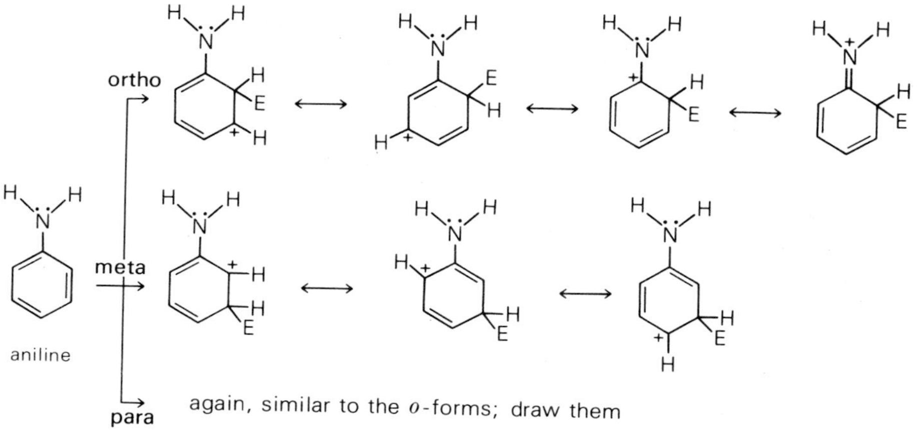

ortho

meta

aniline

para again, similar to the *o*-forms; draw them

The last of the resonance structures for the ortho intermediate is especially favorable since each atom has an octet of electrons around it.

## 7-15 SUMMARY OF FUNCTIONAL GROUP EFFECTS

There is clearly a difference in activating power between different substituents, for example, an —OH and a —$CH_3$. By competitive reactions in which a mixture of 1 mole of phenol, $C_6H_5OH$, and 1 mole of toluene, $C_6H_5CH_3$, is treated with 1 mole of $Br_2$ (and a catalyst), it can be shown by isolating the products that the phenol reacts much faster than the toluene. An order of reactivity can thus be established (Table 7-8). The strongest activators (and ortho-para directors) are those containing atoms with unshared electrons next to the ring, such as oxygen and nitrogen. The strongest deactivators (and meta directors) usually contain either a formal positive charge or a multiple-bond attachment on the atom next to the ring.

**Table 7-8 A summary of activating and directing effects**

| **Ortho-para directors (activators)** | **Meta directors (deactivators)** |
|---|---|
| *Electron-releasing (donating):* *unshared electrons next to the ring* | *Electron-withdrawing (attracting):* *multiple bonds next to the ring* |
| $-\ddot{N}R_2$  $-\ddot{N}HR$  $-\ddot{N}H_2$ | $-\overset{+}{N}(CH_3)_3$ |
| $-\ddot{\underset{\cdot\cdot}{O}}H$ | $-NO_2$ |
| | $-CN$ |
| | $-SO_3H$ |
| $-\ddot{\underset{\cdot\cdot}{O}}CH_3$  $(-\ddot{\underset{\cdot\cdot}{O}}R)$ | $-\overset{O}{\overset{\|}{C}}-H$  $-\overset{O}{\overset{\|}{C}}-CH_3$  $(-\overset{O}{\overset{\|}{C}}-R)$ |
| $-\ddot{N}H-COCH_3$ | $-\overset{O}{\overset{\|}{C}}-OH$  $(-\overset{O}{\overset{\|}{C}}-OR)$ |
| $-\ddot{\underset{\cdot\cdot}{O}}-COCH_3$ | |
| $-CH_3$  $(-R)$ | $-\overset{O}{\overset{\|}{C}}-NH_2$ |
| $-\ddot{\underset{\cdot\cdot}{X}}\colon$ (—halogens: special case) | $-\overset{+}{N}H_3$ |
| $-C_6H_5$ | (—H) |
| (—H) | |

## 7-16 PRINCIPLES OF HIGHER SUBSTITUTION

Since this section is a preview of later material, only a few special examples are discussed here. In general, when several functional groups are present in an aromatic system, the position taken by a new incoming group is determined by the additive influence of *each* function already present. When there is a choice, however, the more strongly activating functional groups (such as $—NH_2$, —OH, and their derivatives) will take precedence.

*Example* 1:

$$\text{o-xylene} \xrightarrow[\text{0°; 95\% yield}]{\text{Br}_2\ \text{Fe (I}_2\text{);}} \text{4-bromo-o-xylene}$$

*o*-xylene 4-bromo-*o*-xylene

In *o*-xylene each $—CH_3$ directs to its ortho and para position. However, steric effects predict the observed product rather than 3-bromo-*o*-xylene, which would place the —Br and $—CH_3$ in adjacent positions.

*Example* 2:

$$\text{N,N-dimethylaniline} \xrightarrow[\text{5–10°; 60\% yield}]{\text{HNO}_3\text{; H}_2\text{SO}_4} \text{N,N-dimethyl-m-nitroaniline}$$

*N, N*-dimethylaniline *N, N*-dimethyl-*m*-nitroaniline

This result is not unexpected if it is noted that the reaction is being carried out in strong acid solution. The positively charged *N,N*-dimethylanilium ion is undergoing reaction.

$H_3C—\overset{H}{N^+}—CH_3$ (attached to a benzene ring)

*Example* 3:

$$\text{p-cymene} \xrightarrow[\text{0–5°; HOAc 80\% yield}]{\text{HNO}_3\text{; H}_2\text{SO}_4} \text{2-nitro-p-cymene}$$

*p*-cymene 2-nitro-*p*-cymene

As in Example 1, all positions are activated by the two alkyl groups; however, steric *and* electronic effects predict the observed product.

*Example* 4:

$$\text{m-hydroxybenzaldehyde (CHO, OH)} \xrightarrow[\text{FeBr}_3]{\text{Br}_2} \text{2-bromo-5-hydroxybenzaldehyde (CHO, Br, OH)}$$

Note the influence of the activating substituent (—OH) over the deactivating one (—CHO).

1. Write the structure of the predicted major product from the succinoylation of

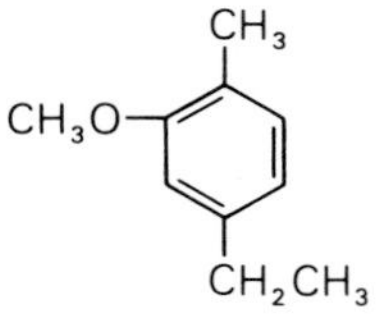

(1-ethyl-2-methoxy-4-methylbenzene: ring bearing $CH_3$, $CH_3O$ and $CH_2CH_3$) and of (ring bearing $CH_3$, $CH_3O$ and $CH(CH_3)_2$)

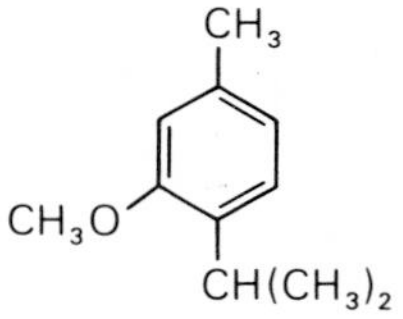

2. Predict and name the major dinitration product (obtained in 60% yield) of benzoic acid. This reaction requires mixed acid at a temperature of 140° for 3 hr.

3. Predict and name the major mononitration product (obtained in 80% yield) of benzaldehyde. This transformation requires fuming nitric acid and concentrated sulfuric acid at 5 to 10°. Why do you suppose a higher temperature (and less strenuous acid conditions) are not employed?

## 7-17 INDIRECT METHODS OF SYNTHESIS

When it is impossible or impractical to obtain a compound by direct substitution, it is necessary to have a group present which will direct the desired incoming group to the correct position. This directing group must then be removed or modified. Again, this section must be considered a preview, since some of these reactions will be discussed in later chapters.

**Trinitrobenzene (TNB) from trinitrotoluene (TNT):** Although nitrobenzene can be nitrated under strenuous conditions, further nitration requires such forcing conditions, since the ring is very deactivated, that extensive oxidation and decomposition result.

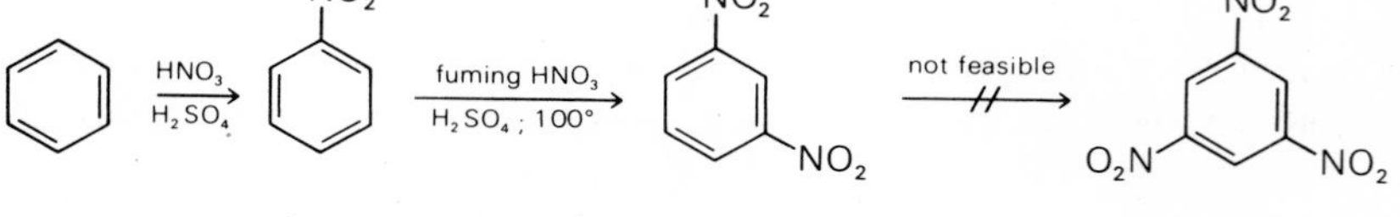

Benzene $\xrightarrow[H_2SO_4]{HNO_3}$ nitrobenzene ($NO_2$) $\xrightarrow[H_2SO_4;\ 100°]{\text{fuming } HNO_3}$ m-dinitrobenzene ($NO_2$, $NO_2$) $\xrightarrow{\text{not feasible}}$ 1,3,5-trinitrobenzene ($NO_2$, $O_2N$, $NO_2$)

An indirect route utilizes the activating effect of the methyl group. The entire conversion from toluene to the commericial explosive TNT can be carried out in a single reaction vessel.

$\xrightarrow[H_2SO_4]{HNO_3}$

minor intermediate
why?

TNT

The individual steps and intermediates are shown above. Note that the route via 2,6-dinitrotoluene is expected to be relatively unimportant because of steric interference.

Alkyl side chains on an aromatic system can be oxidized by permanganate to the corresponding acid. In this particular example, the sodium salt of the acid is very readily decarboxylated in solution, giving trinitrobenzene (TNB).

TNT $\longrightarrow$ 2,4,6-trinitrobenzoic acid $\xrightarrow{NaHCO_3}$ [sodium 2,4,6-trinitrobenzoate] $\xrightarrow{\Delta}$ TNB $+ \; CO_2\uparrow$

**Picric acid (2,4,6-trinitrophenol):** The synthesis of this compound also requires an indirect method. Whereas phenol is easily mononitrated, further nitration causes extensive oxidation and decomposition.

OH, HNO$_3$ → OH, NO$_2$ + OH, NO$_2$ —not feasible→ O$_2$N, OH, NO$_2$, NO$_2$

phenol *o*-nitrophenol *p*-nitrophenol

A possible route is

Cl —HNO$_3$, H$_2$SO$_4$→ [ write the appropriate intermediates ] → Cl, O$_2$N, NO$_2$, NO$_2$

chlorobenzene 2,4,6-trinitrochlorobenzene

Cl, O$_2$N, NO$_2$, NO$_2$ —OH$^-$, Δ→ OH, O$_2$N, NO$_2$, NO$_2$ + Cl$^-$

picric acid

The replacement of an aromatic halogen by hydroxide occurs here because of the electron-withdrawing effect of the nitro groups. This is an example of a ***nucleophilic aromatic substitution***.

> The hydroxyl hydrogen of 2,4,6-trinitrophenol is so acidic that the compound is commonly called picric acid. In order to understand why this is so, remove the proton, —OH, and write the many possible resonance structures for the anion.

***m*-Bromotoluene:** An example of a rather simple compound requiring indirect synthesis is *m*-bromotoluene. Recall that direct bromination of toluene or alkylation of bromobenzene would be expected to give primarily ortho and para disubstituted compounds. One method starts with *p*-nitrotoluene, which can be readily reduced to the amino compound and then monobrominated under carefully specified conditions.

toluene $\xrightarrow[H_2SO_4]{HNO_3}$ *p*-nitrotoluene $\xrightarrow{Sn/HCl}$ *p*-toluidine $\xrightarrow{Br_2}$ 2-bromo-4-methylaniline

The amino group can then be removed by conversion to the diazonium salt (see Chap. 16), which is readily decomposed by heating with $H_3PO_2$.

2-bromo-4-methylaniline $\xrightarrow[(HCl + NaNO_2)]{HONO;\ 0\text{-}5°}$ $[\text{diazonium salt } (^{+}N_2)]\ Cl^-$ $\xrightarrow[\Delta]{H_3PO_2}$ *m*-bromotoluene

## 7-18 ACTIVATED SUBSTRATES

Some compounds are so activated by substituents that further reactions cannot be stopped short of multiple substitution under ordinary conditions. Special precautions and other methods (discussed later) must be used to prepare the corresponding mono- and disubstituted products.

Phenol (OH) $\xrightarrow[\approx 100\%\ yield]{3Br_2\ very\ fast}$ 2,4,6-tribromophenol (Br, Br, Br; OH) + 3HBr

Aniline ($NH_2$) $\xrightarrow[\approx 100\%\ yield]{3Br_2\ very\ fast}$ 2,4,6-tribromoaniline (Br, Br, Br; $NH_2$) + 3HBr

## SUGGESTED READINGS

### Aromatic substitution

Ault, A.: The Activating Effect of Fluorine in Electrophilic Aromatic Substitution, *J. Chem. Educ.*, **43**, 329 (1966). Cites evidence that in certain compounds a fluorine atom activates the position para to it.

Duewell, H.: Aromatic Substitution, *J. Chem. Educ.*, **43**, 138 (1966). Discusses activation and orientation in terms of the intermediate-state stability.

Jones, M. M.: Activation of Small Molecules by Coordination, *J. Chem. Educ.*, **41**, 493 (1964). Discusses the generation of electrophiles, free radicals, and nucleophiles.

Marsi, K. L., and S. H. Wilen: Friedel-Crafts Alkylation, *J. Chem. Educ.*, **40**, 214 (1963).

Meislich, H.: Teaching Aromatic Substitution: A Molecular Orbital Approach, *J. Chem. Educ.*, **44**, 153 (1967).

Stewart, R.: The Reactive Intermediates of Organic Chemistry, *J. Chem. Educ.*, **38**, 308 (1961).

Waack, R.: The Stability of the "Aromatic Sextet," *J. Chem. Educ.*, **39**, 469 (1962).

**Organometallics and heterocycles**

Kaesz, H. D.: Organometallic Derivatives of the Transition Elements, *J. Chem. Educ.*, **40**, 159 (1963).

Katrizky, A. R.: Teaching Heterocyclic Chemistry, *J. Chem. Educ.*, **42**, 636 (1965). Emphasizes chemistry of six-membered heterocycles.

Rochow, E. G.: The Direct Synthesis of Organometallic Compounds, *J. Chem. Educ.*, **43**, 58 (1966).

## PROBLEMS

★**1.** Given the following heats of hydrogenation, is there any evidence of resonance stabilization of the benzene ring by the vinyl group in styrene? Show your reasoning clearly.

| $CH_2{=}CH_2$ | benzene | $C_6H_5CH_2CH_3$ | $C_6H_5CH{=}CH_2$ |
|---|---|---|---|
| 32.8 kcal/mole | 49.8 | 48.9 | 77.5 |

**2**. Given the following heats of hydrogenation, compare the resonance energy of the two conjugated dienes.

| $CH_2{=}CH{-}CH_2CH_3$ | $CH_2{=}CH{-}CH{=}CH{-}CH_3$ | $CH_2{=}CH{-}CH{=}CH_2$ |
|---|---|---|
| 30.3 kcal/mole | 54.1 | 57.1 |

$CH_2{=}CH{-}CH_2{-}CH{=}CH_2$

60.8

★**3**. Draw the structure(s) of all the dibromoanthracenes which can give only two possible tribromoanthracenes on further reaction with bromine and a catalyst.

**4**. Give the structures and names of all the dimethylnaphthalenes. How many possible monochloro isomers can each give? Could the isomeric dimethylnaphthalenes be distinguished by this method?

**5.** Give the expected monosubstitution product(s) from the following reactions and explain fully the observed orientation using structural formulas but a minimum of words. Explain why the starting material reacts either at a slower or at a faster rate than benzene. Note that the compounds in (*a*) to (*c*) are isomers.

★(*a*) (*i*) $C_6H_5$—CO—$NHCH_3$ (*ii*) $C_6H_5$—NH—$COCH_3$ $\xrightarrow{H_2SO_4}$

(*b*) (*i*) $C_6H_5$—O—CO—$CH_3$ (*ii*) $C_6H_5$—CO—O—$CH_3$ (*iii*) $C_6H_5$—$CH_2$—$CO_2H$ $\xrightarrow[H_2SO_4]{HNO_3}$

★(*c*) (*i*) o-xylene ($CH_3$, $CH_3$) (*ii*) m-xylene ($CH_3$, $CH_3$) (*iii*) p-xylene ($CH_3$, $CH_3$) $\xrightarrow[FeBr_3]{Br_2}$

(*d*) p-$C(CH_3)_3$—$C_6H_4$—$CH_3$ + $CH_2$=CH—$CH_3$ $\xrightarrow[AlCl_3]{trace}$

(*e*) $C_6H_5Br$ $\xrightarrow[\text{1.1 equiv } AlCl_3 \text{ in } CS_2]{CH_3COCl}$

★(*f*) $C_6H_5$—$CH_3$ $\xrightarrow[\text{2.1 equiv } AlCl_3 \text{ in nitrobenzene}]{\text{succinic anhydride}}$

**6**. On the basis of the stability of the transition state, explain the orientation and rate of bromination of:

(*a*) bromobenzene

(*b*) anisole, $C_6H_5OCH_3$, an ether

(*c*) methyl benzoate, $C_6H_5COOCH_3$, an ester

★**7**. 2,4,6-Trinitrotoluene is a relatively acidic hydrocarbon. Explain why a proton is readily removed from the methyl group.

**8**. Show how you could prepare each of the following compounds from benzene, toluene, or one of the xylenes. Note that the order in which substituents are introduced is often important.

★(*a*) $C_6H_4$ with $COCH_3$ and Br (meta)

★(*b*) $C_6H_4$ with $COCH_3$ and Br (para)

(*c*) $C_6H_3$ with $CH_3$, $NH_2$, $CH_3$ (2,5-dimethylaniline)

★(*d*) $C_6H_2$ with $CH_3$, $CH_3$, Br, $O_2N$

(*e*) $C_6H_4$ with $NH_2$ and Cl (meta)

★(*f*) $C_6H_4$ with $NH_2$ and Cl (para)

(*g*) $C_6H_3$ with $CH_3$, $CH_3$, $SO_3H$

# Chapter Eight

## NOMENCLATURE AND STRUCTURE

Compounds containing halogen atoms, (F), Cl, Br, I, are classified as 1°, 2°, or 3° alkyl, allyl, benzyl, vinyl, aryl, or alkynyl depending upon the organic group to which the halogen is attached. Halogen atoms are considered substituents, not functional groups, in naming organic compounds. Examples of organic halides are shown in Table 8-1.

Vinyl and aryl halides are less reactive than alkyl halides, but allyl and benzyl halides are very much more reactive in the silver nitrate test (discussed later). The structural similarity between the members in each pair is shown in Fig. 8-1. The halogen atoms in vinyl and aryl compounds are bound more closely to the carbon atoms, whereas the allyl and benzyl *cations*, formed by ionization of the halogen atoms, are resonance-stabilized, and thus are easily formed.

**Table 8-1 Representative organic halides**

| | | |
|---|---|---|
| $CH_3Cl$ (primary alkyl)<br>methyl chloride<br>(chloromethane) | $(H_3C)_2CH—Br$ (secondary alkyl)<br>isopropyl bromide<br>(2-bromopropane) | $(CH_3)_3CI$ (tertiary alkyl)<br>*tert*-butyl iodide<br>(2-iodo-2-methylpropane) |
| $CHI_3$ (polyhalogenated)<br>iodoform<br>(triiodomethane) | $CH_2{=}CH—Cl$ (vinyl)<br>vinyl chloride<br>(chloroethylene) | $CH_2{=}CH—CH_2—Br$ (allyl)<br>allyl bromide<br>(3-bromo-1-propene) |
| $C_6H_5F$ (aryl)<br>fluorobenzene | $C_6H_5CH_2Cl$ (benzyl)<br>benzyl chloride<br>($\alpha$-chlorotoluene) | $H—C{\equiv}C—I$ (alkynyl)<br>iodoacetylene |

# Halides

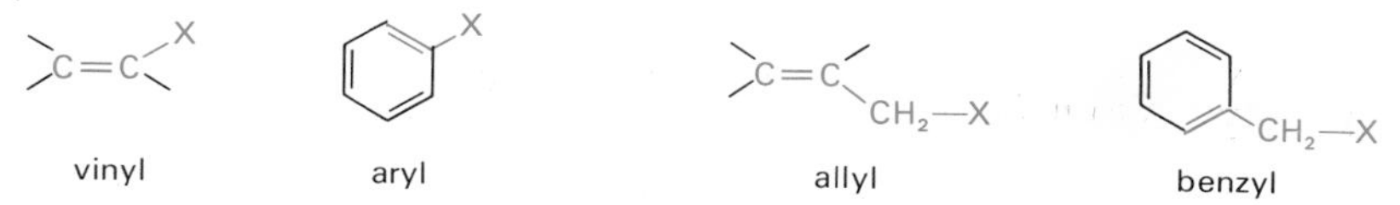

**Figure 8-1 Comparison of vinyl and aryl halides and allyl and benzyl halides**

## APPLICATIONS

Besides being valuable intermediates for chemical syntheses, organic halides have a wide variety of practical uses. Almost all of them, however, are toxic. Exposure, even in low concentrations, over prolonged periods may cause liver damage.

Both carbon tetrachloride, $CCl_4$, and trichloroethylene, $CHCl{=}CCl_2$, are used in the dry-cleaning industry; fats and greases are soluble in these nonpolar solvents. Carbon tetrachloride is also used in fire extinguishers but may generate phosgene, $COCl_2$, an extremely toxic gas, if used in conjunction with water.

$$CCl_4 + H_2O \xrightarrow{\Delta} COCl_2 + 2HCl$$

Ethyl chloride, $CH_3CH_2Cl$, is used as a local anesthetic, which is applied to the area from an aerosol bomb. Chloroform, $CHCl_3$, has been used as an anesthetic but is extremely toxic. Iodoform, $CHI_3$, is used as an antiseptic and has a characteristic hospital-like odor.

Some polyhalogenated compounds are used both as dispersing gases in aerosol containers and as refrigerants; they are known as *Freons*.

| $CCl_3F$ | $CCl_2F_2$ | $CClF_3$ |
|---|---|---|
| trichlorofluoromethane<br>Freon-11 | dichlorodifluoromethane<br>Freon-12 | chlorotrifluoromethane<br>Freon-13 |

$CBrF_3$ — bromotrifluoromethane, Freon-13-B1

$CClF_2—CClF_2$ — 1,2-dichlorotetrafluoroethane, Freon-114

$CF_3—CF_3$ — hexafluoroethane, Freon-116

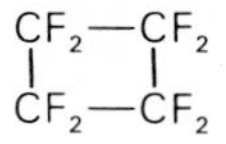

$CF_2—CF_2$ / $CF_2—CF_2$ (ring) — octofluorocyclobutane, Freon-C-318

The use of polychlorinated organic compounds as insecticides has increased significantly in recent years. Some common ones are 1,1-bis-(*p*-chlorophenyl)-2,2,2-trichloroethane (DDT), chlordan, and heptachlor; the latter two are prepared from chlordene.

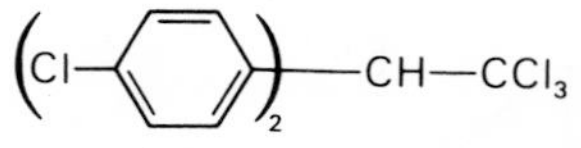

$(Cl—C_6H_4)_2—CH—CCl_3$

DDT

chlordene $\xrightarrow{Cl_2 \text{ addition}}$ chlordan

chlordene $\xrightarrow{Cl_2 \text{ substitution}}$ heptachlor + HCl

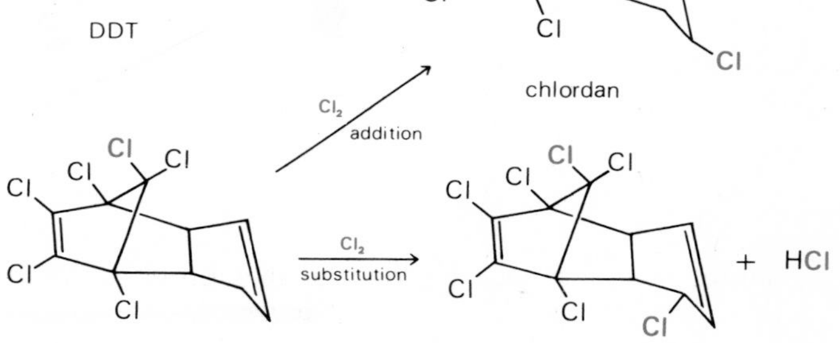

## PREPARATION

### 8-1 ADDITION OF HALOGENS AND HYDROGEN HALIDES TO MULTIPLE BONDS

Halogens and hydrogen halides add easily and stereospecifically to multiple bonds by an electrophilic mechanism. These reactions have already been discussed in Secs. 4-5 and 4-8 (alkenes), Sec. 5-6 (alkynes), and Sec. 6-3 (dienes). Reviewing pertinent material for this section is an excellent method of coordinating the many types of organic reactions; these reactions will usually be discussed under both ***Reactions*** and ***Preparations***.

### 8-2 HALOGENATION OF HYDROCARBONS

Although the photochemical halogenation of aliphatic and alicyclic hydrocarbons and separation of the possible isomers is usually not a feasible laboratory method for the preparation of these compounds, side chains of aromatic hydrocarbons (methyl groups in particular) readily undergo substitution. A free-radical initiator, such as air ($O_2$) or peroxides, may be used in addition to heat and/or light. These reactions give the monobromo isomer almost exclusively when 1 equiv of bromine is used (see Sec. 2-5).

$$C_6H_5\text{-}CH_3 \xrightarrow[h\nu;\ \Delta]{Br_2} C_6H_5\text{-}CH_2Br + HBr$$

toluene — benzyl bromide

> Write a reasonable mechanism for the above reaction.

Compounds containing halogen atoms on the aromatic ring are prepared by the usual electrophilic halogenation reactions (see Chap. 7).

$$CH_3\text{-}C_6H_4\text{-}CH_3 \xrightarrow[\text{ionic mechanism}]{Br_2/FeBr_3} CH_3\text{-}C_6H_3(Br)\text{-}CH_3 + HBr$$

*p*-xylene — 2-bromo-*p*-xylene

$$CH_3\text{-}C_6H_4\text{-}CH_3 \xrightarrow[\text{free-radical mechanism}]{Br_2;\ \Delta;\ h\nu} CH_3\text{-}C_6H_4\text{-}CH_2Br + HBr$$

α-bromo-*p*-xylene
(*p*-methylbenzyl bromide)

> Under what conditions would you expect to obtain 4,4'-dibromobibenzyl from bibenzyl? How might you alter the conditions to obtain α,α'-dibromobibenzyl?
>
> $$C_6H_5\text{-}\overset{\alpha'}{CH_2}\text{-}\overset{\alpha}{CH_2}\text{-}C_6H_5$$
>
> (ring positions 1'–6' and 1–6)
>
> bibenzyl

## 8-3 USE OF *N*-BROMOSUCCINIMIDE

Allylic and benzylic positions are readily brominated under free-radical conditions with *N*-bromosuccinimide (NBS). The NBS appears to furnish a low concentration of $Br_2$ molecules, which then dissociate and act as free-radical chain carriers.

*Examples*:

$$CH_3{-}CH{=}CH_2 + \text{N-bromosuccinimide (NBr)} \xrightarrow[\text{dry } CCl_4]{h\nu} CH_2Br{-}CH{=}CH_2 + \text{succinimide (N-H)}$$

*N*-bromosuccinimide    succinimide

$$C_6H_5CH_3 \xrightarrow[h\nu]{\text{NBS in dry } CCl_4} C_6H_5CH_2Br$$

Generally allylic ***methylene*** groups undergo bromination with NBS more readily than allylic ***methyl*** groups. Consider the radical stability in the two cases.

$$CH_3(CH_2)_2CH_2{-}CH{=}CH{-}CH_3 \xrightarrow[\Delta;\ 60\%\ \text{yield}]{\text{NBS in dry } CCl_4} CH_3(CH_2)_2CH(Br){-}CH{=}CH{-}CH_3$$

2-heptene    4-bromo-2-heptene

In the presence of traces of water or with very polar substrates which undergo rapid electrophilic substitution, reactions of NBS lead to bromination of an aromatic ring. For example, water, an alcohol, or a phenol would be expected to provide low concentrations of HOBr, which could then lead to bromination of the ring by polarization of HOBr ($\overset{\delta-}{HO}{-}\overset{\delta+}{Br}$).

$$\text{succinimide-}\overset{\delta-}{N}{-}\overset{\delta+}{Br} + \overset{\delta+}{H}{-}\overset{\delta-}{OH} \longrightarrow \text{succinimide-}N{-}H + HOBr$$

*Example*:

$$C_6H_5OH \xrightarrow{\text{NBS}} p\text{-}BrC_6H_4OH$$

In fact, NBS in water is a convenient source of HOBr, which readily adds to olefins (Sec. 4-9).

$$CH_3{-}CH{=}CH_2 \xrightarrow[\text{presence of } H_2O]{\text{NBS}} CH_3{-}CH(OH){-}CH_2Br$$

## 8-4 HALIDES FROM ALCOHOLS, ALDEHYDES, AND KETONES

Alcohols react with HX, $PX_3$, and $SOCl_2$ affording good yields of organic halides. Aldehydes, RCHO, and ketones, $R_2C{=}O$, give dihalides with $PCl_5$ or $PBr_5$ (see Sec. 5-4). Some of these preparations have been mentioned in earlier chapters and will be discussed in more detail in Chap. 9.

*Examples*:

$$\underset{\text{OH}}{CH_2}-(CH_2)_4-\underset{\text{OH}}{CH_2} \xrightarrow[\substack{(KI\ +\ H_3PO_4)\\ 85\%\ \text{yield}}]{HI} \underset{\text{I}}{CH_2}-(CH_2)_4-\underset{\text{I}}{CH_2} + 2H_2O$$

$$\underset{\text{a ketone}}{(CH_3)_2CH-CH_2-\underset{\|\atop O}{C}-CH_2-CH(CH_3)_2} \xrightarrow[50\%\ \text{yield}]{PCl_5;\ 70°} \underset{\text{a } geminal\text{-dihalide}}{(CH_3)_2CH-CH_2-\overset{Cl}{\underset{Cl}{C}}-CH_2-CH(CH_3)_2} + POCl_3$$

Note that *geminal*-dihalides can be converted to aldehydes or ketones on treatment with ***dilute base*** but are converted to acetylenes with hot ***concentrated base***.

> Name the compounds in the above examples. Formulate the reaction of each halide with dilute and with concentrated base. Name the products.

## 8-5 HALIDE EXCHANGE: $S_N2$ AND $S_N1$ MECHANISMS

An excellent method of preparing simple alkyl iodides (not vinyl, aryl, or alkynyl halides) is the treatment of an alkyl chloride or bromide with sodium iodide in acetone. Sodium iodide forms a complex with acetone and is readily soluble; sodium bromide and sodium chloride are only sparingly soluble in hot acetone and precipitate as the reaction proceeds.

*General*: $$RCl\ (\text{or } RBr) + NaI \xrightarrow[\text{acetone}]{\Delta;\ \text{dry}} R-I + \underset{\text{insoluble in acetone}}{NaCl\downarrow\ (\text{or } NaBr)}$$

The mechanism for this reaction depends on the structure of the organic halide undergoing reaction. Primary and secondary halides are displaced by the nucleophile $I^-$ in a bimolecular slow step. Hence, this is known as an $S_N2$ reaction mechanism (***s***ubstitution, ***n***ucleophilic, ***bi***molecular). The displacement (substitution) occurs in such a way that the iodine-carbon bond is forming while the chlorine- or bromine-carbon bond is breaking. The reaction profile can be expressed by an energy diagram (Fig. 8-2). Although there are many transition states in this reaction, the one of highest energy is usually labeled on an energy diagram.

**Figure 8-2 Reaction profile of $S_N2$ displacement reactions**

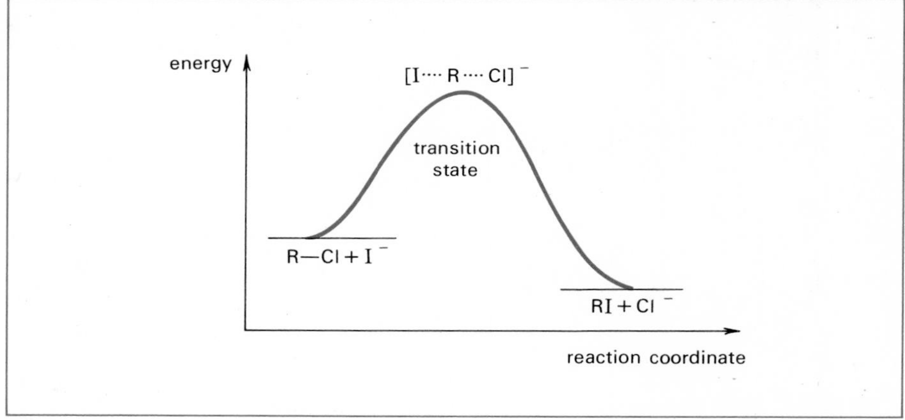


*Mechanism for primary and secondary halides*:

$$CH_3{-}CH_2{-}\underset{\displaystyle H}{\overset{\displaystyle CH_3}{\underset{|}{\overset{|}{C}}}}{-}Cl + I^- \xrightarrow[S_N2]{\text{slow}} \left[ \underset{\displaystyle H}{I\cdots \overset{Et\diagdown\ \diagup CH_3}{C}\cdots Cl} \right]^- \longrightarrow I{-}\underset{\displaystyle H}{\overset{\displaystyle CH_2CH_3}{\underset{|}{\overset{|}{C}}}}{-}CH_3 + Cl^-$$

transition state

Halides that form a relatively stable carbonium ion by ionization, such as tertiary alkyl, allyl, and benzyl halides, undergo unimolecular ionization as the slow step in this substitution.

*Mechanism for tertiary, allyl, and benzyl halides*:

$$CH_3{-}\underset{\displaystyle CH_3}{\overset{\displaystyle CH_2CH_3}{\underset{|}{\overset{|}{C}}}}{-}Cl + I^- \xrightarrow[S_N1]{\text{slow}} \left[ CH_3{-}\overset{+}{C}\begin{matrix} \diagup CH_2CH_3 \\ \diagdown CH_3 \end{matrix} \right] \longrightarrow CH_3{-}\underset{\displaystyle CH_3}{\overset{\displaystyle CH_2CH_3}{\underset{|}{\overset{|}{C}}}}{-}I + Cl^-$$

planar carbonium ion intermediate

This mechanism is characterized as an $S_N1$ mechanism (*s*ubstitution, *n*ucleophilic, *uni*molecular). Note that the reaction profile of an $S_N1$ reaction mechanism (Fig. 8-3) contains a small "valley," indicating the stability of the discrete carbonium ion intermediate formed in the slow step of this reaction. Although an $S_N1$ mechanism is characterized by the formation of a carbonium ion intermediate, there are many transition states involved: those leading up to the intermediate, which are indicative of the ionization process, and those going from the intermediate to products, which represent the carbon-iodine bond formation. The $S_N1$ and $S_N2$ mechanisms have very different stereochemical implications, as will be discussed in Chap. 12.

The role of the solvent in $S_N1$ reactions is very important. The more polar the solvent, the more readily is the carbon-halogen bond broken. Tertiary alkyl, allyl, and benzyl halides are not ionic compounds but ionize only in polar solvents, in which the charge on the carbonium ion can be dispersed by interaction with the electrons of the solvent.

$$(H_3C)_2\overset{\delta+}{C}{=}\overset{\delta-}{O}\cdots\overset{+}{C}\cdots\overset{\delta-}{O}{=}\overset{\delta+}{C}(CH_3)_2 \quad \text{with } \overset{+}{C}\cdots\overset{\delta-}{O}{=}\overset{\delta+}{C}(CH_3)_2$$

A characteristic side reaction which may be observed when an $S_N1$ mechanism is the predominant pathway is *elimination*, which is favored by the possible formation of highly substituted double bonds.

*Elimination side reaction*: $\left[CH_3{-}\overset{+}{C}(CH_3){-}CH(H)CH_3\right] \longrightarrow (H_3C)_2C{=}C(H)CH_3 + H^+$

Recall that a carbonium ion is also an intermediate in the acid-catalyzed dehydration of an alcohol (Sec. 4-1). In the example cited above, it would not be surprising to find at least small quantities of the corresponding olefin. The other olefin which might be formed would be less stable than the trisubstituted one.

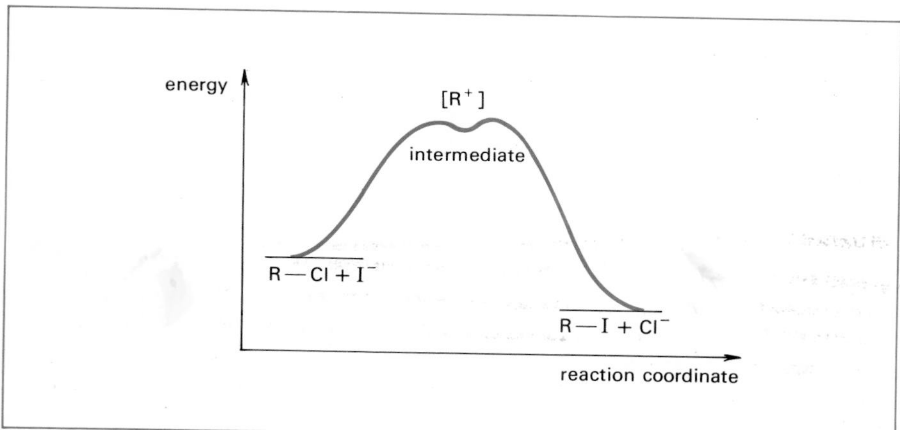


**Figure 8-3 Reaction profile of $S_N1$ displacement reactions**

## REACTIONS

### 8-6 HYDROLYSIS WITH DILUTE BASE

In general, halides (except aryl, vinyl, and alkynyl) are transformed to the corresponding alcohol by treatment with water or dilute base. Table 8-2 summarizes the mechanistic routes by which the simplest halides are solvolyzed.

**Table 8-2**
**Halide solvolysis**

| *Halide* | *Type* | *Mechanism* |
|---|---|---|
| $CH_3Cl$ | 1° | $S_N2$ |
| $CH_3CH_2Cl$ | 1° | $S_N2$ |
| $(CH_3)_2CHCl$ | 2° | mainly $S_N2$ |
| $(CH_3)_3CCl$ | 3° | $S_N1$ |

For some halides, particularly secondary halides, under certain conditions the $S_N1$ and $S_N2$ mechanistic pathways seem to compete as routes to observed products. With these compounds ***a high*** $OH^-$ ***concentration*** favors the $S_N2$ pathway, accompanied by fair amounts of products formed in an $E_2$ elimination (see Sec. 4-2); ***a low*** $OH^-$ ***concentration*** favors the $S_N1$ ionization, which is accompanied by lesser amounts of $E_1$ elimination products. There is little competition of the $S_N2$ substitution pathway for tertiary halides for two reasons: (1) ionization produces a relatively stable tertiary carbonium ion, and (2) the steric interference of the alkyl groups on the tertiary carbon effectively prevents the approach of the hydroxide ion or water molecule to the reacting carbon atom. After ionization and formation of a planar carbonium ion, the interference is much reduced.

Not only is the base concentration a factor in these solvolyses, but the polarity of the solvent is an important factor in determining the rate of reaction. Since the $S_N1$ pathway involves a carbonium ion intermediate and polar solvents will more readily solvate this ion, the $S_N1$ mechanism is favored by polar solvents. In the $S_N2$ pathway, the starting materials and the transition state are equally charged, and although polar solvents will slightly enhance the reaction rate, the degree of rate acceleration is not so great as that for an $S_N1$ reaction.

$$S_N1:\quad R{-}X \xrightarrow{\text{slow}} \underset{\text{intermediate}}{[R^+]} \xrightarrow[HO^-]{\text{fast}} \text{products}$$

$$S_N2:\quad R{-}X + OH^- \xrightarrow{\text{slow}} \underset{\text{transition state}}{[HO\cdots R\cdots X]^-} \longrightarrow \text{products}$$

## 8-7 GENERAL $S_N2$ REACTIONS OF HALIDES

Primary and secondary halides undergo $S_N2$ displacement by a variety of negative ions and nucleophilic molecules. Those which form new carbon-carbon bonds are especially useful for synthesizing new organic compounds. Listed in Table 8-3 are some general and specific examples; the last three are important alkylation reactions, which will be discussed in detail in Chap. 14.

**Table 8-3**
**General and specific examples of $S_N2$ reactions**

Halides to alcohols:

$$R{-}X + OH^- \longrightarrow R{-}OH + X^-$$

$$C_6H_{11}{-}Br + OH^- \longrightarrow C_6H_{11}{-}OH + Br^-$$

cyclohexyl bromide → cyclohexanol

Hydrolysis:

$$R{-}X + H_2O \longrightarrow R{-}OH + HX$$

$$CH_3CH_2CH_2Cl + H_2O \xrightarrow{\Delta} CH_3CH_2CH_2OH + HCl$$

*n*-propyl chloride → *n*-propyl alcohol

Williamson ether synthesis:

$$R{-}X + R'O^- \longrightarrow R{-}O{-}R' + X^-$$

primary or secondary alkyl halide; alkoxide ion; an ether

$$CH_3{-}I + CH_3CH_2O^-Na^+ \longrightarrow CH_3{-}O{-}CH_2{-}CH_3 + Na^+I^-$$

sodium ethoxide → methyl ethyl ether

Nitrile synthesis:

$$R{-}X + CN^- \longrightarrow R{-}CN + X^-$$

$$CH_3CH_2CH_2Br + CN^- \longrightarrow CH_3CH_2CH_2CN + Br^-$$

1-bromopropane → 1-cyanopropane (butyronitrile)

Acetylene synthesis:

$$R{-}X + R'{-}C{\equiv}C^- \longrightarrow R'{-}C{\equiv}C{-}R + X^-$$

$$CH_3I + CH_3{-}C{\equiv}C^-Na^+ \longrightarrow CH_3{-}C{\equiv}C{-}CH_3 + Na^+I^-$$

sodium methylacetylide → dimethylacetylene (2-butyne)

**Amine alkylation:**

$$R{-}X + 2NH_3 \longrightarrow R{-}NH_2 + NH_4I$$

This newly formed amine may react further with the alkyl halide

$$\underset{\text{ethyl iodide}}{CH_3CH_2I} + \underset{\text{ethylamine}}{CH_3CH_2NH_2} \longrightarrow \underset{\text{diethylamine}}{(CH_3CH_2)_2NH} + HI$$

**Malonic ester alkylation:**

$$R{-}X + {}^{-}CH(CO_2Et)(CO_2Et) \longrightarrow R{-}CH(CO_2Et)_2 + X^-$$

$$CH_3CH_2Br + \underset{\text{diethyl sodium malonate}}{Na^{+-}CH(CO_2Et)_2} \longrightarrow \underset{\text{diethyl ethylmalonate}}{CH_3CH_2{-}CH(CO_2Et)_2} + Na^+Br^-$$

**Acetoacetic ester synthesis:**

$$R{-}X + {}^{-}CH(COCH_3)(CO_2Et) \longrightarrow R{-}CH(COCH_3)(CO_2Et) + X^-$$

$$\underset{\text{2-phenyl-1-bromoethane}}{C_6H_5{-}CH_2CH_2Br} + \underset{\text{sodium ethyl acetoacetate}}{Na^{+-}CH(COCH_3)(CO_2Et)}$$

$$\downarrow$$

$$C_6H_5{-}CH_2CH_2{-}CH(COCH_3)(CO_2Et) + Na^+Br^-$$

**Cyanoacetic ester synthesis:**

$$R{-}X + {}^{-}CH(CN)(CO_2Et) \longrightarrow R{-}CH(CN)(CO_2Et) + X^-$$

$$CH_3I + \underset{\text{sodium ethyl cyanoacetate}}{Na^{+-}CH(CN)(CO_2Et)} \longrightarrow \underset{\text{ethyl methylcyanoacetate}}{CH_3{-}CH(CN)(CO_2Et)} + X^-$$

## 8-8 THE GRIGNARD REAGENT

The direct reaction of alkyl and aryl halides with metallic magnesium in a dry solvent gives the Grignard reagent, a valuable intermediate in synthetic organic chemistry.

$$R{-}X \quad (\text{or } Ar{-}X) \xrightarrow[\text{dry ether}]{\text{Mg in}} [R{-}Mg{-}X] \quad (\text{or } [Ar{-}Mg{-}X])$$

Use of this reagent in the preparation of hydrocarbons was illustrated in Chap. 2, and its use in the synthesis of alc[illegible] will be discussed in the next chapter.

## 8-9 AROMATIC CYANO SUBSTITUTION

Aromatic halides usually undergo nucleophilic substitution only when the system is activated by $-NO_2$, $-CN$, or other strongly electron-withdrawing groups. The replacement of halide by cyanide, however, is a useful reaction which can be carried out with KCN and $Cu_2(CN)_2$ in hot dimethylformamide (DMF), $(CH_3)_2N{-}CHO$; in hot pyridine; or in hot dimethylsulfoxide (DMSO), $CH_3{-}\overset{\overset{O}{\|}}{S}{-}CH_3$

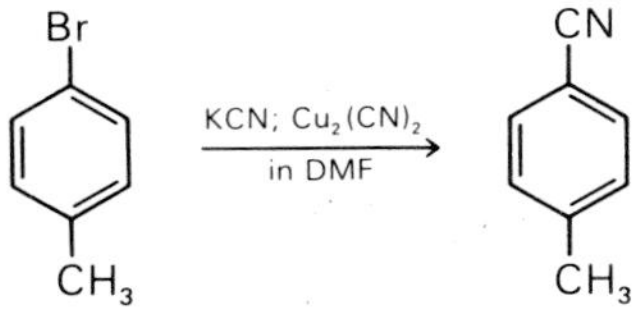

$$p\text{-}CH_3C_6H_4Br \xrightarrow[\text{in DMF}]{\text{KCN; } Cu_2(CN)_2} p\text{-}CH_3C_6H_4CN$$

*p*-bromotoluene *p*-cyanotoluene

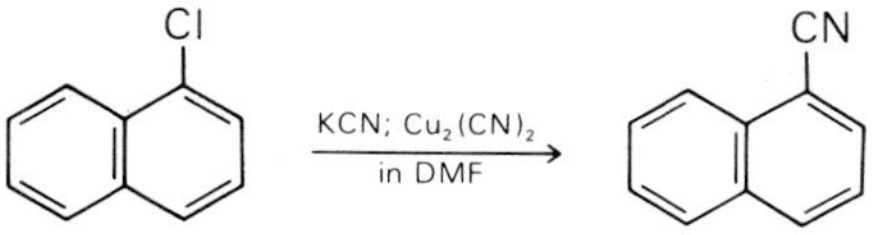

$$C_{10}H_7Cl \xrightarrow[\text{in DMF}]{\text{KCN; } Cu_2(CN)_2} C_{10}H_7CN$$

α-chloronaphthalene α-cyanonaphthalene

## 8-10 NUCLEOPHILIC AROMATIC SUBSTITUTION OF ACTIVATED SUBSTRATES

Aryl halides must be activated by strong electron-withdrawing substituents, such as $-NO_2$ or $-CN$, in the ortho and para positions in order to undergo a facile $S_N2$ reaction. Electron-withdrawing groups have very little effect when they occupy the meta position.

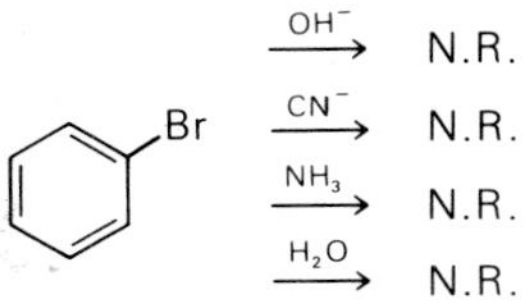

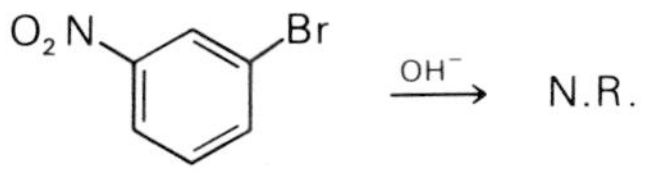

$$C_6H_5Br \xrightarrow{OH^-} \text{N.R.} \qquad C_6H_5Br \xrightarrow{CN^-} \text{N.R.} \qquad C_6H_5Br \xrightarrow{NH_3} \text{N.R.} \qquad C_6H_5Br \xrightarrow{H_2O} \text{N.R.}$$

$$m\text{-}O_2N{-}C_6H_4{-}Br \xrightarrow{OH^-} \text{N.R.}$$

The preparation of picric acid from 2,4,6-trinitrochlorobenzene with base illustrates this displacement when activating groups are at the ortho and para positions.

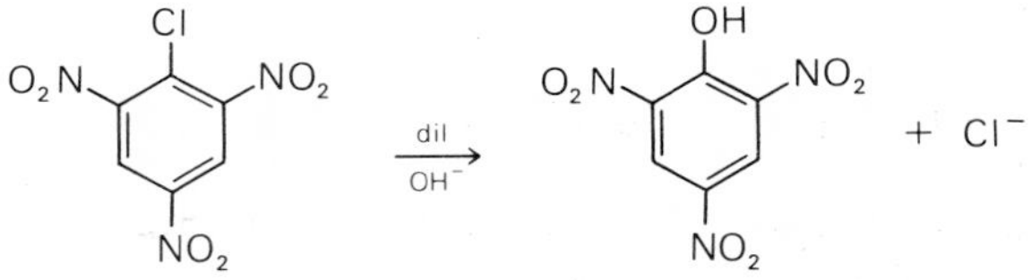

Cl O$_2$N NO$_2$ NO$_2$ $\xrightarrow[OH^-]{dil}$ OH O$_2$N NO$_2$ NO$_2$ + $Cl^-$

picric acid

The factors determining the ease and mechanism of this substitution can be seen by looking at the hydrolysis of a simpler compound, *p*-nitrobromobenzene. The activating group is the same, and any resonance effects due to the nitro group in the para position hold equally well for the two ortho nitro groups.

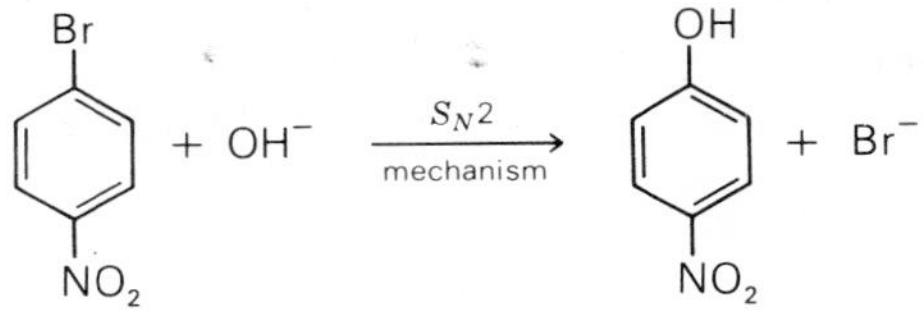

Br NO$_2$ + $OH^-$ $\xrightarrow[\text{mechanism}]{S_N2}$ OH NO$_2$ + $Br^-$

*p*-nitrobromobenzene *p*-nitrophenol

*Mechanism*: The resonance forms for the starting material indicate a low electron density at the halogen-bearing carbon. Similar forms can be written for the ortho nitrohalobenzenes.

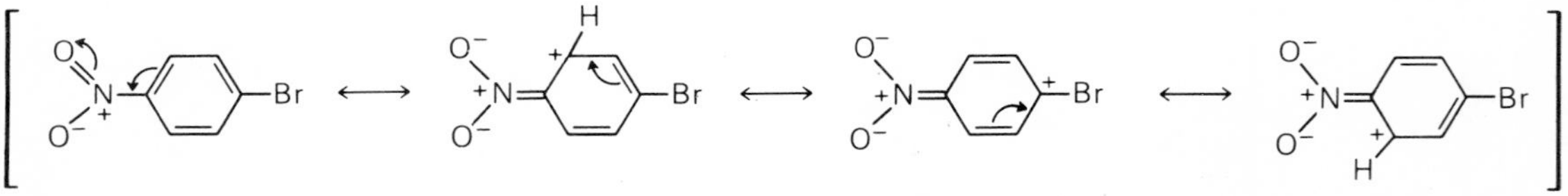

resonance structures of *p*-nitrobromobenzene

This facilitates attack by the hydroxide ion or other nucleophile. Loss of the $Br^-$ ion yields *p*-nitrophenol.

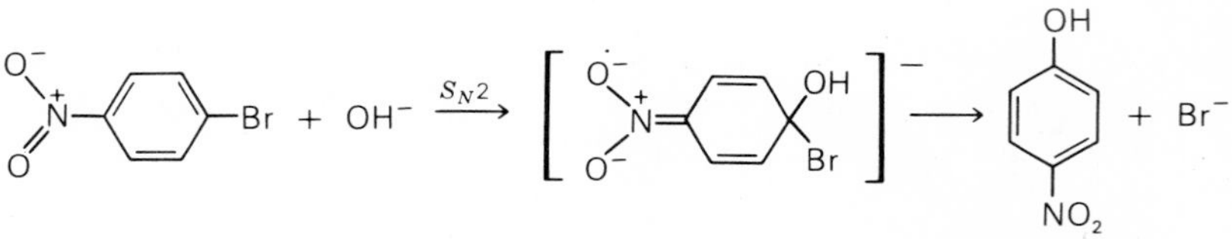

+ $OH^-$ $\xrightarrow{S_N2}$ [ ]$^-$ ⟶ + $Br^-$

Why do meta nitro groups have very little effect?

The $S_N1$ pathway is not a feasible mechanism for displacement of aromatic halides, since the halogen is tightly bound to the carbon atom. The valence-bond description attributes some double-bond character to the carbon-halogen bond; the molecular-orbital picture shows the halogen-aromatic-ring overlap.

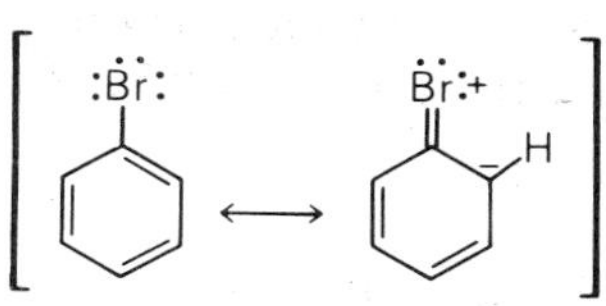

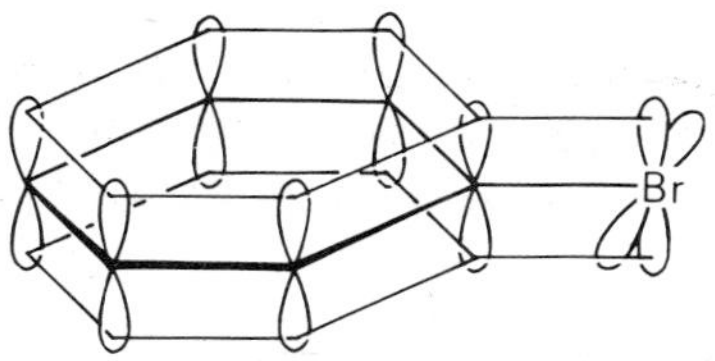

:Br: ⟷ Br:+ H

Br

## 8-11 BENZYNES; DIELS-ALDER REACTIONS AND CYCLOADDITIONS

Treatment of *o*-bromofluorobenzene with reagents which form organometallic compounds at the carbon-bromine bond leads to products arising from ***benzyne***, a very reactive intermediate.

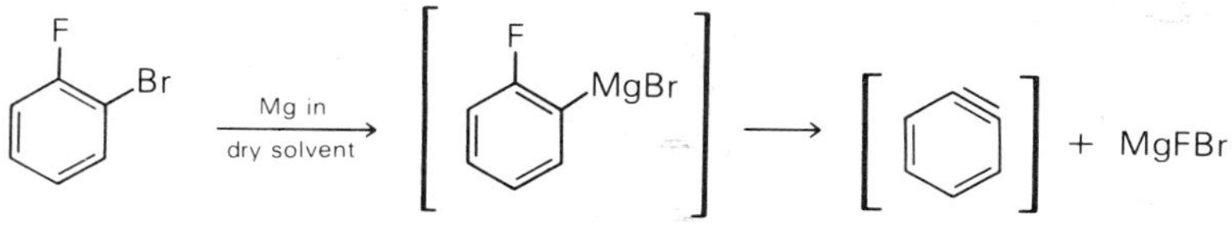

F, Br —Mg in dry solvent→ [F, MgBr] → [benzyne] + MgFBr

benzyne intermediate

The newly-formed "triple bond" in the aromatic system reacts rapidly with itself or gives Diels-Alder reaction products in the presence of reactive dienes.

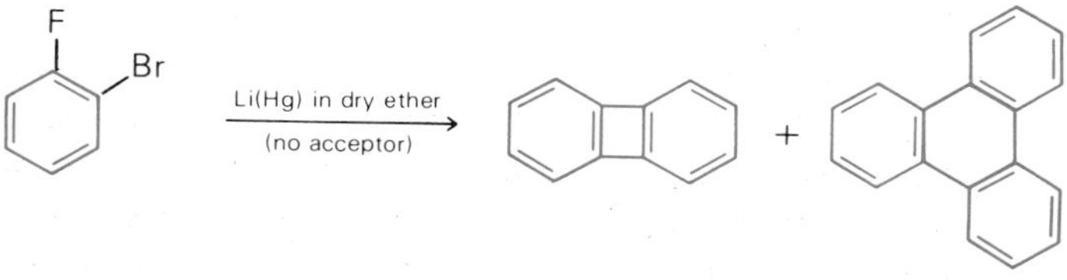

F, Br —Li(Hg) in dry ether (no acceptor)→ diphenylene 24% + triphenylene 3%

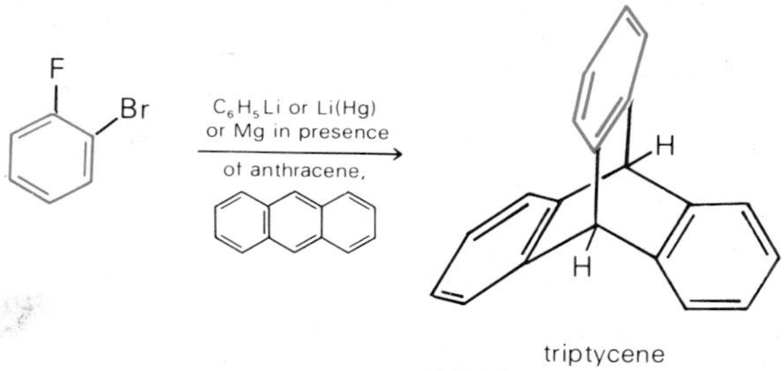

F, Br —$C_6H_5Li$ or Li(Hg) or Mg in presence of anthracene→ triptycene (H, H)

triptycene
28% (from Mg in dry THF)

F, Br — Mg in dry furan →

naphthalene-1, 4-epoxide

Benzyne intermediates can also be generated from aryl halides by other reagents, such as $NaNH_2$. The diazonium salt derived from anthranilic acid has also been used as an intermediate.

$NH_2$, $CO_2H$ — HONO; diazotization in base → [ $N_2^+$, $CO_2^-$ ] —Δ→ [ ] + $N_2$ + $CO_2$

anthranilic acid

Use of the benzyne intermediate allows the formation of products which are difficult to obtain by other means. Substituted triptycenes, for example, are now readily prepared.

F, Br — [ $N_2^+$, $CO_2^-$ ] Δ; Y →  Y

## QUALITATIVE ANALYSIS

Alkyl and aryl halides are insoluble in cold concentrated sulfuric acid and can be separated from many polar impurities in this manner. Other qualitative tests are like those for inorganic halides. In the Beilstein test (not for F), a copper wire which has been heated to redness is reheated with a trace of a halogen-containing compound. A characteristic green flame indicates the presence of a halogen.

A solution of alcoholic silver nitrate on treatment with an alkyl (*not* ordinary aryl) halide gives a precipitate of the silver halide. The ionizing conditions lead to reaction via the $S_N1$ pathway, the most immediate positive tests being given by those halides which form a stable carbonium ion intermediate.

| allyl, benzyl, 3° | >> | 2° > 1° | >> | vinyl, aryl, $CHCl_3$, $CCl_4$ |
|---|---|---|---|---|
| immediate precipitate | | very rapid precipitation | | inert |

The order of halogen reactivity is

I > Br > Cl

Organic fluorides do not react under these conditions.

## SUGGESTED READINGS

### Synthesis and reactions

Berliner, E.: The Current State of Positive Halogenating Agents, *J. Chem. Educ.*, **43**, 124 (1966).

Bunnett, J. F.: The Chemistry of Benzyne, *J. Chem. Educ.*, **38**, 278 (1961).

Goldwhite, H.: The Side-chain Halogenation of *n*-Alkyl Benzenes, *J. Chem. Educ.*, **37**, 295 (1960).

Ibne-Rasa, K. M.: Equations for Correlation of Nucleophilic Reactivity, *J. Chem. Educ.*, **44**, 89 (1967). Extensive discussion of nucleophiles and their reactions.

Joiner, C. R.: Pesticide Residue Control under the Food, Drug, and Cosmetic Act, *J. Chem. Educ.*, **38**, 370 (1961). Describes the common chlorinated hydrocarbon pesticides and how they are detected in food.

### Kinetics

DeWolfe, R. H.: Kinetics in the Study of Organic Reaction Mechanisms, *J. Chem. Educ.*, **40**, 95 (1963).

Zimmerman, H. K.: Method for Determining Order of a Reaction, *J. Chem. Educ.*, **40**, 356 (1963).

## PROBLEMS

★**1.** Draw a structure and name the example for each of the following:

(*a*) an 8-carbon benzylic fluoride

(*b*) two 4-carbon primary chlorides

(*c*) a 6-carbon aryl bromide

(*d*) three 10-carbon diiodides containing a benzylic and an aryl halogen

(*e*) two 5-carbon secondary dibromides

(*f*) five 10-carbon primary trifluorides

(*g*) two 7-carbon tertiary chlorides

★**2.** Give a specific example of a halide containing seven carbons which undergoes an $S_N2$ displacement with dilute base. Sketch and label the energy diagram for this reaction.

★**3.** Give a specific example of a halide containing three carbons which undergoes an $S_N1$ hydrolysis. Draw and label the energy diagram for this reaction.

**4.** Give a specific example of:

★(*a*) nucleophilic aromatic displacement of a fluorine atom by ammonia

(*b*) the synthesis of

R
R

using a benzyne intermediate

★(*c*) a solvolysis which proceeds faster in acetone than in chloroform, (***Hint***: Which is the more polar solvent?)

(*d*) the synthesis of $(R)_2C(CO_2Et)_2$

(*e*) the addition of a hydrogen halide to a double bond (show mechanism)

(*f*) the use of *N*-bromosuccinimide to prepare a naphthalene-containing compound

★(*g*) the free-radical chlorination of an aryl methyl group

(*h*) seven different halogen-containing compounds which give a negative silver nitrate test

★(*i*) a tertiary halide which gives a negative Beilstein test

(*j*) the preparation of a 7-carbon ***geminal***-dihalide which is subsequently treated with $NaNH_2$

★(*k*) a reaction with alkoxide ion

★**5.** Although the low-temperature bromination of propene in solution yields 1,2-dibromopropane, the high-temperature (200°) gas-phase bromination yields 3-bromopropene. Explain fully.

**6.** Name the starting material and give the structural formula *and* name of the product. If no reaction occurs, write N.R. Describe by a phrase or a few words the type of mechanism by which the reaction proceeds.

(*a*) $\xrightarrow{Br_2}$

(*b*) Br $\xrightarrow{\text{dil. } OH^-}$

(*c*) Br $\xrightarrow[\text{KOH}]{\text{alc}}$

(*d*) O, N—Br, O + $\xrightarrow[\Delta]{H_2O}$

(*e*) $CH_3$, $CH_3$ + O, N—Br, O $\xrightarrow[h\nu]{\Delta}$

(*f*) $CH_3$ $\xrightarrow[h\nu]{Br_2}$ (main product)

(*g*) product in (*f*) $\xrightarrow{H_2O}$

(*h*) $CH_3CH_2CH_2O^-K^+$ + $CH_2—CH_2—Br$ $\longrightarrow$

(*i*) Bromobenzene $\xrightarrow{NH_3}$

(*j*) o-Bromonitrobenzene (Br, $NO_2$) $\xrightarrow{KCN}$

★ (*k*) Bromobenzene $\xrightarrow{KCN}$

(*l*) o-Bromotoluene (Br, $CH_3$) $\xrightarrow[\text{in pyridine}]{KCN \; Cu_2(CN)_2,\ \Delta}$

(*m*) $^{-}CH(CO_2CH_3)(CN)$ + $C_6H_5CH_2CH_2Br$ $\longrightarrow$

★(*n*) o-Bromofluorobenzene (F, Br) $\xrightarrow[\text{dry ether}]{\text{Mg in}}$

(*o*) Benzene $\xrightarrow[FeBr_3]{Br_2}$

(*p*) product in (*o*) $\xrightarrow[\Delta]{Cu}$ $C_{12}H_{10}$

(*q*) Benzene $\xrightarrow[h\nu]{Br_2}$

(*r*) p-Xylene ($CH_3$, $CH_3$) (xs) $\xrightarrow[h\nu]{Br_2}$

(*s*) product in (*r*) $\xrightarrow{Na}$

★(*t*) m-Bromonitrobenzene (Br, $NO_2$) $\xrightarrow{H_2O}$

(*u*) Bromobenzene + $CH_3—C\equiv\bar{C}\overset{+}{Na}$ $\longrightarrow$

(*v*) $CH_3—\underset{\underset{O}{\|}}{C}—C_6H_5$ $\xrightarrow[\text{2. } NaNH_2]{\text{1. } PBr_5}$

(*w*) $C_6H_5CCl_3$ $\xrightarrow[AgNO_3]{\text{alc.}}$

## REVIEW PROBLEM SET FOR CHAPS. 1 TO 8

**1.** Determine whether or not the following molecules have dipole moments and indicate their direction:

(*a*) durene (1,2,4,5-tetramethylbenzene: $H_3C$, $CH_3$, $H_3C$, $CH_3$)

durene

(*d*) $C_6H_5—\overset{\overset{O}{\|}}{C}—C_6H_5$

benzophenone

(*b*) *cis*-1,2-dimethylcyclopropane

(*c*) *trans*-2-butene

(*e*) carbon dioxide, $CO_2$

(*f*) carbon monoxide, CO

**2.** Write Lewis structures (dot formulas) for the following molecules, indicating formal charges where appropriate.

(*a*) phosphoric acid, $H_3PO_4$

(*b*) dimethyl sulfoxide, $CH_3—\overset{\overset{\displaystyle O}{\|}}{S}—CH_3$ (DMSO)

(*c*) nitrous oxide, $N_2O$ (has a N—N bond)

(*d*) tetramethylammonium chloride (ionic)

(*e*) hydrazoic acid, $HN_3$ (linear)

**3.** (*a*) Because of the resonance stabilization of the resulting anions, certain compounds are more acidic than might otherwise be expected. Draw reasonable resonance structures for the anions of the following compounds formed by removal of a hydrogen atom from the position indicated.

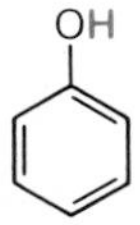

phenol (benzene ring bearing OH)

$CH_3NO_2$ nitromethane

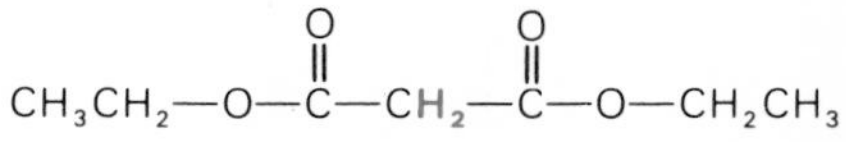

$CH_3CH_2—O—\overset{\overset{\displaystyle O}{\|}}{C}—CH_2—\overset{\overset{\displaystyle O}{\|}}{C}—O—CH_2CH_3$ diethyl malonate

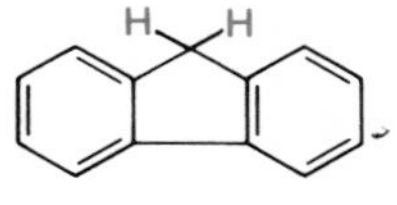

fluorene (H, H on the central $CH_2$)

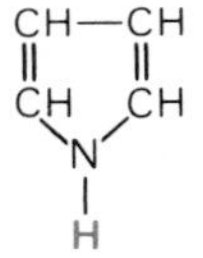

pyrrole: CH=CH, CH, CH, N—H ring

(*b*) Draw the LCAO (molecular-orbital) pictures for the anions of the compounds in part (*a*).

**4.** Name the following compounds:

(*a*) $CH_3—CH_2—\underset{\underset{\displaystyle C_6H_5}{|}}{CH}—\overset{\overset{\displaystyle OH}{|}}{CH}—$(cyclopropyl)

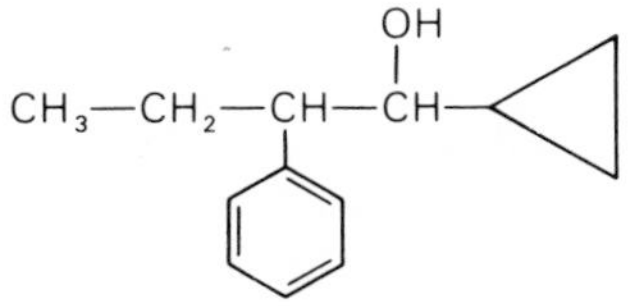

(*b*) cyclohexane chair with H and OH on one carbon, HO and H on another

(*c*) cyclohexadiene ring with $H_3C$ and $CH_3$ on one carbon

(*d*) $\underset{\underset{\displaystyle CH_3}{|}}{CH_3—CH}$—CH=CH—$CH_2—\overset{\overset{\displaystyle CH_3}{|}}{CH}—CH_3$ (H, H on the double-bond carbons, trans)

(*e*) $CH_3—\overset{\overset{\displaystyle CH_3}{|}}{CH}—\overset{\overset{\displaystyle CH_3}{|}}{CH}—CH_2—CH_2—\underset{\underset{\displaystyle CH_3}{|}}{\overset{\overset{\displaystyle CH_3}{|}}{C}}—CH_3$

(*f*) benzene ring with Br and $NO_2$ on adjacent carbons

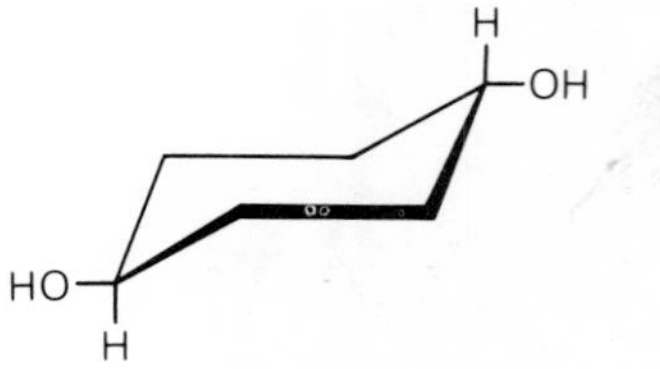

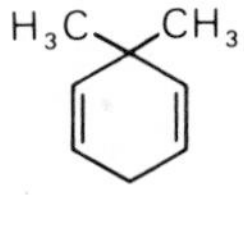

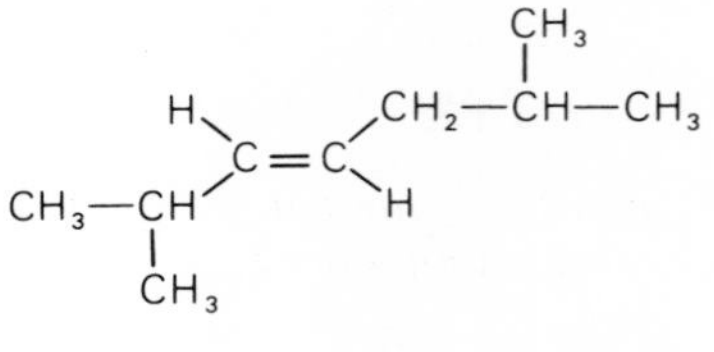

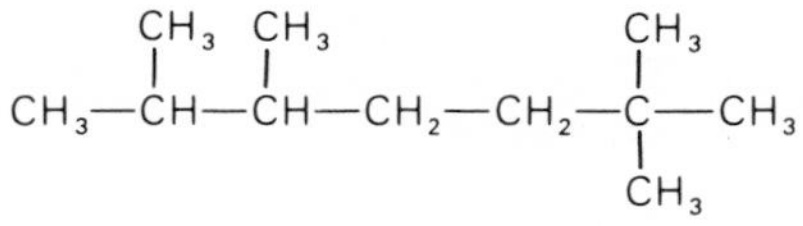

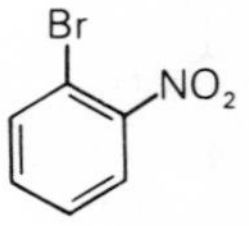

**5.** Write the structural formulas of the following compounds:

(*a*) ***trans*-4-*tert***-butylcyclohexylmagnesium bromide

(*b*) *o*-nitroethylbenzene

(*c*) 1-methylcyclopentanol

(*d*) vinylcyclohexane

(*e*) ***cis***-1,4-cyclohexanediol

(*f*) 3-(*p*-bromophenyl)-1-pentene

(*g*) phenylallylacetylene

**6.** Name the starting materials and give the structural formula and name of the product(s). If no reaction occurs, write N.R.

(*a*) $CH_3—C{\equiv}C—H \xrightarrow[H_2SO_4]{H_2O;\ Hg^{++}SO_4^{--}}$

(*b*) $C_6H_5—C{\equiv}C—H \xrightarrow{Cu(NH_3)_2^+}$

(*c*) $H_5C_6(H)C{=}C(C_6H_5)H \xrightarrow[CH_2I_2]{\text{Zn-Cu couple}}$

(*d*) $CH_3CHBrCHBrCH_3 \xrightarrow{Zn}$

(*e*) 1,2-dimethylcyclohexene $\xrightarrow[\text{pressure}]{H_2/Pd}$ (show the preferred conformation)

(*f*) cyclohexene $\xrightarrow[\text{work-up}]{O_3;\ \text{oxidative}}$

(*g*) cyclohexene $\xrightarrow[\Delta \text{ or } h\nu]{NBS}$

(*h*) $C_6H_5C(CH_3)_3 \xrightarrow[1.1 \text{ equiv } AlCl_3 \text{ in } CS_2]{CH_3COCl}$

(*i*) $C_6H_5—CH(OH)—CH_3 \xrightarrow{PBr_5}$

(*j*) $[CH_3MgBr] \xrightarrow[2.\ H_3O^+]{1.\ CO_2}$

**7.** Compound **A**, $C_{14}H_{12}$, gives no reaction with $Ag(NH_3)_2^+$ but decolorizes bromine, yielding compound **B**, $C_{14}H_{12}Br_2$. Treatment of **B** with alcoholic KOH gives compound **C**, $C_{14}H_{10}$, which still gives no reaction with $Ag(NH_3)_2^+$. Ozonization of **A** followed by reductive work-up yields only benzaldehyde. Give the structures of **A**, **B**, and **C**.

**8.** Compound **A**, $C_{10}H_{20}O_2$, reacted with acetyl chloride to give compound **B**, $C_{14}H_{24}O_4$. Dehydration of **A** gave compound **C**, $C_{10}H_{16}$, which gave no Diels-Alder adduct with maleic anhydride. Hydrogenation of **C** gave compound **D**, $C_{10}H_{20}$. Compound **C** readily decolorized bromine, affording **E**, which gave compound **F**, $C_{10}H_{12}$, on treatment with alcoholic KOH. F liberated 2 moles of methane on treatment with $CH_3MgCl$ and gave **D** on hydrogenation.

$KMnO_4$ oxidation of **C** gave a diacid which readily lost $CO_2$ (indicating that both carboxyl groups are on the same carbon) affording compound **G**. Treatment of cyclohexylmagnesium iodide with $CO_2$ and then with water gave **G**.

Give the structure of compounds **A** to **G**.

# Part Two:
# Oxygen- and Nitrogen-containing Organic Compounds

# Chapter Nine

## NOMENCLATURE

The class of compounds known as ***alcohols*** contains an —OH group attached to a saturated carbon atom. The IUPAC ending for alcohols is *-ol*. The corresponding aromatic compounds, ***phenols***, Ar—OH, have different chemical properties and undergo reactions different from those of alcohols (see Chap. 10). The saturated alcohols belong to the $C_nH_{2n+2}O$ homologous series, as do the corresponding saturated ethers, R—O—R. Compare the formula and structure of ethyl alcohol, $CH_3—CH_2\ddot{\underset{..}{O}}H$, with those of dimethyl ether, $CH_3—\ddot{\underset{..}{O}}—CH_3$.

> To what homologous series does allyl alcohol, $CH_2{=}CH—CH_2OH$, belong? Which other classes of compounds belong to this same series? Illustrate with specific examples.

Alcohols are designated primary, secondary, or tertiary, depending on the degree of substitution of the carbon atom to which the —OH functional group is attached (see Table 9-1).

Examples of alcohols which do not belong to the saturated series are shown in Table 9-2. Note that some may also be classified as allylic or benzylic alcohols. Compounds with two and three —OH functional groups are ***diols*** and ***triols***.

> **1.** Classify each of the alcohols in Table 9-1 as primary, secondary or tertiary.
>
> **2.** Write the structure for each $C_5$ alcohol in this homologous series and name it according to the IUPAC system.
>
> **3.** The $C_5$ alcohols are called pentyl alcohols in the trivial system. Following the trivial names for the butanols, can you assign a trivial name to each of the $C_5$ alcohols? (***Hint***: One is named neopentyl alcohol.)

# Alcohols

**Table 9-1**
**Nomenclature of the $C_1$ to $C_4$ alcohols**

| | | |
|---|---|---|
| $C_1$: | $CH_3OH$<br>methanol<br>(methyl alcohol) | |
| $C_2$: | $CH_3CH_2OH$<br>ethanol<br>(ethyl alcohol) | |
| $C_3$: | $CH_3CH_2CH_2OH$<br>1-propanol<br>(*n*-propyl alcohol) | $CH_3\underset{\substack{\vert \\ OH}}{C}HCH_3$<br>2-propanol<br>(isopropyl alcohol) |
| $C_4$: | $CH_3CH_2CH_2CH_2OH$<br>1-butanol<br>(*n*-butyl alcohol) | $CH_3\underset{\substack{\vert \\ OH}}{C}HCH_2CH_3$<br>2-butanol<br>(*sec*-butyl alcohol) |
| | $CH_3\underset{\substack{\vert \\ CH_3}}{C}HCH_2OH$<br>2-methyl-1-propanol<br>(isobutyl alcohol) | $CH_3{-}\overset{\substack{CH_3 \\ \vert}}{\underset{\substack{\vert \\ CH_3}}{C}}{-}OH$<br>2-methyl-2-propanol<br>(*tert*-butyl alcohol) |

**Table 9-2 Examples of alcohol nomenclature**

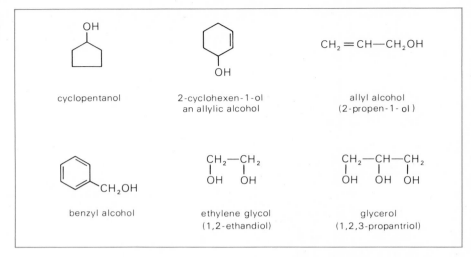

| | | |
|---|---|---|
| cyclopentanol | 2-cyclohexen-1-ol<br>an allylic alcohol | $CH_2{=}CH{-}CH_2OH$<br>allyl alcohol<br>(2-propen-1-ol) |
| $C_6H_5CH_2OH$<br>benzyl alcohol | $HOCH_2{-}CH_2OH$<br>ethylene glycol<br>(1,2-ethandiol) | $HOCH_2{-}CH(OH){-}CH_2OH$<br>glycerol<br>(1,2,3-propantriol) |

## HYDROGEN BONDING

Comparison of the boiling points of the hydrogen halides with their molecular weights reveals the abnormally high boiling point of HF (Fig. 9-1).

| | HF | HCl | HBr | HI |
|---|---|---|---|---|
| b.p. | 19° | −84° | −67° | −35° |
| mol. wt. | 20 | 36.5 | 81 | 128 |

A similar comparison of the boiling points of a series of organic compounds of approximately the same molecular weight shows that alcohols and acids also have higher boiling points than hydrocarbons, halides, or ethers.

| | $CH_3CH_2CH_2CH_2CH_3$ | $CH_3CH_2CH_2Cl$ | $CH_3CH_2OCH_2CH_3$ |
|---|---|---|---|
| b.p. | 36° | 47° | 35° |
| mol. wt. | 72 | 78.5 | 74 |

| $CH_3CH_2CH_2CH_2OH$ | $CH_3CH_2COOH$ |
|---|---|
| 118° | 141° |
| 74 | 74 |

These differences can be explained in terms of the additional energy required to break the weak bonds between molecules of HF, alcohols, and acids during vaporization. These bonds, called ***hydrogen bonds*** are

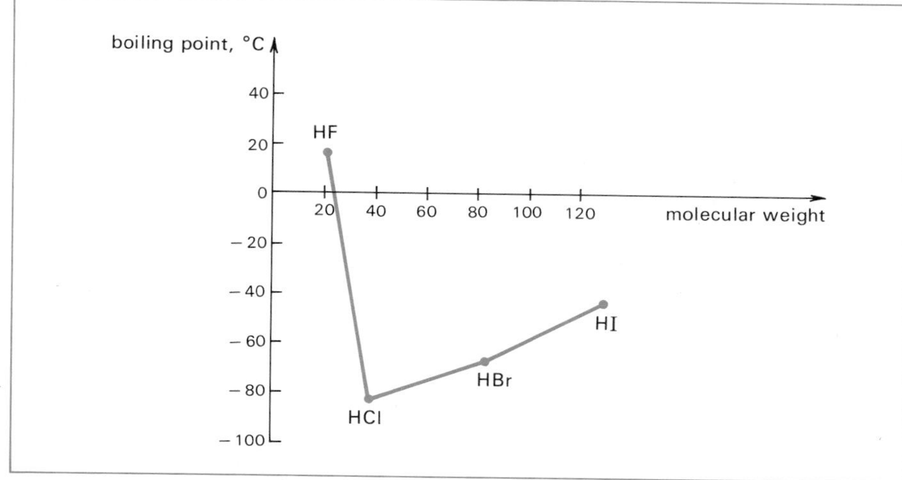


**Figure 9-1 Boiling points of hydrogen halides**

formed when a hydrogen atom acts as a bridge between two very electronegative elements (commonly, fluorine, oxygen, and nitrogen) (see Fig. 9-2). Although hydrogen bonds are weak compared to ionic or covalent bonds, they can be significant in accounting for the relative boiling points of alcohols, acids, and other similar polar compounds. Hydrogen bonding between different parts of the same molecule (***intramolecular bonds***) often determines the preferred configuration of the molecule. Some examples of intermolecular and intramolecular

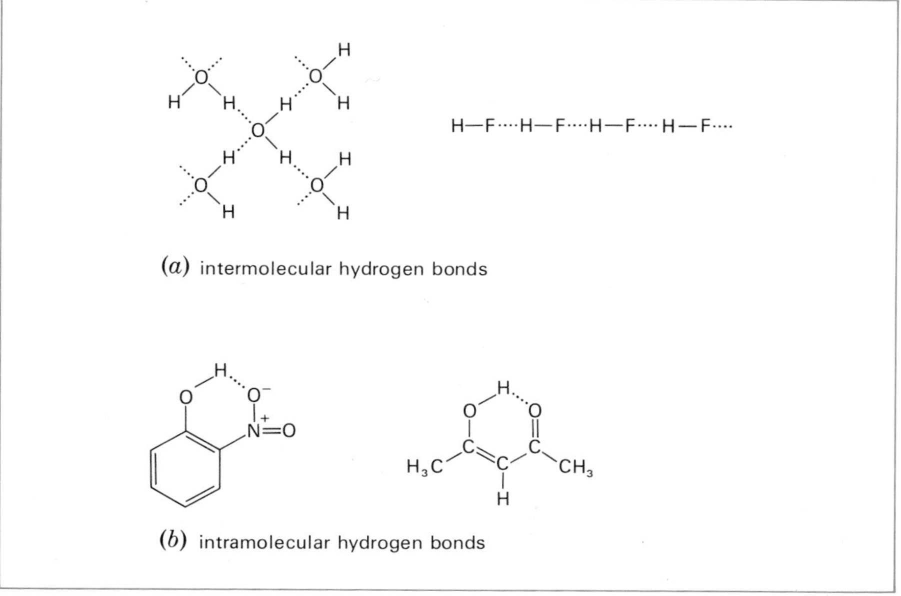


**Figure 9-2 Hydrogen-bonded molecules**

hydrogen-bonded molecules are shown in Fig. 9-2. Hydrogen-bonded molecules are also said to be ***associated***.

It must be emphasized that electronegative elements can participate in hydrogen bonding only when the geometry permits the proton to overlap with the orbitals of these atoms. For intramolecular hydrogen bonding, ring size is an important factor, and a hydrogen-bonded ring other than a five- or a six-membered one is rare. Carbon is not very electronegative, and thus hydrogen bonding is seldom found to be important between carbon and hydrogen in ordinary organic molecules.

## REACTIONS

### 9-1 REACTIONS WITH METALS

Most alkali metals (Li, Na, K) and alkaline-earth metals (Mg, Ca, Ba) will react with $C_1$ to $C_8$ alcohols. Aluminum also reacts slowly with these compounds. These reactions, in which the alcohol loses a hydrogen ion, demonstrate the very weak acidity of alcohols.

*General*: $R{-}OH + Na \longrightarrow R{-}O^- Na^+ + \frac{1}{2}H_2\uparrow$

an alkoxide

*Specific*: $(CH_3)_3C{-}OH + K \longrightarrow (CH_3)_3C{-}O^-K^+ + \frac{1}{2}H_2\uparrow$

*tert*-butyl alcohol — potassium *tert*-butoxide

The saltlike products, $RO^-M^+$, are known as ***alkoxides***; for example, $CH_3CH_2O^-Na^+$ is sodium ethoxide. Alkoxides are strong bases which give the original alcohol and hydroxide ions on treatment with water.

$$CH_3O^- Na^+ + H_2O \longrightarrow CH_3OH + Na^+ OH^-$$

sodium methoxide — methanol

### 9-2 INORGANIC ACID HALIDES OF PHOSPHORUS AND SULFUR

The phosphorus halides are often employed in the synthesis of organic halides from alcohols, where relatively mild conditions are desirable (Sec. 8-4). The compounds commonly available are phosphorus trichloride, $PCl_3$, phosphorus pentachloride, $PCl_5$, phosphorus tribromide, $PBr_3$, and phosphorus pentabromide, $PBr_5$. The latter is prepared directly: $PBr_3 + Br_2 \longrightarrow PBr_5$. Although the corresponding iodides are not used, the combination of ***red*** phosphorus and iodine can be used to produce alkyl iodides.

$$CH_3CH_2CH_2CH_2OH \xrightarrow[I_2;\ \Delta]{\text{red P}} CH_3CH_2CH_2CH_2I + H_3PO_3$$

Often $PBr_3$ (or red phosphorus and bromine) is chosen as the reagent for the preparation of secondary and tertiary halides from the corresponding alcohols, since the use of HBr may cause extensive elimination and rearrangement of these alcohols (see Sec. 9-4).

Of the sulfur-containing halides, thionyl chloride, $SOCl_2$, provides alkyl chlorides of high purity, since the other products of the reaction are gases.

$$CH_3CH(OH)CH_3 + SOCl_2 \longrightarrow CH_3CH(Cl)CH_3 + SO_2\uparrow + HCl\uparrow$$

Thionyl chloride and phosphorus trichloride and pentachloride are also used in the preparation of acid chlorides from acids (Sec. 7-10). Of these three reagents, only $PCl_5$ or $PBr_5$ is generally used for the preparation of *geminal*-dihalides from aldehydes and ketones.

$$C_6H_5-\overset{O}{\overset{\|}{C}}-H \xrightarrow{PCl_5} C_6H_5CHCl_2 + POCl_3$$

benzaldehyde — benzal chloride — phosphorus oxychloride

## 9-3 HYDROGEN HALIDES

Many of the common alcohols are commercially available, and most others can be synthesized by use of the appropriate Grignard reagent (see Sec. 9-14 to 9-16). The reaction of an alcohol with a hydrogen halide is a convenient pathway to the corresponding halide. Often a small quantity of sulfuric acid is added as a catalyst. The order of reactivity of the hydrogen halides is HI > HBr > HCl.

*General*: $R{-}OH + HX \underset{}{\overset{H^+}{\rightleftharpoons}} R{-}X + H_2O$

*Example*: $CH_3CH_2CH_2CH_2OH \xrightarrow[\text{or 48\% HBr}]{H_2SO_4\ +\ NaBr} CH_3CH_2CH_2CH_2Br + H_2O$

*n*-butyl alcohol — *n*-butyl bromide

The mechanism for a specific example is shown below.

*Overall*: $(CH_3)_3C{-}OH + HI \longrightarrow (CH_3)_3C{-}I + H_2O$

*Mechanism*: $(CH_3)_3C{-}\ddot{\underset{..}{O}}{-}H \overset{H^+}{\rightleftharpoons} \left[(CH_3)_3C{-}\overset{H}{\underset{+}{\ddot{O}}}{-}H\right]$

an oxonium ion

$$\left[ (CH_3)_3C-\overset{H}{\underset{+}{\ddot{O}}}\ H \right] \underset{\text{slow}}{\rightleftharpoons} (CH_3)_3C^+ + H_2O \qquad \left[ (CH_3)_3C^+ \right] \xrightarrow[\text{fast}]{I^-} (CH_3)_3CI$$

a carbonium ion (the tertiary butyl carbonium ion)

*Side reaction. elimination*:

$$\left[ H-\overset{H}{\underset{H}{C}}-\overset{+}{C}\begin{matrix} CH_3 \\ CH_3 \end{matrix} \right] \longrightarrow (CH_3)_2C=CH_2 + H^+$$

The formation of the oxonium ion (or oxonium salt) in the first step is a reversible acid-base reaction. Water is a good ''leaving group,'' and the subsequent reaction of the carbonium ion is rapid.

In the case of ethanol and many other simple primary alcohols only small amounts of elimination (dehydration) products are obtained. For secondary alcohols elimination becomes more important. With tertiary alcohols, the olefin or a mixture of possible olefins is often the major product under these conditions. The use of sulfur or phosphorus halides gives a smaller proportion of elimination products.

The relative rate of reaction of various alcohols with hydrochloric acid in the presence of a catalytic amount of zinc chloride provides a basis of identification known as the ***Lucas test*** (Sec. 9-18). For the present it should be noted that the reaction of a primary alcohol with HCl ***requires*** a catalyst ($ZnCl_2$) in order to form good yields of the alkyl chloride in a reasonable time. Secondary, tertiary, allyl, and benzyl alcohols react fairly rapidly without catalysis.

## 9-4 DEHYDRATION OF ALCOHOLS

The acid-catalyzed dehydration of alcohols has already been discussed (Sec. 4-1), but note here the possible rearrangement of the initial intermediate carbonium ion to a more stable one.

*Overall*: $CH_3CH_2CH_2CH_2OH \xrightarrow[HBr]{H^+} CH_3CH_2CH_2CH_2Br$

1-butanol → 1-bromobutane

Side products: $CH_3CH_2CH=CH_2$ and $CH_3-CH=CH-CH_3$

1-butene, 2-butene

Write the mechanism for the formation of the major product, 1-bromobutane, and of the terminal olefin side product. (***Hint***: See the example in Sec. 9-3.)

*Mechanism*: Formation of 2-butene:

$$CH_3CH_2CH_2CH_2OH \xrightleftharpoons{H^+} [CH_3CH_2CH_2CH_2{-}\overset{+}{O}H_2] \qquad \text{Step 1}$$

$$[CH_3CH_2CH_2CH_2{-}\overset{+}{O}H_2] \xrightleftharpoons{-H_2O} [CH_3CH_2CH_2CH_2^+] \qquad \text{Step 2}$$

$$\left[CH_3{-}CH_2{-}CH_2{-}\overset{+}{C}H_2\right] \xrightarrow{\text{1,2 hydride shift}} \left[CH_3{-}CH_2{-}\overset{+}{C}H{-}CH_3\right] \qquad \text{Step 3}$$

1° carbonium ion — 2° carbonium ion

$$\left[CH_3{-}CH_2{-}\overset{+}{C}H{-}CH_3\right] \longrightarrow CH_3{-}CH{=}CH{-}CH_3 + H^+ \qquad \text{Step 4}$$

The formation of the *n*-butyl carbonium ion in steps 1 and 2 is similar to that encountered in Secs. 4-1 and 9-3. In step 3 the driving force for the rearrangement (1,2 hydride shift) is the formation of the more stable secondary carbonium ion. The geometry of the newly formed 2-butene has not been specified, but the more stable form (trans) will be the predominant isomer if the secondary carbonium ion is sufficiently long-lived to permit rotation about the carbon-carbon bond.

**1.** Suggest a mechanism for the formation of each of the possible products in the following reaction. If a given product can be obtained by more than one pathway, note this also.

$$(CH_3)_3C{-}OH \xrightarrow[H^+]{HBr} (CH_3)_3C{-}Br + (CH_3)_2C{=}CH_2 + CH_2{=}CH{-}CH_2{-}CH_3 + CH_3{-}CH{=}CH{-}CH_3$$

**2.** According to your mechanism, what would be the isotopic distribution in each of the above products if you started with:

(*a*) $CH_3{-}C(CH_3)(CD_3){-}OH$ (*b*) $^{14}CH_3{-}C(CH_3)_2{-}OH$

Assume that deuterium atoms react like hydrogen atoms and that $^{12}C$ and $^{14}C$ atoms behave alike.

## 9-5 OXIDATION OF ALCOHOLS

The products obtained from the oxidation of alcohols depend on the type of alcohol undergoing reaction.

$$\underset{\text{1° alcohols}}{R-CH_2-OH} \xrightarrow[\text{fast}]{[O]} \underset{\text{aldehydes}}{R-CHO} \xrightarrow[\text{fast}]{[O]} \underset{\text{acids}}{R-COOH}$$

$$\underset{\text{2° alcohols}}{R-\underset{OH}{\underset{|}{CH}}-R'} \xrightarrow[\text{smoothly}]{[O]} \underset{\text{ketones}}{R-\underset{O}{\underset{\|}{C}}-R'} \qquad \underset{\text{3° alcohols}}{R-\overset{R'}{\overset{|}{\underset{R''}{\underset{|}{C}}}}-OH} \xrightarrow{[O]} \text{N.R.}$$

The most common oxidizing agents are potassium permanganate, $KMnO_4$, or a source of Cr(VI), such as sodium or potassium dichromate, $K_2Cr_2O_7$, sodium chromate, $Na_2CrO_4$, or chromic oxide, $CrO_3$.

Oxidation of primary alcohols is usually not a good method of preparing aldehydes since the product is then oxidized very rapidly to the corresponding acid. When the desired aldehyde has a much lower boiling point than the alcohol, the aldehyde can be removed from the reaction mixture as it is formed, before it is further oxidized to the acid.

$$\underset{\substack{\text{neopentyl alcohol} \\ \text{b.p. 114°}}}{(CH_3)_3C-CH_2OH} \xrightarrow{CrO_3} \underset{\substack{\text{trimethylacetaldehyde} \\ \text{75°}}}{(CH_3)_3C-CHO} \quad \text{(removed as formed)}$$

The oxidation of secondary alcohols to ketones is an excellent synthetic method and usually proceeds in high yields.

$$\underset{\text{2-butanol}}{CH_3-CH_2-\underset{OH}{\underset{|}{CH}}-CH_3} \xrightarrow{KMnO_4} \underset{\substack{\text{2-butanone} \\ \text{(methyl ethyl ketone)}}}{CH_3-CH_2-\underset{O}{\underset{\|}{C}}-CH_3}$$

$$\underset{\text{cyclohexanol}}{C_6H_{11}-OH} \xrightarrow[H^+]{Cr_2O_7^{--}} \underset{\text{cyclohexanone}}{C_6H_{10}=O}$$

Tertiary alcohols are stable to oxidation under the usual conditions. If forcing conditions are used, the alcohol may undergo reactions in which carbon-carbon bonds are ruptured, and a complex mixture of products results.

$$CH_3-\overset{CH_3}{\overset{|}{\underset{CH_3}{\underset{|}{C}}}}-OH \xrightarrow{KMnO_4} \text{N.R. under mild conditions}$$

A good synthetic reaction, also useful in determining organic structures, is the treatment of an allylic or benzylic alcohol with freshly prepared manganese dioxide, $MnO_2$. This reagent is strong enough to oxidize the alcohol to the aldehyde but is unable to oxidize it further to the acid. The $MnO_2$ is reduced to $Mn^{++}$.

$$CH_2{=}CH{-}CH_2OH \xrightarrow[MnO_2]{fresh} CH_2{=}CH{-}CHO$$

allyl alcohol → acrolein

$$C_6H_5{-}CH_2OH \xrightarrow[MnO_2]{fresh} C_6H_5{-}CHO$$

benzyl alcohol → benzaldehyde

## 9-6 ESTER FORMATION

The synthesis of an ester is carried out easily by refluxing a mixture of an organic acid and an alcohol in the presence of a trace of mineral acid such as HCl or $H_2SO_4$. This equilibrium reaction is known as a ***Fischer esterification***.

*General*:

$$R{-}C(=O){-}OH + R'{-}OH \overset{H^+}{\rightleftharpoons} R{-}C(=O){-}O{-}R' + H_2O$$

an acid + an alcohol ⇌ an ester

*Specific*:

$$CH_3{-}C(=O){-}OH + CH_3OH \overset{H_2SO_4}{\rightleftharpoons} CH_3{-}C(=O){-}O{-}CH_3 + H_2O$$

acetic acid + methyl alcohol ⇌ methyl acetate

$$CH_3{-}C(=O){-}OH + CH_3CH_2OH \overset{H^+}{\rightleftharpoons} CH_3{-}C(=O){-}O{-}CH_2CH_3 + H_2O$$

acetic acid + ethyl alcohol ⇌ ethyl acetate

Usually the equilibrium is shifted to the side of the ester by using an excess of the alcohol (or the acid if it is the less valuable compound) or by removing the water as it is formed. For the present, we shall be concerned only with esters derived from acetic acid, acetyl chloride, and acetic anhydride, namely, ***acetates***. The reagents shown below were discussed briefly under Friedel-Crafts acylation in Secs. 7-9 and 7-10.

Acid chlorides:

$$CH_3{-}C(=O){-}Cl + CH_3CH_2OH \longrightarrow CH_3{-}C(=O){-}O{-}CH_2CH_3 + HCl$$

acetyl chloride + ethyl alcohol → ethyl acetate

Anhydrides:

$$\underset{\text{acetic anhydride}}{(CH_3-CO)_2O} + \underset{n\text{-propyl alcohol}}{CH_3-CH_2-CH_2-OH} \longrightarrow \underset{n\text{-propyl acetate}}{CH_3-C(=O)-O-CH_2CH_2CH_3} + \underset{\text{acetic acid}}{CH_3CO_2H}$$

Esters of inorganic acids and organic alcohols are valuable commercial products. For instance, nitroglycerine is readily prepared by the esterification of nitric acid with glycerol.

$$\underset{\substack{\text{glycerine}\\ \text{(glycerol)}}}{CH_2(OH)-CH(OH)-CH_2(OH)} \xrightarrow{HNO_3} \underset{\text{nitroglycerine}}{CH_2(ONO_2)-CH(ONO_2)-CH_2(ONO_2)}$$

## PREPARATION

### 9-7 HYDRATION AND HYDROBORATION OF ALKENES

Water can be added to a carbon-carbon double bond in a Markownikoff manner by heating with dilute sulfuric acid (Sec. 4-10) or in an anti-Markownikoff manner by using diborane followed by oxidation with $H_2O_2$ (Sec. 4-12).

### 9-8 HYDROLYSIS OF ALKYL HALIDES: $S_N1$ AND $S_N2$ PATHWAYS

Alcohols are usually not prepared for laboratory use by the hydrolysis of alkyl halides for two reasons: (1) many alcohols are commercially available, and (2) the necessary starting halides are usually obtained from alcohols in the first place. There are situations, however, where this method is chosen.

*General*: $R-X \xrightarrow[\text{dil. }OH^-]{H_2O\text{ or}} R-OH$

*Specific*: $CH_3CH_2CH_2Br \xrightarrow[H_2O]{\Delta} CH_3CH_2CH_2OH + HBr$

The mechanism by which this reaction proceeds depends upon the substrate. Primary and secondary halides usually react by an $S_N2$ displacement with both the alcohol molecule and the hydroxide ion involved in the rate-determining step.

*Overall*: $CH_3CH_2Br \xrightarrow[\text{dil.}]{OH^-} CH_3CH_2OH + HBr \xrightarrow{OH^-} H_2O + Br^-$

*Mechanism*: 1° and 2° alkyl halides: $S_N2$ displacement.

$$HO^- + H(CH_3)(H)C{-}Br \xrightarrow{\text{slow}} \left[ H{-}O\cdots \overset{H\;\;CH_3}{C}\cdots Br \right]^- \xrightarrow{\text{fast}} HOCH_2CH_3 + Br^-$$

transition state

Note that the two carbons and two hydrogens (on the carbon undergoing reaction) all lie in a plane in the transition state.

$$HO\cdots C(H)(CH_3)(H){-}Br$$

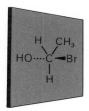

Tertiary alkyl, allyl, and benzyl halides, on the other hand, undergo reaction by way of an $S_N1$ mechanism involving ionization of the carbon-halogen bond in the rate-determining step.

*Mechanism*: $$CH_3{-}C(CH_3)_2{-}Cl \xrightarrow{\text{slow}} \left[ (H_3C)(CH_3)\overset{+}{C}{-}CH_3 \right] Cl^-$$

planar intermediate

The planar *tert*-butyl carbonium ion intermediate is relatively stable compared to primary and secondary ones, as a result of the electron-releasing effect of the methyl groups. Further, the presence of three substituents on the carbon atom undergoing reaction effectively prevents the $OH^-$ from displacing the halide ion by an $S_N2$ reaction because of interference between the groups.

$$\left[ CH_3{-}\overset{+}{C}(CH_3)_2 \right] \xrightarrow[\text{fast } S_N1]{OH^-} CH_3{-}C(CH_3)_2{-}OH$$

$$\left[ CH_3{-}\overset{+}{C}(CH_3)_2 \right] \xrightarrow[\text{competing reaction}]{E_1} CH_2{=}C(CH_3)_2$$

Similarly, the benzyl and allyl carbonium ions involve a resonance-stabilized intermediate which facilitates this ionization.

$$C_6H_5CH_2Br \xrightarrow[OH^-;\ H_2O]{\text{slow } S_N1} \left[ C_6H_5\overset{+}{C}H_2 \longleftrightarrow \text{write resonance structures for the intermediate} \right] \xrightarrow[OH^-]{\text{fast}} C_6H_5CH_2OH$$

benzyl bromide — benzyl cation — benzyl alcohol

## 9-9 REDUCTION OF CARBONYL COMPOUNDS WITH METAL HYDRIDES

Metal hydrides such as $LiAlH_4$ and $NaBH_4$ are good reducing agents and are used for the preparation of alcohols from various carbonyl compounds such as aldehydes, RCHO, ketones, $R_2CO$, acids, RCOOH, and esters, RCOOR'. The more reactive of these hydrides, $LiAlH_4$, combines vigorously with any source of acidic protons ($H^+$, R—O—H, H—O—H, R—COOH) to liberate hydrogen gas.

$$H^- + H^+ \longrightarrow H_2$$

The lithium and aluminum ions combine with the remaining portion of the molecule to form salts. The common organic reduction reactions using $LiAlH_4$ are carried out in dry ether or tetrahydrofuran and require a separate hydrolysis step to free the alcohol from the salt.

$$4R_2C{=}O + LiAlH_4 \longrightarrow [R_2HC{-}O]_4{-}LiAl \xrightarrow{H_3O^+} 4R_2CHOH + Li^+ + Al^{3+} + 4OH^-$$

The fact that $LiAlH_4$ is a stronger reducing agent than $NaBH_4$ can be shown in two ways: (1) $NaBH_4$ can be used in aqueous or alcoholic solution, whereas $LiAlH_4$ reacts with the solvent under these conditions; (2) both these reagents will reduce aldehydes and ketones, but only $LiAlH_4$ will reduce acids and esters. Examples are shown in Table 9-3.

A favorable alternative to the direct reduction of an acid is the reduction of the corresponding methyl or ethyl ester with $LiAlH_4$.

$$R{-}\overset{O}{\overset{\|}{C}}{-}OH + CH_3OH \xrightarrow{H^+} R{-}\overset{O}{\overset{\|}{C}}{-}O{-}CH_3 + H_2O$$

$$R{-}\overset{O}{\overset{\|}{C}}{-}OCH_3 \xrightarrow[2.\ H_3O^+]{1.\ LiAlH_4} R{-}CH_2OH + CH_3OH$$

**Table 9-3**
**Examples of reduction with $LiAlH_4$**

1.

$$R{-}CHO \xrightarrow[2.\ H_3O^+]{1.\ NaBH_4 \text{ or } LiAlH_4} R{-}CH_2OH$$

aldehyde → 1° alcohol

$$C_6H_5{-}CHO \xrightarrow{NaBH_4} C_6H_5{-}CH_2OH$$

benzaldehyde → benzyl alcohol

2.

$$R{-}\overset{O}{\overset{\|}{C}}{-}R' \xrightarrow[2.\ H_3O^+]{1.\ NaBH_4 \text{ or } LiAlH_4} R{-}\underset{OH}{\underset{|}{CH}}{-}R'$$

ketone → 2° alcohol

$$CH_3{-}\underset{O}{\underset{\|}{C}}{-}CH_2CH_3 \xrightarrow[2.\ H_3O^+]{1.\ LiAlH_4} CH_3{-}\underset{OH}{\underset{|}{CH}}{-}CH_2CH_3$$

methyl ethyl ketone → 2-butanol

3.

$$R{-}\overset{O}{\overset{\|}{C}}{-}O{-}H \xrightarrow[2.\ H_3O^+]{1.\ LiAlH_4 \text{ (not } NaBH_4)} R{-}CH_2OH + H_2\uparrow$$

acid → 1° alcohol

$$CH_3{-}CH_2{-}COOH \xrightarrow[2.\ H_3O^+]{1.\ LiAlH_4} CH_3CH_2CH_2OH$$

propanoic acid → 1-propanol

4.

$$R{-}\overset{O}{\overset{\|}{C}}{-}O{-}R' \xrightarrow[2.\ H_3O^+]{1.\ LiAlH_4 \text{ (not } NaBH_4)} R{-}CH_2OH + R'OH$$

ester → 1° alcohol; usually not recovered if R= lower alkyl

$$CH_3{-}\overset{O}{\overset{\|}{C}}{-}O{-}CH_3 \xrightarrow[2.\ H_3O^+]{1.\ LiAlH_4} CH_3CH_2OH + CH_3OH$$

methyl acetate

Methyl esters are commonly used because they are readily prepared and are more soluble in the solvent than the acid or higher-molecular-weight esters. In the reduction of esters, only the primary alcohol derived from the acid is usually recovered; the methyl alcohol is more soluble in water and is removed during the isolation procedure.

Reduction of these carbonyl compounds may also be carried out with hydrogen and a catalyst, but the conditions are often strenuous ones (high temperature, high pressure) which require special hydrogenation apparatus.

## THE GRIGNARD REACTION

**The Grignard reaction is one of the most important reactions in organic chemistry because of its versatility in forming new carbon-carbon bonds.** This reagent, represented as R—Mg—X, was discussed briefly in Chap. 2 as a synthetic route to alkanes, but here its application, especially to the synthesis of alcohols, will be explored extensively.

### 9-10 PREPARATION OF ALKYL GRIGNARD REAGENTS

Alkyl Grignard reagents are prepared by the reaction of an alkyl halide with magnesium in a dry solvent; any water present reacts with the Grignard reagent to yield the hydrocarbon (Sec. 2-7).

*General*: $R{-}X \xrightarrow[\text{or dry THF}]{\text{Mg in dry ether}} [R{-}Mg{-}X]$

*Specific*: $CH_3CH_2Br \xrightarrow[\text{ether}]{\text{Mg in dry}} [CH_3CH_2MgBr]$

bromoethane — ethylmagnesium bromide

$CH_3I \xrightarrow[\text{ether}]{\text{Mg in dry}} [CH_3{-}Mg{-}I]$

methyl iodide — methylmagnesium iodide

The alkyl halide may be primary or secondary; tertiary ones are often less stable for electronic and steric reasons. Chlorides, bromides, or iodides may be used. The choice of the halogen atom in the alkyl halide depends on many factors, including availability (usually Cl > Br > I), cost of materials (usually I > Br > Cl), and reactivity (I > Br > Cl). It may be necessary to take into account the melting point, boiling point, and the ease of manipulation of the halide as well as simplicity of the apparatus. Considering all these factors, the bromides are a good compromise and are most often used. An exception is found in the methyl compounds. Methyl iodide is an easily handled, low-boiling liquid (b.p. 42°), whereas methyl chloride (b.p. −24°) and methyl bromide (b.p. 3.5°) are gases at room temperature.

The use of organolithium reagents, R—Li and Ar—Li, is similar in most respects to that of the Grignard reagents, but the subtle factors dictating the choice of these reagents are beyond the scope of this text. You may consider them as equivalent synthetic intermediates.

### 9-11 PREPARATION OF AROMATIC GRIGNARD REAGENTS

In the aromatic series it is necessary to use *t*etra*h*ydro*f*uran (THF), not ether, when preparing the Grignard reagent from an aryl ***chloride***, which is considerably less reactive than the bromide or iodide.

*General*: $\text{Ar—X} \xrightarrow[\text{ether}]{\text{Mg in dry}} [\text{ArMgX}] \quad \text{X} = \text{I, Br}$

$\text{Ar—X} \xrightarrow[\text{THF}]{\text{Mg in dry}} [\text{ArMgX}] \quad \text{X} = \text{Cl, Br, I}$

*Specific*: $\text{C}_6\text{H}_5\text{—Br} \xrightarrow[\text{ether}]{\text{Mg in dry}} [\text{C}_6\text{H}_5\text{—MgBr}]$

bromobenzene — phenylmagnesium bromide

$p\text{-ClC}_6\text{H}_4\text{Br} \xrightarrow[\text{ether}]{\text{Mg in dry}} [p\text{-ClC}_6\text{H}_4\text{MgBr}]$

*p*-bromochlorobenzene — *p*-chlorophenylmagnesium bromide

In the example of *p*-bromochlorobenzene, note the difference in reactivity of the bromine and chlorine atoms when ether is used as a solvent. If THF were employed, one might have difficulty securing a good yield of the di-Grignard reagent because of side reactions (Sec. 9-12).

### 9-12 SIDE REACTIONS WITH AIR DURING GRIGNARD PREPARATION

At least three constituents of air can react with a Grignard reagent and interfere in the further reaction and isolation procedure, namely, water, oxygen, and carbon dioxide.

$H_2O$: $[\text{CH}_3\text{MgI}] + H_2O \longrightarrow CH_4 + \text{Mg(OH)I}$

$[\text{C}_6\text{H}_5\text{—Mg—Br}] + H_2O \longrightarrow \text{C}_6\text{H}_5\text{—H} + \text{Mg(OH)Br}$

As we have previously noted, the reaction of a Grignard reagent with $H_2O$ or $D_2O$ is an excellent method of preparation of hydrocarbons from halides; however, this is a serious, unwanted side product in other syntheses. The ether or THF must be scrupulously dried, often by distilling the solvents from sodium metal or from $LiAlH_4$.

$$\mathbf{O_2}: \; [CH_3MgI] + O_2 \longrightarrow [CH_3{-}O{-}O{-}MgI] \xrightarrow{H_2O} CH_3OH + Mg(OH)I$$

$$[C_6H_5{-}MgBr] + O_2 \longrightarrow [C_6H_5{-}O{-}O{-}MgBr] \xrightarrow{H_2O} C_6H_5{-}OH + Mg(OH)Br$$

Although this side reaction can be used as a fair method of synthesis of *phenols*, **it is not a feasible synthesis of alcohols** because of the low yields of impure product generally obtained.

$$\mathbf{CO_2}: \; [CH_3MgI] + CO_2 \longrightarrow \left[CH_3{-}\overset{\overset{\displaystyle O}{\|}}{C}{-}O{-}MgI\right] \xrightarrow{H_2O} CH_3COOH + Mg(OH)I$$

$$[C_6H_5{-}MgBr] + CO_2 \longrightarrow \left[C_6H_5{-}\overset{\overset{\displaystyle O}{\|}}{C}{-}OMgBr\right] \xrightarrow{H_2O} C_6H_5{-}COOH + Mg(OH)Br$$

If a solution of a Grignard reagent is poured over Dry Ice (solid $CO_2$) and then treated with dilute mineral acid, excellent yields of the next higher organic acid can be obtained. However, in the reactions discussed below, this acid formation by reaction of the Grignard reagent with atmospheric $CO_2$ can be a serious side reaction.

The Grignard reagent cannot be prepared from a molecule which contains an active-hydrogen functional group, for example, $-CO_2H$, $-OH$, $C_6H_5{-}OH$, $-C{\equiv}C{-}H$, $-NH_2$; a nitro group; another reactive halogen; or any other functional group which reacts with the *incipient* Grignard reagent.

## 9-13 STRUCTURE OF THE GRIGNARD REAGENT

Although many investigations of the structure of various Grignard reagents have been reported, it is clear that no one general formulation correctly represents all Grignard reagents. The detailed structure depends on the organic moiety, the solvent employed, and often on how the reagent is prepared. There seems to be general agreement on the fact that the solvent plays a very important role in the structure and that ethers such as diethyl ether and THF greatly facilitate the reagent formation from the organic halide and magnesium. Studies have indicated that the formation $R_2Mg \cdot MgX_2$ is a reasonable one. We shall omit the various points of debate concerning the structure of the reagent and continue to use the notation R—Mg—X.

Note that the carbon atom in $\overset{\delta-}{R}—\overset{\delta+}{Mg}—X$ is a nucleophile; the carbon bearing the magnesium atom has a great deal of carbanion character. Carbonyl groups contain an electrophilic carbon and are generally highly polar: $>\overset{\delta+}{C}=\overset{\delta-}{O}$. Combination of these two is found to give rise to the formation of a new carbon-carbon bond

$$\overset{\delta-}{R}—\overset{\delta+}{Mg}X + >\overset{\delta+}{C}=\overset{\delta-}{O} \longrightarrow R—\underset{|}{\overset{|}{C}}—\overset{\delta-}{O}—\overset{\delta+}{Mg}X$$

Subsequent treatment with water or dilute acid will release the newly formed alcohol from the salt

$$R—\underset{|}{\overset{|}{C}}—\overset{\delta-}{O}—\overset{\delta+}{Mg}X + \overset{\delta+}{H}—\overset{\delta-}{OH} \longrightarrow R—\underset{|}{\overset{|}{C}}—OH + Mg(OH)X$$

Thus, many different alcohols can be synthesized with this reaction by the proper choice of Grignard reagent and carbonyl substrate. ***Nucleophilic displacements*** (Sec. 8-7), as well as ***nucleophilic additions***, can give rise to new carbon-carbon bonds. In the following sections we shall discuss the synthesis of primary, secondary, and tertiary alcohols.

## 9-14 SYNTHESES OF PRIMARY ALCOHOLS

Two common routes are available for the synthesis of primary alcohols. Route A is the addition of one carbon via formaldehyde, and route B is the addition of two carbon atoms via ethylene oxide, a reactive three-membered-ring ether.

### Route A

*General*: $$[R—MgX] + \underset{\text{formaldehyde}}{H_2C=O} \longrightarrow [R—CO_2—O—MgX] \xrightarrow{H_3O^+} RCH_2OH + Mg(OH)X$$

*Specific*: $$[CH_3CH_2MgBr] + CH_2O \longrightarrow [CH_3CH_2CH_2OMgBr] \xrightarrow{H_3O^+} CH_3CH_2CH_2OH + Mg(OH)Br$$

### Route B

*General*: $[R—MgX] + H_2C\underset{O}{—}CH_2 \longrightarrow [R—CH_2—CH_2OMgX]$

ethylene oxide

$\downarrow H_3O^+$

$RCH_2CH_2OH + Mg(OH)X$

*Specific*: $[CH_3CH_2CH_2CH_2MgBr] + H_2C\underset{O}{—}CH_2 \longrightarrow [C_4H_9—CH_2—CH_2—OMgBr]$

$\downarrow H_3O^+$

$CH_3CH_2CH_2CH_2CH_2CH_2OH + Mg(OH)Br$

> **1.** Name the starting Grignard reagent and the alcohol product in both the specific examples above.
>
> **2.** Write the detailed mechanism for the reaction of each specific Grignard reagent with the given substrate. Identify which of these reactions is a nucleophilic substitution and which is a nucleophilic addition.
>
> **3.** How would you prepare each of the specific Grignard reagents from ethanol and any other necessary compounds?

## 9-15 SYNTHESIS OF SECONDARY ALCOHOLS VIA ALDEHYDES

The reaction of a Grignard reagent with an aldehyde other than formaldehyde, followed by dilute acid hydrolysis, gives rise to a secondary alcohol. These alcohols may be classified as symmetrical, $R_2CHOH$, or unsymmetrical, RR'CHOH, depending on the nature of the two alkyl groups attached to the carbon bearing the —OH group. Thus, there is only one combination of these reagents which gives rise to a symmetrical secondary alcohol, but two choices are possible for the synthesis of unsymmetrical ones. Since the organic product is the center of attention, we shall omit the inorganic product, [Mg(OH)X], in the final step in future discussions.

### Symmetrical secondary alcohols

*General*: $[R—MgX] + R—C(=O)H \longrightarrow \left[ R—\underset{H}{\overset{R}{C}}—OMgX \right] \xrightarrow{H_3O^+} R—\underset{OH}{CH}—R$

*Specific*:

$$\left[ C_6H_5\text{—MgBr} \right] + C_6H_5\text{—C}(=O)\text{—H} \longrightarrow \left[ C_6H_5\text{—}\underset{H}{\overset{OMgBr}{C}}\text{—}C_6H_5 \right] \xrightarrow{H_3O^+} C_6H_5\text{—}\underset{OH}{\overset{H}{C}}\text{—}C_6H_5$$

benzaldehyde

**Unsymmetrical secondary alcohols**

*General*:

$$[\text{R—MgX}] + \text{R'—C}(=O)\text{—H} \xrightarrow{\text{(then } H_3O^+)} \text{R—}\underset{OH}{\text{CH}}\text{—R'}$$

$$[\text{R'—MgX}] + \text{R—C}(=O)\text{—H} \xrightarrow{\text{(then } H_3O^+)} \text{R—}\underset{OH}{\text{CH}}\text{—R'}$$

*Specific*:

$$\left[ C_6H_5\text{—MgI} \right] + CH_3CHO \xrightarrow{\text{(then } H_3O^+)} C_6H_5\text{—}\underset{OH}{\text{CH}}\text{—}CH_3$$

acetaldehyde 1-phenylethanol

$$[CH_3MgI] + C_6H_5\text{—C}(=O)\text{—H} \xrightarrow{\text{(then } H_3O^+)} C_6H_5\text{—}\underset{OH}{\text{CH}}\text{—}CH_3$$

benzaldehyde

## 9-16 SYNTHESIS OF TERTIARY ALCOHOLS VIA KETONES AND ESTERS

Tertiary alcohols can be classified as having three groups alike, $R_3COH$, two groups alike RRR'COH, or no groups alike RR'R''COH, depending on the nature of the alkyl or aryl groups attached to the carbon containing the —OH functional group. Thus, there are three combinations of a Grignard reagent and ketone which can give rise to an alcohol with no groups alike, two combinations for two groups alike, and only one set of reagents for three groups alike.

**Three groups alike**

*General*:

$$[\text{R—MgX}] + \text{R—}\overset{O}{\overset{\|}{C}}\text{—R} \xrightarrow[H_2O)]{\text{(then } NH_4Cl} \text{R—}\underset{R}{\overset{R}{C}}\text{—OH}$$

*Specific*:

$$[CH_3MgI] + CH_3\text{—}\overset{O}{\overset{\|}{C}}\text{—}CH_3 \xrightarrow[H_2O)]{\text{(then } NH_4Cl} CH_3\text{—}\underset{CH_3}{\overset{CH_3}{C}}\text{—OH}$$

acetone

**Two groups alike**

*General*:

$$[R'\text{—MgX}] + R\text{—}\overset{\overset{\displaystyle O}{\|}}{C}\text{—}R \searrow$$

$$[R\text{—MgX}] + R'\text{—}\overset{\overset{\displaystyle O}{\|}}{C}\text{—}R \nearrow$$

$$\left[ R\text{—}\underset{R}{\overset{R'}{C}}\text{—OMgX} \right] \xrightarrow[H_2O)]{\text{(then } NH_4Cl} R\text{—}\underset{R}{\overset{R'}{C}}\text{—OH}$$

*Specific*: $[CH_3MgI]$ + benzophenone (diphenyl ketone) $\xrightarrow{\text{(then } H_2O,\ NH_4Cl)}$ 1,1-diphenylethanol

$\left[ C_6H_5\text{—MgI} \right]$ + acetophenone (methyl phenyl ketone) $\xrightarrow{\text{(then } NH_4Cl,\ H_2O)}$ 1,1-diphenylethanol

benzophenone
(diphenyl ketone)

acetophenone
(methyl phenyl ketone)

1,1-diphenylethanol

**No groups alike**

*General*:

$$[R\text{—MgX}] + R'\text{—}\overset{\overset{\displaystyle O}{\|}}{C}\text{—}R'' \xrightarrow[H_2O)]{\text{(then } NH_4Cl} R\text{—}\underset{R''}{\overset{R'}{C}}\text{—OH}$$

Tertiary alcohols and certain allylic and benzylic alcohols

$$\sim CH{=}CH\text{—}\underset{OH}{CH}\text{—}CH_2\text{—} \quad \text{and} \quad C_6H_5\text{—}\underset{OH}{CH}\text{—}CH_2\sim$$

an allylic alcohol — a benzylic alcohol

readily undergo dehydration to olefins, dienes, or alkenes resembling styrene on treatment with strong acid. All these alcohols form relatively stable carbonium ions by protonation and loss of a water molecule. Although this dehydration reaction may be a useful synthetic step, even in conjunction with the Grignard reaction, **milder hydrolysis conditions must be employed when tertiary alcohols are to be obtained**. Instead of mineral acids, dilute solutions of ammonium chloride are usually used. These solutions are very weakly acidic owing to the hydrolysis of the ammonium ion:

$$NH_4^+ + H_2O \rightleftharpoons NH_4OH + H^+$$

Further, the combination of ammonium and magnesium salts is more easily handled in the isolation procedure.

> **1.** Write the other two combinations of reagents which will give rise to the general tertiary alcohol.
>
> **2.** In a similar manner, formulate the three Grignard syntheses of 1-phenyl-1-cyclohexylethanol. Name the starting materials.

The reaction of a Grignard reagent with an ester gives a tertiary alcohol which must have at least two groups alike.

*Overall*: $2[\mathrm{R{-}MgX}] + \mathrm{R'{-}\overset{\overset{\large O}{\|}}{C}{-}O{-}R''} \xrightarrow{\text{(then } H_2O)} \mathrm{R'{-}\underset{\underset{\large R}{|}}{\overset{\overset{\large OH}{|}}{C}}{-}R} + \mathrm{R''OMgX}$

*Mechanism*: $\left[\mathrm{\overset{\delta-}{R}{-}\overset{\delta+}{MgX}}\right] + \mathrm{R'{-}\overset{\overset{\large O}{\|}}{C}{-}O{-}R''} \xrightarrow{\text{slow}} \left[\mathrm{R'{-}\underset{\underset{\large R}{|}}{\overset{\overset{\large O{-}MgX}{|}}{C}}{-}O{-}R''}\right]$ **I**

$\downarrow$ spontaneously, $-\mathrm{R''OMgX}$

$\mathrm{R'{-}\underset{\underset{\large R}{|}}{\overset{\overset{\large OH}{|}}{C}}{-}R} \xleftarrow[H_2O]{NH_4Cl} \left[\mathrm{R'{-}\underset{\underset{\large R}{|}}{\overset{\overset{\large OMgX}{|}}{C}}{-}R}\right]$ **II** $\xleftarrow[\text{very fast}]{\text{RMgX}} \mathrm{R'{-}\overset{\overset{\large O}{\|}}{C}{-}R}$

$[\mathrm{R''OMgX}] \xrightarrow{H_2O} \mathrm{R''OH} + \mathrm{Mg(OH)X}$

Follow the mechanism closely and note these points: (1) The first intermediate, I, is formed in a slow step, but, once formed, it spontaneously loses an alkoxymagnesium halide, R''OMgX, where R''OH is the alcohol from which the starting ester may have been prepared

$\mathrm{R'{-}COOH} + \mathrm{R''OH} \xrightarrow{H^+} \mathrm{R'{-}COOR''} + H_2O$

(2) Here the ketone intermediate, II, reacts with the Grignard reagent many times faster than the original ester. Thus, this ketone cannot be isolated. (3) The reaction of a ketone with a Grignard reagent, the next step, has been shown above; the tertiary alcohol is then released by $NH_4Cl$-$H_2O$ hydrolysis. (4) For every mole of starting ester 2 moles of the Grignard reagent are consumed. (5) Since the alcohol portion of the ester is not found in the principal organic product, it makes little difference which starting alcohol is used. Generally a methyl or ethyl

ester is prepared because methanol and ethanol are inexpensive and readily available, these lower-molecular-weight esters are fairly soluble in ether or THF, and the methyl and ethyl groups provide a minimum steric interference to the incoming Grignard reagent. Finally, they are readily removed from the desired tertiary alcohol in the isolation procedure.

*Specific*: $2[C_6H_5\text{—}MgBr] + C_6H_5\text{—}\overset{O}{\overset{\|}{C}}\text{—}OCH_3 \xrightarrow[H_2O)]{(\text{then } NH_4Cl}$ $(C_6H_5)_3C\text{—}OH$ + $CH_3OH$

methyl benzoate

triphenylmethanol

$$2[CH_3MgI] + C_6H_5\text{—}\overset{O}{\overset{\|}{C}}\text{—}OCH_3 \xrightarrow[H_2O)]{(\text{then } NH_4Cl} C_6H_5\text{—}C(CH_3)_2\text{—}OH + CH_3OH$$

2-phenyl-2-propanol

**1.** Formulate the mechanism for the synthesis of the tertiary alcohols in each of the specific examples above.

**2.** Suppose 1 mole of methylmagnesium bromide is added to 1 mole of ethyl benzoate and then $NH_4Cl$-$H_2O$ is added. What organic compounds would you expect to isolate? How much of each, assuming a nearly quantitative yield?

**3.** Give a specific example of the synthesis of a tertiary alcohol in which all three groups are alike, employing an ester and $CH_3CH_2MgBr$.

## SYNTHESIS PROBLEMS: THE APPROACH

Since the Grignard reaction is a versatile method for the preparation of alcohols, from which other compounds can subsequently be prepared, this is an excellent place to explain in detail how to approach multistep synthetic problems. Rather than specifying any particular starting materials for the first few examples, let us try to work back from a desired alcohol to the simplest compounds we have studied, and by this method determine a series of reactions which can be used to prepare the alcohol. Usually certain organic starting materials will be given in the statement of the problem.

*Example* 1: Show how you would synthesize

$$C_6H_5-CH_2-\underset{\displaystyle OH}{\underset{|}{CH}}-CH_2-CH_3$$

The first questions to ask when attempting the synthesis of a complex molecule are: What type of molecule is this? What functional group (or groups) does it contain? After the various syntheses for this class of compound have been recalled, the question becomes: If *all* reagents and compounds were available, what particular combination would afford this compound in one (or two) steps?

For instance, the molecule in this example is a secondary alcohol, which can be prepared by treating an aldehyde with a Grignard reagent (followed by dilute acid hydrolysis). This suggests two routes.

*Route A*:

$$C_6H_5-CH_2-CHO + [CH_3CH_2MgBr] \xrightarrow{\text{(then } H_3O^+\text{)}} C_6H_5-CH_2-\underset{\displaystyle OH}{\underset{|}{CH}}-CH_2-CH_3$$

This particular route now requires the synthesis of phenylacetaldehyde and ethylmagnesium bromide.

$$CH_3CH_2Br \xrightarrow[\text{dry ether}]{\text{Mg in}} [CH_3CH_2MgBr]$$

$$CH_3CH_2OH \xrightarrow[\text{or } H^+ \text{ and HBr}]{PBr_3 \text{ or } PBr_5} CH_3CH_2Br$$

or

$$CH_2{=}CH_2 \xrightarrow{HBr} CH_3CH_2Br$$

Recall that ethanol and ethylene are related by the following reactions:

$$CH_3CH_2OH \xrightarrow[Al_2O_3;\ \Delta]{H^+;\ \Delta \text{ or}} CH_2{=}CH_2 + H_2O$$

$$CH_2{=}CH_2 \xrightarrow[\substack{2.\ H_2O;\ \Delta \\ \text{or hydroboration}}]{1.\ H_2SO_4} CH_3CH_2OH$$

The aldehyde syntheses discussed so far are the oxidation of a primary alcohol and the ozonization of an alkene followed by reductive work-up. In the absence of better methods, which will be discussed in Chap. 13, the former can be used noting the difficulty with overoxidation.

$$C_6H_5-CH_2-CH_2-OH \xrightarrow[H^+;\ \text{low temp.}]{Cr_2O_7^{--}} C_6H_5-CH_2-CHO$$ remove as formed to prevent overoxidation

$$C_6H_6 \xrightarrow[FeBr_3]{Br_2} C_6H_5-Br \xrightarrow[\text{dry ether}]{\text{Mg in}} [C_6H_5-MgBr] \xrightarrow[2.\ H_3O^+]{1.\ H_2C\overset{O}{-}CH_2} C_6H_5-CH_2CH_2OH$$

Starting with benzene, we can add the necessary two carbon fragment via ethylene oxide.
Thus, by route A we have achieved the synthesis from ethanol, ethylene oxide, and benzene.

> Show how you can prepare ethanol from coke, limestone, water, and other inorganic reagents.

In synthesis problems we shall always assume that all inorganic reagents and all organic or inorganic solvents are available, but an organic solvent may not be used as a reagent unless it is synthesized or given in a statement of the problem.

*Route B*

$$[C_6H_5-CH_2-MgBr] + CH_3-CH_2-CHO \xrightarrow{(\text{then } H_3O^+)} C_6H_5-CH_2-\underset{OH}{CH}-CH_2CH_3$$

The other combination of reagents requires benzyl bromide and propionaldehyde. For the halide, two routes are available: convert benzyl alcohol to the bromide or halogenate toluene in the ***side chain*** under free-radical conditions:

$$C_6H_5CH_3 \xrightarrow{\text{NBS; } h\nu \text{ or } Br_2;\ \Delta} C_6H_5CH_2Br \xrightarrow[\text{ether; dil. conditions}]{\text{Mg in dry}} [C_6H_5-CH_2-MgBr]$$

$$C_6H_5CH_2OH \xrightarrow{PBr_3 \text{ or } PBr_5 \text{ or } HBr\ (H^+)} C_6H_5CH_2Br$$

> Summarize the above syntheses via routes A and B on *one* diagram showing structural formulas of starting material, products, and reagents.

*Example* 2: Synthesize 2,3-dimethyl-3-pentanol.

This is a tertiary alcohol with three different groups on the carbon bearing the —OH functional group, which suggests a Grignard synthesis involving a ketone; three combinations are possible. Note that an ester and a Grignard reagent ***cannot*** be used here, since esters yield only tertiary alcohols with at least two groups alike.

*Route A*:

$$[CH_3CH_2MgCl] + CH_3{-}\overset{\overset{O}{\|}}{C}{-}CH(CH_3)_2 \xrightarrow[H_2O)]{\text{(then } NH_4Cl} CH_3CH_2{-}\underset{OH}{\overset{H_3C}{C}}{-}\overset{CH_3}{CH}{-}CH_3$$

methyl isopropyl ketone

$$CH_3CH_2OH \xrightarrow[\text{which can be used here)}]{\text{(list at least 3 reagents}} CH_3CH_2Cl \xrightarrow[\text{dry ether}]{\text{Mg in}} [CH_3CH_2MgCl]$$

$$CH_3{-}\underset{OH}{CH}{-}CH(CH_3)_2 \xrightarrow[CrO_3]{KMnO_4 \text{ or}} CH_3{-}\underset{\underset{O}{\|}}{C}{-}CH(CH_3)_2$$

3-methyl-2-butanol

$$[CH_3MgI] + (CH_3)_2CH{-}CHO \xrightarrow{\text{(then } H_3O^+)} CH_3{-}\underset{OH}{CH}{-}CH(CH_3)_2$$

3-methyl-2-butanol

↑ (then $H_3O^+$)

$$CH_3CHO + (CH_3)_2CHMgBr$$

> Indicate a synthesis of $[CH_3MgI]$ and of $[(CH_3)_2CHMgBr]$.

Working back, this route requires methyl isopropyl ketone, which in turn can be prepared from the corresponding alcohol by oxidation. This alcohol can be prepared by two different methods.

*Route B*

$$[(CH_3)_2CH{-}Mg{-}Br] + CH_3{-}CH_2{-}\underset{\underset{O}{\|}}{C}{-}CH_3 \xrightarrow[H_2O)]{\text{(then } NH_4Cl} CH_3CH_2{-}\underset{OH}{\overset{H_3C}{C}}{-}\overset{CH_3}{CH}{-}CH_3$$

methyl ethyl ketone

Work this route back to simpler materials.

*Route C*

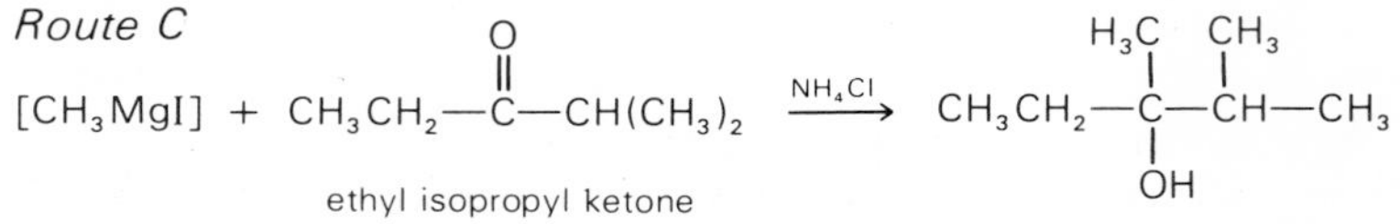

$$[CH_3MgI] + CH_3CH_2{-}\overset{\overset{\displaystyle O}{\|}}{C}{-}CH(CH_3)_2 \xrightarrow{NH_4Cl} CH_3CH_2{-}\underset{\underset{\displaystyle OH}{|}}{\overset{\overset{\displaystyle H_3C}{|}}{C}}{-}\overset{\overset{\displaystyle CH_3}{|}}{CH}{-}CH_3$$

ethyl isopropyl ketone

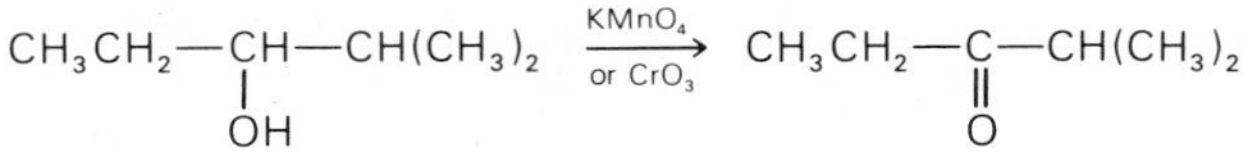

$$CH_3CH_2{-}\underset{\underset{\displaystyle OH}{|}}{CH}{-}CH(CH_3)_2 \xrightarrow[\text{or } CrO_3]{KMnO_4} CH_3CH_2{-}\underset{\underset{\displaystyle O}{\|}}{C}{-}CH(CH_3)_2$$

2-methyl-3-pentanol

Outline two syntheses of 2-methyl-3-pentanol.

In many of these examples several reagents have been shown. This was done only to remind you of the various possibilities which exist for effecting many organic transformations, and hereafter, we shall usually write only one.

If you write the various syntheses of Example 2 on one large piece of paper, as follows:

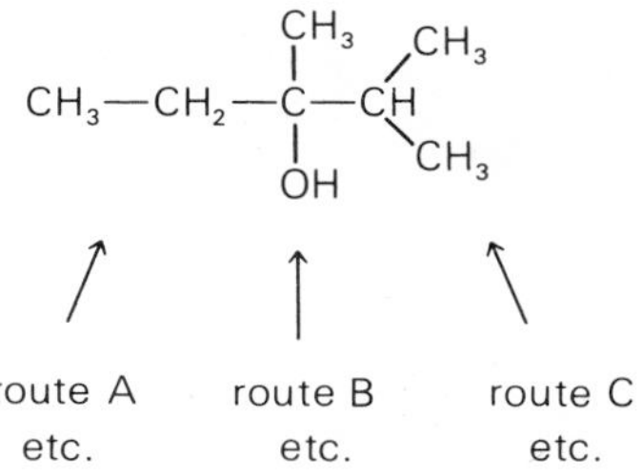

$$CH_3{-}CH_2{-}\underset{\underset{\displaystyle OH}{|}}{\overset{\overset{\displaystyle CH_3}{|}}{C}}{-}CH(CH_3)_2$$

| ↗ | ↑ | ↖ |
|---|---|---|
| route A | route B | route C |
| etc. | etc. | etc. |

you will see that they form a definite pyramid with some of the simplest reactions discussed in the previous eight chapters at the base! Synthesis problems will draw on all your knowledge of organic chemistry; similar problems will be found in the remaining chapters.

*Example* 3: Synthesize

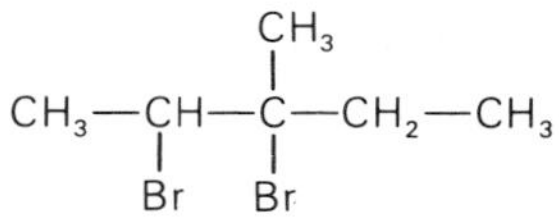

$$CH_3{-}\underset{\underset{\displaystyle Br}{|}}{CH}{-}\underset{\underset{\displaystyle Br}{|}}{\overset{\overset{\displaystyle CH_3}{|}}{C}}{-}CH_2{-}CH_3$$

Here it is clear that the reaction which readily gives rise to this product is

$$CH_3{-}CH{=}C(CH_3)CH_2CH_3 \xrightarrow{Br_2} CH_3{-}\underset{\displaystyle Br}{\underset{|}{C}H}{-}\underset{\displaystyle Br}{\underset{|}{C}}(CH_3)CH_2CH_3$$

Working back, two alcohols can be dehydrated to yield primarily

$$\underset{\text{3-methyl-2-pentanol}}{CH_3{-}\underset{\displaystyle OH}{\underset{|}{C}H}{-}CH(CH_3)CH_2CH_3} \xrightarrow[-H_2O]{\Delta;\ H^+} \underset{\text{3-methyl-2-pentene}}{CH_3{-}CH{=}C(CH_3)CH_2CH_3}$$

$$\Delta;\ H^+ \uparrow -H_2O$$

$$\underset{\text{3-methyl-3-pentanol}}{CH_3CH_2{-}\underset{\displaystyle OH}{\underset{|}{C}}(CH_3)CH_2CH_3}$$

Or, the bromides (derived from these alcohols) can be dehydrohalogenated with alcoholic KOH. The problem is now reduced to the synthesis of either one of these alcohols. The secondary alcohol suggests two different routes using aldehydes and Grignard reagents. The tertiary alcohol can be made via three routes: two involve a ketone (with the appropriate Grignard reagent), and the third involves an ester (specifically, an acetate) and ethylmagnesium halide.

| Continue this problem back to simple compounds. |
|---|

*Example* 4: Synthesize

$$C_6H_5{-}\overset{\displaystyle CH_3}{\overset{|}{\underset{\displaystyle H}{\underset{|}{C}}}}{-}C_6H_{11}$$

Several routes are suggested here: two using hydrogenation in the last step and another using the Grignard reaction with water.

Continue working these back, such that you start with only formaldehyde, $CH_2O$, acetaldehyde, $CH_3CHO$, benzene, toluene, and cyclohexanone. Note that it may not be necessary to use each of these for each route; in fact, some may not be needed at all!

$C_6H_5$—C($CH_3$)=$C_6H_{10}$ $\xrightarrow{H_2/Pt}$ $C_6H_5$—CH($CH_3$)—$C_6H_{11}$ $\xleftarrow{H_2O}$ [$C_6H_5$—C($CH_3$)(MgBr)—$C_6H_{11}$]

$H^+$ Δ, $-H_2O$ ↑ (from $C_6H_5$—C($CH_3$)(OH)—$C_6H_{11}$)

$H_2/Pt$ ↑ (from $C_6H_5$—C(=$CH_2$)—$C_6H_{11}$)

1. $PBr_3$ 2. Mg in dry ether ↑ (from $C_6H_5$—C($CH_3$)(OH)—$C_6H_{11}$)

Δ $Al_2O_3$ ↑ (from $C_6H_5$—CH($CH_2OH$)—$C_6H_{11}$)

Recall the fact that benzene can be converted to acetophenone, $C_6H_5$—C(=O)—$CH_3$, by Friedel-Crafts acylation.

Further, cyclohexanone,

(cyclohexanone structure: six-membered ring with C=O)

can be reduced to cyclohexanol with $NaBH_4$ (or with $LiAlH_4$ followed by hydrolysis).

*Example* 5: Synthesize $CH_3$—CH═CH—CH(Br)—$CH_3$ from any $C_1$, $C_2$, and $C_3$ organic compounds.

One possible final step is the treatment of 2-pentene with *N*-bromosuccinimide (NBS) in $CCl_4$ ($h\nu$).

$$CH_3\text{—}CH{=}CH\text{—}CH_2\text{—}CH_3 \xrightarrow[\text{in dry } CCl_4]{NBS;\,h\nu} CH_3\text{—}CH{=}CH\text{—}\underset{\displaystyle Br}{\underset{|}{CH}}\text{—}CH_3$$

A subtle detail of this problem was mentioned in the previous chapter; namely, allylic *methylene* groups undergo bromination with NBS more readily than allylic *methyl* groups. This problem is now reduced to one which is similar to Example 3.

## QUALITATIVE TESTS

### 9-17 SODIUM METAL

Alcohols containing fewer than nine carbon atoms are usually reactive toward metallic sodium and can be identified by the fact that the reaction visibly evolves hydrogen gas. Higher alcohols react so much more slowly that the test becomes ambiguous and is no longer of any value.

### 9-18 THE LUCAS TEST

Alcohols of different classes can be differentiated on the basis of their reaction rates with HCl-$ZnCl_2$. The insoluble chloride obtained appears as a white cloudy solution or as a separate layer. Alcohols containing fewer than six carbon atoms are soluble in the reagent and can be tested.

Primary alcohols $\xrightarrow{\text{HCl-ZnCl}_2}$ N.R. (at room temperature within 15 min)

Secondary alcohols $\xrightarrow{\text{HCl-ZnCl}_2}$ Cloudy solution in 5-10 min

Tertiary, allyl, benzyl alcohols $\xrightarrow{\text{HCl-ZnCl}_2}$ *immediate* white solution or separate layer

Phenols $\xrightarrow{\text{HCl-ZnCl}_2}$ N.R. (even at elevated temperatures)

### 9-19 FORMATION OF ACETATES

Primary and secondary alcohols give acetates simply on heating with acetyl chloride or acetic anhydride, whereas tertiary ones require the addition of pyridine, an organic base, for acceptable yields. Acetates generally have characteristic pleasant odors. They can be isolated to provide additional quantitative information concerning the number and type of hydroxyl groups present.

*General*: $$\text{R—OH} + \underset{\text{acetyl chloride}}{\text{CH}_3\text{—C(=O)Cl}} \longrightarrow \underset{\text{an acetate}}{\text{R—O—C(=O)CH}_3} + \text{HCl}$$

$$R\text{—}OH + CH_3\text{—}\overset{\displaystyle O}{\overset{\|}{C}}\text{—}O\text{—}\overset{\displaystyle O}{\overset{\|}{C}}\text{—}CH_3 \longrightarrow R\text{—}O\text{—}C\!\!\begin{array}{l}\nearrow\!\!\!\!\!\!= O\\ \searrow CH_3\end{array} + CH_3\text{—}COOH$$

acetic anhydride — an acetate

*Specific*:

$$CH_3\text{—}\underset{\displaystyle OH}{\underset{|}{C}H}\text{—}CH_2CH_3 + CH_3COCl \longrightarrow CH_3\text{—}\underset{\displaystyle O\text{—}COCH_3}{\underset{|}{C}H}\text{—}CH_2\text{—}CH_3 + HCl$$

*sec*-butyl alcohol — *sec*-butyl acetate

$$CH_3\text{—}\overset{\displaystyle CH_3}{\overset{|}{\underset{\displaystyle CH_3}{\underset{|}{C}}}}\text{—}OH + CH_3COCl \longrightarrow \text{N.R.}$$

(Recall that tertiary alcohols require pyridine.)

**1.** Compound A, $C_4H_{10}O_2$, on treatment with acetyl chloride gives $C_6H_{12}O_3$, but when the reaction is carried out in the presence of pyridine, $C_8H_{14}O_4$ is obtained. Write a structure for A.

Since compound A is in the $C_nH_{2n+2}O_2$ homologous series, it must contain only alcohol or ether functions. Further, from the data, both must be alcohols, of which one is primary or secondary and the other is tertiary. Write the structure and formulate the reactions with acetyl chloride.

**2.** Compound X, $C_6H_{14}O_2$, gives $C_{10}H_{18}O_4$ on treatment with acetic anhydride only if pyridine is present; there is no reaction in the absence of pyridine. Write a structure for compound X and suggest a synthesis from acetone.

## SUGGESTED READINGS

Bordwell, F. G., and K. M. Wellman: A Rapid Test to Distinguish Tertiary from Primary or Secondary Alcohols, *J. Chem. Educ.*, **39**, 308 (1962). Uses $CrO_3$-$H_2SO_4$ in water.

Donohue, J.: On Hydrogen Bonds, *J. Chem. Educ.*, **40**, 598 (1963).

Phelan, N. F., H. H. Jaffé, and M. Orchin: A Molecular Orbital Description of the Non-classical Ion in 1,2-rearrangements, *J. Chem. Educ.*, **44**, 626 (1967).

Swinehart, J. S.: The Decolorization of Baeyer's Reagent [$KMnO_4$] by Primary and Secondary Alkanols, *J. Chem. Educ.*, **41**, 392 (1964).

Young, W. G.: Unexpected Rearrangement and Lack of Rearrangement in Allylic Systems, *J. Chem. Educ.*, **39**, 455 (1962).

## PROBLEMS

★**1.** Write the structure and name each of the isomeric heptanols, $C_7H_{16}O$, according to the IUPAC system. Label each as primary, secondary, or tertiary. Give a reasonable synthesis of each alcohol using a Grignard reaction. You may use the following organic starting materials and any necessary solvents and inorganic reagents:

$CH_2O$ $\quad$ $CH_3CHO$ $\quad$ $CH_3CH_2CHO$ $\quad$ $CH_2{-}CH_2$ (bridged by O)

**2.** Use benzene and toluene in addition to the compounds given in Prob. 1 to synthesize each of the following:

(*a*) $C_6H_5CH_2{-}C(CH_3)_2{-}OH$

★(*b*) $C_6H_5CH_2{-}CHD{-}CH_2D$

★(*c*) $C_6H_5CH_2{-}CH(OH){-}C_6H_5$

(*d*) $C_6H_5{-}C(CH_3)_2{-}C(CH_3)_2{-}C_6H_5$

(*e*) $C_6H_5CH_2{-}C(CH_3)(OH){-}CH_2C_6H_5$

**3.** Name the starting material and give the structural formula and name of the product(s) for each of the following reactions. If no reaction occurs, write N.R.

★(*a*) p-$ClC_6H_4Cl$ $\xrightarrow[\text{2. } CO_2 \quad \text{3. } H_3O^+]{\text{1. Mg in dry ether}}$

★(*b*) $[CH_3CH_2CH_2MgBr]$ + $CH_3CH_2CO_2CH_3$ $\xrightarrow[H_2O]{NH_4Cl}$

(*c*) $C_6H_5{-}C(=O){-}C_6H_5$ + $[C_6H_5{-}MgBr]$ $\xrightarrow{H_2O}$

★(*d*) $CH_3CH_2CH(OH){-}CH_3$ $\xrightarrow[H^+]{K_2Cr_2O_7}$

★(*e*) $C_6H_5CHCl_2$ $\xrightarrow[OH^-]{\text{dil.}}$

★(*f*) $CH_3CH_2OH$ + Na $\longrightarrow$

★(*g*) product in (*f*) + $(CH_3)_3CBr$ $\longrightarrow$

(*h*) O (ring ketone) $\xrightarrow{NaBH_4}$

★(*i*) $CH_2Cl$ (on benzene ring) $\xrightarrow[\text{acetone } \Delta]{\text{NaI in}}$

(*j*) CHO / $CH_3$ (on benzene ring) $\xrightarrow[2.\ H_3O^+]{1.\ LiAlH_4}$

(*k*) product in (*j*) $\xrightarrow{HBr}$

(*l*) product in (*k*) $\xrightarrow[\substack{2.\ CO_2 \\ 3.\ H_3O^+}]{1.\text{ Mg in dry ether}}$

★(*m*) $[CH_3CH_2CH_2MgI]$ + $H_2C—CH_2$ (bridged by O) $\xrightarrow{H_3O^+}$

**★4.** Write a structural formula for each molecular formula given below. (***Hint***: Start with $C_6H_6$.)

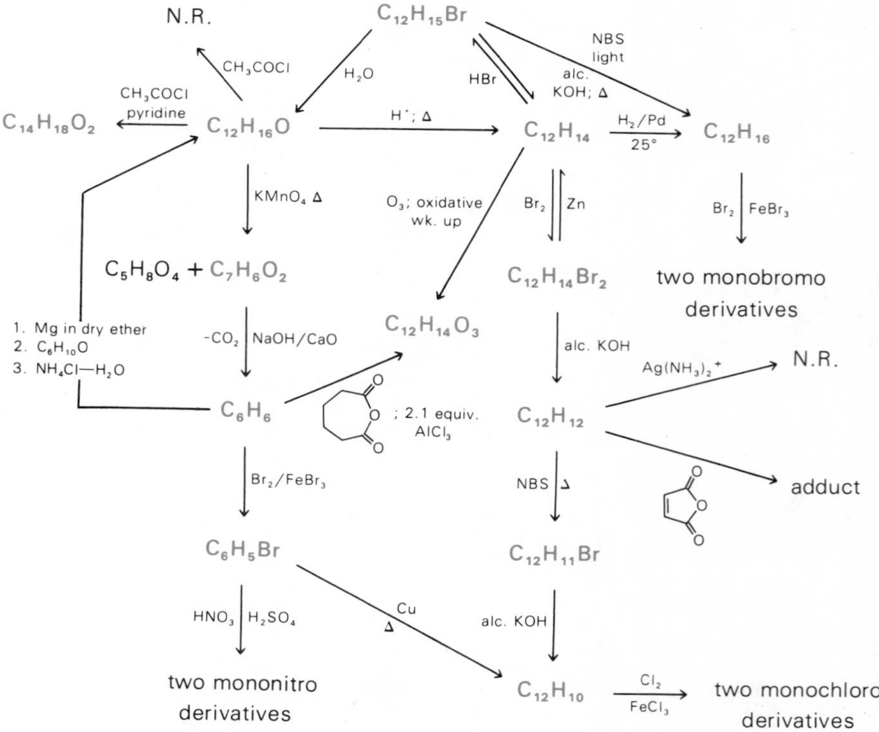

★**5.** Compound **A**, $C_7H_{16}O_2$, gave compound **B**, $C_{11}H_{20}O_4$, on treatment with acetyl chloride in pyridine. Dehydration of **A** gave compound **C**, $C_7H_{12}$, which gave no Diels-Alder adduct with maleic anhydride. Hydrogenation of **C** gave compound **D**, $C_7H_{16}$.

Compound **C** readily decolorized bromine, yielding compound **E**, which in turn gave compound **F**, $C_7H_8$, on treatment with alcoholic KOH. Compound **F** gave a precipitate with $Ag(NH_3)_2^+$ and liberated 2 moles of methane on treatment with $CH_3MgI$. Hydrogenation of **F** yielded **D**.

Compound **C** was oxidized by $KMnO_4$ to compound **G** (a diacid), which readily lost carbon dioxide, giving compound **H**. Treatment of isopropylmagnesium iodide first with carbon dioxide and then with water gave **H**.

Identify compounds **A** to **H**.

**6.** Given as starting materials the eight saturated alcohols having not more than four carbon atoms, devise syntheses of the following compounds utilizing the Grignard reagent:

★(*a*) 2,3-dimethyl-2-pentanol

(*b*) 2,3,4-trimethyl-3-pentanol

★(*c*) 2,4-dimethylpentane

(*d*) 3-ethyl-2-pentene

# Chapter Ten

Unlike ordinary alcohols, phenols, Ar—OH, have a fairly acidic hydrogen. For instance, phenols dissolve in sodium hydroxide but not in the weaker base sodium bicarbonate. The phenoxide anion formed is stabilized by resonance. Phenols may be considered the enol form of cyclohexadienones, in which the equilibrium lies almost entirely on the enol side.

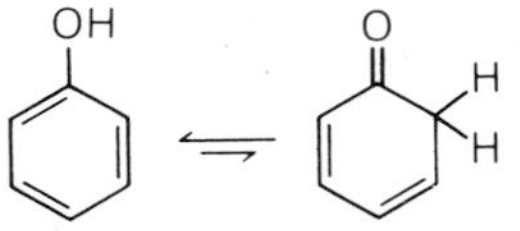

OH O H H

The driving force for the predominance of this enol form is the formation of the six-$\pi$-electron aromatic system. Phenols are extremely reactive in electrophilic aromatic substitution because of the electron donation of the unshared electrons on the oxygen atom (Sec. 7-18).

In general, a phenol cannot be converted directly to the corresponding halide, but the phenolic function can be removed readily in high yield under mild conditions (Sec. 10-8).

## NOMENCLATURE

Many aromatic hydroxy compounds are known by trivial names, which are retained in the IUPAC system when they are of long standing. In complicated cases, the —OH is designated as a substituent on the aromatic system (see Table 10-1).

# Phenols

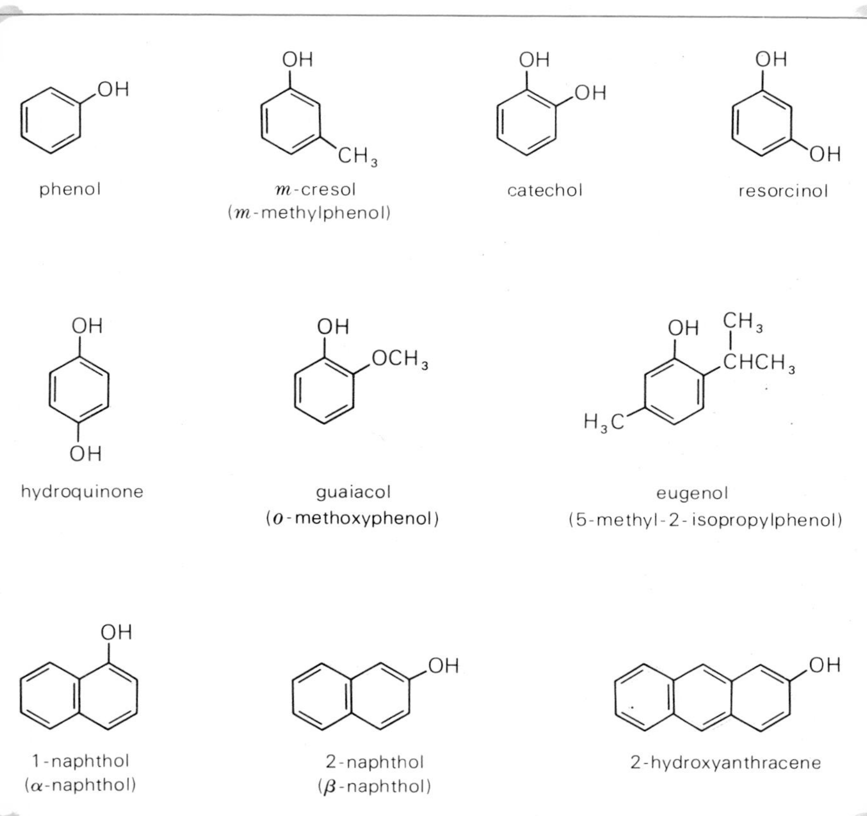


**Table 10-1**
**Examples of phenol nomenclature**

## PREPARATION

### 10-1 FUSION OF SULFONIC ACID SALTS

Sulfonic acids, Ar—$SO_3H$, derived from the reversible reaction of aromatic hydrocarbons with $H_2SO_4$ or oleum, can be converted to salts, for example, Ar—$SO_3^-K^+$, by treatment with dilute base (Sec. 7-7). Fusion of these salts with molten KOH at high temperatures leads to the formation of phenoxides, the salts of phenols.

*Example*

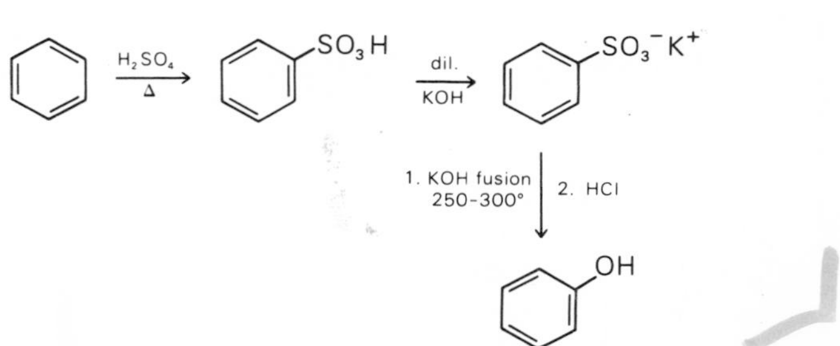


The phenol itself is liberated by treating the cooled reaction mixture with dilute acid. Obviously this reaction cannot be used where base- or heat-sensitive functional groups are present. Even under favorable circumstances the yields are only fair to good.

### 10-2 PHENOLS VIA DIAZONIUM SALTS

Probably the best general method for the preparation of phenols is the decomposition of an aryldiazonium salt, Ar—$N_2^+$, in the presence of dilute acid. These salts are prepared from primary aromatic amines, Ar—$NH_2$, at low temperatures using nitrous acid, HONO, which is generated in solution from HCl or $H_2SO_4$ and $NaNO_2$. Since these aryldiazonium salts are unstable when dry, they are usually used in solution.

*Examples*

$NH_2$ (aniline) $\xrightarrow[(HCl\ +\ NaNO_2)\ 0\text{-}5°]{HNO_2}$ [ $N_2^+Cl^-$ (benzenediazonium chloride) ] $\xrightarrow[\Delta]{H_3O^+}$ OH (phenol) + $N_2\uparrow$

aniline — benzenediazonium chloride — phenol

3-bromo-4-aminotoluene

$\xrightarrow[0\text{-}5°]{H_2SO_4,\ NaNO_2}$ [ $N_2^+HSO_4^-$ ] $\xrightarrow[\Delta\ 85\%\ \text{yield}]{H_2O,\ H_2SO_4}$ $+ N_2\uparrow$

3-bromo-4-hydroxytoluene

This is a convenient route to phenols since many aromatic compounds readily undergo nitration, and the subsequent reduction can be accomplished in good yield by a metal-acid system.

$\xrightarrow[H_2SO_4]{HNO_3}$ nitrobenzene $\xrightarrow[HCl]{\text{Sn or Fe}}$ aniline

## 10-3 PHENOLS VIA THE GRIGNARD REAGENT

The usual side reaction of Grignard reagents with oxygen can be used as a fair preparative method of phenols. In the example below the reaction of phenylmagnesium chloride with oxygen gives off energy in the form of light (rather than heat), a phenomenon known as *chemiluminescence*.

Cl $\xrightarrow[\text{dry THF}]{\text{Mg in}}$ [ MgCl ] $\xrightarrow{O_2}$ [ O—O—MgCl ] $\xrightarrow{H_3O^+}$ OH

## 10-4 DISPLACEMENTS ON ACTIVATED HYDROCARBONS

Phenols, such as *o*- and *p*-nitrophenol and picric acid, can be prepared by treatment of the corresponding halonitro compound with base (see Sec. 8-10).

$$p\text{-}ClC_6H_4NO_2 \xrightarrow{OH^-} p\text{-}HOC_6H_4NO_2 + Cl^-$$

The substitution occurs only when highly electron-withdrawing substituents are located in the ortho and para positions of the halobenzene. The resonance forms of these ortho and para halonitro compounds indicate a low electron density at the carbon bearing the halogen atom, thus facilitating the attack of the $OH^-$.

*Mechanism*: $O_2N{-}C_6H_4{-}Cl + OH^- \longrightarrow [O_2N{-}C_6H_4(Cl)(OH)]^- \longrightarrow O_2N{-}C_6H_4{-}OH + Cl^-$

A notable exception to this activation requirement is the ***industrial*** reaction of chlorobenzene with hot concentrated base at high temperatures. This is the basis for the Dow Chemical Company process, a commercial source of phenols.

Industrial preparation: $\underset{\text{chlorobenzene}}{C_6H_5Cl} \xrightarrow[\text{pressure}]{OH^-;\ \Delta} \underset{\text{phenol}}{C_6H_5OH} + Cl^-$

# REACTIONS

## 10-5 ACIDITY

Ordinary alcohols are nonacidic. Phenols are weakly acidic and dissolve in dilute sodium hydroxide but *not* in dilute sodium bicarbonate; the stronger organic acids, those containing the carboxyl group, $R{-}CO_2H$, will dissolve in both. The resonance stabilization of the phenoxide ion is a strong driving force for the formation of the anion.

A comparison of phenol and cyclohexanol is shown in Fig. 10-1.

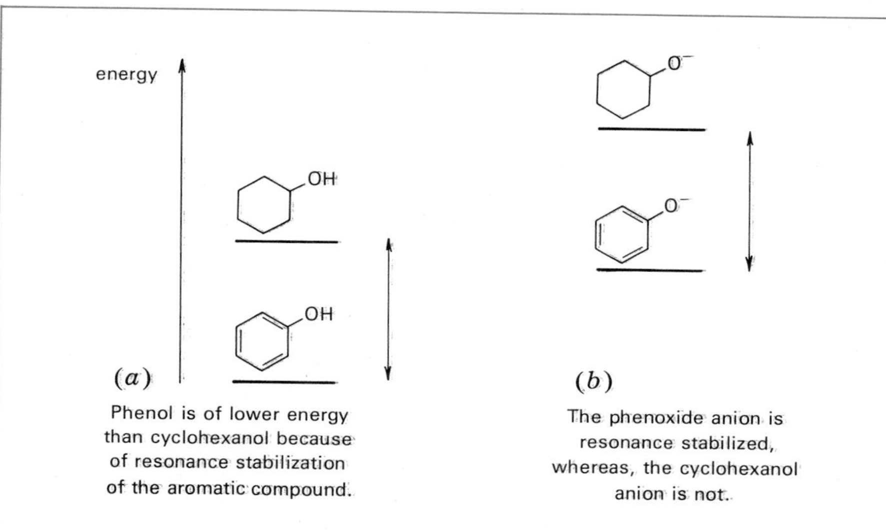
energy
OH
OH
$O^-$
$O^-$
(a)
Phenol is of lower energy than cyclohexanol because of resonance stabilization of the aromatic compound.
(b)
The phenoxide anion is resonance stabilized, whereas, the cyclohexanol anion is not.

**Figure 10-1** **Relative stability of phenol, cyclohexanol, and their anions**

## 10-6 ETHER FORMATION

Phenols can be converted to the corresponding methyl or ethyl ethers by the reaction of the phenoxide ion with dimethyl or diethyl sulfate. Although both alkyl groups can be displaced, the second requires more strenuous conditions.

$$C_6H_5O^-Na^+ + CH_3{-}O{-}SO_2{-}O{-}CH_3 \longrightarrow C_6H_5OCH_3 + CH_3SO_4^-\,Na^+$$

sodium phenoxide — dimethyl sulfate — anisole — sodium methylsulfate

The phenoxide ion also displaces the halogen atom of primary and secondary alkyl halides; tertiary halides undergo extensive elimination

(Sec. 8-7). Simple aromatic halides are unreactive toward ordinary displacement reactions.

$$C_6H_5O^-K^+ + CH_3CH_2I \longrightarrow C_6H_5OCH_2CH_3 + K^+I^-$$

potassium phenoxide; ethyl iodide; ethyl phenyl ether

$$o\text{-}CH_3OC_6H_4OH + CH_2{=}CH{-}CH_2Br \xrightarrow[85\%\ \text{yield}]{K_2CO_3\ \text{in acetone};\ \Delta} o\text{-}CH_3OC_6H_4{-}O{-}CH_2{-}CH{=}CH_2$$

guaiacol; allyl bromide; allyl guaiacol ether

### 10-7 ESTER FORMATION

Phenols do not undergo simple Fischer esterification in a reasonable time, and the equilibrium generally lies toward the left.

$$R{-}C(=O){-}OH + C_6H_5OH \xrightarrow{H^+} \text{N.R. in an appreciable time}$$

Instead of the simple reaction with an organic acid, a more *reactive* derivative of the organic acid is used with the salt of the phenol. The reactions are generally irreversible.

$$C_6H_5{-}O^-Na^+ + CH_3{-}C(=O){-}Cl \longrightarrow C_6H_5{-}O{-}C(=O){-}CH_3 + Na^+Cl^-$$

sodium phenoxide; acetyl chloride; phenyl acetate

### 10-8 REMOVAL OF THE PHENOLIC —OH GROUP

Recently a hydrogenolysis reaction has been discovered in which phenolic hydroxyl groups are readily removed under mild conditions. Several heterocyclic reagents can be used, but 1-phenyl-5-chlorotetrazole is preferred, followed by hydrogenolysis of the ether with 5% palladium-on-charcoal in ethanol or THF at 35°.

4-hydroxybiphenyl ($p$-phenylphenol) + Cl—C(=N—N=N—N—$C_6H_5$) $\xrightarrow[\text{acetone}]{K_2CO_3 \text{ in}}$ biphenyl-O—C(tetrazole, N—$C_6H_5$)

$\downarrow$ $H_2$, Pd-on-C (80% yield)

biphenyl + O=C(tetrazole, N—H, N—$C_6H_5$) + HCl

Using 1-phenyl-5-chlorotetrazole, the following phenols have been reduced (yields in parentheses); formulate the reactions:

**1.** 2-naphthol (65%)

**2.** guaiacol (86% anisole)

**3.** $p$-chlorophenol (70% benzene; hydrogenolysis also of C—Cl bond)

## 10-9 ELECTROPHILIC AROMATIC SUBSTITUTION

The very facile electrophilic aromatic substitution reactions of phenols and their salts were discussed in Sec. 7-18. You should review these reactions, noting particularly the ortho-para substitution patterns involved.

resorcinol $\xrightarrow[\text{ZnCl}_2 \text{ (cat.)}]{CH_3CO_2H}$ 2,4-dihydroxyacetophenone ($COCH_3$)

Phenols undergo nitrosation at low temperatures in the presence of nitrous acid.

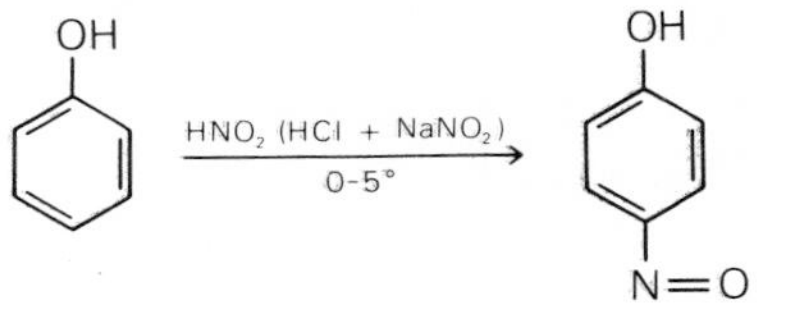

$$\text{phenol} \xrightarrow[0\text{-}5^\circ]{HNO_2\ (HCl + NaNO_2)} p\text{-nitrosophenol}$$

phenol p-nitrosophenol

How is this nitrosonium ion, $NO^+$, formed? Propose a mechanism for this reaction, assuming it to be an electrophilic aromatic substitution.

## 10-10 THE CLAISEN REARRANGEMENT

Phenyl allyl ethers rearrange, simply on heating to about 140°, to give the corresponding ortho substituted phenol.

*Specific*:

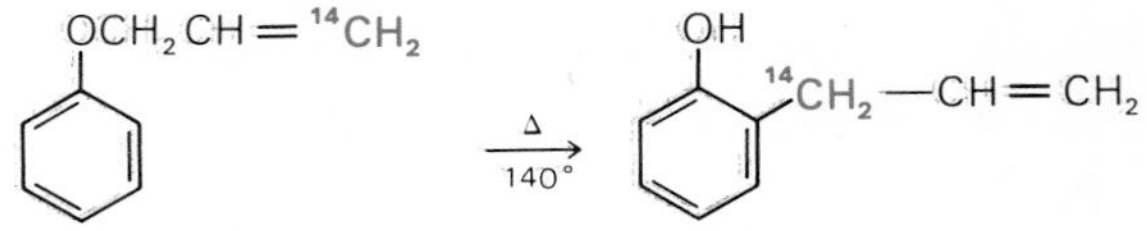

$$C_6H_5OCH_2CH{=}^{14}CH_2 \xrightarrow[140^\circ]{\Delta} o\text{-}HOC_6H_4{-}^{14}CH_2{-}CH{=}CH_2$$

If the terminal carbon is labeled with $^{14}C$, this carbon is adjacent to the aromatic ring in the final product. A six-membered transition state leads initially to the dienone intermediate, which then tautomerizes readily, as expected, to the observed phenol.

*Mechanism*:

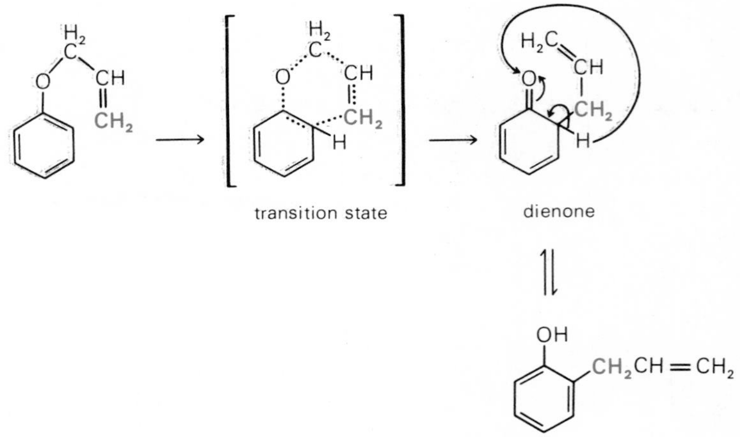

transition state

dienone

$$\rightleftharpoons \; o\text{-}HOC_6H_4CH_2CH{=}CH_2$$

The position of the labeled carbon in the product was shown by oxidation of the methyl ether of the $^{14}C$ substituted compound, which produces $CO_2$ with a normal $^{12}C$ isotopic content. Since oxidation of the phenol itself would lead to considerable oxidation of the aromatic ring, the compound is first converted to an ether, which is relatively stable under these oxidative conditions.

$$o\text{-}CH_3OC_6H_4{}^{14}CH_2-CH=CH_2 \xrightarrow[\Delta]{KMnO_4} [o\text{-}CH_3OC_6H_4{}^{14}CH_2CO_2H] + CO_2$$

$$[o\text{-}CH_3OC_6H_4{}^{14}CH_2CO_2H] \xrightarrow[\Delta]{KMnO_4} o\text{-}CH_3OC_6H_4{}^{14}CO_2H + CO_2$$

Decarboxylation of the *o*-methoxybenzoic acid finally gives all the radioactive carbon as $^{14}CO_2$.

$$o\text{-}CH_3OC_6H_4{}^{14}COOH \xrightarrow{\Delta} C_6H_5OCH_3 + {}^{14}CO_2$$

## QUALITATIVE TESTS

Phenols are often identified by the fact that they dissolve in strong bases, such as sodium hydroxide, but not in sodium bicarbonate; organic acids usually dissolve in both, and alcohols dissolve in neither.

A dilute yellow-orange solution of ferric chloride, $FeCl_3$, will usually change color (varying from green to violet to brown) on treatment with a phenol or enol. The color is due to the complex mixture of oxidation products obtained.

## SUGGESTED READINGS

### Phenols

Clevenger, S.: Flower Pigments, *Sci. Am.*, **216** (6), 84 (1964). A discussion of various heterocyclic phenols found in nature.

Offenhauer, R. D.: The Direct Esterification of Phenols, *J. Chem. Educ.*, **41**, 39 (1964).

Steelink, C.: What is Humic Acid?, *J. Chem. Educ.*, **40**, 379 (1963). Discusses the composition of the mixture of phenolic derivatives obtained by extracting soil with base.

### Chemiluminescence

Haas, J.H., Jr.: Chemiluminescent Reactions in Solution, *J. Chem. Educ.*, **44**, 396 (1967). Discusses specific chemical systems which demonstrate chemiluminescence.

McElroy, W.D., and H.H. Seliger: Biological Luminescence, *Sci., Am.*, **207** (6), 76 (1962). Discusses the phenomenon as observed in many biological systems, with emphasis on the firefly material, luciferin.

## PROBLEMS

**1.** Name the starting material and give the structural formula and name of the product(s). If no reaction occurs, write N.R.

★(*a*) *o*-cresol $\xrightarrow{KHCO_3}$

(*b*) Br, OH + $CH_3CH_2CH_2OH \xrightarrow{H^+}$

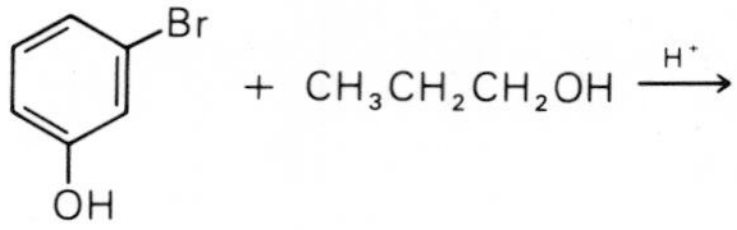

★(*c*) 2,4,6-tribromophenol $\xrightarrow[0\text{-}5°]{HCl\text{-}NaNO_2}$

★(*d*) $CO_2H$ + OH, OH $\xrightarrow{H^+}$

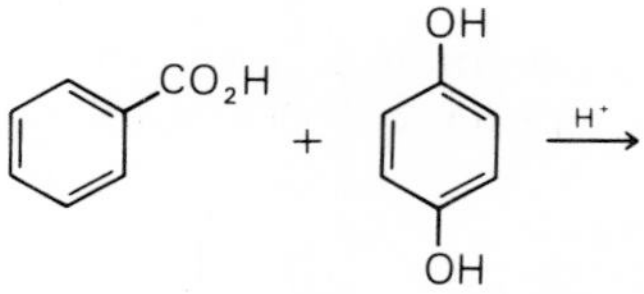

(*e*) α-naphthol $\xrightarrow{NaOH}$

(*f*) $CH_3$, $OCH_2C{=}CH_2$, $CH_3$ $\xrightarrow{\Delta}$

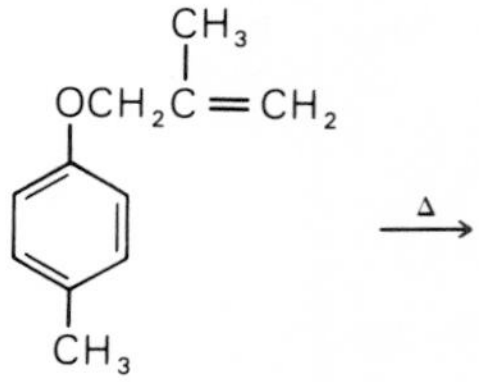

★(*g*) $SO_3H$ $\xrightarrow[3.\ H_3O^+]{1.\ \text{dil. KOH} \quad 2.\ \text{fuse with KOH}}$

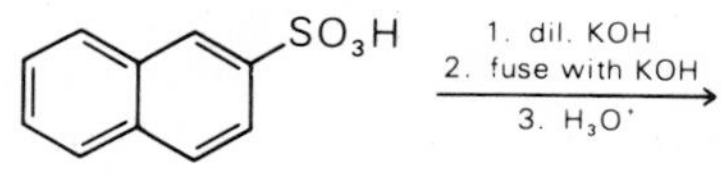

★(*h*) $CH_3$, $CH_3$ $\xrightarrow[3.\ HONO\ \text{at}\ 0\text{-}5° \quad 4.\ H_3O^+;\ \Delta \quad 5.\ CH_3OSO_2OCH_3;\ KOH]{1.\ HNO_3\text{-}H_2SO_4 \quad 2.\ Fe/HCl}$

(*i*) $C(CH_3)_3$, $CH_3$ $\xrightarrow[3.\ \text{dil. HCl} \quad 4.\ NaOH \quad 5.\ CH_3CH_2CH_2\overset{O}{\overset{\|}{C}}Cl]{1.\ H_2SO_4 \quad 2.\ \text{KOH fusion}}$

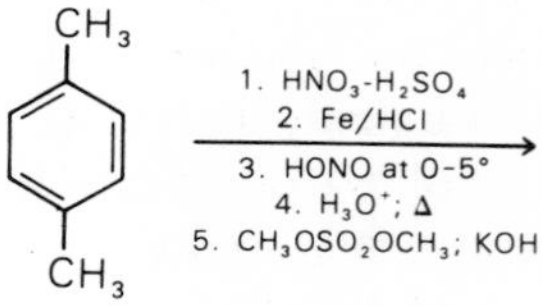

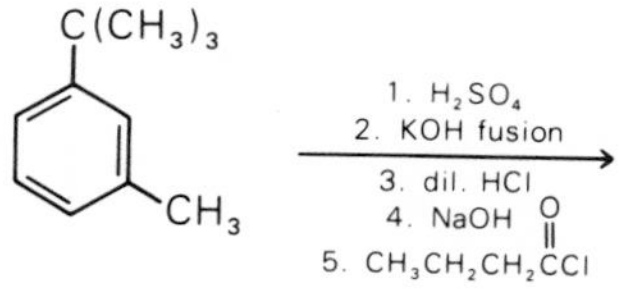

(*j*) $NO_2$ $\xrightarrow[3.\ \Delta;\ H_3O^+ \quad 4.\ NaOH]{1.\ Sn/HCl \quad 2.\ HCl\text{-}NaNO_2,\ 0°}$

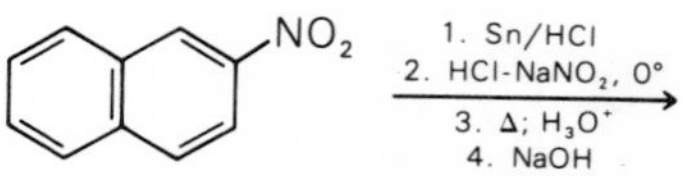

★**2.** Suppose you were given the following pure compounds in separate test tubes. How could you rapidly distinguish between them by chemical means? Name these compounds.

(*a*) $CH{=}CH_2$ $OCH_3$ OH, $CH{=}CH_2$

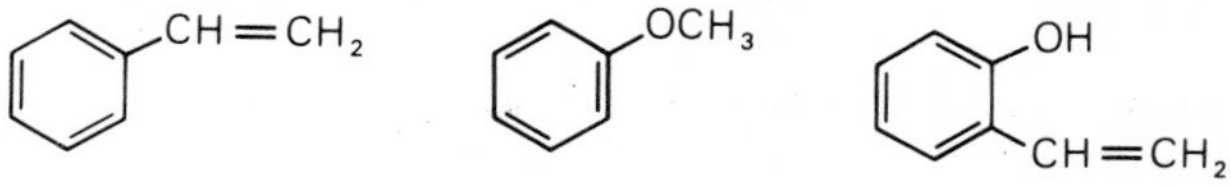

(*b*) (o-methylphenol: OH, $CH_3$) (benzene–$CH_2OH$) (benzene–$CO_2H$)

**3.** Synthesize the following compounds using only benzene, toluene, any of the $C_1$ to $C_4$ aldehydes, and any necessary solvents and inorganic reagents.

(*a*) $C_6H_5$–O–C(=O)–$CH_2CH_3$

★(*b*) $O^-K^+$ / $CH_3$ (para-substituted benzene)

(*c*) OH / $CH_2CH{=}CH_2$ / N=O

★(*d*) O–$CH_2CH_2CH_2CH_3$ (on benzene)

via a diazonium salt reaction

# Chapter Eleven

Organic ethers, R—O—R', are chemically unreactive and are often used as solvents. Diethyl ether and the cyclic ether tetrahydrofuran are excellent solvents for Grignard syntheses (Sec. 9-11). Diethyl ether is also a common anesthetic.

The ether function can occur as part of a ring structure, as in tetrahydrofuran.

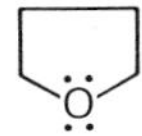

tetrahydrofuran

Unlike the open-chain ethers smaller heterocycles, such as ethylene oxide

$$H_2C\text{—}CH_2$$
$$\diagdown\ddot{\underset{\cdot\cdot}{O}}\diagup$$

ethylene oxide

are quite reactive since ring-opening reactions relieve the strain.

Most dialkyl ethers are liquids, but many alkyl aromatic and diaryl ones are solids. Diethyl ether is commonly used as an extraction solvent not only because of its ability to dissolve many organic compounds but also because it is readily removed at its boiling point, 35°.

## NOMENCLATURE

There are two systems of naming organic ethers. The IUPAC system denotes the alkoxyl group, RO—, as a substituent on the longest chain;

# Ethers

$CH_3OCH_2CH_3$ is named methoxyethane. The other method names each alkyl or aryl group on the oxygen atom followed by the word ether. This name is written as three (or two) separate words; $CH_3OCH_2CH_3$ is named methyl ethyl ether. The smaller of the two groups is named first:

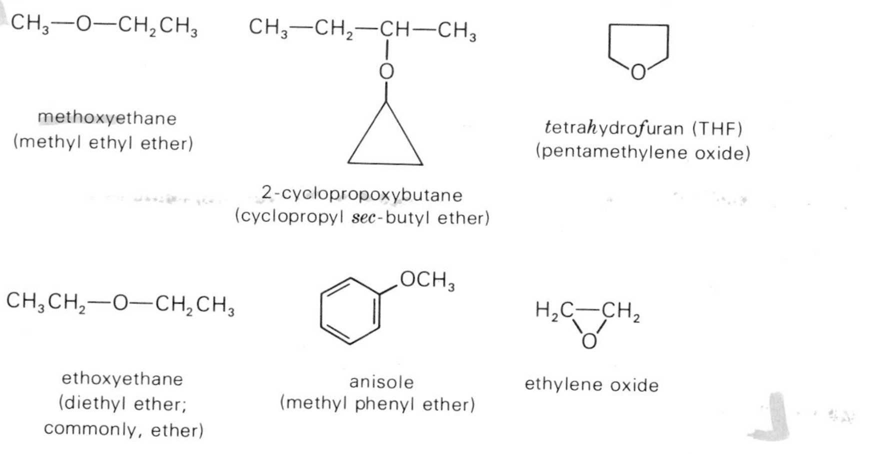


methoxyethane (methyl ethyl ether)

2-cyclopropoxybutane (cyclopropyl *sec*-butyl ether)

*t*etra*h*ydro*f*uran (THF) (pentamethylene oxide)

ethoxyethane (diethyl ether; commonly, ether)

anisole (methyl phenyl ether)

ethylene oxide

## PREPARATION

Ethers are commonly prepared by three methods: (1) the reaction of an organic halide with an alkoxide or phenoxide anion (the Williamson synthesis), (2) dehydration of alcohols to yield dialkyl ethers, and (3) the reaction of a phenoxide anion with dimethyl or diethyl sulfate.

## 11-1 THE WILLIAMSON SYNTHESIS

Alkoxides and phenoxides are formed by treating an alcohol with metallic sodium or a phenol with sodium hydroxide.

Alkoxide formation: $R{-}OH \xrightarrow{Na} RO^- Na^+ + \frac{1}{2}H_2$

Phenoxide formation: $C_6H_5OH \xrightarrow{NaOH} C_6H_5O^- Na^+ + H_2O$

These sodium salts can displace the halogen atom from a primary or secondary halide via an $S_N2$ reaction pathway.

*General*: $RO^- + R'{-}CH_2{-}X \longrightarrow R{-}O{-}CH_2R' + X^-$

*Specific*:

$(CH_3)_2CH{-}OH \xrightarrow{Na} (CH_3)_2CH{-}O^- Na^+ \xrightarrow{CH_3CH_2Br} (CH_3)_2CH{-}O{-}CH_2CH_3$

isopropyl alcohol — sodium isopropoxide — 2-ethoxypropane (ethyl isopropyl ether)

*Mechanism*: $S_N2$ displacement.

$(CH_3)_2CH{-}O^- + CH_2CH_3(Br) \longrightarrow (CH_3)_2CH{-}O{-}CH_2CH_3 + Br^-$

This reaction, known as the Williamson synthesis, can be used to prepare either symmetrical or unsymmetrical ethers. Tertiary halides cannot be used, since the reaction is carried out in the presence of a strong base; the major product is an olefin formed by an $E_2$ elimination (Sec. 8-7). Aryl and vinyl halides cannot be used, because they are unreactive in $S_N2$ reactions (Sec. 8-7).

*Examples*:

$C_6H_5{-}O^-Na^+ \xrightarrow{CH_3CH_2Br} C_6H_5{-}O{-}CH_2CH_3 + Br^-$

sodium phenoxide — ethyl phenyl ether

$o\text{-}NO_2C_6H_4{-}OH \xrightarrow[\text{2. } CH_3CH_2CH_2CH_2Br \text{ 80\% yield}]{\text{1. } K_2CO_3 (K^+ \text{ salt formation})} o\text{-}NO_2C_6H_4{-}O{-}CH_2CH_2CH_2CH_3$

*o*-nitrophenol — *o*-*n*-butoxynitrobenzene (butyl *o*-nitrophenyl ether)

## 11-2 SYMMETRICAL ETHERS FROM ALCOHOLS

The reaction of an alcohol with sulfuric acid yields products which depend upon the structure of the alcohol and the reaction conditions employed. Tertiary alcohols, for example, give almost exclusively olefins that are products of dehydration.

$$(CH_3)_3C{-}OH \xrightarrow[140°]{H^+} (CH_3)_2C{=}CH_2 + H_2O$$

The intermediate tertiary carbonium ion is readily formed and is considerably stabilized by the alkyl substituents (Sec. 9-4). Primary alcohols, and to some extent secondary alcohols, react with sulfuric acid at 140° to form the symmetrical ether.

$$2CH_3CH_2OH \xrightarrow[140°]{H_2SO_4} \underset{\text{b.p. 35°; removed as formed}}{CH_3CH_2{-}O{-}CH_2CH_3} + H_2O$$

Even with ethanol, significant amounts of ethylene are formed at 150°.

$$CH_3CH_2OH \xrightarrow[150°]{H_2SO_4} CH_2{=}CH_2 + H_2O$$

The primary and secondary carbonium ions are relatively unstable and react quickly with the alcohol to give a protonated ether, which is in equilibrium with the ether itself.

*Mechanism*:

$$CH_3CH_2\ddot{\underset{..}{O}}H \xrightarrow{H^+} [CH_3CH_2\overset{+}{\underset{..}{O}}H_2] \xrightarrow{-H_2O} [CH_3\overset{+}{C}H_2] \xrightarrow{CH_3CH_2\ddot{O}H}$$

$$[CH_3CH_2{-}\overset{+}{\underset{H}{\ddot{O}}}{-}CH_2CH_3] \rightleftharpoons CH_3CH_2{-}\ddot{\underset{..}{O}}{-}CH_2CH_3 + H^+$$

Phenolic ethers cannot be formed by reaction with sulfuric acid for two reasons: (1) sulfonation of phenols takes place readily at temperatures well below 140°, and (2) because phenols have a lower electron density at the oxygen atom, the initial protonation does not occur easily.

$$\left[ C_6H_5{-}\ddot{\underset{..}{O}}{-}H \longleftrightarrow (\text{cyclohexadienyl anion}){=}\overset{+}{O}{-}H \longleftrightarrow \text{and other forms} \right]$$

## 11-3 ALKYL ARYL ETHERS FROM DIALKYL SULFATES

Phenoxide anions can displace alkyl groups from dimethyl sulfate, $CH_3O—SO_2—OCH_3$, or diethyl sulfate, $CH_3CH_2O—SO_2—OCH_2CH_3$, in the same manner that they displace halide ions from primary or secondary alkyl halides.

*Mechanism*:

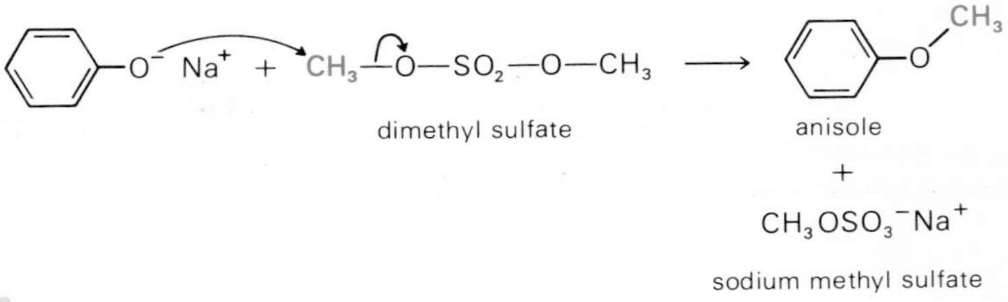

$$C_6H_5—O^- \ Na^+ + CH_3—O—SO_2—O—CH_3 \longrightarrow C_6H_5—O—CH_3 + CH_3OSO_3^-Na^+$$

dimethyl sulfate; anisole; sodium methyl sulfate

Both alkyl groups may undergo displacement, but the second requires more strenuous conditions, since it involves the attack of the negatively charged phenoxide anion on the negatively charged methyl sulfate anion. When the phenol is valuable, a 1:1 molar ratio is employed; only the first alkyl group is utilized.

## 11-4 EPOXIDES

Three-membered cyclic ethers, known as ***epoxides*** or ethylene oxides, are highly strained and very reactive toward nucleophilic attack. Epoxides are commonly prepared in the laboratory by the reaction of an alkene with a ***peracid***, $R—\overset{O}{\overset{\|}{C}}—O—O—H$, which in turn can be formed from an organic acid or anhydride and hydrogen peroxide. Common examples are peracetic acid, trifluoroperacetic acid, $CF_3CO_3H$, perbenzoic acid, and monoperphthalic acid.

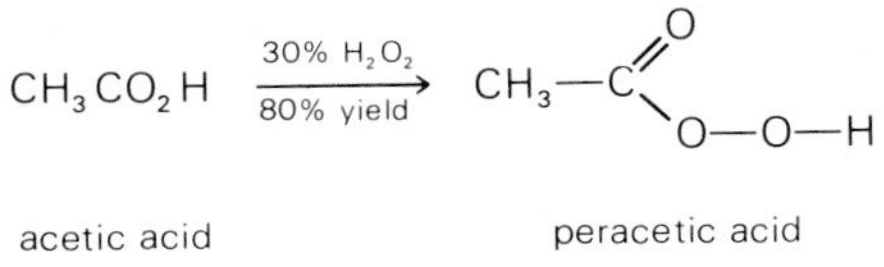

$$CH_3CO_2H \xrightarrow[80\% \text{ yield}]{30\% \ H_2O_2} CH_3—C(=O)—O—O—H$$

acetic acid; peracetic acid

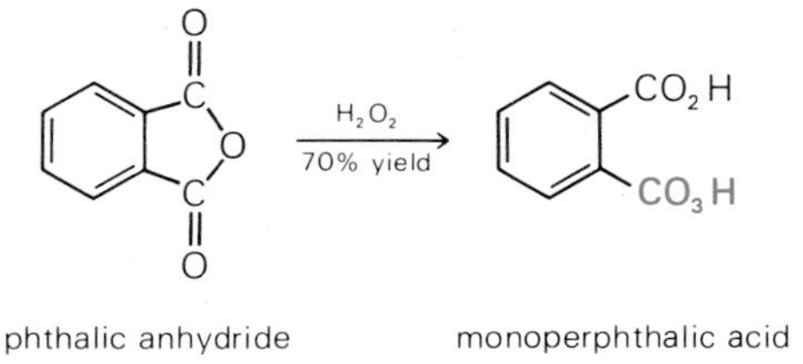

$$\text{phthalic anhydride} \xrightarrow[70\% \text{ yield}]{H_2O_2} C_6H_4(CO_2H)(CO_3H)$$

phthalic anhydride; monoperphthalic acid

When treated with an alkene, the highly reactive peracid gives the corresponding epoxide, in which the stereochemistry of the alkene substituents is preserved in the product.

$$\underset{\textit{trans}\text{-stilbene}}{H_5C_6(H)C{=}C(H)C_6H_5} \xrightarrow[75\%\ \text{yield}]{CH_3CO_3H} \underset{\textit{trans}\text{-stilbene oxide}}{H_5C_6(H)C{-}C(H)C_6H_5\ (\text{epoxide, }O\text{ bridge})} + CH_3CO_2H$$

$$\underset{\text{cyclohexene}}{C_6H_{10}} \xrightarrow{C_6H_5CO_3H} \underset{\text{cyclohexene oxide}}{C_6H_{10}O} + C_6H_5COOH$$

The commercial preparation of ethylene oxide employs an internal $S_N2$ displacement on ethylene chlorohydrin. Halohydrins and base can also be used in the laboratory, and good yields are obtained, although elimination and halogen displacement are often competing reactions.

$$\underset{\text{ethylene}}{CH_2{=}CH_2} \xrightarrow[NaOH]{Cl_2} \underset{\text{ethylene chlorohydrin}}{CH_2(OH){-}CH_2(Cl)} \xrightarrow{\text{base}} CH_2(O^-){-}CH_2(Cl) \longrightarrow \underset{\text{ethylene oxide}}{H_2C{-}CH_2\ (\text{bridged by }O)}$$

The specific ring-opening reaction of ethylene oxide with Grignard reagents has already been discussed as a method of preparing primary alcohols (Sec. 9-14). Many other nucleophiles also react readily. In addition, epoxides are readily opened in acid-catalyzed reactions.

*Overall*:

$$H_2C{-}CH_2\ (\text{bridged by }O) \xrightarrow[H^+]{H_2O} CH_2(OH){-}CH_2(OH)$$

*Mechanism*:

$$H_2C{-}CH_2\ (\text{bridged by }\ddot{O}) \xrightarrow{H^+} H_2C{-}CH_2\ (\text{bridged by }{}^{+}\ddot{O}{-}H) \xrightarrow{\ddot{O}H_2} CH_2(OH){-}CH_2(\overset{+}{O}H_2) \xrightarrow{-H^+} CH_2(OH){-}CH_2(OH)$$

## REACTIONS

### 11-5 CLEAVAGE BY HBr AND HI

Ordinary alkyl ethers are unreactive toward most reagents but can be cleaved by HBr or HI, yielding the corresponding alkyl halides and water.

*General*: $R{-}\ddot{\underset{..}{O}}{-}R' \xrightarrow{2HBr} R{-}Br + R'{-}Br + H_2O$

*Specific*: $(CH_3)_2CH{-}\ddot{\underset{..}{O}}{-}CH_2CH_3 \xrightarrow{2HBr} (CH_3)_2CHBr + CH_3CH_2Br + H_2O$

The mechanism involves protonation of the ether [Eq. (*a*)] followed by carbon-oxygen bond cleavage to give an alcohol and the more stable carbonium ion [Eq. (*b*)]. Note that the secondary, rather than the primary, carbonium ion forms. It then combines with the halide ion [Eq. (*c*)].

*Mechanism*: $$(CH_3)_2CH{-}\ddot{\underset{..}{O}}{-}CH_2CH_3 \rightleftharpoons \left[(CH_3)_2CH{-}\underset{+}{\overset{H}{\ddot{O}}}{-}CH_2CH_3\right] \qquad (a)$$

oxonium ion

$$\left[(CH_3)_2CH{-}\underset{+}{\overset{H}{\ddot{O}}}{-}CH_2CH_3\right] \longrightarrow [(CH_3)_2\overset{+}{C}H] + HO{-}CH_2CH_3 \qquad (b)$$

$$[(CH_3)_2\overset{+}{C}H] \xrightarrow{Br^-} (CH_3)_2CH{-}Br \qquad (c)$$

An alternative pathway for Eqs. (*b*) and (*c*) is the direct displacement of the alcohol from the oxonium ion by the halide ion, which can be observed with strong nucleophiles.

$$\left[(CH_3)_2CH{-}\underset{+}{\overset{H}{\ddot{O}}}{-}CH_2CH_3\right] \xrightarrow{Br^-} (CH_3)_2CH{-}Br + HO{-}CH_2CH_3$$

The alcohol is then converted to the halide via the mechanism discussed in Sec. 9-3.

$$CH_3CH_2OH \xrightarrow{HBr} [CH_3CH_2\overset{+}{O}H_2] \xrightarrow{Br^-} CH_3CH_2Br + H_2O$$

Since the ether cleavage involves an intermediate carbonium ion, traces of olefin may be formed.

Side reactions: $$[(CH_3)_2\overset{+}{C}H] \xrightarrow{-H^+} CH_2{=}CH{-}CH_3$$

$$[CH_3CH_2^{\,+}] \xrightarrow{-H^+} CH_2{=}CH_2$$

Cyclic ethers are also readily opened by hydrogen bromide and hydrogen iodide. 1,4- and 1,5-Dihalides are obtained in good yield from tetrahydrofuran and tetrahydropyran.

*Examples*:

$$\text{tetrahydrofuran} \xrightarrow[\substack{(KI\,+\,H_3PO_4)\\95\%\ \text{yield}}]{HI} \underset{|\qquad\qquad\qquad\ \ |}{\underset{I\qquad\qquad\qquad\ \ I}{CH_2CH_2CH_2CH_2}}$$

tetrahydrofuran 1,4-diiodobutane

$$\text{tetrahydropyran} \xrightarrow[H^+]{HBr} Br-CH_2CH_2CH_2CH_2CH_2-Br$$

tetrahydropyran 1,5-dibromopentane (pentamethylene bromide)

> Write a reasonable mechanism for one of these ring-opening reactions.

On cleavage by HI or HBr phenyl alkyl ethers give the phenol and an alkyl halide. Since phenols do not react with HBr or HI, aryl halides are not formed.

*Overall*:

$$C_6H_5OCH_3 \xrightarrow{HI} C_6H_5OH + CH_3I$$

*Mechanism*:

$$C_6H_5\ddot{O}CH_3 \underset{}{\overset{H^+}{\rightleftharpoons}} \left[C_6H_5\overset{+}{\ddot{O}}(H)CH_3\right]$$

$$\left[C_6H_5\overset{+}{\ddot{O}}(H)CH_3\right] \xrightarrow{I^-} C_6H_5\ddot{O}H + CH_3I$$

## 11-6 AROMATIC SUBSTITUTION OF PHENOLIC ETHERS

Phenolic ethers like phenols, are ortho-para directors and only slightly less reactive than the corresponding phenols.

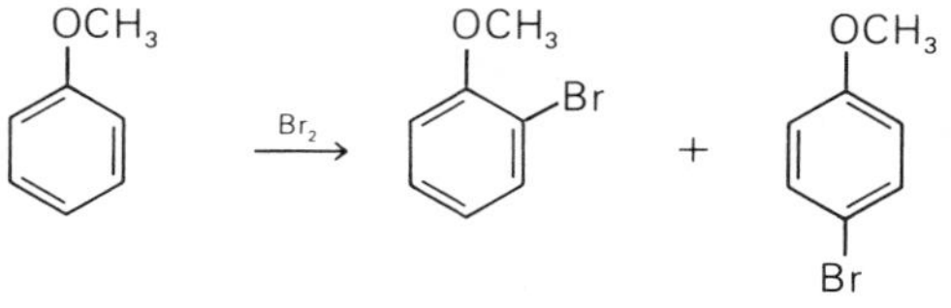

$$\text{anisole} \xrightarrow{Br_2} o\text{-bromoanisole} + p\text{-bromoanisole}$$

anisole $\quad$ *o*-bromoanisole $\quad$ *p*-bromoanisole

## 11-7 ETHERS AS SOLVENTS

Diethyl ether, tetrahydrofuran, 1,4-dioxane, and diglyme

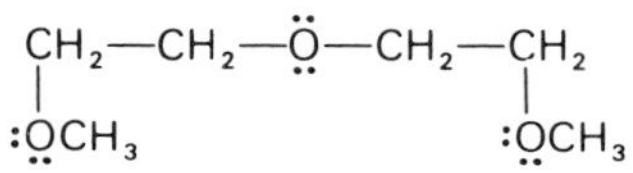

$$CH_3\ddot{O}-CH_2-CH_2-\ddot{O}-CH_2-CH_2-\ddot{O}CH_3$$

diglyme

are common solvents, particularly in Grignard reactions. Because the unshared pairs of electrons of the oxygen atom in these compounds can be donated to positive species and coordinated with them, they readily solvate centers of low electron density.

## PROBLEMS

**1.** Name each of the following compounds using a consistent system of nomenclature:

★(*a*) Br—$C_6H_4$—$OCH_3$ (para)

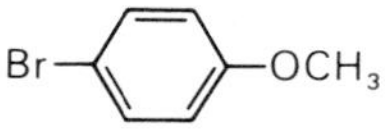

(*b*) $(CH_3)_2CH—O—CH(CH_3)_2$

★(*c*) $CH_3—C(CH_3)_2—O—C_6H_{11}$ (cyclohexyl)

★(*d*) [six-membered ring containing O]

(*e*) $C_5H_9—O—CH_2CH_3$ (cyclopentyl)

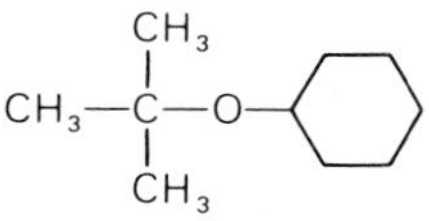

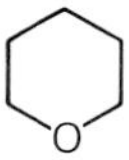

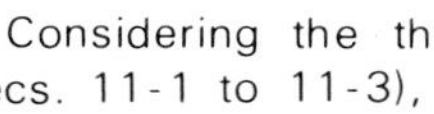

★(*f*) [naphthalene with $OCH_3$ at position 2]

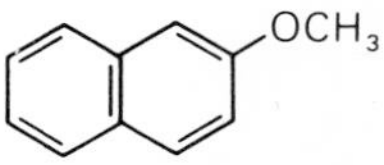

**2.** Considering the three methods of ether synthesis discussed in this chapter (Secs. 11-1 to 11-3), choose the most appropriate method for the preparation of each compound in Prob. 1.

**3.** Give the product(s) and mechanism for each of the following reactions:

(*a*) ethylene oxide + HCN $\longrightarrow$

(*b*) $(CH_3)_3COCH_2CH_3 \xrightarrow{HBr} CH_3CH_2Br + (CH_3)_2C{=}CH_2 + H_2O$

★(*c*) $C_6H_5$—$OCH_3$ + N-bromosuccinimide (N—Br) $\xrightarrow{H_2O}$ Br—$C_6H_4$—$OCH_3$ + succinimide (N—H)

**★4.** Suggest a mechanism for the following reaction:

$C_6H_5OCH_2CH_2Br \xrightarrow[2.\ H_2O]{1.\ Mg} C_6H_5OH + CH_2{=}CH_2 + Mg(OH)Br$

# Chapter Twelve

There are three types of isomerism, structural (Chap. 2), geometrical (Chaps. 3 and 4), and optical; the last is discussed in this chapter. ***Optical isomers*** are compounds which have the same atoms attached to each other, but the order of attachment to a given atom (and the arrangement of the atoms in space) is different. We shall see that the fundamental criterion is that the two isomers are not superimposable. The formal relationship of the three types of isomerism and examples of each are shown in Table 12-1. The spatial arrangement of atoms is extremely important in biological systems, where a delicate balance of interactions is maintained; e.g., two optical isomers may have very different biological effects.

**Table 12-1**
**Isomerism**

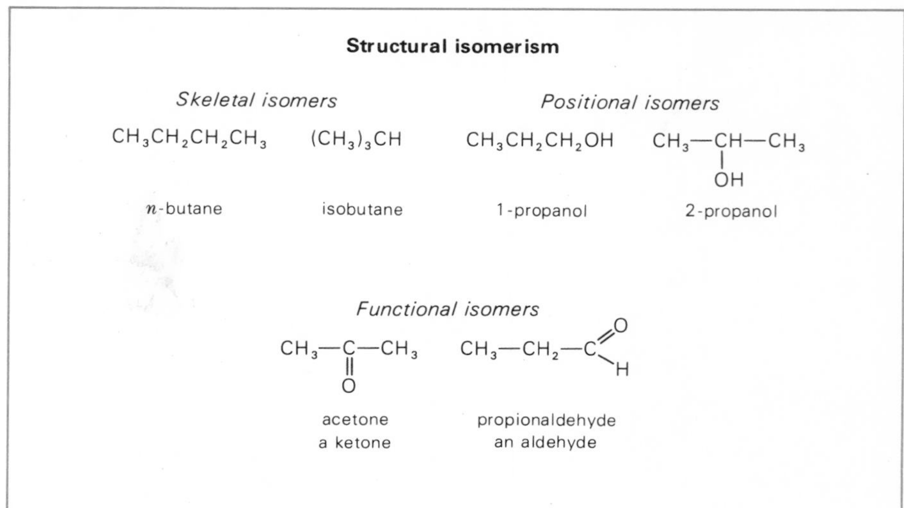

# Optical Isomerism and Stereospecificity

**Stereoisomerism**

*GEOMETRICAL ISOMERISM*

*Carbon-carbon double bonds*

$H_3C(H)C{=}C(H)CH_3$ — *cis*-2-butene

$H_3C(H)C{=}C(CH_3)H$ — *trans*-2-butene

*Carbon-nitrogen double bonds*

$H_3C(H)C{=}N{-}OH$ — *anti*, H and OH "trans"

$H_3C(H)C{=}N{-}OH$ — *syn*, H and OH "cis"

*Cyclic compounds*

1,3-dichlorocyclobutane (Cl, H on each ring carbon) — cis; trans

*OPTICAL ISOMERISM*

*Compounds with asymmetric carbons*

A—C(B)(E)—D; D—C(B)(E)—A

*Ring compounds*

1,2-dimethylcyclopropane ($H_3C$, H; H, $CH_3$) — two enantiomers

*Allenes*

$H(Br)C{=}C{=}C(Br)H$; $Br(H)C{=}C{=}C(H)Br$

*Overcrowded, nonplanar molecules, biphenyls, and others*

In this text molecules with four different groups attached to a given carbon atom, such as $CH_3CHBrCl$ or $CH_3CH(NH_2)COOH$, have been written without regard to this spatial consideration; but the actual arrangement is important and must often be taken into account. The two isomers of $CH_3CHBrCl$ are mirror images, which cannot be made superimposable by any rotational manipulations (see Fig. 12-1). You will find a set of molecular models extremely valuable in helping to visualize the spatial configuration of organic molecules and especially those of optical isomers discussed in this chapter.

**Figure 12-1 The optical isomers of $CH_3CHBrCl$**

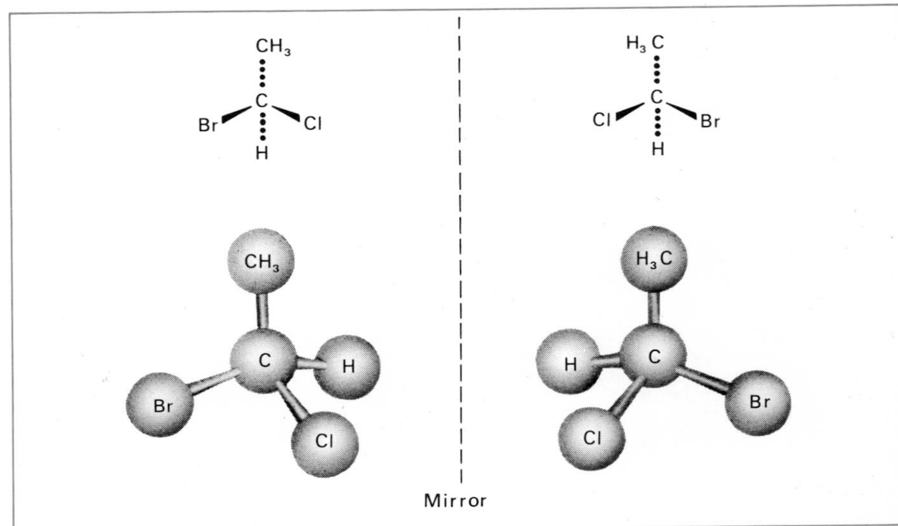


## OPTICAL ACTIVITY AND ASYMMETRIC CENTERS

### 12-1 ASYMMETRIC CRYSTALS

Quartz crystals, found in nature, are hemihedral (Fig. 12-2) and have a ***sense*** or ***handedness***. They are identical except in their three-dimensional geometries, which are like an object and its mirror image. A pair of shoes and hands also bear this relationship to each other. Not only do some crystals exhibit this phenomenon, but it can also be attributed to certain molecules. Although every molecule has a mirror image, only those which are ***not superimposable*** with their mirror images are optical isomers. Examining crystals of sodium ammonium tartrate, $NaO_2C—CH(OH)—CH(OH)—COONH_4$, with a hand lens, Pasteur found that they also had a discernible handedness. He was able to arrange the crystals into two piles simply by separating them on the

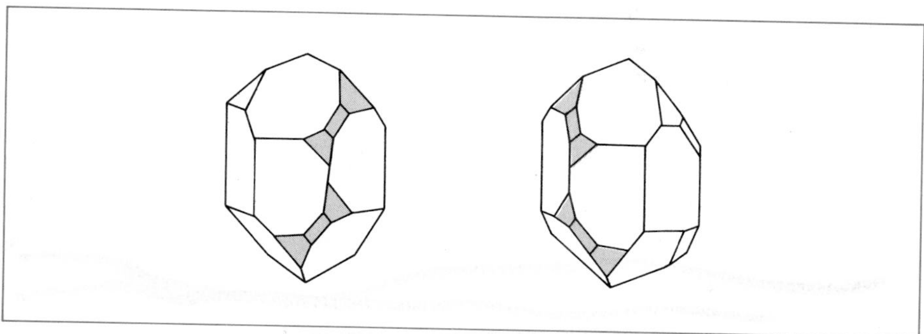

**Figure 12-2 Hemihedral quartz crystals**

basis of their apparent handedness. When dissolved in water, each of the two solutions also showed a handedness, as revealed by a crude polarimeter, which indicated that neither the crystals *nor* the molecules were superimposable on their mirror images.

## 12-2 THE POLARIMETER

It is important to discuss at the outset the method by which optical isomers can be detected qualitatively and analyzed quantitatively. In order to study optical isomers, they must be detectable. Instruments like the polarimeter described below *do not create* the optical properties of the molecules studied; they only reveal them.

Light whose rays are oriented in one direction is called *plane-polarized light*. Polarization can be accomplished by passing ordinary light through a piece of calcite, a crystalline form of calcium carbonate. If polarized light is now passed through a single quartz crystal, the plane of light will be found to have undergone a rotation, either to the right or to the left, when it emerges (Fig. 12-3). If a given quartz crystal is found to rotate light to the right, its mirror image will rotate light to the left. Just as a single quartz crystal rotates plane-polarized light, so also do *solutions* containing single optical isomers. The only physical property of two optical isomers of a given molecule which is different is the *direction* in which the isomer rotates plane-polarized light. The extent of rotation is the same. This ability of molecules to rotate plane-polarized light is known as *optical activity*.

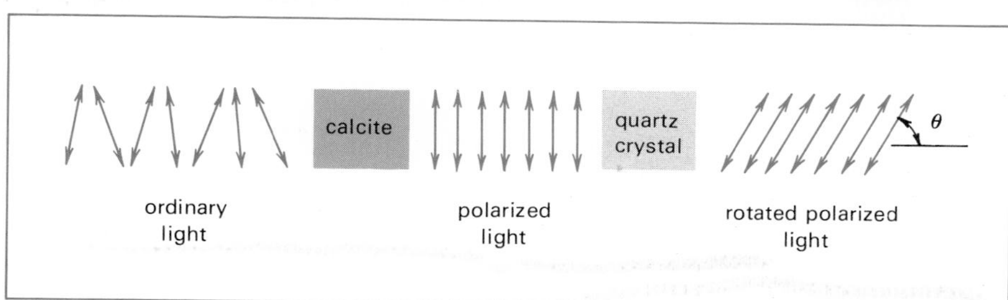


**Figure 12-3 Schematic polarization and rotation of light**

The instrument used to measure the direction of this rotation in solution qualitatively and its extent quantitatively is known as a *polarimeter* (see Fig. 12-4). The lamp is a source of radiation of a given wavelength; the D line of sodium (5893 Å) is commonly used. The polarizer and analyzer are analogous to two pieces of commercial Polaroid glass or plastic which allow maximum transmission only of light polarized in one plane. The sample tube of known length, often 10 cm, is allowed to reach constant temperature before readings are taken. If the analyzer permits maximum transmission in a clockwise direction (to the right) it is designated, by convention, *dextrorotatory* or (+); rotation of the analyzer to the left is called *levorotatory* or (−).

**Figure 12-4 Schematic diagram of polarimeter**

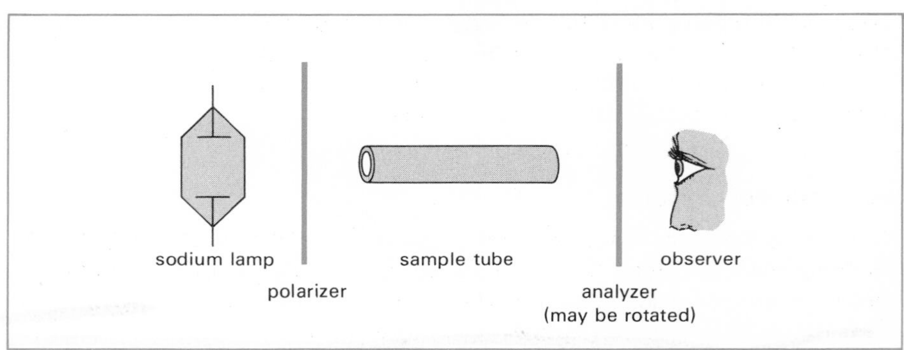


### 12-3 POLARIMETRIC MEASUREMENTS

The *specific rotation*, designated $\alpha$, is a physical property of a given optical isomer which depends on the *wavelength of light* $\lambda$, the *temperature* $T$, the *solvent* employed, and the *concentration* $c$ at which the measurement is made. The observed rotation $a$ is related to the specific rotation in the following way:

For solutions:

$$[\alpha]_{\lambda}^{T^\circ} = \frac{100 \cdot a}{1(\text{cm}/10) \cdot c(\text{g}/100\text{ ml soln.})}$$

Thus, the notation, $[\alpha]_{\text{D}}^{25^\circ} = -30^\circ$ (0.1 in $H_2O$) means that the specific rotation $\alpha$ at 25°C using the D line of sodium is 30° to the left when measured at a concentration of 0.1 g in 100 ml of aqueous solution. Rotations are often observed in organic solvents or in solutions of acid or base. The solvent or solution must be named when reporting specific rotations, since the sign of rotation can change with solvent.

Only separated optical isomers can rotate plane-polarized light; optically inactive molecules, i.e., those which are superimposable on their mirror images, or a 1 : 1 mixture of the two optical isomers of a given substance produce no rotation.

## 12-4 COMMON TERMS ILLUSTRATED WITH AMINO ACIDS

Most naturally occurring amino acids, RCH($NH_2$)COOH, are capable of exhibiting optical isomerism, although only one isomer is usually prevalent in nature. Alanine, $CH_3—\overset{*}{C}H(NH_2)—COOH$, is the simplest optically active natural amino acid. It contains one asymmetric carbon atom (starred), a carbon to which four ***different*** groups are attached. This is one condition which gives rise to optical activity; others are discussed later in this chapter. In the discussion of optical activity of the asymmetric-carbon type, it is often convenient to label the asymmetric carbon atom with a star.

These two isomers of alanine have identical physical properties except for the ***direction*** in which they rotate plane-polarized light; the extent, or magnitude, of rotation of pure isomers is identical.

H
$H_3C$—C—COOH
$NH_2$

H
HOOC—C—$CH_3$
$NH_2$

An equimolar mixture of the two isomers is called a ***racemate, racemic mixture***, or D,L ***pair***.[†] In this text we shall not consider the racemate a separate isomer despite the fact that it has physical properties different from those of the individual constituent isomers. For example, the density of D- and L-alanine is 1.401 g/ml, whereas the density of the racemate is 1.424. The optically active isomers of a given pair are also known as ***enantiomers*** or ***optical antipodes***.

These two forms can be represented in three dimensions, although we have not yet specified which isomer rotates light to the right (or left). These are the relative configurations of the two isomers. In order to specify the ***absolute configuration***, i.e., to determine which of the two isomers actually rotates to the right (or left), there must be common agreement on a ***reference compound***.

## 12-5 ABSOLUTE CONFIGURATION

Glyceraldehyde, $CHO—\overset{*}{C}HOH—CH_2OH$, has a single asymmetric carbon atom. The isomer with the positive rotation was arbitrarily assigned the following absolute configuration by Emil Fischer in 1891:

H, CHO, $HOCH_2$, OH (C)

CHO
H—C—OH
$CH_2OH$

D(+)-glyceraldehyde

CHO, H, HO, $CH_2OH$ (C)

CHO
HO—C—H
$CH_2OH$

L(−)-glyceraldehyde

[†] The lowercase letters *d* and *l* were used in the past to designate rotations and isomers; this older notation will not be used in this text.

This arbitrary assignment was shown to be the actual one by x-ray analysis techniques in 1951. It is fortunate that Fischer's assignment turned out to be correct; for it means that all the known compounds which had been related to D(+)-glyceraldehyde were also correctly related in terms of their absolute configuration. The signs + and − are used to show the *direction* of rotation; the letters D and L refer to the absolute configuration of the compound. **There is no necessary, general correlation between the sign of rotation and the absolute configuration.** For instance, there are many pairs of optical isomers of the D(−) and L (+) type.

## 12-6 CAHN-INGOLD-PRELOG CONVENTION

Another method of designating the absolute configuration of asymmetric centers, known as the *Cahn-Ingold-Prelog convention*, is being used. It assigns a relative sequence to substituents, A, B, D, E, located on a carbon atom C. If, on looking at the tetrahedral arrangement of the carbon atom from the side opposite to that of the substituent of lowest priority (E), the order A ⟶ B ⟶ D is clockwise, the designation is R (Latin *rectus*, straight or right); if the order A ⟶ B ⟶ D is counterclockwise, the designation is S (Latin *sinister*, left).

A→B→D is clockwise; thus, R

A→B→D is counterclockwise; thus, S

The substituents A, B, D, and E are assigned a priority, A being highest, on the basis of *highest atomic number*. Hence, the halogens are in the order I, Br, Cl, F. If the substituent contains a *group* of atoms, the highest priority is given to the group in which the *first* atom has the highest number. For instance, if the substituents are $CH_3$, OH, and $NH_2$, the order or priority (on the basis of atomic number) is OH, $NH_2$, and $CH_3$. If there are two or more substituents with same *first* atom, the priority is assigned on the basis of the *second* atom or combined second atoms. Thus, in assigning relative priorities to —COOH and —CHO, the order would be —COOH and then —CHO. In more complicated cases, one must proceed along the chain in order to determine the priority.

There are certain advantages to the D,L notation, and since the R,S convention has not yet received universal acceptance, we shall not use it in this text.

## 12-7 FISCHER PROJECTIONS

On paper it is relatively easy to represent molecules containing only one asymmetric carbon. With more complex molecules, three-dimensional representations become more difficult to draw. For two-dimensional representation of molecules containing several asymmetric carbons we may use either tetrahedral drawings, which place the carbon atoms in the center of a tetrahedron with the substituents at the vertices, or Fischer projections derived from these tetrahedral drawings, in which the carbon chain (back of the plane of the paper) is drawn as a vertical line and the substituents (projecting out from the plane of the paper) are placed at the ends of the horizontal ones. The intersections of the vertical and horizontal lines represent the carbon atoms of the chain.

Consider the four-carbon sugars (CHO—$\overset{*}{C}$HOH—$\overset{*}{C}$HOH—$CH_2OH$) shown in Table 12-2. In the tetrahedral representations $C_2$ and $C_3$ are not shown but are located at the centers of the two tetrahedrons. Fischer projections of these compounds, also in Table 12-2, simply show the substituents and imply $C_2$ and $C_3$ at the intersections.

**Table 12-2 Representations of the tetroses**

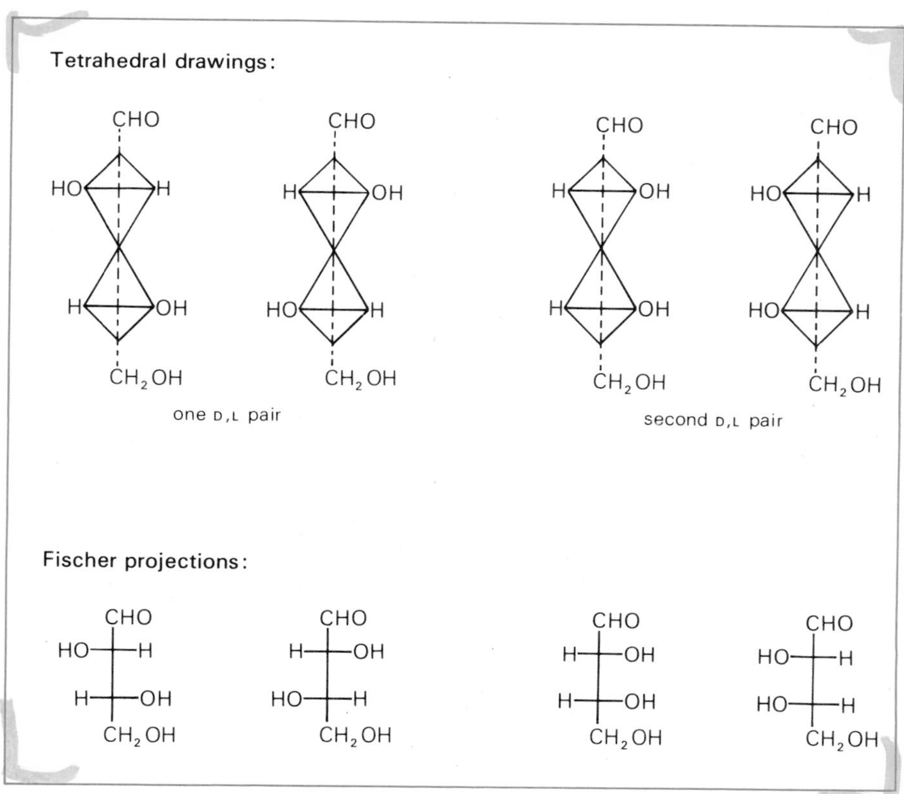

Suppose we wish to compare two projection drawings; e.g., do (*a*) and (*b*) represent a single isomer, or do they represent a D,L pair?

$CH_3$ / H—OH / COOH (*a*)   $CH_3$ / H—OH / COOH (*a*)   OH / $H_3C$—COOH / H (*b*)   OH / $H_3C$—COOH / H (*b*)

Note that (*a*) and (*b*) are projections in which the vertical substituents are behind the plane of the paper and the horizontal ones are in front of it. In this text we shall adopt the ***permutation*** convention for answering these questions. A single interchange of two substituents, by this convention, inverts the configuration; a pair of interchanges restores the original configuration even though the resulting representation may be in an unfamiliar form. Note that by this convention each optical isomer has 12 different representations, and there will also be 12 for its mirror image. No even number of exchanges can possibly transform one isomer to its mirror image. Let us make the following two interchanges on (*b*) and examine the results: (1) interchange —$CH_3$ and —OH and (2) interchange —H and —COOH. The result is (*c*),

$CH_3$ / HO—H / COOH

(*c*)

the mirror image of (*a*); thus, (*a*) and (*b*) represent a D,L pair.

Show the relationship of the following pairs:

1. H / HO—$CH_2OH$ / CHO   and   $CH_2OH$ / HO—H / CHO

2. CHO / H—OH / H—OH / $CH_2OH$   and   OH / H—CHO / HO—$CH_2OH$ / H

## 12-8 COMPOUNDS CONTAINING MORE THAN ONE DIFFERENT ASYMMETRIC CARBON

Tartaric acid, HOOC—CH(OH)—CH(OH)—COOH, contains two *like* asymmetric carbon atoms; that is, $C_2$ and $C_3$ both contain the substituents —H, —OH, —COOH, and —CH(OH)—COOH. Conversion of one of the carboxyl groups to the sodium salt, $NaOO\overset{1}{C}—\overset{2}{C}H(OH)—\overset{3}{C}H(OH)—\overset{4}{C}OOH$, leads to a structure with two *different* asymmetric carbons: $C_2$ contains —H, —OH, —COONa, and —CH(OH)COOH, whereas $C_3$ contains —H, —OH, —COOH, and —CH(OH)COONa. As illustrated by the sugars in Sec. 12-7, a molecule containing two *different* asymmetric carbon atoms may exist in four isomeric forms. **In general, a molecule with $n$ different asymmetric carbons has $2^n$ isomers and $2^n/2$ D,L pairs.**

> Write structures (Fischer projections) for all the five-carbon sugars, CHO—CHOH—CHOH—CHOH—$CH_2OH$. Note that by convention sugars are written with —CHO group at the top and the —$CH_2OH$ group at the bottom of the structure (Sec. 12-7).

## 12-9 COMPOUNDS CONTAINING LIKE ASYMMETRIC CARBON ATOMS

Molecules which contain like asymmetric carbon atoms will have fewer than $2^n/2$ optical isomers. These like asymmetric centers give rise to meso isomers, which are optically inactive. The tartaric acids present a case in which the molecule contains two *like* asymmetric carbons. Each carbon has the same four groups, —H, —OH, —COOH, and —CH(OH)COOH. There are no conformations of the optically active isomers which are superimposable on their mirror images; however, the meso isomer does possess such conformations. Because meso isomers possess a plane of symmetry,

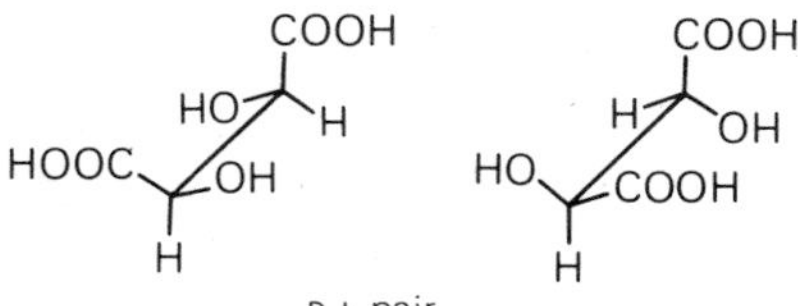

COOH / HO, H / HOOC, OH / H    COOH / H, OH / HO, COOH / H

D,L pair

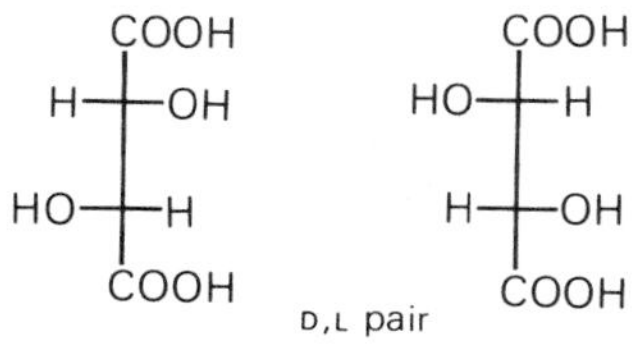

COOH / H—OH / HO—H / COOH    COOH / HO—H / H—OH / COOH

D,L pair

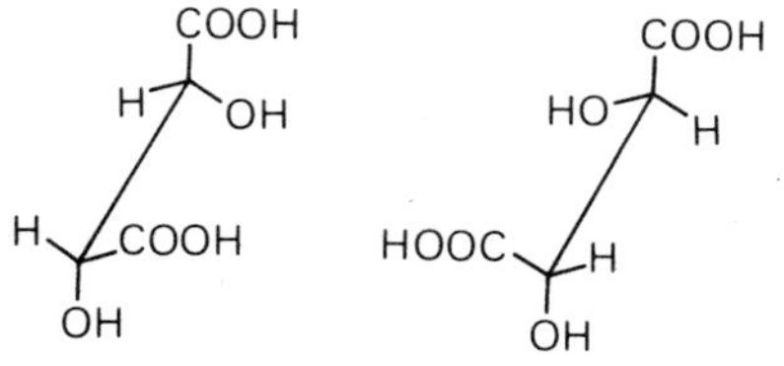

COOH / H, OH / H, COOH / OH    COOH / HO, H / HOOC, H / OH

meso isomer
two conformations

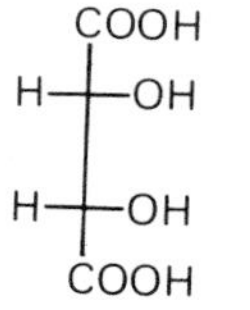

COOH / H—OH / H—OH / COOH

plane-polarized light interacts with the molecule, affording a zero net rotation. Another explanation of the optical inactivity is that the molecule contains a like number of carbon atoms with D and L configuration.

In summary, there are two rules in organic chemistry to which there are *no exceptions* (and such rules in organic chemistry are rare indeed):

**1.** If a molecule is not superimposable on its mirror image, it can exist in D,L forms. The converse is also true.

**2.** If a point or plane of symmetry exists in a molecule, it is an optically inactive form and therefore identical with its mirror image. The converse is also true.

A rapid method of determining whether or not a molecule is optically inactive is to find a point or plane of symmetry. Remember that the primary criterion is whether or not the molecule is superimposable on its mirror image. Some examples of symmetry are shown in Table 12-3.

### 12-10 ADDITIONAL TERMS ILLUSTRATED WITH SUGARS

$CHO—\overset{*}{C}HOH—\overset{*}{C}HOH—\overset{*}{C}HOH—CH_2OH$, the general formulation of five-carbon sugars, shows that the molecules possess three *different* asymmetric carbon atoms and hence $2^3$ or eight optical isomers exist. which form four D,L pairs. These are shown in Table 12-4, where each isomer has arbitrarily been assigned a letter and the isomers are arranged in D,L pairs.

Optical isomers which are mirror images, such as (*a*) and (*b*), (*c*) and (*d*), (*e*) and (*f*), and (*g*) and (*h*), are called *enantiomers* or *optical antipodes*. Isomers which differ only in the configuration at one of several possible optical centers are known as *epimers*. The following isomers are epimers: (*a*) and (*c*), epimeric at $C_4$; (*a*) and (*g*), epimeric at $C_2$; (*d*) and (*g*), epimeric at $C_3$; and others. Optical isomers of a given compound which are not mirror images and which are not identical are known as *diastereoisomers* (*or diastereomers*). The following pairs are diastereoisomers: (*a*) and (*c*), (*b*) and (*c*), (*a*) and (*d*), and others. **All epimers are diastereoisomers, but not all diastereoisomers are epimers; epimers are a special group of diastereoisomers.**

## RESOLUTION AND RACEMIZATION

Suppose propanoic acid is brominated with phosphorus and bromine, how many isomers will be obtained?

$$CH_3CH_2COOH \xrightarrow[\text{red P}]{Br_2} CH_3—\underset{\displaystyle Br}{\underset{|}{\overset{*}{C}H}}—COOH$$

**Table 12-3**
**Examples of molecular symmetries**

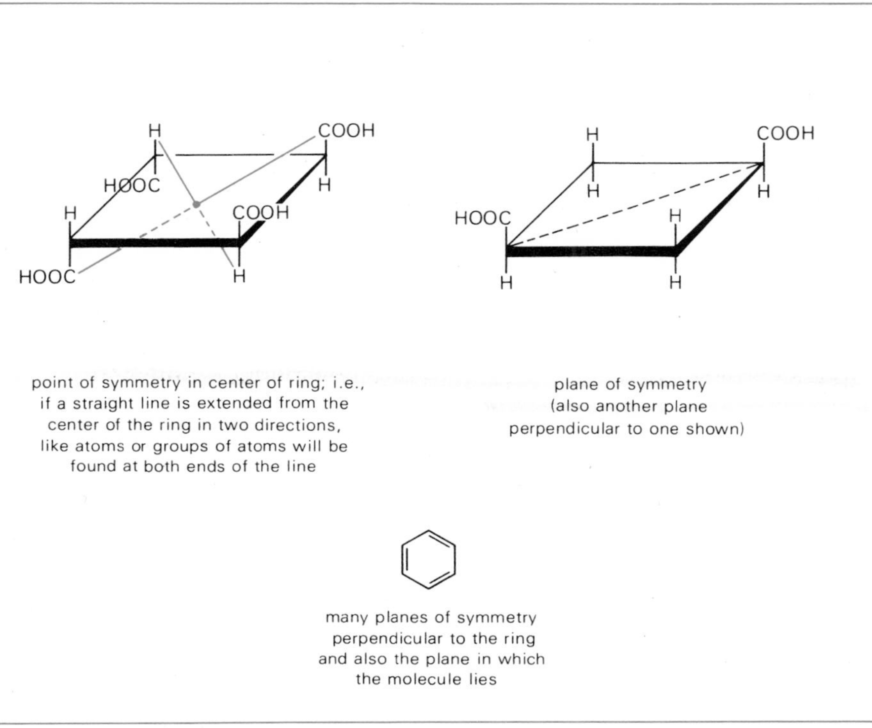


**Table 12-4**
**The aldopentoses**

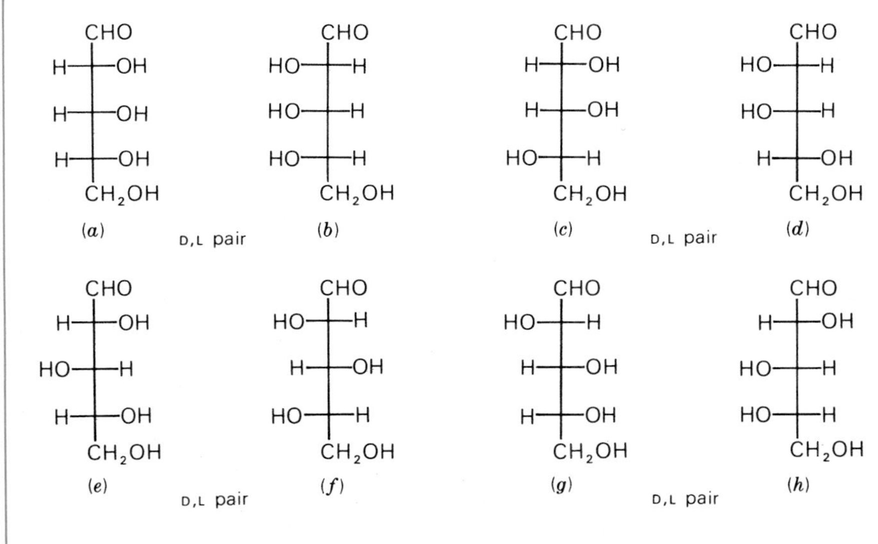

One asymmetric carbon has been created, and thus the reaction mixture, a racemate, is potentially capable of separation into the D isomer and the L isomer.

No optically active product can ever result from a chemical reaction unless one of the reagents itself is optically active or unless the reaction has been carried out under the influence of some optically active agent, such as D or L quartz. The physical properties of D and L isomers are identical except for the sign of optical rotation, and the two isomers cannot be separated without the intervention of some element of asymmetry. **When starting with optically inactive materials in an optically inactive "atmosphere," the product obtained must be a racemic mixture and cannot be the pure D or pure L isomer.**

The separation of a racemate into its constituent optically active isomers is known as a ***resolution***. Since the formation of new asymmetric centers is a common occurrence in organic reactions, the question arises: How can such racemic mixtures be resolved? The principles of the resolution methods employed today were all discovered by Pasteur over 100 years ago! The manner in which they are used have been modified and improved.

## 12-11 MECHANICAL SEPARATION

Hand picking relies on the asymmetry of the gross crystal structure and is not a dependable method of separation. It seldom happens that a mixture will crystallize spontaneously in such a way that the two isomers will form independently of each other; nevertheless, several cases of such a resolution have been reported.

## 12-12 FORMATION OF DIASTEREOISOMERIC SALTS OR DERIVATIVES

The most general method of resolution is the formation of two diastereoisomers from a D,L pair by reaction with a previously resolved compound. Racemic mixtures of acids are a vulnerable target for such a process when they are treated with naturally occurring optically pure bases such as cinchonine, quinine, brucine, or strychnine (see Table 12-5). The acids form salts with the unshared pair of electrons on the nitrogen atom of the organic base.

$$\underset{\text{acid}}{R{-}COOH} + \underset{\text{base}}{\geq N:} \longrightarrow \underset{\text{salt}}{\geq \overset{+}{N}H \quad R{-}COO^-}$$

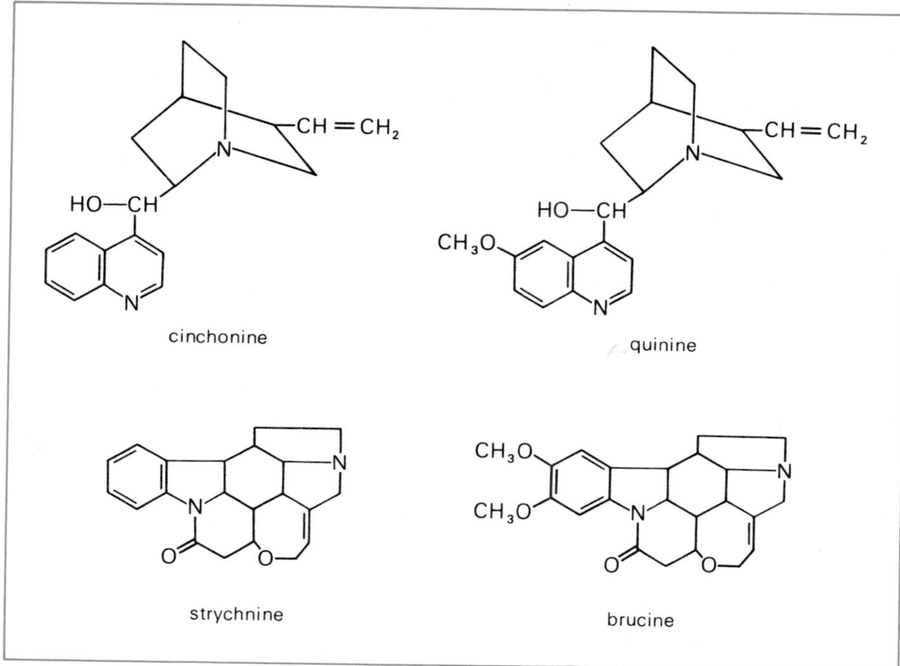


**Table 12-5**
**Natural bases used in resolution of racemic acids**

The salts formed by this process have different properties and, in particular, different solubilities in a variety of pure or mixed solvents. Usually one salt is more soluble than the other, and a separation can be achieved. Decomposition of the salt with HCl or $H_2SO_4$ gives the optical isomer.

$$\text{D,L acid} + \text{L base} \longrightarrow \begin{bmatrix} \text{D acid} \cdot \text{L base salt} \\ \text{L acid} \cdot \text{L base salt} \end{bmatrix}$$

racemic mixture — from natural sources — mixture of diastereoisomers

$$\xrightarrow[\text{fractional crystallization}]{\text{separation by}} \begin{cases} \text{D acid} \cdot \text{L base salt} \xrightarrow{\text{dil. H}^+} \text{D acid} \\ \text{L acid} \cdot \text{L base salt} \xrightarrow{\text{dil. H}^+} \text{L acid} \end{cases} + \text{L base} \cdot \text{HCl}$$

Compounds which are not acids or bases can often be converted to acidic or basic derivatives, which can be resolved as previously described and then regenerated by reagents that do not affect the asymmetric center. Alcohols, for instance, can be resolved via the phthalate or succinate half ester. Hydrolysis of the resolved half ester yields the optically pure alcohol.

$$\text{phthalic anhydride} + R{-}\overset{*}{C}H(R'){-}OH \longrightarrow C_6H_4(COO\overset{*}{C}HRR')(COOH)$$

phthalic anhydride — D,L alcohol — D,L phthalate half ester

Although the separation of diastereoisomeric compounds is common, it is not without some difficulties. For example, it may be nearly impossible to obtain the compounds as crystalline materials from oily residues. There may be so little difference in the solubility of the diastereoisomers that a separation is not feasible. Finally, although the less soluble diastereoisomer may be obtained by this procedure, it may be necessary to repeat the entire procedure with a different resolving agent in order to obtain the other enantiomer.

### 12-13 ENZYMATIC RESOLUTION

Some resolutions have been accomplished by allowing an organism to grow in the presence of, i.e., metabolize, a D,L mixture. Often only one of the isomers will be destroyed, leaving the other intact. Pasteur found that treatment of a dilute solution of D,L-ammonium tartrate with *Penicillium glaucum* led to the destruction of the D isomer faster than that of the L isomer. These transformations can also be accomplished with the use of enzymes, which are optically active protein catalysts. A drawback to this procedure is that since one isomer is generally destroyed or transformed and therefore not available, other systems or methods must be employed to obtain it.

Enzyme-catalyzed transformations of this type are extremely important in biological systems. In fact, enzymes are capable of assisting in the transformation of symmetrical, optically inactive molecules to those which exhibit optical activity.

### 12-14 RACEMIZATION

The process in which a single optical isomer is transformed into a D,L mixture, or racemate, is called *racemization*. Many optical antipodes undergo such a reversion or racemization on heating or simply on standing in solution.

A common cause of racemization is enolization at the asymmetric center. For example, assume that the following ketone has been resolved.

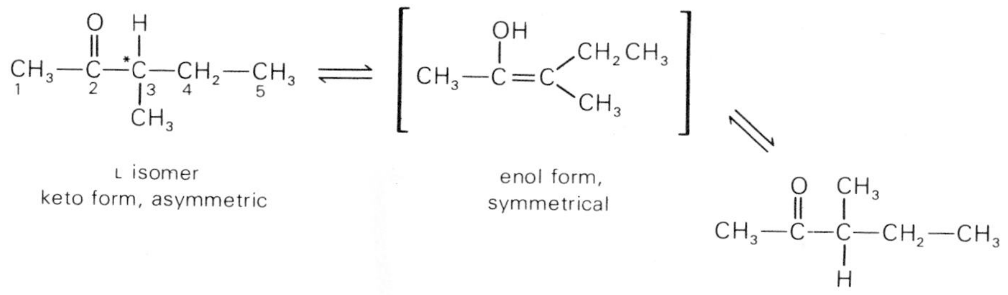

$$\underset{\substack{\text{L isomer}\\ \text{keto form, asymmetric}}}{\underset{1}{CH_3}-\underset{2}{\overset{\overset{\displaystyle O}{\|}}{C}}-\underset{\underset{\displaystyle CH_3}{|3}}{\overset{\overset{\displaystyle H}{|}}{\overset{*}{C}}}-\underset{4}{CH_2}-\underset{5}{CH_3}} \rightleftharpoons \underset{\substack{\text{enol form,}\\ \text{symmetrical}}}{\left[CH_3-\overset{\overset{\displaystyle OH}{|}}{C}=C\begin{matrix}CH_2CH_3\\ CH_3\end{matrix}\right]} \rightleftharpoons \underset{\text{D isomer}}{CH_3-\overset{\overset{\displaystyle O}{\|}}{C}-\underset{\underset{\displaystyle H}{|}}{\overset{\overset{\displaystyle CH_3}{|}}{C}}-CH_2-CH_3}$$

In solution this keto form is in equilibrium with the enol form, in which the asymmetry at $C_3$ has been destroyed by the introduction of a double bond. The enol proton may then return with equal probability to $C_3$ from either the top or the bottom of the double-bond plane. This process gives rise to an equal number of both isomers and, hence, to a racemic mixture. **Any process which destroys the asymmetry of an optical isomer results in racemization.**

## OPTICAL ACTIVITY OF CYCLOALKANES

### 12-15 GENERAL CONSIDERATIONS

We shall find it convenient to divide molecules into several general classes in order to determine the number of possible stereoisomers quickly. In all cases the principal criterion will apply: **A molecule which is not superimposable on its mirror image is optically active.** The fist class of compounds, already considered in previous sections, is that containing an **asymmetric carbon atom.** In this section are considered **substituted cycloalkanes**, which also contain asymmetric carbons. This division, which is continued later in the chapter for *allenes* and *overcrowded molecules*, is somewhat artificial but is helpful in determining the elements of symmetry which may be present. Recall that if an element of symmetry is found, the molecule is not capable of optical isomerism.

Although it has been shown that all cycloalkanes except cyclopropanes (and perhaps some cyclobutanes) exist in nonplanar conformations, at room temperature the conformations are in dynamic equilibrium such that the carbons of the ring may be considered planar for the purposes of determining the number of possible optical isomers. This simplifies the counting process considerably. For example, it is true that the preferred conformation of a cyclohexane is a chair form; nevertheless, the ring flip is so rapid at room temperature that the time-averaged position of the six carbon atoms defines a plane.

### 12-16 SPECIFIC EXAMPLES OF SUBSTITUTED $C_3$ TO $C_6$ CYCLOALKANES

We shall first consider the 1,2-dibromocyclopropanes. There are three possible isomers: the cis, which is a meso form (optically inactive) and the trans, which consists of a D,L pair.

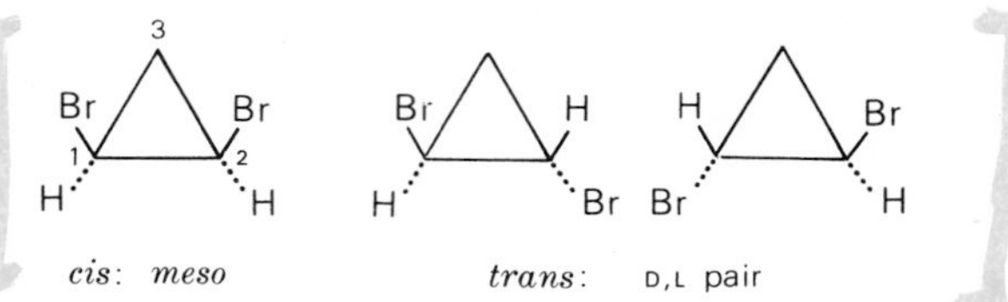


*cis*: *meso* *trans*: D,L pair

Note that the cis isomer has a plane of symmetry which bisects the $C_1$—$C_2$ bond and slices $C_3$ and its two hydrogen atoms in half. In this text we shall keep track of the stereoisomers by a four-column table, like Table 12-6, which lists the compound, the total number of stereoisomers, the number optically active (counting each isomer only once), and finally a brief description of the isomers. Usually you will find it helpful to draw each isomer or, better, make a model of it in order to see clearly whether or not it contains symmetry elements.

**1.** Draw all the isomers of 1,2,3-tribromocyclopropane. In order to find all possible combinations of substituted cycloalkanes, it is suggested that you consider first the isomer with no substituent up, i.e., above the plane, then the cases of one substituent up, two substituents up, etc. Note, however, that in this particular case, one up (two down) is the same as two up (one down).

**2.** Draw *all* the isomers of dibromodichlorocyclobutane. Summarize this information in a table like Table 12-6. Note that it is possible to have two halogen atoms on a given carbon atom.

Let us consider the problem of drawing all the dichlorocyclopentanes and discussing the stereochemistry. We may begin the process of combination and permutation by placing a chlorine atom on any of the five equivalent carbons and asking how many different positions are available for the second.

**1.** Place one chlorine atom on the ring:

**2.** Positions available for second chlorine: three ($C_1$, $C_2$, and $C_3$). Note that $C_2$ is equivalent to $C_5$ and $C_3$ is equivalent to $C_4$. The 1,1 isomer is denoted inactive rather than meso since there is only one possible 1,1 isomer.

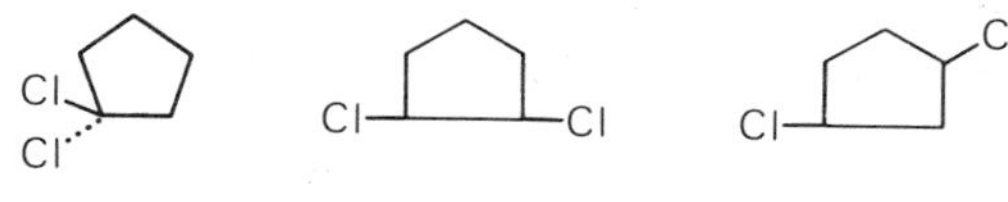


1,1 isomer 1,2 isomer 1,3 isomer

**3.** Since the compounds in part 2 represent the structural isomers, what are the possible stereochemical relationships of the chlorine atoms in the two isomers? They have the following formulas:

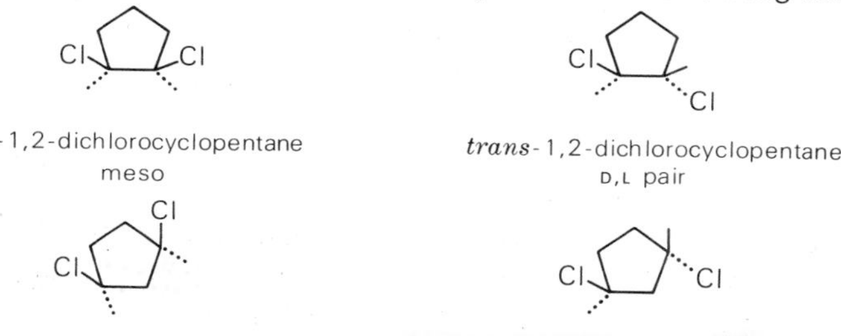


*cis*-1,2-dichlorocyclopentane
meso

*trans*-1,2-dichlorocyclopentane
D,L pair

*cis*-1,3-dichlorocyclopentane
meso

*trans*-1,3-dichlorocyclopentane
D,L pair

**4.** Tabulation

| *Compound* | *Total possible number of stereoisomers* | *Number optically active* | *Comments* |
|---|---|---|---|
| Dichlorocyclopentane | 7 | 4 | 1,1 isomer: inactive<br>1,2 isomers: cis-meso, trans D,L pair<br>1,3 isomers: cis-meso, trans D,L pair |

In the counting process note that there can be no 1,4 isomers because they are identical with 1,3 isomers. Here, as in many cases, numbering the compounds and naming them will avoid duplication.

**1.** Using the process described for dichlorocyclopentane, draw all the dimethylcyclohexanes. Note that both *cis*- and *trans*-1,4-dimethylcyclohexane are meso isomers since there is a plane of symmetry in each isomer which bisects $C_1HCH_3$ and $C_4HCH_3$. There is an additional plane of symmetry in the cis isomer.

**2.** Draw all the inositols, 1,2,3,4,5,6-hexahydroxycyclohexanes.

**3.** Show the preferred conformation of each isomer in part 2.

**Table 12-6 1,2-Dibromo- and 1,2,3-tribromocyclopropanes**

| Compound | Total possible number of stereoisomers | Number optically active | Comments |
|---|---|---|---|
| 1,2-dibromocyclopropanes | 3 | 2 | cis: meso<br>trans: D,L pair |
| 1,2,3-tribromocyclopropanes | 2 | 0 | cis, cis: meso<br>cis, trans: meso |

## OPTICAL ACTIVITY OF CUMULENES

*Cumulenes* are organic compounds containing at least one carbon atom which is bonded to other atoms by two double bonds. The simplest of these are known as ***allenes***, $R_2C{=}C{=}CR_2$. Recall that the molecular-orbital pictures of allenes show that the substituents on the terminal carbons lie in perpendicular planes (Sec. 6-2). Thus, certain substituted allenes, R—CH=C=CH—R, show optical activity (Fig. 12-5). The next higher cumulenes, R—CH=C=C=CHR, have their terminal substituents in the same plane (Fig. 12-5) and are capable of existing in cis-trans modifications but not of showing optical activity. Note that in the allenes and higher cumulenes containing an odd number of cumulated carbons that the elements of symmetry to be examined are two planes: one bisects $C_1$ and its substituents and includes $C_n$ and its substituents; the other includes $C_1$ and its substituents and bisects $C_n$ and its substituents, where $C_1$ and $C_n$ are the terminal cumulated carbons. If either plane is a plane of symmetry, the molecule is optically inactive.

**Figure 12-5 Representative cumulenes**

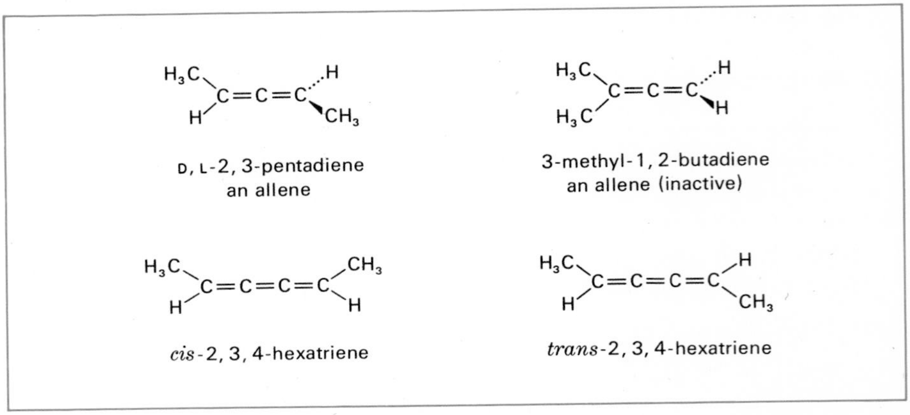

$H_3C(H)C{=}C{=}C(H)CH_3$

D, L-2, 3-pentadiene
an allene

$(H_3C)_2C{=}C{=}CH_2$

3-methyl-1, 2-butadiene
an allene (inactive)

$H_3C(H)C{=}C{=}C{=}C(CH_3)H$

*cis*-2, 3, 4-hexatriene

$H_3C(H)C{=}C{=}C{=}C(H)CH_3$

*trans*-2, 3, 4-hexatriene

## OPTICAL ACTIVITY DUE TO MOLECULAR OVERCROWDING

### 12-17 OPTICALLY ACTIVE BIPHENYLS

Bulky substituents located on the ortho positions of a biphenyl molecule prevent free rotation around the bond joining the two aromatic rings. Ortho-substituted biphenyl compounds exhibit molecular asymmetry and optical activity if two conditions hold: (1) the ortho substituents are large enough to prevent free rotation and (2) the molecule is unsymmetrically substituted. Although the two biphenyl rings are not rigidly held in a perpendicular conformation, it is convenient for symmetry purposes to consider them so.

Which substituents are large enough to prevent free rotation? It has been found that —H, —F, —OH, and —$OCH_3$, which are among the smallest common substituents, do *not* prevent rotation. Next in size are —COOH and —$NO_2$, which prevent rotation, but the isomers are fairly readily racemized in solution at room temperature. If these latter two substituents occur in conjunction with much bulkier ones such as —I, —Br, —Cl, and —$CH_3$, optical isomers are quite stable and racemize only at higher temperatures. Examples are given in Table 12-7.

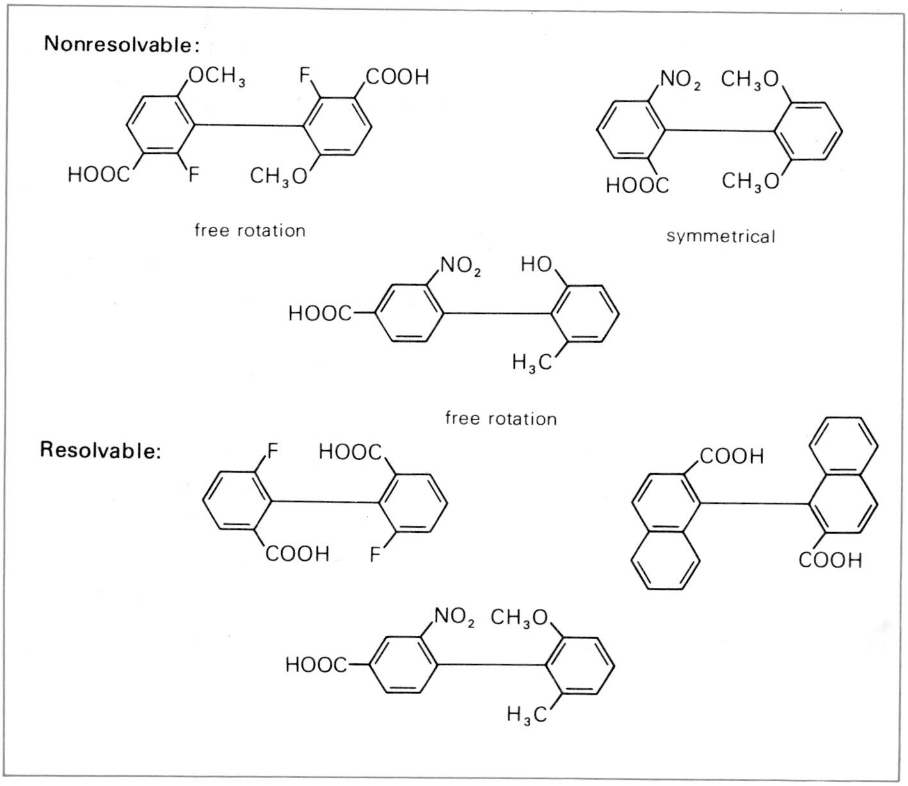

Nonresolvable:

OCH$_3$ F COOH
HOOC F CH$_3$O

free rotation

NO$_2$ CH$_3$O
HOOC CH$_3$O

symmetrical

NO$_2$ HO
HOOC—
H$_3$C

free rotation

Resolvable:

F HOOC
COOH F

COOH
COOH

NO$_2$ CH$_3$O
HOOC—
H$_3$C

**Table 12-7 Optical activity of some biphenyls**

### 12-18 HELICAL MOLECULAR ASYMMETRY

In the last class of molecules to be considered the optical activity is due to the asymmetry of the whole molecule. Often these are compounds which are overcrowded and distortion of the normal bond angle occurs in order to reduce nonbonded interactions. In a sense the gross geometry resembles part of a helical turn. A given helix (or spiral staircase) may be denoted as right-handed or left-handed, depending on whether you move clockwise or counterclockwise while advancing up the helix (or staircase). Hexahelicine is the trivial name of a distorted molecule; it has been resolved and shows an extremely high optical rotation.

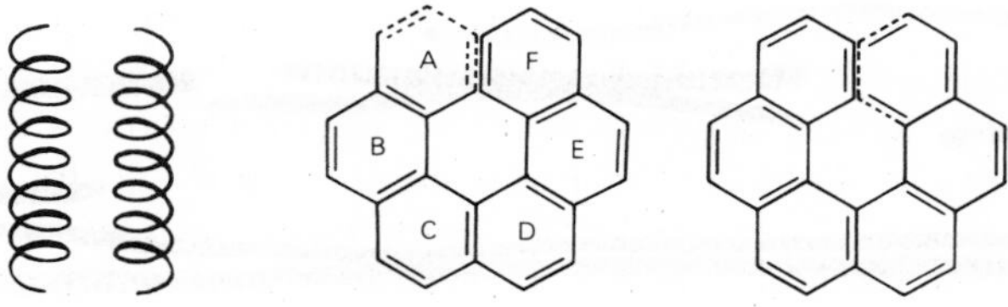


a pair of helices D and L isomers of hexahelicine

## STEREOSPECIFICITY OF CHEMICAL REACTIONS

It must be emphasized that starting with optically inactive chemicals and solvents in an optically inactive atmosphere, pure optically active isomers cannot be formed. The racemates ***always*** obtained must be resolved by the intervention of an optically active agent in order to obtain the pure antipode. Many chemical reactions are of this type; several are shown as examples. A discussion of stereospecificity at this point in the text provides an opportunity to review some of the reactions previously studied. For example, two of the reactions which generate asymmetric centers are the formation of a tertiary alcohol via the Grignard reaction and the addition of HCN to an aldehyde.

$$[CH_3MgI] + C_6H_5{-}\underset{\underset{O}{\|}}{C}{-}CH_2CH_3 \xrightarrow{H_2O} C_6H_5{-}\overset{CH_3}{\underset{OH}{\overset{|}{\underset{|}{{}^{*}C}}}}{-}CH_2CH_3$$

$$CH_3CHO + HCN \longrightarrow CH_3{-}\overset{OH}{\underset{H}{\overset{|}{\underset{|}{{}^{*}C}}}}{-}CN$$

### 12-19 ASYMMETRIC SYNTHESIS

Many chemical reactions which begin with a pure optical isomer yield a compound with preserved optical integrity. This is true of reactions which either do not affect the asymmetric center, e.g., the conversion of an acid to an acid chloride, or affect it in a known, predictable manner, e.g., $S_N2$ reactions.

$$\underset{\text{D isomer}}{CH_3CH_2\text{—}\underset{\substack{|\\CH_3}}{CH}\text{—}COOH} \xrightarrow{SOCl_2} \underset{\text{D isomer}}{CH_3CH_2\text{—}\underset{\substack{|\\CH_3}}{CH}\text{—}COCl}$$

$$\underset{\text{D isomer}}{CH_3CH_2\text{—}\underset{\substack{|\\Br}}{CH}\text{—}CH_3} \xrightarrow[\text{acetone}]{\text{NaI in}} \underset{\text{L isomer}}{CH_3CH_2\text{—}\overset{\substack{I\\|}}{CH}\text{—}CH_3}$$

Reactions which take place by backside displacement of a group or ion are called $S_N2$ reactions or ***Walden inversions***, since the reaction is a bimolecular, nucleophilic substitution which inverts the absolute configuration. Taking NaI in acetone as an example, the C—I bond is being formed while the C—Br bond is being broken.

$$I^- \;\; \underset{\text{D isomer}}{CH_2CH_3\text{—}\overset{\substack{CH_3\\|}}{\underset{\substack{|\\H}}{C}}\text{—}Br} \longrightarrow \left[\begin{matrix} CH_3CH_2\;\;CH_3 \\ I\cdots C\cdots Br \\ | \\ H \end{matrix}\right]^- \longrightarrow \underset{\text{L isomer}}{I\text{—}\overset{\substack{CH_3\\|}}{\underset{\substack{|\\H}}{C}}\text{—}CH_2CH_3} + Br^-$$

Thus, starting with a compound of known configuration, the product will be of the opposite absolute configuration if the $S_N2$ pathway is followed. Remember that in the absence of additional information, this statement cannot be used to predict the direction of rotation of the product. The Walden inversion, or $S_N2$ mechanism, is a common solvolytic displacement pathway for primary and secondary halides.

The stereochemistry of products obtained via an $S_N2$ mechanism is to be contrasted with that from an $S_N1$ mechanism; the latter products are racemic (or nearly so), since the intermediate planar carbonium ion may add the attacking anion from either the top or the bottom of the plane. **In general, $S_N2$ reactions (Walden inversions) proceed with inversion of configuration, and $S_N1$ reactions result in racemization.**

Molecules which already contain an asymmetric center may induce a predominance of one isomer (diastereoisomer) over another if the newly created center is close to the already established one. This is known as ***asymmetric induction***. A case which has been extensively studied is the Grignard reaction of optically active aldehydes and ketones. Note that the approach of the Grignard reagent will be determined by the steric effects of the groups adjacent to the incipient asymmetric center.

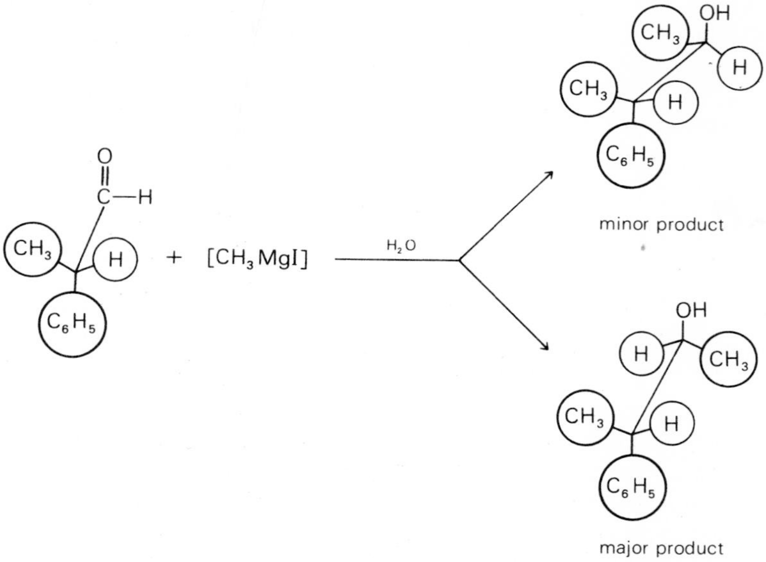

$$CH_3,\ H,\ C_6H_5\text{-CHO} + [CH_3MgI] \xrightarrow{H_2O}$$

minor product

major product

The two diastereoisomers are not formed in equal amounts; the major product is the one obtained by attack of the carbonyl group from the side which is flanked by the smallest group, in this case, —H.

### 12-20 GEOMETRICAL STEREOSPECIFICITY

It is profitable to review briefly several reactions which are stereospecific in the ***geometrical*** sense: hydrogenation of multiple bonds (Sec. 4-4), hydroxylation of double bonds (Sec. 4-6), formation of cyclopropane via the Simmons-Smith reaction (Chap. 3), halogenation, hydrohalogenation, and hypohalogenation of multiple bonds (Secs. 4-5, 4-8, and 4-9).

The catalytic hydrogenation of double and triple bonds takes place primarily by cis addition, although there are cases known in which skeletal rearrangement takes place in the presence of the catalyst metals, such as Pt, Pd, and Ni.

Treatment of an alkene with $KMnO_4$ in dilute basic solution at low temperatures has been used for the formation of cis glycols. The cyclic intermediate formed is then cleaved by breaking Mn—O bonds.

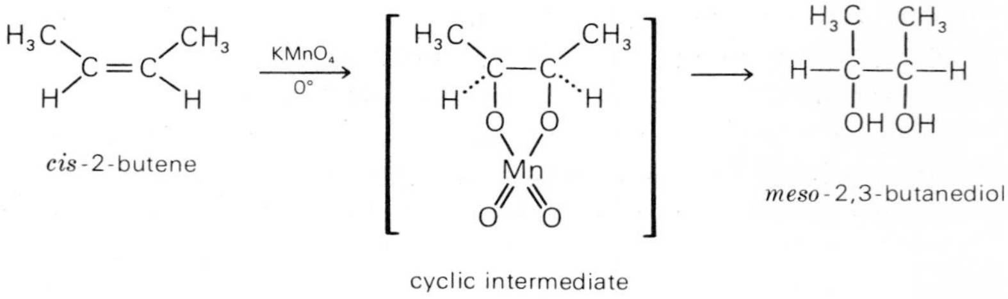

$$H_3C(H)C{=}C(H)CH_3 \xrightarrow[0^\circ]{KMnO_4} [\text{cyclic intermediate}] \longrightarrow H_3C\text{-}CH(OH)\text{-}CH(OH)\text{-}CH_3$$

*cis*-2-butene

cyclic intermediate

*meso*-2,3-butanediol

*trans*-2-butene $\xrightarrow[0^\circ]{KMnO_4}$ [cyclic manganate ester] $\longrightarrow$ D,L-2,3-butanediol

cyclohexene $\longrightarrow$ *cis*-1,2-cyclohexanediol

OH (*a*) OH (*e*) H H

preferred conformation of cis isomer

Since the requisite five-membered intermediate cannot assume a trans configuration, this gives rise to cis glycols in the absence of rearrangement reactions. If the starting olefin is the cis isomer, the product is the meso glycol; trans olefins, by such a cis addition give the D,L racemate. Small-ring olefins can have only the cis double-bond configuration and thus always lead initially to the meso isomer.

The Simmon-Smith reaction produces cyclopropane derivatives from olefins and an organozinc intermediate, I—$CH_2$—ZnI, produced from methylene iodine, $CH_2I_2$, and a zinc-copper couple, Zn—Cu. In this case also the addition of the one-carbon fragment takes place with cis addition, and the stereochemical integrity of the starting olefin is preserved. Cyclic olefins give rise to bicyclic products.

*cis*-2-butene $\xrightarrow[\text{Zn—Cu couple}]{CH_2I_2}$ *cis*-1,2-dimethylcyclopropane

*trans*-2-butene $\xrightarrow[\text{Zn—Cu couple}]{CH_2I_2}$ *trans*-1,2-dimethylcyclopropane

cyclohexene $\xrightarrow[\text{Zn—Cu couple}]{CH_2I_2}$ norcarane (bicyclo[4.1.0]heptane)

The Diels-Alder reaction (Chap. 6), an example of a cis cycloaddition, affords six-membered rings (adducts) by the 1,4 addition of an olefin to a diene. In these adducts the geometry of the olefin is maintained.

1,3-butadiene + maleic acid $\xrightarrow{\Delta}$ [transition state] $\longrightarrow$ *cis*-4-cyclohexene-1,2-dicarboxylic acid

1,3-butadiene + fumaric acid $\xrightarrow{\Delta}$ [transition state] $\longrightarrow$ trans isomer

The reactions discussed previously in this section have been cis additions or cycloadditions; additions to multiple bonds can also occur by trans addition. Three reactions which exemplify such additions are the reaction of a halogen, $X_2$, a hydrohalic acid, HX, and a hypohalous acid, HOX, to an olefin (or acetylene), examples of which are shown below; note that in all cases there is an electrophilic attack by $H^+$ or $X^+$, followed by backside attack of the $X^-$ or $OH^-$.

*cis*-2-butene + $Br_2$ $\longrightarrow$ [cyclic bromonium ion] $\xrightarrow{Br^-}$ $CH_3$—CH(Br)—CH(Br)—$CH_3$ D,L isomer

*trans*-2-butene + $Br_2$ $\longrightarrow$ [cyclic bromonium ion] $\xrightarrow{Br^-}$ $CH_3$—CH(Br)—CH(Br)—$CH_3$ meso isomer

cyclohexene $\xrightarrow{HBr}$ bromocyclohexane

The reaction of cyclohexene with HBr cannot be used to determine the stereochemical course of addition, but the reaction of 1,2-dideuterocyclohexene with HBr does demonstrate the stereospecificity.

1,2-dideuterocyclohexene $\xrightarrow{HBr}$ *trans*-1,2-dideuterobromocyclohexane; preferred conformation

> Formulate the reactions of hypobromous acid with *cis*-2-butene, *trans*-2-butene, and cyclohexene. Make projection drawings or use models to show the preferred conformation, on the basis of steric considerations, of each product.

## SUGGESTED READINGS


Baxter, J. N.: Systematic Names for the Tartaric Acids, *J. Chem. Educ.*, **41**, 619 (1964).

Cahn, R. S.: An Introduction to the Sequence Rule, *J. Chem. Educ.*, **41**, 116 (1964).

Cammarata, A.: Optical Studies in Organophosphorus Chemistry, *J. Chem. Educ.*, **43**, 64 (1966).

Cram, D. J.: Recent Advances in Stereochemistry, *J. Chem. Educ.*, **37**, 317 (1960).

Eliel, E. L.: Teaching Organic Stereochemistry, *J. Chem. Educ.*, **41**, 73 (1964).

Glasser, L.: Teaching Symmetry: The Use of Decorations, *J. Chem. Educ.*, **44**, 502 (1967). Shows various types of symmetries found in works of M. Escher, a Dutch artist.

Ingraham, L. L.: Three-dimensional Effects in Biochemistry, *J. Chem. Educ*, **41**, 66 (1964).

Kauffman, G. B.: Foundations of Nitrogen Stereochemistry: Alfred Werner's Inaugural Dissertation, *J. Chem. Educ.*, **43**, 155 (1966).

Lyle, R. E., and G. G. Lyle: A Brief History of Polarimetry, *J. Chem. Educ.*, **41**, 308 (1964).

Natta, G.: Precisely Constructed Polymers, *Sci. Am.*, **205** (2), 33 (1961). Discusses stereospecific catalytic processes for synthesizing "stereoregular" polymers from optically active hydrocarbons.

Noyce, W. K.: Stereoisomerism of Carbon Compounds, *J. Chem. Educ.*, **38**, 23 (1961).

Thompson, H. B.: The Criterion for Optical Isomerism, *J. Chem. Educ.*, **37**, 530 (1960).

Williams, F. T.: Resolution by the Method of Racemic Modification, *J. Chem. Educ.*, **39**, 211 (1962).

## PROBLEMS

**1.** Make a table like that in the example for the compounds listed. It will be helpful to write projection formulas or make a model for each of the stereoisomers.

| Compounds | Total possible number of stereoisomers | Number of optically active forms | Comment (number of cis, trans, meso, D, L pairs, etc.) |
|---|---|---|---|
| 000. (chlorobenzene structure, Cl) | 0 | 0 | |
| 00. 1,2-dichloroethylene | 2 | 0 | one cis<br>one trans |
| 0. $HO_2C—CHOH—CHOH—CO_2H$ | 3 | 2 | one meso<br>one D, L pair |

★(*a*) 2,4-diphenyl-1,3-cyclobutanedicarboxylic acid (truxillic acids)

(*b*) (decalin ring structure with OH) β-decalol (also show the preferred conformations)

★(*c*) 4-bromo-1,4-dimethylcyclohexanol (preferred conformations)

★(*d*) $CH_2(NH_2)CO_2H$, glycine

(*e*) $CH_3CH(NH_2)CO_2H$, alanine

★(*f*) ($H_2C$=C($H_3C$)– cyclohexene ring –$CH_3$), limonene

★(*g*) $HC{\equiv}C{-}C{\equiv}C{-}CH{=}C{=}CH{-}CH{=}CH{-}CH{=}CHCH_2CO_2H$, mycomycin

(*h*) $C_6H_5CH(OH)—CH(NHCH_3)CH_3$, ephedrine

(*i*) $H_3C$–(cyclohexanone ring, O)–$CH(CH_3)_2$, menthone

(*j*) $HOCH_2—CH(OH)—CH(OH)—CHO$

(*k*) $C_6H_5CH_2CH(NH_2)CH_3$, amphetamine

★(*l*) (ring structure with $CH_3$) methylcyclopentenophenanthrene

★(*m*) 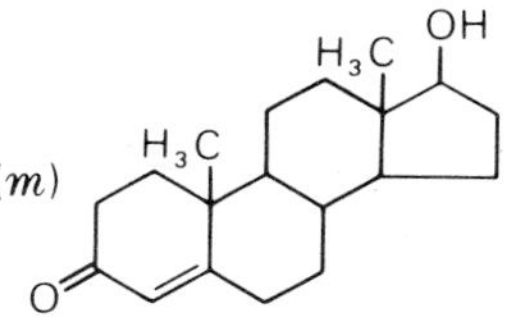 testosterone

(*n*) 1,2-dimethylcyclobutane

★(*o*)

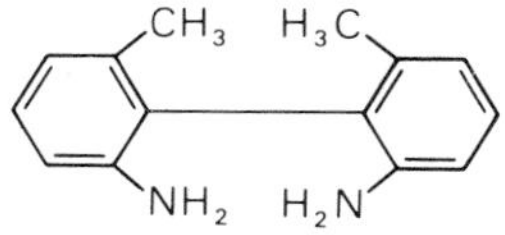

★(*p*)

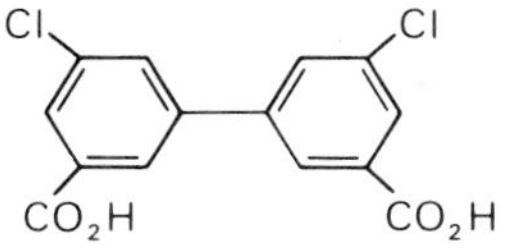

(*q*) $CH_3(CH_2)_4—CH{=}CH—CH_2—CH{=}CH—(CH_2)_7CO_2H$

(*r*)

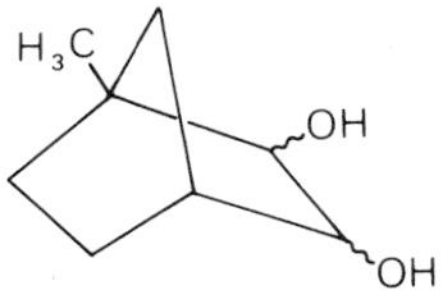

**2.** Each of the following compounds has been resolved. State clearly the source of the optical activity and the total number and type of stereoisomers expected.

★(*a*)

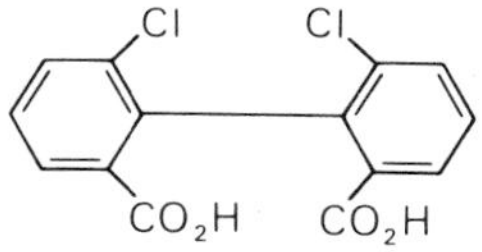

★(*b*)

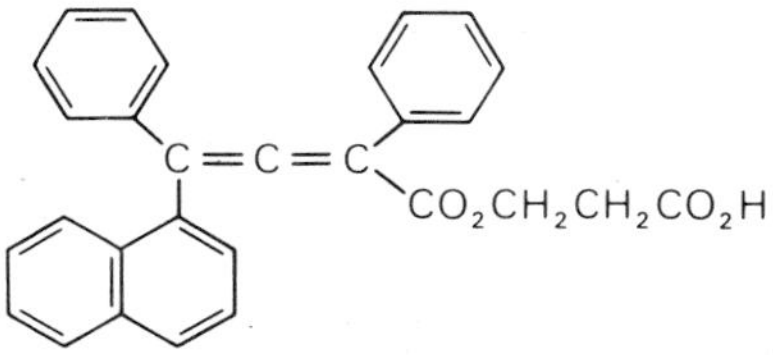

(*c*) 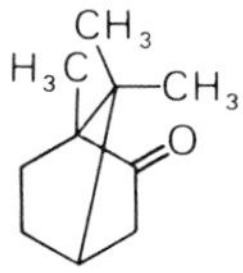 camphor

★(*d*) $CH_3—\overset{+}{N}(—O^-)(CH_2CH_3)—CH_2CH_2CH_3$

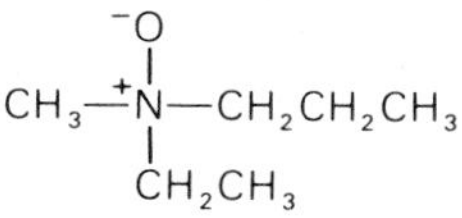

★(*e*) cyclooctene

(*f*)

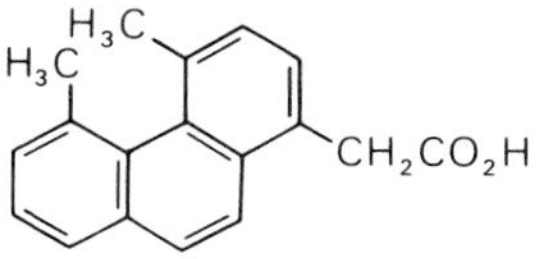

★**3.** It has *not* been possible to resolve the following compounds. State the reason clearly.

(*a*) $CH_3—\ddot{N}(CH_3CH_2)—C_6H_5$

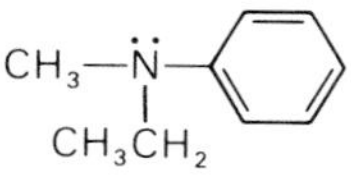

(*b*)

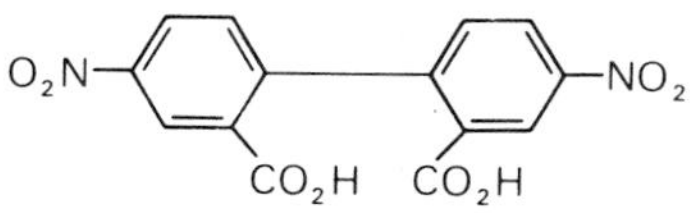

(*c*) $CH_3CH{=}C{=}C{=}CHC_6H_5$

(*d*) 1,2,3,4,5-pentachlorocyclopentane

(*e*) *meso*-tartaric acid

★**4.** Using Fischer projections, draw all the aldohexoses, $CHO—(CHOH)_4—CH_2OH$.

# Chapter Thirteen

The functional groups of aldehydes and ketones both contain a carbonyl group

$$\underset{\text{aldehyde}}{\mathrm{RC}{\overset{\displaystyle /\!\!/ \mathrm{O}}{\underset{\displaystyle \diagdown \mathrm{H}}{}}}} \qquad\qquad \underset{\text{ketone}}{\mathrm{R{-}\overset{\overset{\displaystyle O}{\|}}{C}{-}R}}$$

Because of their similar structures, they undergo many of the same reactions. The general organization of this chapter is dictated by these similarities. The nomenclature of these two classes is discussed, followed by separate sections on their preparation. The reactions are discussed together in the third section. Aldehydes and ketones undergo many condensation reactions, giving rise to the formation of carbon-carbon bonds, and these important reactions are discussed in the next section. The last part of this chapter discusses the qualitative tests used in distinguishing aldehydes from ketones.

## NOMENCLATURE OF ALDEHYDES AND KETONES

Aldehydes, R—CHO, and ketones, R—CO—R', may be named either by the common (trivial) system or by the IUPAC system. For aldehydes, the common name is formed from the trivial name of the ***acid*** containing the same number of carbon atoms by dropping the -*ic* ending and adding the suffix -***aldehyde***. The IUPAC system employs the -***al*** ending on the IUPAC hydrocarbon name. The trivial name for $CH_3CH_2CH_2CHO$, for example, is butyraldehyde; the IUPAC name is butanal.

The common system of ketone nomenclature names each of the alkyl or aryl groups attached to the carbonyl carbon and adds the word ketone.

# Aldehydes and Ketones

For example, $CH_3CH_2COCH(CH_3)_2$ is named ethyl isopropyl ketone. The IUPAC ending for ketones is *-one*. The above example is also named 2-methyl-3-pentanone (see Table 13-1).

## PREPARATION OF ALDEHYDES

Since aldehydes are intermediate in oxidation state between alcohols and acids, it is reasonable to expect that methods of synthesis can be devised in which aldehydes can be prepared either by the oxidation of primary alcohols or by reduction of the corresponding acids and their derivatives.

$$R\text{—}CH_2OH \xrightarrow[\text{slow}]{[O]} R\text{—}CHO \xrightarrow[\text{fast}]{[O]} R\text{—}CO_2H$$

This is the case; however, the newly formed aldehyde is often more susceptible to further oxidation than the original primary alcohol. On the other hand, the aldehyde may be more readily reduced to the alcohol than the starting acid is reduced to the aldehyde. It has become a challenge for the organic chemist to find reagents which will effect the desired transformation without consuming the aldehyde by further oxidation or reduction reactions.

### 13-1 OXIDATION OF PRIMARY ALCOHOLS

The preparation of aldehydes by oxidation of the corresponding primary alcohols with warm permanganate solution, $KMnO_4$, or some form of Cr(VI), such as $CrO_3$ or $K_2Cr_2O_7$, is generally a poor method since the aldehyde itself is more readily oxidized to the corresponding acid under these same conditions.

$$R\text{—}CH_2OH \xrightarrow[\text{slow}]{[O]} R\text{—}CHO \xrightarrow[\text{fast}]{[O]} R\text{—}CO_2H$$

**Table 13-1 Examples of aldehyde and ketone nomenclature**

| Acids | Aldehydes | Ketones |
|---|---|---|
| $HCOOH$<br>formic acid | $H{-}C({=}O){-}H$<br>formaldehyde<br>(methanal) | $CH_3{-}C({=}O){-}CH_3$<br>dimethyl ketone<br>(2-propanone; commonly, acetone) |
| $CH_3COOH$<br>acetic acid | $CH_3CHO$<br>acetaldehyde<br>(ethanal) | $CH_3{-}C({=}O){-}CH_2{-}CH_3$<br>methyl ethyl ketone<br>(2-butanone) |
| $CH_3CH_2COOH$<br>propionic acid | $CH_3CH_2CHO$<br>propionaldehyde<br>(propanal) | $CH_3CH_2{-}C({=}O){-}CH_2CH_3$<br>diethyl ketone<br>(3-pentanone) |
| $CH_3CH_2CH_2COOH$<br>butyric acid | $CH_3CH_2CH_2CHO$<br>butyraldehyde<br>(butanal) | $CH_3{-}C({=}O){-}C(CH_3)_3$<br>methyl *tert*-butyl ketone<br>(3,3-dimethyl-2-butanone; commonly, pinacolone) |
| $C_6H_5COOH$<br>benzoic acid | $C_6H_5CHO$<br>benzaldehyde | cyclopropanone |
| $CCl_3COOH$<br>trichloroacetic acid | $CCl_3CHO$<br>trichloroacetaldehyde<br>(commonly, chloral) | 1,3-cyclopentadione |
| | $C_{10}H_7CHO$<br>β-naphthaldehyde | $C_6H_5{-}C({=}O){-}CH_3$<br>methyl phenyl ketone<br>(commonly, acetophenone) |

Of course, there are cases in which this difficulty is avoided: if the aldehyde has a lower boiling point than the alcohol, the product can be removed from the reaction mixture by distillation as it is formed (Sec. 9-5).

The oxidation of primary *allylic* and *benzylic* alcohols to the aldehyde with freshly prepared manganese dioxide, $MnO_2$, is a fairly good method of preparation. While $MnO_2$ is strong enough to effect the desired oxidation ($MnO_2 \longrightarrow Mn^{++}$), it is not a strong enough oxidizing agent to convert aldehydes to acids (Sec. 9-5).

## 13-2 HYDROLYSIS OF TERMINAL GEMINAL-DIHALIDES

*geminal*-Dihalides are hydrolyzed to aldehydes or ketones in good yield simply on treatment with warm dilute base. Terminal *geminal*-dihalides give aldehydes; internal ones give ketones (Sec. 8-4). The mechanism may reasonably proceed by either of the pathways outlined:

$$CH_3—CHCl_2 \xrightarrow[2OH^-]{dil.} \left[ CH_3—\underset{H}{\overset{OH}{C}}—OH \right] \xrightarrow{-H_2O} CH_3CHO$$

$$CH_3—CHCl_2 \xrightarrow[OH^-]{dil.} \left[ CH_3—\underset{H}{\overset{OH}{C}}—Cl \right] \xrightarrow{-HCl} CH_3CHO$$

Both the intermediates shown are known to be unstable and would be expected to yield the aldehyde.

This hydrolysis reaction is especially useful in the aromatic series, where the corresponding dihalide is readily available by photochemical free-radical side-chain halogenation (Sec. 8-3).

$$C_6H_5—CH_3 \xrightarrow[h\nu;\ \Delta]{2Cl_2} C_6H_5—CHCl_2 \xrightarrow[\text{or dil. } OH^-]{H_2O;\ \Delta} C_6H_5—CHO$$

## 13-3 ROSENMUND REDUCTION (ACID CHLORIDES)

The reduction of acid chlorides to aldehydes, known as the *Rosenmund reduction*, is somewhat tricky to carry out effectively. The reaction involves catalytic hydrogenolysis under conditions that must be carefully controlled to avoid further reduction to the alcohol.

$$R—C\overset{O}{\underset{Cl}{\lessgtr}} \xrightarrow[\text{sulfur-quinoline poison}]{H_2/Pd \text{ on } BaSO_4} R—C\overset{O}{\underset{H}{\lessgtr}} + HCl$$

This reaction is carried out using a palladium catalyst (supported on $BaSO_4$) which has been partially deactivated or "poisoned" by the presence of a mixture of sulfur and quinoline.

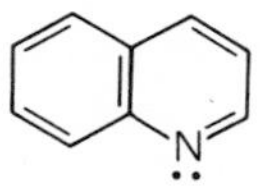

quinoline

The reaction has been applied successfully to aliphatic and, especially, aromatic acid chlorides.

## 13-4 SOMMELET REACTION

This preparation of aldehydes involves conversion of a primary halide to an amine salt, followed by acid hydrolysis.

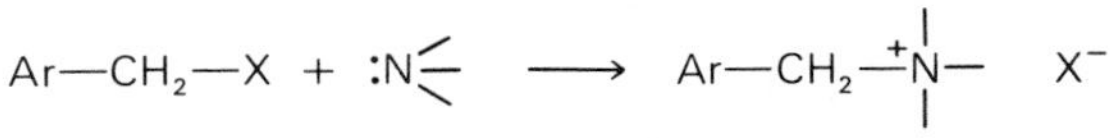

$$Ar{-}CH_2{-}X + :N\lessgtr \longrightarrow Ar{-}CH_2{-}\overset{+}{N}{-} \quad X^-$$

HMTA HMTA salt

The reagent for the conversion of the halide to the salt is *h*exa*m*ethyl-ene*t*etr*a*mine (HMTA), which is formed by the condensation of form-aldehyde with ammonia. Note the all-chairlike conformation of the rings in the product.

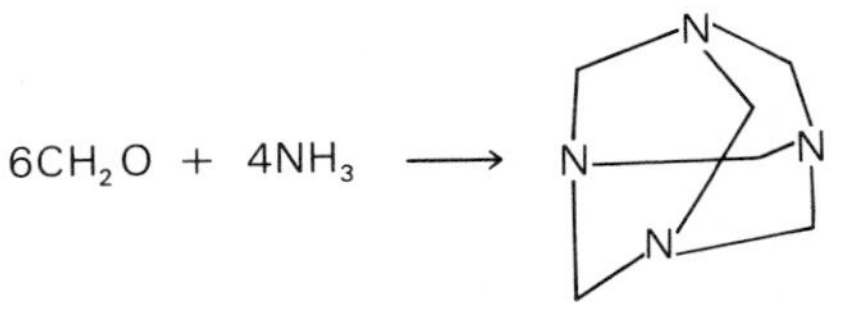

$$6CH_2O + 4NH_3 \longrightarrow \text{HMTA}$$

HMTA

HMTA reacts with halides, particularly benzyl halides, in aqueous ethanol to form a salt which can be decomposed to the corresponding aldehyde by refluxing with dilute acid. The yields of aldehydes are good to excellent when benzyl halides are used.

$$C_6H_5CH_2Br \xrightarrow[H_2O\text{-}EtOH]{HMTA} [\text{salt}] \xrightarrow{H_3O^+} C_6H_5CHO$$

benzyl bromide benzaldehyde

The availability of benzyl halides from photochemical free-radical halo-genation of the corresponding methylhydrocarbons makes this an attrac-tive synthetic route for mono-, di-, and higher-substituted aromatic aldehydes.

$$m\text{-xylene} \xrightarrow[h\nu]{2Br_2} \alpha,\alpha'\text{-dibromo-}m\text{-xylene} \xrightarrow[2.\ H_3O^+;\ \Delta]{1.\ 2HMTA\ in\ H_2O\text{-}EtOH} \text{isophthaldehyde}$$

m-xylene — α,α'-dibromo-m-xylene — isophthaldehyde

## 13-5 ALDEHYDES FROM NITRILES

At least two common methods are available for the synthesis of aldehydes from nitriles, R—C≡N, also called ***cyanides***. The syntheses can be applied to aliphatic or aromatic nitriles; the yields in both cases are only fair.

In the first method stannous chloride, $SnCl_2$, in hydrochloric acid is a good reducing agent ($Sn^{++} \longrightarrow Sn^{4+}$) and nitriles, especially aliphatic ones, can be converted to a tin salt with this reagent. Decomposition of this salt with water yields the aldehyde.

$$R{-}C{\equiv}N \xrightarrow[2.\ H_2O]{1.\ SnCl_2/HCl} R{-}CHO$$

Lithium aluminum hydride, $LiAlH_4$, in ether will reduce some nitriles under carefully controlled conditions, giving mainly the imine, which can be hydrolyzed to the corresponding aldehyde and ammonia.

*General*:

$$R{-}C{\equiv}N \xrightarrow{LiAlH_4} [(R{-}CH{=}N)_4{-}LiAl] \xrightarrow{H_2O} [R{-}CH{=}N{-}H] \xrightarrow{H_2O} R{-}CHO + NH_3$$

an aldimine

*Specific*:

$$\text{cyclopropanecarbonitrile} \xrightarrow[50\%\ yield]{1.\ LiAlH_4\quad 2.\ H_2O} \text{cyclopropanecarboxaldehyde}$$

cyclopropanecarbonitrile — cyclopropanecarboxaldehyde

Imines, also known as ***Schiff bases***, are the products of the equilibrium of aldehydes or ketones with amines, $R{-}NH_2$, or ammonia, $NH_3$. Aldehydes form ***aldimines***; ketones form ***ketimines*** (Sec. 13-14).

> Suggest a mechanism for the hydrolysis of an aldimine to the aldehyde.

Since excess $LiAlH_4$ will reduce a nitrile to the corresponding primary amine, $R—CH_2NH_2$, this side reaction must be minimized in the formation of aldehydes by using only the calculated quantity of $LiAlH_4$.

### 13-6 ALDEHYDES VIA THE GRIGNARD REACTION

Treatment of ethyl orthoformate, $HC(OCH_2CH_3)_3$, with a Grignard reagent gives the next higher aldehydediethyl acetal.

$$\underset{\text{1-pentylmagnesium bromide}}{CH_3(CH_2)_3CH_2MgBr} + \underset{\text{ethyl orthoformate}}{HC(OCH_2CH_3)_3} \longrightarrow \underset{n\text{-hexaldehyde diethyl acetal}}{CH_3(CH_2)_3CH_2—CH(OCH_2CH_3)_2} + CH_3CH_2OMgBr$$

$$CH_3(CH_2)_3CH_2CH(OCH_2CH_3)_2 \xrightarrow{H_3O^+} \underset{n\text{-hexaldehyde}}{CH_3(CH_2)_4CHO} + 2CH_3CH_2OH$$

Acid hydrolysis of the acetal liberates the aldehyde (see also Sec. 13-13 for acetal reactions). Ethyl orthoformate is prepared in one step as follows:

$$2CHCl_3 + 6CH_3CH_2OH + 6Na \longrightarrow 2CH(OCH_2CH_3)_3 + 3H_2\uparrow + 6NaCl$$

**1.** Suggest a mechanism for the formation of ethyl orthoformate.

**2.** Suggest a mechanism for the reaction of a Grignard reagent with ethyl orthoformate.

## PREPARATION OF KETONES

Most of the preparations of ketones are quite different from those of aldehydes, since aldehydes are easily oxidized terminal functional groups. However, secondary alcohols are smoothly oxidized to ketones (Sec. 9-5), and *geminal*-dihalides are hydrolyzed to ketones (Sec. 13-7).

### 13-7 HYDROLYSIS OF INTERNAL GEMINAL-DIHALIDES

In the same manner that aldehydes can be prepared from terminal *geminal*-dihalides (Sec. 13-2), ***ketones*** result from the hydrolysis of internal *geminal*-dihalides. Since aliphatic *geminal*-dihalides are usually prepared from the desired carbonyl compound and $PX_5$, the preparation is not particularly useful, but the hydrolysis reaction can be used in the aromatic series, where *geminal*-dihalides can be obtained by photochemical halogenation.

$$C_6H_5-CH_2-C_6H_5 \xrightarrow[h\nu]{2Cl_2} C_6H_5-CCl_2-C_6H_5 \xrightarrow[OH^-]{H_2O} C_6H_5-\overset{O}{\overset{\|}{C}}-C_6H_5$$

> **1.** In the example above, the ketone could be prepared via a Friedel-Crafts acylation reaction. Formulate this reaction.
>
> **2.** Name the compounds in the example above.

### 13-8 FIVE AND SIX-MEMBERED CYCLIC KETONES

Our discussion of cycloalkanes and a study of appropriate models pointed out the fact that cyclopropane and cyclobutane are highly strained molecules but cyclopentane and cyclohexane are relatively strain-free. Higher-membered cycloalkanes assume conformations which are also free of strain effects. The formation of five- and six-membered cyclic ketones by strongly heating the barium or calcium salt of the corresponding open-chain diacid is in accord with these observations.

$$(CH_2)_4(CO_2H)_2 \xrightarrow{Ba(OH)_2} \left[ (CH_2)_4(CO_2^-)_2 \; Ba^{++} \right] \xrightarrow{\Delta} \text{cyclopentanone} + CO_2\uparrow + BaO\downarrow$$

adipic acid — cyclopentanone

The open-chain diacid is treated with barium or calcium hydroxide to form the salt, which is then dried and strongly heated. The ketone is removed by distillation as it is formed. Although cyclopentanone and cyclohexanone are obtained in fair yield, the higher and lower members in the series give negligible yields. The three- and four-membered ring systems are highly strained and must be prepared by other methods. With the larger rings, it is difficult to get the ends of the diacid close enough to effect the cyclization. Note that with the higher diacids, a polymeric structure for the salt competes effectively with the cyclic structure.

$$[Ba^{++}\ {}^-O_2C-(CH_2)_n-CO_2^-\ Ba^{++}\ {}^-O_2C-(CH_2)_n-CO_2^-\ Ba^{++}\ {}^-O_2C-(CH_2)_n-CO_2^-]$$

### 13-9 METHYL ARYL KETONES VIA THE GRIGNARD REAGENT

Aromatic methyl ketones can be prepared in fair yield by the reaction of methylmagnesium iodide with an aryl cyanide, followed by hydrolysis of the imine salt intermediate.

$$C_6H_5CN \xrightarrow{[CH_3MgI]} \left[ C_6H_5C(=NMgX)CH_3 \right] \xrightarrow{H_2O} \left[ C_6H_5C(=NH)CH_3 \right] \xrightarrow{H_2O} C_6H_5COCH_3 + NH_3$$

benzonitrile → imine → acetophenone

The imine intermediate in this reaction is similar to that encountered in the reduction of nitriles to aldehydes with $LiAlH_4$ (Sec. 13-5). This reaction is seldom used since other methods of synthesis are more reliable, particularly the Friedel-Crafts acetylation discussed in Sec. 7-9.

### 13-10 KETONES FROM ACID CHLORIDES AND DIALKYL CADMIUM COMPOUNDS

The direct reaction between a Grignard reagent and an acid chloride is an ineffective synthesis of ketones because the ketone, once formed, reacts much faster with the Grignard reagent than the starting acid chloride does, even at low temperatures. An indirect method must be sought. Treatment of an alkyl Grignard reagent with anhydrous cadmium chloride, $CdCl_2$, gives the dialkyl cadmium compound, $R_2Cd$.

$$2[R{-}MgX] + CdCl_2 \text{ (dry)} \longrightarrow [R_2Cd] + 2MgXCl$$

The dialkyl cadmium compound reacts in much the same way as a Grignard reagent, but it is less reactive; thus, it is able to effect the transformation of an acid chloride to a ketone but reacts only slowly with the ketone itself. The cadmium product of the first substitution, RCdCl, may undergo the same reaction with another equivalent of the acid chloride.

$$R'-C(=O)Cl + RCdCl \longrightarrow R'-\overset{O}{\overset{\|}{C}}-R + CdCl_2$$

## 13-11 FRIEDEL-CRAFTS ACYLATION[†]

Methyl ketones can be prepared via Friedel-Crafts acetylation of aromatic compounds with acetyl chloride and aluminum chloride in nitrobenzene or carbon disulfide.

$$\text{biphenyl} \xrightarrow[\text{2. } H_3O^+]{\text{1. } CH_3COCl \quad \text{1.1 equiv. } AlCl_3 \text{ in } CS_2} \text{4-acetylbiphenyl } (C_6H_5-C_6H_4-COCH_3)$$

biphenyl 4-acetylbiphenyl

Higher acid chlorides give the corresponding ketones.

$$C_6H_6 + C_6H_5-COCl \xrightarrow[\text{2. } H_3O^+]{\text{1. 1.1 equiv } AlCl_3 \text{ in } CS_2} C_6H_5-\overset{O}{\overset{\|}{C}}-C_6H_5$$

benzene benzoyl chloride benzophenone

Cyclic anhydrides yield keto acids. Succinic anhydride is commonly used which allows four carbon atoms to be added to an aromatic system at one time.

$$Br-C_6H_5 + \text{succinic anhydride} \xrightarrow[\text{2. } H_3O^+]{\text{1. 2.1 equiv. } AlCl_3 \text{ in } C_6H_5NO_2} Br-C_6H_4-CO-CH_2-CH_2-COOH$$

This is the first step in the synthesis of many naphthalene compounds from substituted benzenes, a sequence which is discussed in Sec. 15-22.

The mechanism of the Friedel-Crafts acylation, which was discussed in Sec 7-9, shows that each carbonyl group in the acid chloride or anhydride is complexed by 1 equiv of $AlCl_3$; the additional 0.1 equiv of $AlCl_3$ acts as a catalyst in the reaction.

[†] See also Secs. 7-9 and 7-10.

## REACTIONS OF ALDEHYDES AND KETONES

Aldehydes and ketones are unsaturated in the sense that they contain a carbonyl group which has a carbon-oxygen double bond, $>C=O$. The carbon and oxygen atoms are bound by both a $\sigma$ and a $\pi$ bond (Fig. 13-1). Since oxygen is the more electronegative element, the best resonance structures in the valence-bond treatment place the negative charge on the oxygen atom.

**Figure 13-1 LCAO representation of the carbonyl group**

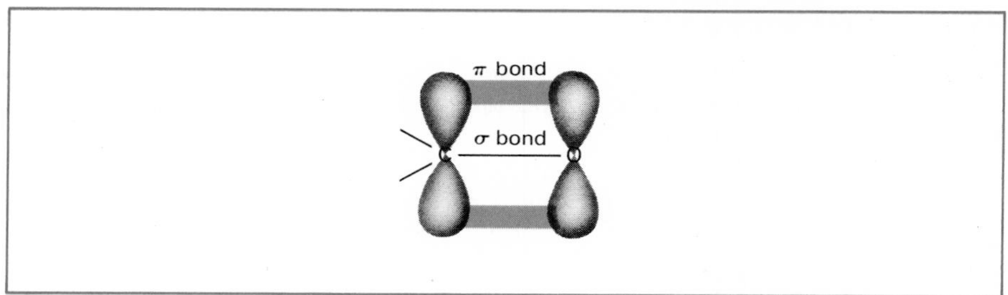


$$\left[ >C=O \longleftrightarrow >\overset{+}{C}-\overset{-}{O} \right]$$

The reactions of aldehydes and ketones are mainly those of nucleophilic attack on the carbon atom of the carbonyl group and those due to the enolizable hydrogen atoms $\alpha$ to the carbonyl.

$$\left[ -CH_2-\underset{\underset{O}{\|}}{C}\diagup \rightleftharpoons -CH=\underset{\underset{OH}{|}}{C}- \right]$$

It is important to note that the hydrogen atom attached directly to the carbonyl group of aldehydes, —CHO, is *not* readily removed.

### 13-12 REDUCTION

With the availability of hydride reducing agents such as $LiAlH_4$ and $NaBH_4$, catalytic hydrogenation of aldehydes and ketones (to primary and secondary alcohols) has been relegated to second place among methods for such reductions in the laboratory (Sec. 9-9). On an industrial scale, however, catalytic reduction is used almost exclusively, and the search for more effective catalysts and optimum reaction conditions goes on steadily.

$$R-CHO \xrightarrow[\substack{2.\ H_3O^+ \\ \text{or} \\ NaBH_4}]{1.\ LiAlH_4} R-CH_2OH$$

$$R-\underset{\underset{O}{\|}}{C}-R' \xrightarrow[\substack{2.\ H_3O^+ \\ \text{or} \\ NaBH_4}]{1.\ LiAlH_4} R-\underset{\underset{OH}{|}}{CH}-R'$$

The total reduction of these carbonyl compounds to the corresponding hydrocarbon is usually accomplished by one of the following three routes. The presence of other functional groups in the molecule will dictate whether the reduction will be most effective in acidic, basic, or neutral solution.

**Acidic conditions:** Reduction under acidic conditions is usually accomplished by treatment of the ketone with amalgamated zinc, Zn(Hg), in dilute HCl. Exposure of a clean surface of zinc metal to a mercuric salt, commonly mercuric chloride, $HgCl_2$, results in the deposition of a thin layer of mercury on the zinc surface. The zinc and mercury metals unite, in nonstoichiometric proportions, to give ***amalgamated zinc***.

$$Zn^0 + Hg^{++} \longrightarrow Zn^{++} + Hg^0$$

$$Hg^0 + Zn^0 \longrightarrow Zn(Hg)$$

Other metals can be similarly amalgamated, although zinc is preferred for this organic reaction, known as the ***Clemmenson reduction***. Treatment of the amalgam with dilute HCl slowly produces hydrogen on the metallic surface, where the ketone is reduced to the hydrocarbon.

$$Ar—\underset{\underset{O}{\|}}{C}—R \xrightarrow[HCl]{Zn(Hg)} Ar—CH_2—R$$

This method of reduction is unsatisfactory for aldehydes because they often give a mixture of products. Aliphatic-aromatic ketones which contain no acid-sensitive groups react smoothly; excellent yields are usually obtained. This reaction has proved to be especially effective for the reduction of keto acids derived from Friedel-Crafts acylation with succinic anhydride.

$$C_6H_5—\overset{\overset{O}{\|}}{C}—CH_3 \xrightarrow[HCl \; 80\% \text{ yield}]{Zn(Hg)} C_6H_5—CH_2—CH_3$$

acetophenone ethylbenzene

$$C_6H_5—\underset{\underset{O}{\|}}{C}—CH_2—CH_2—COOH \xrightarrow[HCl \; 90\% \text{ yield}]{Zn(Hg)} C_6H_5—\overset{\gamma}{C}H_2—\overset{\beta}{C}H_2—\overset{\alpha}{C}H_2—COOH$$

β-benzoylpropionic acid

γ-phenylbutyric acid
4-phenylbutanoic acid, IUPAC

**Basic Conditions:** The Wolff-Kishner reduction consists of the reduction of a hydrazone under basic conditions.

$$>C{=}O + H_2N{-}NH_2 \longrightarrow >C{=}N{-}NH_2 + H_2O$$

aldehyde or ketone — hydrazine — a hydrazone

$$>C{=}N{-}NH_2 \xrightarrow[\Delta]{\text{base}} >CH_2 + N_2\uparrow$$

a hydrazone

The preparation of hydrazones from hydrazine, $H_2N{-}NH_2$, will be discussed in Sec. 13-14; however, it is of interest here to note that both aldehydes and ketones are reduced by treatment with hydrazine and a strong base at elevated temperatures. The presence of base-sensitive groups in the aldehyde or ketone dictates the use of other methods of reduction.

$$C_6H_5{-}\overset{O}{\overset{\|}{C}}{-}CH_3 \xrightarrow[(-H_2O)]{H_2N-NH_2} C_6H_5{-}\underset{CH_3}{\underset{|}{C}}{=}N{-}NH_2 \xrightarrow{KOH} C_6H_5{-}CH_2CH_3 + N_2\uparrow$$

acetophenone — acetophenone hydrazone — ethylbenzene

**Neutral conditions:** Treatment of sulfur-containing organic compounds with a hydrogen-metal system usually leads to cleavage of sulfur-carbon bonds (desulfurization). The reaction of aldehydes or ketones with ethylene dithiol, $CH_2SH{-}CH_2SH$, leads to the formation of thioketals.

$$\underset{R}{\overset{R'}{>}}C{=}O + \underset{SH\ \ SH}{CH_2CH_2} \longrightarrow \underset{R}{\overset{R'}{>}}C\underset{S-CH_2}{\overset{S-CH_2}{<}} + H_2O$$

aldehyde or ketone, R' = —H or alkyl — ethylene dithiol — a thioketal

This reaction is discussed in detail in Sec. 13-14. Here we wish to show that treatment of thioketals with a catalyst, freshly prepared Raney nickel, leads to the corresponding hydrocarbon.

$$\underset{R}{\overset{R}{>}}C\underset{S-CH_2}{\overset{S-CH_2}{<}} \xrightarrow[H_2]{Ra(Ni)} \underset{R}{\overset{R}{>}}CH_2 + CH_3CH_3\uparrow + H_2S\uparrow$$

Both the thioketal formation and desulfurization reactions take place under mild neutral conditions.

Raney nickel is prepared by treating nickel-aluminum alloy with base; the aluminum atoms in the metallic structure are removed by oxidation with strong base, leaving finely divided nickel metal saturated with hydrogen gas.

$$NiAl_2 + 6OH^- \longrightarrow Ni\downarrow + 2AlO_3^{3-} + 3H_2\uparrow$$

## 13-13 NUCLEOPHILIC ADDITIONS TO THE CARBONYL GROUP

Nearly all strong nucleophiles, whether ions, for example, $CN^-$, $R^-$, or molecules, for example, $\ddot{N}H_3$, $H_2\ddot{O}$, will attack the low-electron-density center about the carbon atom of an aldehyde or ketone carbonyl group.

**1.** The Grignard reaction with aldehydes and ketones has been discussed before in detail (Chap. 9 Alcohols).

**2.** Hydrogen cyanide adds to carbonyl groups of aldehydes in the expected manner, yielding cyanohydrins. An important consequence of this new carbon-carbon bond formation is that subsequent hydrolysis of the cyanohydrin gives the $\alpha$ hydroxy acid.

$$CH_3CH_2CHO \xrightarrow{HCN} CH_3CH_2{-}\underset{\displaystyle OH}{\underset{|}{CH}}{-}CN \xrightarrow{H_3O^+} CH_3{-}CH_2{-}\underset{\displaystyle OH}{\underset{|}{CH}}{-}COOH$$

propionaldehyde — propionaldehyde cyanohydrin — $\alpha$-hydroxybutyric acid

Unlike HCN, hydrogen halides do not generally add to these carbonyl functions; the equilibrium lies in the opposite direction.

$$R{-}\overset{\displaystyle O}{\overset{\|}{C}}{-}R' + H{-}X \rightleftharpoons R{-}\underset{\displaystyle X}{\underset{|}{\overset{\displaystyle OH}{\overset{|}{C}}}}{-}R'$$

R' = —H or alkyl

**3.** Although the equilibrium of the addition of water to aldehydes and ketones usually lies on the side of the carbonyl compound, alcohols do undergo appreciable reaction.

$$R{-}\overset{\displaystyle O}{\overset{\|}{C}}{-}R' + H_2O \rightleftharpoons R{-}\underset{\displaystyle OH}{\underset{|}{\overset{\displaystyle OH}{\overset{|}{C}}}}{-}R'$$

R' = —H or alkyl

Aldehydes give first ***hemiacetals*** and, on reaction with an additional equivalent of alcohol, give ***acetals***.

*General*:

$$\mathrm{R{-}CHO + R'OH \rightleftharpoons R{-}\overset{\displaystyle OH}{\underset{\displaystyle H}{C}}{-}OR' \overset{R'OH}{\rightleftharpoons} R{-}\overset{\displaystyle OR'}{\underset{\displaystyle H}{C}}{-}OR' + H_2O}$$

*Specific*:

$$\mathrm{\underset{acetaldehyde}{CH_3CHO} + \underset{ethyl\ alcohol}{CH_3CH_2OH} \rightleftharpoons \underset{acetaldehyde\ ethyl\ hemiacetal}{CH_3{-}\overset{\displaystyle OH}{\underset{\displaystyle H}{C}}{-}OCH_2CH_3}}$$

$$\mathrm{\overset{EtOH}{\rightleftharpoons} \underset{acetaldehyde\ diethyl\ acetal}{CH_3{-}\overset{\displaystyle OCH_2CH_3}{\underset{\displaystyle H}{C}}{-}OCH_2CH_3} + H_2O}$$

The reverse reaction, hydrolysis of an acetal, proceeds rapidly in the presence of traces of acid, but the base-catalyzed hydrolysis is much slower.

Although ketones give hemiketals on treatment with alcohols, the further reaction leading to ketals is much more difficult and is seldom achieved directly.

$$\mathrm{R{-}\overset{\displaystyle O}{\overset{\|}{C}}{-}R' + R''OH \rightleftharpoons R{-}\overset{\displaystyle OH}{\underset{\displaystyle OR''}{C}}{-}R' \overset{R''OH}{\rightleftharpoons} R{-}\overset{\displaystyle OR''}{\underset{\displaystyle OR''}{C}}{-}R' + H_2O}$$

We shall not be concerned here with the indirect synthesis of ketals; however, ketals of 1,2-glycols and their sulfur analogs can be formed directly. Often used are ethylene glycol, $HO{-}CH_2{-}CH_2{-}OH$; ethylene dithiol, $HS{-}CH_2{-}CH_2{-}SH$, which is the sulfur analog; and 2-mercaptoethanol, $HS{-}CH_2{-}CH_2{-}OH$, which combines both functional groups.

$$\mathrm{\underset{acetone}{(H_3C)_2C{=}O} + \underset{ethylene\ glycol}{HO{-}CH_2{-}CH_2{-}OH} \rightleftharpoons \underset{acetone\ ethylene\ ketal}{(H_3C)_2C\langle O{-}CH_2{-}CH_2{-}O\rangle} + H_2O}$$

> Write the structure of the products from the preparation of ketals from ethylene dithiol and 2-mercaptoethanol and review the reduction of thioketals by Raney nickel (Sec. 13-12).

**4.** Sodium bisulfite, $NaHSO_3$, adds to the carbonyl group of aldehydes, methyl ketones, and a few cyclic ketones, to give the sodium bisulfite adduct. **It adds as $H^+$ and $NaSO_3^-$**, rather than as $Na^+$ and $HSO_3^-$, **the sulfur atom becomes bound to the carbonyl carbon atoms.** This reaction is useful in the separation and purification of compounds that readily form the adduct, which is insoluble in aqueous ethanol. The bisulfite adduct can be converted to a cyanohydrin by treatment with aqueous cyanide, thus eliminating the use of liquid HCN, which is extremely toxic. Recall the hydrolysis of cyanohydrins to $\alpha$ hydroxy acids.

$$\mathrm{RHC}^{\delta+}{=}\mathrm{O}^{\delta-} + \mathrm{Na}\overset{\delta+}{\mathrm{H}}\ \overset{\delta-}{\mathrm{SO_3}} \xrightarrow[\mathrm{H_2O}]{\mathrm{EtOH}} \mathrm{R{-}CH(SO_3^-Na^+){-}OH} \xrightarrow{\mathrm{CN^-}} \mathrm{R{-}CH(CN){-}OH} + \mathrm{NaSO_3^-}$$

solid adduct — a cyanohydrin

## 13-14 REACTIONS OF AMMONIA AND RELATED MOLECULES; PREPARATION OF SOLID DERIVATIVES OF CARBONYL COMPOUNDS

Qualitative organic analysis, the identification of organic compounds by spectral methods and by known reactions, is an important aspect of organic chemistry. The training of an organic chemist may include an entire course in just this subject. For example, suppose you have an unknown (liquid) compound, which you have shown to be a ketone (by the rapid tests discussed in the next section). Which of the many known (or as yet unknown!) ketones is your particular compound?

One of the chemical methods used to determine the identity of an unknown compound is the conversion of the unknown ketone, *by a known reaction sequence*, to a second compound which is known (or which can be prepared from known starting materials). This second compound is called a ***derivative***, and the reagents are usually chosen so that the derivative is a solid; solids can be purified readily by recrystallization. The melting point and mixture melting point with a known sample can be determined. Of course, the probability of correctly identifying the unknown is increased by preparing two or more derivatives and comparing them with like compounds of a known sample. All the derivatives of aldehydes and ketones discussed here are prepared from reagents structurally related to ammonia (or hydrazine, $H_2N{-}NH_2$, which is also structurally related to ammonia).

**Imines:** Although aldehydes or ketones are in equilibrium with ***aldimines*** or ***ketimines*** in the presence of ammonia, the equilibrium usually lies toward the carbonyl compound; these unstable ***imines***, or ***Schiff bases***, are ***not*** used as derivatives. Imines are known to be intermediates in the reduction of nitriles (Sec. 13-5) and in the Grignard reaction of nitriles (Sec. 13-9).

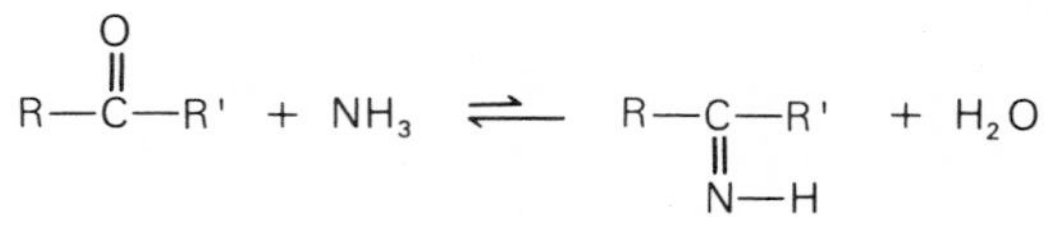

$$R-\overset{O}{\overset{\|}{C}}-R' + NH_3 \rightleftharpoons \underset{\underset{N-H}{\|}}{R-C-R'} + H_2O$$

R = —H or alkyl; an imine

**Oximes:** Hydroxylamine, $H_2N-OH$, gives **aldoximes from aldehydes and ketoximes from ketones.** Since the carbon-nitrogen double bond prevents both rotation and ammonialike inversion, two geometrical isomers are possible.

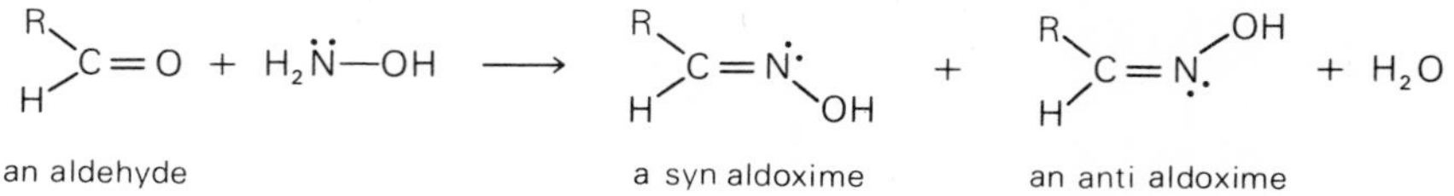

$$\begin{matrix}R\\ \quad\ C=O\\ H\end{matrix} + H_2\ddot{N}-OH \longrightarrow \begin{matrix}R\\ \quad\ C=\ddot{N}\\ H \qquad\qquad OH\end{matrix} + \begin{matrix}R \qquad\qquad OH\\ \quad\ C=N\\ H\end{matrix} + H_2O$$

an aldehyde; a syn aldoxime; an anti aldoxime

For aldehydes, the syn isomer (compare cis, "same") is the one in which the —H and —OH are on the same side of the carbon-nitrogen double bond; in the anti isomer (compare trans, "across") they are on opposite sides.

Ketoximes may be named in two ways since the relationship between the —OH and the —R groups is not inherently determined.

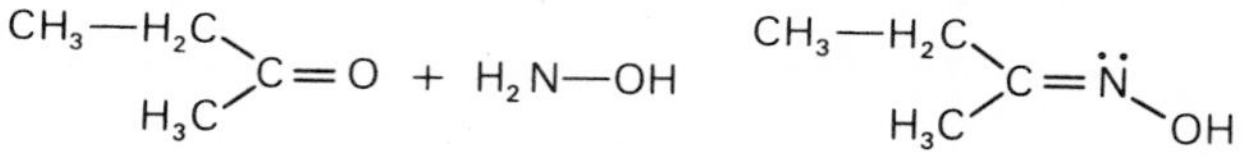

$$\begin{matrix}CH_3-H_2C\\ \qquad\quad C=O\\ H_3C\end{matrix} + H_2N-OH \qquad \begin{matrix}CH_3-H_2C\\ \qquad\quad C=\ddot{N}\\ H_3C \qquad\qquad OH\end{matrix}$$

methyl ethyl ketone; *syn*-methyl ethyl ketoxime (*anti*-ethyl methyl ketoxime)

As would be expected on steric grounds, the isomer formed in larger amounts is the one in which the —OH and the larger —R group bear an anti relationship. At least traces of the other isomer can usually be found. This geometrical isomerism plays an important role in the Beckmann rearrangement of oximes (Sec. 15-26).

Aldoximes can be dehydrated with phosphorus pentoxide, $P_2O_5$; the nitrile (cyanide) thus formed may be subjected to further transformations.

$$R-CH=N-OH \xrightarrow{P_2O_5} R-C\equiv N + H_2O$$

**Hydrazones:** Hydrazine, $H_2N-NH_2$, reacts with aldehydes and ketones to give hydrazones.

*General*: 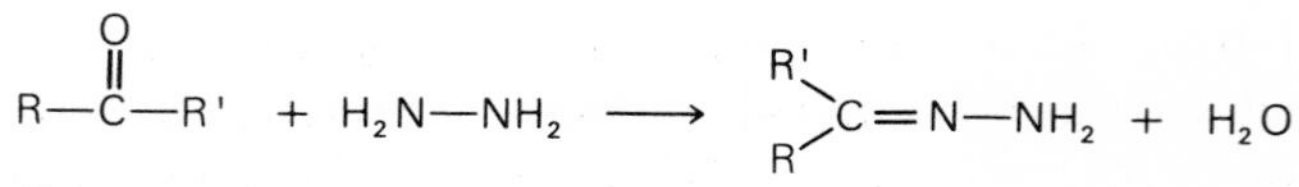
$$R-\overset{O}{\overset{\|}{C}}-R' + H_2N-NH_2 \longrightarrow \begin{matrix}R'\\ \quad\ C=N-NH_2\\ R\end{matrix} + H_2O$$

R' = —H or alkyl

*Specific*: Br–$C_6H_4$–C(=O)–$CH_3$ $\xrightarrow{H_2N-NH_2}$ Br–$C_6H_4$–C(=N–$NH_2$)–$CH_3$

*p*-bromoacetophenone → *p*-bromoacetophenone hydrazone

Recall the use of hydrazones in the Wolff-Kishner reduction (Sec. 13-12). The mechanism for the formation of all these related derivatives involves nucleophilic attack on the carbonyl group.

$$RR'C^{\delta+}{=}O^{\delta-} + H_2\ddot{N}{-}NH_2 \rightleftharpoons \left[RR'C(O^-)(\overset{+}{N}H_2{-}NH_2)\right]$$

$$\left[RR'C(O^-)(\overset{+}{N}H(H){-}NH_2) \rightleftharpoons RR'C(OH)(\ddot{N}H{-}NH_2)\right]$$

$$\left[RR'C(OH)(\ddot{N}H{-}NH_2) \underset{}{\overset{+H^+}{\rightleftharpoons}} RR'C(\overset{+}{O}H_2)(\ddot{N}H{-}NH_2) \overset{-H_2O}{\rightleftharpoons} RR'C{=}\overset{+}{N}H{-}NH_2\right]$$

$$\left[RR'C{=}\overset{+}{N}(H){-}NH_2\right] \overset{-H^+}{\rightleftharpoons} RR'C{=}\ddot{N}{-}NH_2$$

Hydrazone derivatives are not greatly increased in molecular weight over the original carbonyl compound and therefore are often liquids or low-melting solids. Thus three phenyl-substituted hydrazines are commonly used:

| $C_6H_5$–NH–$NH_2$ | $O_2N$–$C_6H_4$–NH–$NH_2$ | $O_2N$–$C_6H_3(NO_2)$–NH–$NH_2$ |
|---|---|---|
| phenylhydrazine | *p*-nitrophenylhydrazine | 2,4-dinitrophenylhydrazine (2,4-DNPH) |

The last of these compounds forms highly colored 2,4-dinitrophenylhydrazones, which range from yellow to deep red, depending on the extent of conjugation of the newly formed derivative.

> **1.** Formulate the reactions of acetaldehyde and acetophenone with (*a*) hydrazine and (*b*) the three phenyl-substituted hydrazines (total of eight equations).
>
> **2.** Calculate the percent increase in weight of the derivative over the starting carbonyl compound in all eight cases.

**Semicarbazones:** Semicarbazide, $H_2N—NH—CO—NH_2$, which is an amide derivative of hydrazine, reacts with aldehydes and ketones giving semicarbazones. When it is kept in mind that this is a substituted hydrazine, there should be no confusion about which of the $—NH_2$ groups of semicarbazide undergoes reaction.

$$\underset{\text{acetaldehyde}}{CH_3CHO} + \underset{\text{semicarbazide}}{H_2NNH—CONH_2} \longrightarrow \underset{\text{acetaldehyde semicarbazone}}{CH_3CH{=}N—NH—CONH_2} + H_2O$$

$$\underset{\text{cyclopentanone}}{C_5H_8{=}O} + \underset{\text{semicarbazide}}{H_2NNH—CONH_2} \longrightarrow \underset{\text{cyclopentanone semicarbazone}}{C_5H_8{=}N—NH—CONH_2} + H_2O$$

> Write the reaction of each of the reagents discussed in Sec. 13-14 (omit $NH_3$) with acetone, cyclopentanone, and benzaldehyde (total of 18 equations).

### 13-15 THE HALOFORM REACTION

Methyl ketones, $CH_3—CO—$, and certain other compounds react with hypohalite ions, $XO^-$, affording the salt of a carboxylic acid, $—COO^-$, and the corresponding haloform, $CHX_3$, from which the reaction derives its name.

$$R—CO—CH_3 \xrightarrow[\text{base}]{X_2} R—COO^- + CHX_3$$

The haloform reaction not only provides a rapid qualitative test for certain functional groups but also is of considerable importance in the preparation of carboxylic acids. For example, the formation of aryl methyl ketones, $Ar—CO—CH_3$, via the Friedel-Crafts acylation can provide the desired starting material for this preparation of aromatic carboxylic acids.

The reagent, hypohalite ion, $XO^-$, is prepared from halogen and a base. Iodine is commonly used. Chlorine is cheaper and is used on a preparative scale; bromine may also be used.

$$I_2 + 2NaOH \longrightarrow \underset{\text{sodium hypoiodite}}{Na^+OI^-} + Na^+I^- + H_2O$$

$$Na^+OI^- \xrightleftharpoons{H_2O} \underset{\text{hypoiodous acid}}{HOI} + Na^+\ OH^-$$

Methyl ketones, $CH_3$—CO—; secondary alcohols which can be oxidized to methyl ketones under the conditions of the reaction, $CH_3-\underset{OH}{\underset{|}{C}}H-$; acetaldehyde but no other simple aldehyde; and ethanol but no other primary alcohol—all these react with the reagent, giving the salt of the next lower carboxylic acid and the haloform. Hypoiodite is preferred for the identification tests because iodoform, $CHI_3$, is a solid yellow compound with a characteristic iodine odor, whereas the liquids, chloroform, $CHCl_3$, and bromoform, $CHBr_3$, may be lost from the reaction mixture as gases and, hence, not isolated or identified when the reaction is carried out in an open vessel. To isolate the carboxylic acid, a separate acidification step is necessary.

*General*: $$R-\underset{O}{\underset{\|}{C}}-CH_3 \xrightarrow[I_2]{NaOH} \underset{\text{iodoform}}{CHI_3\downarrow} + R-CO_2^- \xrightarrow{H^+} R-COOH$$

*Specific*: $$\underset{\text{methyl ethyl ketone}}{CH_3-\underset{O}{\underset{\|}{C}}-CH_2-CH_3} \xrightarrow[I_2]{KOH} CHI_3\downarrow + \underset{\text{potassium propionate}}{CH_3CH_2COO^-\ K^+}$$

*Mechanism*: $$\underset{\text{keto form}}{CH_3-\underset{O}{\underset{\|}{C}}-CH_2-CH_3} \rightleftharpoons \underset{\text{enol}}{\left[CH_2=\underset{OH}{\underset{|}{C}}-CH_2-CH_3\right]}$$

$$\left[CH_2=\underset{OH}{\underset{|}{C}}-CH_2-CH_3\right] + HOI \longrightarrow \left[\underset{I}{\underset{|}{C}H_2}-\overset{OH}{\overset{|}{\underset{OH}{\underset{|}{C}}}}-CH_2-CH_3\right] \xrightarrow{-H_2O}$$

$$\underset{\text{keto}}{\mathrm{CH_2I{-}C({=}O){-}CH_2CH_3}} \rightleftharpoons \underset{\text{enol}}{\left[\mathrm{CHI{=}C(OH){-}CH_2CH_3}\right]} \xrightarrow{\mathrm{HOI}} \left[\mathrm{CHI_2{-}C(OH)_2{-}CH_2CH_3}\right] \xrightarrow{-\mathrm{H_2O}} \mathrm{CHI_2{-}C({=}O){-}CH_2CH_3}$$

$$\mathrm{CHI_2{-}C({=}O){-}CH_2CH_3} \rightleftharpoons \left[\mathrm{CI_2{=}C(OH){-}CH_2CH_3}\right] \xrightarrow{\mathrm{HOI}} \left[\mathrm{CI_3{-}C(OH)_2{-}CH_2CH_3}\right] \underset{}{\overset{-\mathrm{H_2O}}{\rightleftharpoons}} \mathrm{CI_3{-}C({=}O){-}CH_2{-}CH_3}$$

$$\mathrm{CI_3{-}C({=}O){-}CH_2{-}CH_3} \xrightarrow{\mathrm{OH^-}} [\mathrm{CI_3^-}] + \mathrm{CH_3CH_2CO_2H} \xrightarrow[\mathrm{H_2O}]{\mathrm{NaOH}} \mathrm{CHI_3} + \mathrm{CH_3CH_2CO_2^-\ Na^+}$$

Note these three facts about the reaction mechanism: (1) halomethyl ketones undergo this reaction and are intermediates in it; (2) they are formed by addition to the enol form of the ketone; and (3) the trihalo-substituted carbonyl compound is extremely susceptible to attack by hydroxide ion as a result of the electron-withdrawing effect of both the halogens and the oxygen atom on the adjacent carbon.

### 13-16 PINACOL-PINACOLONE REARRANGEMENT

Ketones, on treatment with amalgamated magnesium, Mg(Hg), prepared in a manner similar to Zn(Hg) (Sec. 13-12), yield a 1,2-glycol after hydrolysis. (Aldehydes give a complex mixture of products.) On treatment with acid, this *vicinal*-diol undergoes rearrangement, the methyl group migrating ***with its pair of electrons***, i.e., a methide shift, to give a ketone.

$$2\ \underset{\text{acetone}}{\mathrm{(H_3C)_2C{=}O}} \xrightarrow[2.\ \mathrm{H_3O^+}]{1.\ \mathrm{Mg(Hg)}} \underset{\text{pinacol (2,3-dimethylbutane-2,3-diol)}}{\mathrm{CH_3{-}C(CH_3)(OH){-}C(CH_3)(OH){-}CH_3}} \xrightarrow[\mathrm{H^+}]{\text{cat.}} \underset{\text{pinacolone (methyl } t\text{-butyl ketone)}}{\mathrm{CH_3{-}C(CH_3)(CH_3){-}C({=}O){-}CH_3}}$$

These latter ketones and their subsequent reaction products are often difficult to synthesize by other methods. The name of this reaction is derived from the compounds formed from acetone. The mechanism of the rearrangement follows. Note that the proton is a catalyst.

$$(CH_3)_2C(OH)-C(OH)(CH_3)_2 \xrightarrow{H^+} \left[ (CH_3)_2C(\overset{+}{O}H_2)-C(OH)(CH_3)_2 \right] \xrightarrow{-H_2O} \left[ (CH_3)_2\overset{+}{C}-C(OH)(CH_3)_2 \right]$$

pinacol — an oxonium ion — a carbonium ion

$$\downarrow \text{1,2-}CH_3^- \text{ shift}$$

$$(CH_3)_3C-CO-CH_3 \xleftarrow{-H^+} \left[ (CH_3)_3C-\overset{+}{C}(CH_3)-OH \right]$$

pinacolone

Alkyl aryl ketones, such as acetophenone, undergo pinacol formation with amalgamated aluminum (foil). Diaryl ketones readily undergo the pinacol reaction in isopropyl alcohol in the sunlight; the pinacol, insoluble in the alcohol, is obtained directly in very pure form. This latter reaction strikingly demonstrates the ease and usefulness of some photochemical reactions.

$$2\,(H_5C_6)_2C{=}O + (H_3C)_2CH{-}OH \xrightarrow{h\nu} C_6H_5{-}\underset{OH}{\overset{H_5C_6}{C}}{-}\underset{OH}{\overset{C_6H_5}{C}}{-}C_6H_5 + (H_3C)_2C{=}O$$

benzophenone — isopropyl alcohol — benzpinacol — acetone

$$C_6H_5{-}\underset{OH}{\overset{H_5C_6}{C}}{-}\underset{OH}{\overset{C_6H_5}{C}}{-}C_6H_5 \xrightarrow[\text{in } CH_3CO_2H]{\Delta;\ I_2 \text{ cat.}} C_6H_5{-}\underset{H_5C_6}{\overset{C_6H_5}{C}}{-}\underset{\|}{\overset{}{C}}{-}C_6H_5 \ (C{=}O)$$

benzpinacol — benzpinacolone

## 13-17 CYCLIC TRIMERIZATION OF ALDEHYDES

Although formaldehyde is readily obtained as an aqueous solution, evaporation of this solution leads to a solid which is a mixture of the linear polymer, ***paraformaldehyde***, and the cyclic trimer, ***trioxane***.

$$-CH_2-O-(CH_2-O)_x-CH_2-O- \xrightarrow{\Delta} CH_2O\uparrow \xleftarrow{\Delta} (CH_2O)_3$$

paraformaldehyde — formaldehyde — trioxane

Thermal decomposition of either of these leads to gaseous formaldehyde, which may be used directly in transformations, such as the Grignard reaction.

In a similar manner, concentration of aqueous acetaldehyde solutions leads mainly to ***paraldehyde***, the cyclic trimer. Acetaldehyde (b.p. 20°) can be obtained by treating the trimer with warm acid. Higher aldehydes can be obtained without difficulty in the aldehyde form, rather than as the trimer.

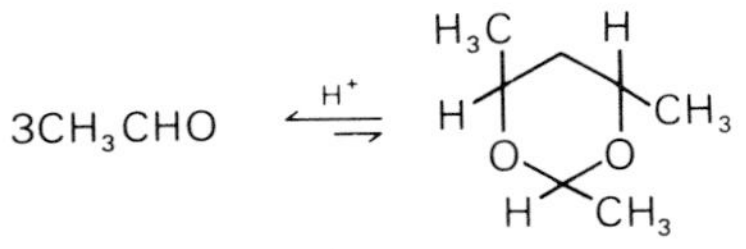

$$3CH_3CHO \underset{}{\overset{H^+}{\rightleftharpoons}} \text{(cyclic trimer: 2,4,6-trimethyl-1,3,5-trioxane)}$$

paraldehyde

> Trichloroacetaldehyde (chloral, the well-known knockout drops) is an interesting example of a stable compound with two hydroxyl groups on the same carbon. Why do you suppose that this particular diol functional group is stabilized? 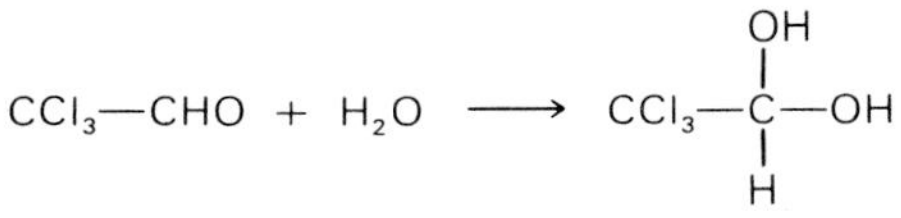
>
> $$CCl_3\text{—}CHO + H_2O \longrightarrow CCl_3\text{—}C(OH)_2\text{—}H$$
>
> chloral → chloral hydrate

## 13-18 CYCLIC DEHYDRATION OF KETONES

Unlike the aldehydes discussed in the previous section, even the simplest ketone, acetone, is stable with respect to trimerization; however, ketones do undergo a cyclic trimerization ***with the loss of water*** under the influence of sulfuric or hydrochloric acid.

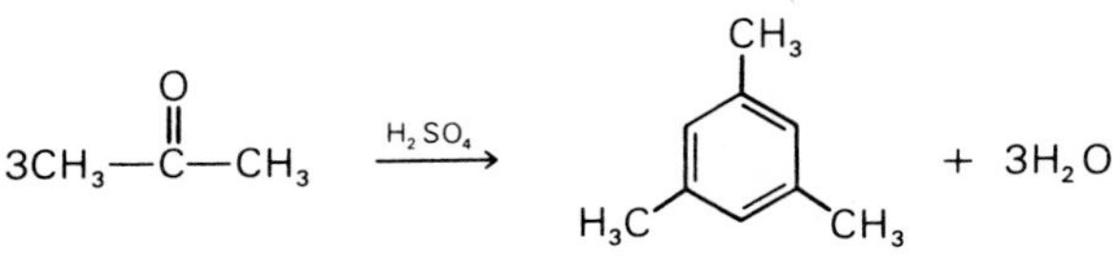

$$3CH_3\text{—}\overset{O}{\overset{\|}{C}}\text{—}CH_3 \xrightarrow{H_2SO_4} \text{(1,3,5-trimethylbenzene)} + 3H_2O$$

mesitylene

Some very interesting compounds result, especially from cyclic ketones. Although the yields are often only fair, the starting materials are usually cheap. The reaction proceeds by condensation of a carbonyl group with an $\alpha$ $CH_2$— group of another molecule.

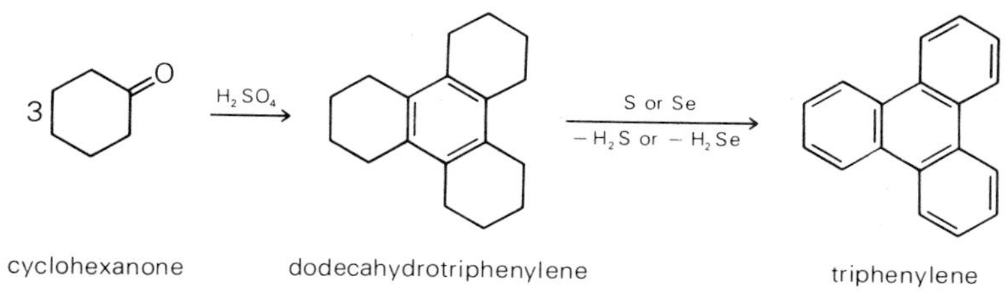

$$3 \text{ cyclohexanone} \xrightarrow{H_2SO_4} \text{dodecahydrotriphenylene} \xrightarrow[-H_2S \text{ or } -H_2Se]{S \text{ or } Se} \text{triphenylene}$$

cyclohexanone dodecahydrotriphenylene triphenylene

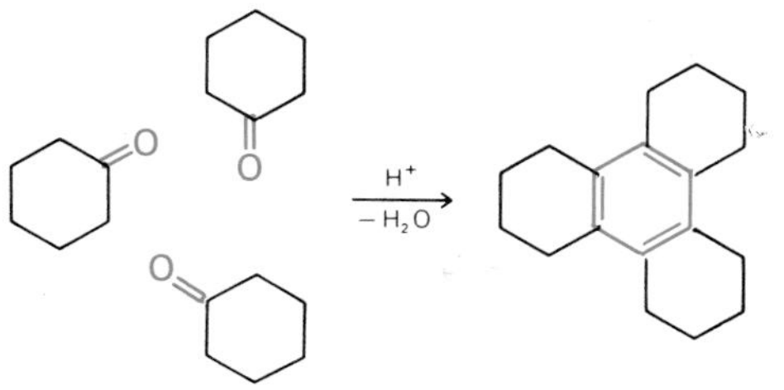

$$\xrightarrow[-H_2O]{H^+}$$

> **1.** How might you prepare 1,3,5-triphenylbenzene?
>
> **2.** Write the structure of the product expected from the reaction of 2-butanone with sulfuric acid. How might this product react with sulfur or selenium?

## CONDENSATION REACTIONS OF ALDEHYDES AND KETONES

The formation of new carbon-carbon bonds is not only of special interest to the organic chemist but is also of vital importance in biological systems, particularly in pathways by which natural products are synthesized. Aldehydes and ketones undergo a variety of condensation reactions, usually in the presence of base. Many of these laboratory reactions have counterparts in plants and animals. All these condensation reactions can be readily understood and systematized by noting three factors: the polarization of the carbonyl group, the enolization of $\alpha$ hydrogens, and the enhanced stability of the newly formed $\alpha,\beta$-unsaturated carbonyl compounds.

### 13-19 ALDOL CONDENSATION

In the presence of base the enol form of an aldehyde or ketone readily loses a proton, and the resonance-stabilized ion can then attack the carbonyl function of a second molecule. To illustrate the reaction, consider the condensation of acetaldehyde to a new $\beta$-hydroxyaldehyde, commonly called *aldol*, which can then readily lose a water molecule forming an $\alpha,\beta$-unsaturated aldehyde, crotonaldehyde.

*Overall*:

$$2CH_3CHO \xrightarrow[-H_2O]{OH^- \text{ cat.}} \left[ CH_3—\underset{\displaystyle OH}{\underset{|}{CH}}—CH_2—CHO \right] \xrightarrow[-H_2O]{} CH_3—CH{=}CH—CHO$$

acetaldehyde — aldol — crotonaldehyde

Note that the hydroxide ion is a catalyst and that three factors, carbonyl polarization, enolization, and stability of $\alpha,\beta$-unsaturated carbonyl compounds, are all important to the mechanism.

*Mechanism*:

$$CH_3—C(=O)H \rightleftharpoons [CH_2{=}C(OH)H]$$

keto form — enol

$$[CH_2{=}C(OH)H] \xrightarrow[-H_2O]{\text{slow} \; OH^-} [CH_2{=}C(O^-)H \longleftrightarrow {}^-CH_2—C(=O)H]$$

$$[{}^-CH_2—C(=O)H] + CH_3—C(=O)H \xrightarrow{\text{fast}} [CH_3—\overset{\displaystyle O^-}{\overset{|}{CH}}—CH_2—C(=O)H] \xrightarrow{H_2O}$$

$$CH_3—\underset{\displaystyle OH}{\underset{|}{CH}}—CH_2—C(=O)H \rightleftharpoons \left[ CH_3—\underset{\displaystyle OH}{\underset{|}{CH}}—CH{=}C(OH)H \right] + OH^-$$

keto — enol

aldol
($\beta$-hydroxybutyraldehyde)

$$\left[ CH_3—\underset{\displaystyle OH}{\underset{|}{CH}}—CH{=}C(O—H)H \right] \xrightarrow{{}^-OH} CH_3—CH{=}CH—CHO + H_2O + {}^-OH$$

enol form of aldol — crotonaldehyde

This condensation reaction ***cannot*** be used to advantage with two different aldehydes, since four possible condensation products will be obtained and may be difficult to separate.

$$R—CH_2—CHO + R'—CH_2—CHO \longrightarrow RCH_2—CH{=}\underset{\displaystyle R}{\underset{|}{C}}—CHO$$

$$+ R'CH_2—CH{=}\underset{\displaystyle R'}{\underset{|}{C}}—CHO + RCH_2—CH{=}\underset{\displaystyle R'}{\underset{|}{C}}—CHO + R'CH_2—CH{=}\underset{\displaystyle R}{\underset{|}{C}}—CHO$$

The mixed adol condensation, discussed in the next section, is an exception.

The aldol condensation is also a reaction observed with ketones containing an $\alpha$ hydrogen atom. The condensation product of acetone can be dehydrated to an $\alpha,\beta$-unsaturated ketone.

$$2CH_3-\overset{O}{\overset{\|}{C}}-CH_3 \xrightarrow[-H_2O]{OH^-} CH_3-\overset{O}{\overset{\|}{C}}-CH_2-\underset{OH}{\underset{|}{C}}(CH_3)_2 \xrightarrow[\Delta]{I_2} CH_3-\underset{O}{\underset{\|}{C}}-CH=C(CH_3)_2$$

## 13-20 MIXED ALDOL CONDENSATION

A mixed aldol condensation can be carried out between two different aldehydes only under two conditions: (1) one of the reactants has no $\alpha$ hydrogens and thus cannot enolize, and (2) the second carbonyl component, which does have an $\alpha$ hydrogen, is added slowly to a mixture of the first reactant and dilute base.

$$C_6H_5-CHO \text{ (with base)} + CH_3CHO \text{ (added slowly)} \xrightarrow[OH^-]{dil.} C_6H_5-CH=CH-CHO + H_2O$$

cinnamaldehyde

$$C_6H_5-CHO + C_6H_5-\overset{O}{\overset{\|}{C}}-CH_3 \xrightarrow{OH^-} C_6H_5-CH=CH-\underset{O}{\underset{\|}{C}}-C_6H_5 + H_2O$$

benzalacetophenone

> Formulate a reasonable mechanism for each of the above examples.

## 13-21 CANNIZZARO REACTION

The Cannizzaro reaction is the simultaneous oxidation and reduction (***disproportionation***) of an aldehyde having no $\alpha$ hydrogen atoms to the corresponding alcohol and acid (salt) in the presence of strong (30 to 60%) base. A separate acidification step is necessary in order to obtain the acid itself. Similar oxidation-reductions are carried out in living cells under milder conditions by the action of enzyme systems.

*Specific*:

$$2\,C_6H_5-CHO \xrightarrow[KOH;\,\Delta]{conc.} C_6H_5-CH_2OH + C_6H_5-CO_2^-\,K^+ \xrightarrow{H^+} C_6H_5-COOH$$

benzaldehyde → benzyl alcohol + potassium benzoate → benzoic acid

*Mechanism*:

$$C_6H_5{-}\overset{\overset{\displaystyle O}{\|}}{C}{-}H + HO^- \rightleftharpoons \left[ C_6H_5{-}\overset{\overset{\displaystyle O^-}{|}}{\underset{\underset{\displaystyle OH}{|}}{C}}{-}H \right]$$

$$\left[ C_6H_5{-}\overset{\overset{\displaystyle O^-}{|}}{\underset{\underset{\displaystyle OH}{|}}{C}}{-}H + C_6H_5{-}\overset{\overset{\displaystyle O}{\|}}{C}{-}H \right] \longrightarrow \left[ \underset{\text{a weak acid}}{C_6H_5{-}\overset{\overset{\displaystyle O}{\|}}{C}{-}OH} + \underset{\text{a strong base}}{C_6H_5{-}\overset{\overset{\displaystyle O^-}{|}}{\underset{\underset{\displaystyle H}{|}}{C}}{-}H} \right]$$

$$\left[ C_6H_5{-}\overset{\overset{\displaystyle O}{\|}}{C}{-}OH + C_6H_5{-}\overset{\overset{\displaystyle O^-}{|}}{\underset{\underset{\displaystyle H}{|}}{C}}{-}H \right] \rightleftharpoons C_6H_5{-}\overset{\overset{\displaystyle O}{\|}}{C}{-}O^- + C_6H_5{-}CH_2OH$$

$$C_6H_5{-}CO_2^- \xrightarrow{H^+} C_6H_5{-}CO_2H$$

> Write the products from the Cannizzaro reaction of each of these molecules: formaldehyde, triphenylacetaldehyde, and trimethylacetaldehyde.

### 13-22 CROSSED CANNIZZARO REACTION

By properly choosing the reagents and reaction conditions, the Cannizzaro reaction can be carried out between two aldehydes neither of which contains an $\alpha$ hydrogen atom. One of the components is usually formaldehyde, which is more readily oxidized to the acid than most other aldehydes.

$$C_6H_5{-}CHO + CH_2O\ (xs) \xrightarrow[OH^-;\ \Delta]{conc.} C_6H_5{-}CH_2OH + HCO_2^- \xrightarrow{H^+} HCO_2H$$

An interesting example of the aldol condensation used in combination with the crossed Cannizzaro reaction is the preparation of pentaerythritol, tetra(hydroxymethyl)methane. It consists of three successive aldol condensations on acetaldehyde, followed by a crossed Cannizzaro reaction with formaldehyde.

$$CH_3CHO + CH_2O\ (xs) \xrightarrow{OH^-} \left[ HO—CH_2—\underset{CH_2OH}{\overset{CH_2OH}{\overset{|}{\underset{|}{C}}}}—CHO \right] \xrightarrow[CH_2O]{OH^-} \underset{\text{pentaerythritol}}{C(CH_2OH)_4} + HCO_2^-$$

Pentaerythritol is used in the manufacture of plastics and resins; its tetranitrate (ester) is an extremely powerful explosive.

> Write the structure of the $C_{10}H_{20}O_5$ compound formed by treating cyclohexanone with excess formaldehyde (in base).

## QUALITATIVE TESTS

### 13-23 OXIDATION REACTIONS

Both $Ag^+$ and $Cu^{++}$ are mild oxidizing agents which are reduced to $Ag^0$ and $Cu^+$ by aliphatic aldehydes, which in turn are oxidized to carboxylic acids. Tests have been devised which use certain complexes of these ions. Tollens' test uses $Ag(NH_3)_2^+$, Benedict's solution is composed of $Cu(citrate)_2^{--}$, and Fehling's test uses $Cu(tartrate)_2^{--}$.

$$\underset{\text{citric acid}}{HO_2C—CH_2—\underset{CO_2H}{\underset{|}{C}}(OH)—CH_2—CO_2H} \qquad \underset{\text{tartaric acid}}{HO_2C—CH(OH)—CH(OH)—CO_2H}$$

Tollens' test is positive for all aldehydes but the other two are positive only for aliphatic aldehydes. All three are negative for ketones.

Tollens' test: $R—CHO + \underset{\text{colorless solution}}{Ag(NH_3)_2^+} \longrightarrow \underset{\text{silver mirror}}{Ag^0\downarrow} + R—CO_2^- \xrightarrow{H^+} R—CO_2H$

Benedict's test: $R—CHO + \underset{\text{deep blue solution}}{Cu(citrate)_2^{--}} \longrightarrow \underset{\text{cuprous oxide usually red}}{Cu_2O\downarrow} + R—CO_2^-$

Fehling's test: $R—CHO + \underset{\text{deep blue solution}}{Cu(tartrate)_2^{--}} \longrightarrow Cu_2O\downarrow + R—CO_2^-$

It is interesting to note that Tollens' test is also known as the ***silver-mirror test***, since a test tube cleaned with warm dilute nitric acid followed by complete rinsing with distilled water can be silvered by the metal deposited in this reaction.

Another positive test for aldehydes is the ***Schiff test***, which consists of treating the unknown with a colorless dye. The solution turns pink to violet with aldehydes; ketones give no reaction. The chemistry of this reaction is complex, but in general the aldehyde changes the structure of the dye.

### 13-24 SODIUM BISULFITE

It was pointed out in Sec. 13-13 that aldehydes, unhindered methyl ketones, and some cyclic ketones form an alcohol-insoluble adduct with sodium bisulfite, $NaHSO_3$. This reaction can often be used as a rapid qualitative test as well as a means of separating these carbonyl compounds from a mixture. On treatment with either dilute acid or base the adduct yields the organic carbonyl compound.

**1.** Using sodium bisulfite, show how the components in each of the following pairs can be obtained in pure form: acetone and isopropyl alcohol; ethyl alcohol and acetaldehyde.

**2.** Review Sec. 13-15 (the haloform reaction) and show how the following compounds can be differentiated using this test: ethanol and methanol; propionaldehyde and acetaldehyde; and acetophenone and phenylacetaldehyde.

### 13-25 SOLID DERIVATIVES

Review Sec. 13-14 and note that the rapid formation of high-molecular-weight derivatives, such as 2,4-dinitrophenylhydrazones, of aldehydes and ketones may also serve as a qualitative test for the presence of these compounds in addition to establishing their identity by determinations of melting point and mixture melting point. For example, acetaldehyde (b.p. 21°) and acetone (b.p. 56°) form *p*-nitrophenylhydrazones melting at 129° and 152°, respectively.

Acetone phenylhydrazone has a melting point of 42°, whereas the literature values for the melting point of acetaldehyde phenylhydrazone are 63 and 99°. Suggest a reason for two melting points for the latter compound.

## SUGGESTED READINGS

### Qualitative tests

Daniels, R., C. C. Rush, and L. Bauer: The Fehling and Benedict Tests, *J. Chem. Educ.*, **37**, 205 (1960).

Morrison, J. D.: Qualitative Test for Ketones, Aromatic Aldehydes, and Aliphatic Aldehydes, *J. Chem. Educ.*, **42**, 554 (1965). Describes the use of $CrO_3$-$H_2SO_4$ in water.

Seelye, R. N., and T. A. Turney: The Iodoform Reaction, *J. Chem. Educ.*, **36**, 572 (1959).

Shine, H. J.: Preparation of 2,4-Dinitrophenylhydrazones: Demonstrating Acid Catalysis, *J. Chem. Educ.*, **36**, 575 (1959).

### Keto-enol tautomerism

Dawber, J. G., and M. M. Crane: Keto-Enol Tautomerism: A Thermodynamics and Kinetic Study, *J. Chem. Educ.*, **44**, 150 (1967). Study of acetoacetic ester.

Lockwood, K. L.: Solvent Effect on the Keto-Enol Equilibrium of Acetoacetic Ester, *J. Chem. Educ.*, **42**, 481 (1965).

Ward, C. H.: Keto-Enol Tautomerism of Ethyl Acetoacetate, *J. Chem. Educ.*, **39**, 95 (1962). Describes the experimental determination of enol content.

### Others

Hurd, C. D.: Hemiacetals, Aldals and Hemialdals, *J. Chem. Educ.*, **43**, 527 (1966).

Moore, D. R.: The Art and the Science of Perfumery, *J. Chem. Educ.*, **37**, 434 (1960).

Schultz, H. P., and J. P. Sichels: The Pyrolytic Decomposition of Carboxylate Salts to Ketones, *J. Chem. Educ.*, **38**, 300 (1961).

## PROBLEM SET I

*This problem set is designed to aid you in studying and rereading Chap. 13. It also provides a review of previous chapters. Each of the following examples has been taken from the literature and illustrates a reaction discussed in this chapter in the section indicated. Complete the names and structures where necessary and answer the additional questions.*

### Section 13-1

**1.** $\underset{\text{name?}}{H{-}C{\equiv}C{-}CH_2OH} \xrightarrow[\text{40\% yield}]{CrO_3;\ H^+} \underset{\text{propiolaldehyde}}{H{-}C{\equiv}C{-}CHO}$

## Section 13-2

2. *p*-xylene $\xrightarrow[\text{50\% yield}]{4Br_2;\ h\nu}$ [ name? structure? ] $\xrightarrow[H_2SO_4\ \text{80\% yield}]{2H_2O}$ terephthaldehyde (CHO / CHO)

What is the overall yield of the aldehyde from the hydrocarbon?

## Section 13-3

3. mesitoyl chloride ($CH_3$, COCl, $H_3C$, $CH_3$) $\xrightarrow[\text{no poison 75\% yield}]{H_2;\ \Delta\ \text{in xylene}\ Pd/BaSO_4}$ mesitaldehyde ($CH_3$, CHO, $H_3C$, $CH_3$)

The Rosenmund reduction is usually carried out by bubbling hydrogen through a warm or hot solution of the acid chloride in which the catalyst (usually poisoned) is suspended. Why do you suppose no poison is required in the above example?

4. *β*-naphthoyl chloride $\xrightarrow[\text{sulfur-quinoline 80\% yield}]{H_2\ \text{in xylene}\ Pd/BaSO_4}$ *β*-naphthaldehyde

5. 3-phenanthroyl chloride $\xrightarrow[\text{no poison 90\% yield}]{Pd/BaSO_4\ 180°;\ H_2}$ 3-phenanthraldehyde

## Section 13-4

6. 1-chloromethylnaphthalene $\xrightarrow[2.\ H_2O\ \text{75\% yield}]{1.\ \text{HMTA}}$

7. *p*-nitrobenzyl chloride ($NO_2$, $CH_2Cl$) $\xrightarrow[\text{60\% yield}]{1.\ \text{HMTA}\ 2.\ H_3O}$

8. *n*-heptyl iodide $\xrightarrow[\text{45\% yield}]{1.\ \text{HMTA}\ 2.\ H_3O^+;\ \Delta}$ *n*-heptaldehyde

removed as formed by steam distillation

## Section 13-5

9. β-naphthonitrile $\xrightarrow{HCl}$ [imido chloride: $C_{10}H_7$–C(Cl)=N–H] $\xrightarrow[HCl]{SnCl_2}$

[$C_{10}H_7$–CH=NH · HCl · $SnCl_4$] $\xrightarrow[75\%\ yield]{H_2O;\ \Delta}$ β-naphthaldehyde

aldimine-stannic chloride-hydrochloride complex

## Section 13-6

10. 9-bromophenanthrene $\xrightarrow[\substack{3.\ H_2SO_4 \\ 45\%\ yield}]{\substack{1.\ Mg\ in\ dry\ ether \\ 2.\ HC(OEt)_3}}$ phenanthrene-9-aldehyde

(9-phenanthrenecarboxaldehyde)

## Section 13-7

11. *o*-xylene $\xrightarrow[75\%\ yield]{\substack{4Br_2 \\ h\nu;\ 150^\circ}}$ [name? structure?] $\xrightarrow[75\%\ yield]{1:1\ EtOH\text{-}H_2O(KO_2C\text{-}CO_2K)}$ *o*-phthalaldehyde

overall yield = ?

## Section 13-9

12. 9-cyanophenanthrene $\xrightarrow[\substack{2.\ H_3O^+ \\ 55\%\ yield}]{1.\ CH_3MgI}$ 9-acetylphenanthrene

## Section 13-11

13. nicotinic acid (3-pyridinecarboxylic acid, $CO_2H$) $\xrightarrow{SOCl_2}$ 3-pyridine-COCl $\xrightarrow[2.\ H_3O^+]{1.\ C_6H_6;\ AlCl_3}$ 3-benzoylpyridine (pyridyl–C(=O)–C$_6$H$_5$)

nicotinic acid

3-benzoylpyridine
95% overall yield

14. ClOC(H)C=C(H)COCl + benzene (xs) $\xrightarrow[2.\ H_3O^+\ 80\%\ yield]{1.\ 2.6\ equiv\ AlCl_3}$ 1,4-diphenyl-2-buten-1,4-dione

## Section 13-12

15. 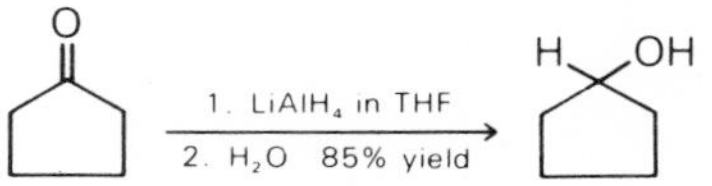 cyclopentanone $\xrightarrow[\text{2. } H_2O \text{ 85\% yield}]{\text{1. } LiAlH_4 \text{ in THF}}$ cyclopentanol (H, OH)

16. 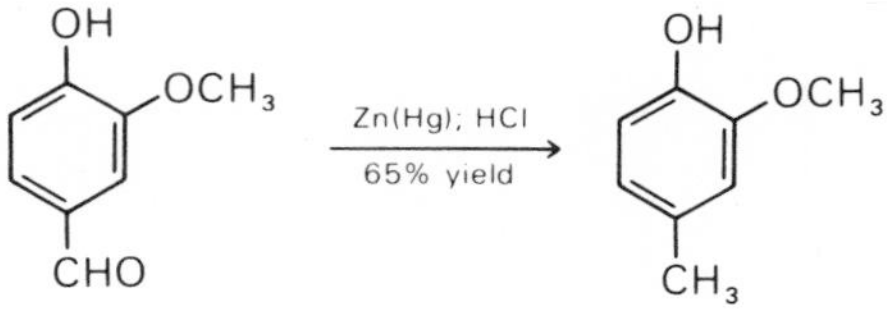 OH, $OCH_3$, CHO $\xrightarrow[\text{65\% yield}]{Zn(Hg);\ HCl}$ OH, $OCH_3$, $CH_3$

vanillin — creosol

17. 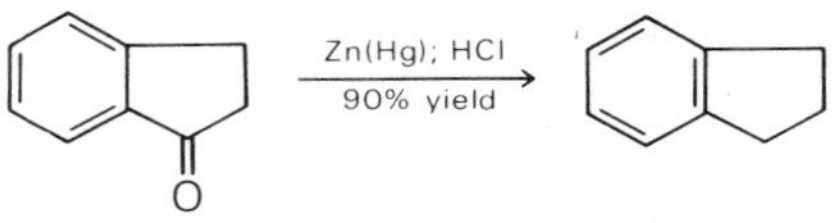 $\xrightarrow[\text{90\% yield}]{Zn(Hg);\ HCl}$

1-indanone — name?

18. 2-acetylphenanthrene $\xrightarrow[\text{45\% yield}]{Zn(Hg);\ HCl}$ 2-ethylphenanthrene

19. 6-ketoundecanedioic acid $\xrightarrow[\text{90\% yield}]{H_2NNH_2;\ KOH}$ undecanedioic acid

20. phenyl *n*-hexyl ketone $\xrightarrow[\text{45\% yield}]{H_2N{-}NH_2;\ KOH}$

## Section 13-13

21. *m*-nitrobenzaldehyde $\xrightarrow[\text{25°; 5 days 85\% yield}]{CH_3OH(xs),\ HCl(trace)}$ *m*-nitrobenzaldehyde dimethylacetal

## Section 13-14

22. 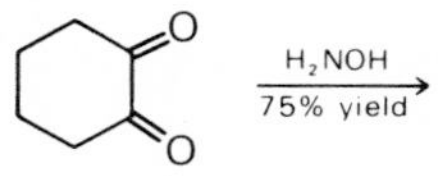 1,2-cyclohexanedione $\xrightarrow[\text{75\% yield}]{H_2NOH}$ 1,2-cyclohexanedione dioxime

1,2-cyclohexanedione

### Section 13-16

**23.** The pinacolone rearrangement is a concerted migration of the alkyl group with a simultaneous loss of the water molecule. Note the similarity to the nitrous acid deamination of an $\alpha$ hydroxy amine.

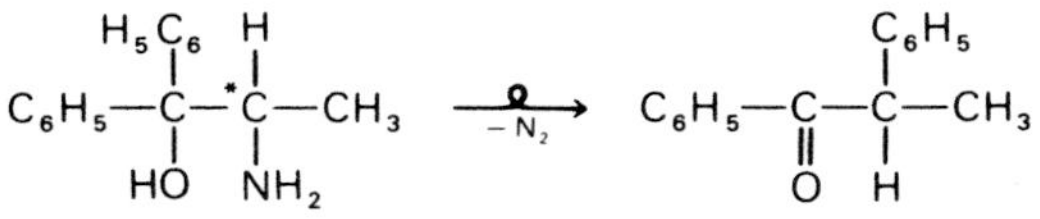

$$C_6H_5-C(C_6H_5)(OH)-\overset{*}{C}H(NH_2)-CH_3 \xrightarrow[-N_2]{} C_6H_5-C(=O)-C(C_6H_5)(H)-CH_3$$

D isomer L isomer

### Section 13-17

**24.** Other common hydrates are formed from glyoxal and ketonalonaldehyde in reactions like that of chloral (p. 286). Write the structure for each hydrate.

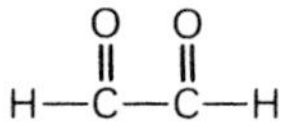

$$H-\overset{O}{\overset{\|}{C}}-\overset{O}{\overset{\|}{C}}-H \quad \text{and} \quad H-\overset{O}{\overset{\|}{C}}-\overset{O}{\overset{\|}{C}}-\overset{O}{\overset{\|}{C}}-H$$

glyoxal ketomalonaldehyde

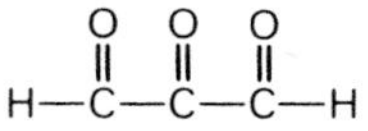

### Section 13-21

**25.** *m*-hydroxybenzaldehyde $\xrightarrow[2.\ H_3O]{1.\ 50\%\ KOH}$ 94% ***each*** of the corresponding alcohol and acid

### Section 13-22

**26.** 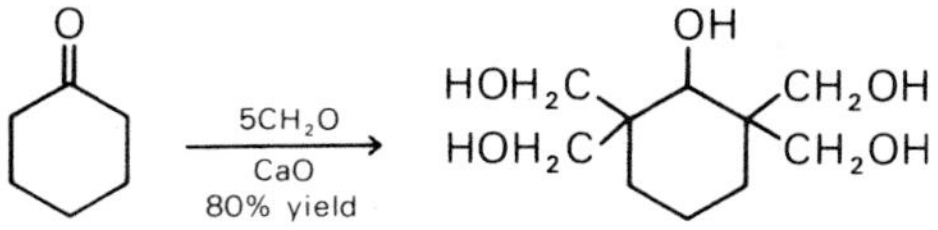 cyclohexanone $\xrightarrow[\text{CaO, 80\% yield}]{5CH_2O}$ 2,2,6,6-tetra(hydroxymethyl)-cyclohexanol

### Section 13-23

**27.** vanillin $\xrightarrow[2.\ H_3O^+\ 80\%\ \text{yield}]{1.\ Ag_2O;\ NaOH}$ vanillic acid

## PROBLEM SET II

**1.** Name the starting material and give the structural formula ***and*** name of the product(s). If no reaction occurs, write N.R.

★(*a*) 1-naphthaldehyde (CHO) $\xrightarrow{50\%\ KOH}$

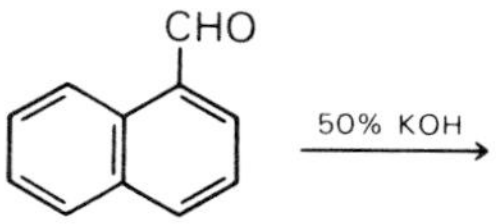

★(*b*) p-benzenedicarbaldehyde (CHO, CHO) $\xrightarrow[2.\ H_3O\quad 3.\ \Delta;\ Al_2O_3]{1.\ CH_3MgI\ (xs)}$

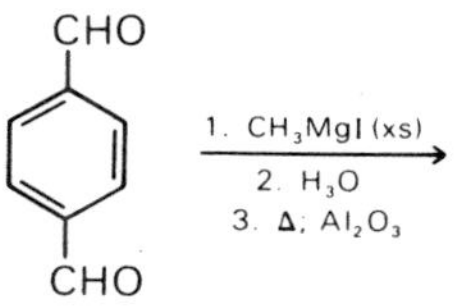

★(*c*) $C_6H_5-\overset{O}{\overset{\|}{C}}-$(2-naphthyl) $\xrightarrow{C_6H_5NHNH_2}$ ? $\xrightarrow[\Delta]{KOH}$ ?

★(*d*) 1-methylnaphthalene ($CH_3$) $\xrightarrow[\text{2. } (NH_3 + CH_2O \longrightarrow)?\ \text{3. } H_3O^+]{\text{1. 1 equiv NBS; } h\nu}$

(*e*) $C_6H_5-\overset{O}{\overset{\|}{C}}-C_6H_5$ $\xrightarrow{NaHSO_3}$

(*f*) $C_6H_5CH_3$ $\xrightarrow[\text{2. } H_3O^+\ \text{3. Zn/HCl}]{\text{1. } (CH_3CO)_2O;\ \text{2.1 equiv } AlCl_3 \text{ in } C_6H_5NO_2}$

★(*g*) $CH_3-\overset{O}{\overset{\|}{C}}-$cyclohexyl $\xrightarrow[\text{2. } NaNH_2]{\text{1. } PCl_5}$

(*h*) p-$O_2N-C_6H_4-CHO$ $\xrightarrow{MnO_2}$

★(*i*) m-$Br-C_6H_4-\overset{O}{\overset{\|}{C}}-CH_3$ $\xrightarrow[\text{2. } PBr_3]{\text{1. } NaBH_4}$

(*j*) m-$CH_3CH_2-C_6H_4-CHO$ $\xrightarrow{Ag(NH_3)_2^+}$

**2.** Name the starting material and give the structural formula *and* name of the product(s). If no reaction occurs, write N.R.

(*a*) 2,5-dimethylphenyl ring ($CH_3$, $CH_3$) bearing $CH_2-CHO$ $\xrightarrow[\Delta]{OH^-}$

Formulate a reasonable mechanism for this reaction.

(*b*) o-$C_6H_4(CHO)_2$ $\xrightarrow[\Delta]{\text{conc. } OH^-}$

★(*c*) m-$CH_3-C_6H_4-CHO$ $\xrightarrow[\text{40\% NaOH}]{H-\overset{O}{\overset{\|}{C}}-H\ (xs)}$

(*d*) 2,2-dimethylcyclohexanone ($CH_3$, $CH_3$) $\xrightarrow[\text{conc. base}]{H_2CO(xs)}$

★(*e*) $CH_3-\overset{O}{\overset{\|}{C}}-CH_2-CH_2-\overset{O}{\overset{\|}{C}}-CH_3$ $\xrightarrow[\text{2. Ra (Ni)}]{\text{1. } HSCH_2CH_2SH\ (xs)}$

(*f*) $CH_3-C(C_6H_5)(C_6H_{11})-CH_2-CH_2-CHO \xrightarrow[2.\ P_2O_5]{1.\ NH_2OH}$

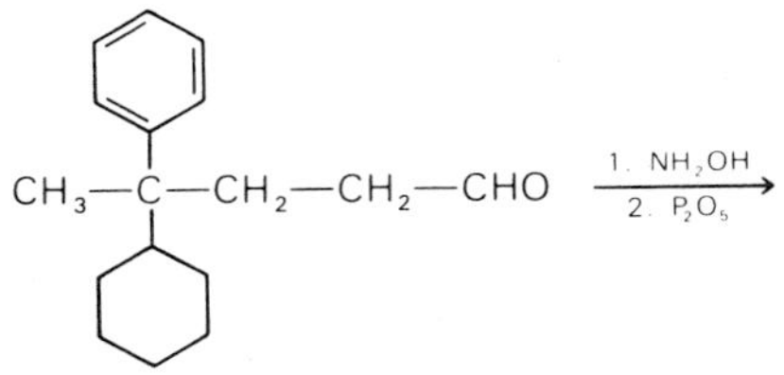

(*g*) 1-tetralone $\xrightarrow[\Delta]{H_2SO_4\ (xs)}$ (cyclic trimerization product)

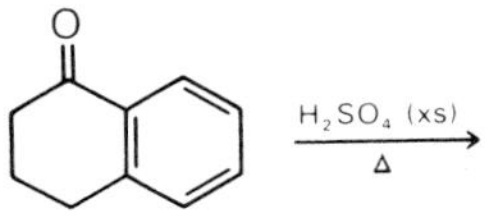

★(*h*) o-$CH_3C_6H_4CH_2CHO$ + m-$BrC_6H_4CH_2CHO$ $\xrightarrow[\Delta]{OH}$

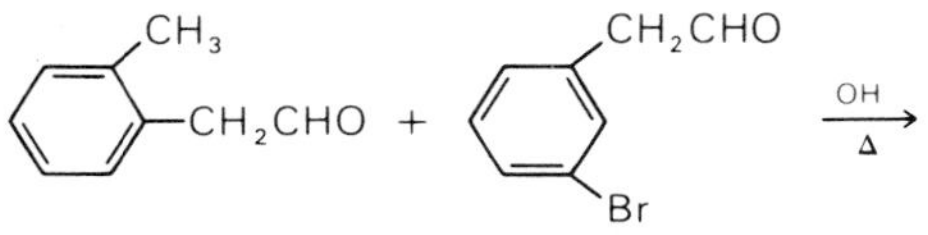

(*i*) o-$CH_3C_6H_4CHO + OH^-$ $\xrightarrow{\text{add } m\text{-}BrC_6H_4CH_2CHO}$

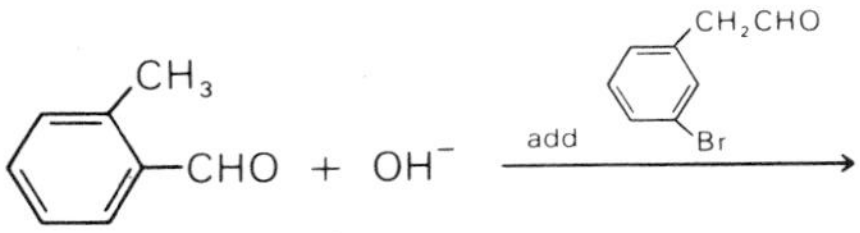

Formulate a reasonable mechanism for this reaction.

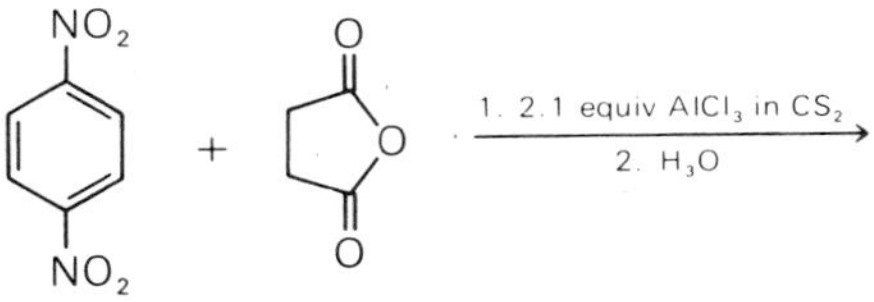

(*j*) $[(CH_3)_2CH]_2Cd + CH_3-CH_2-C(CH_3)_2-C(=O)-CH-CH(C_6H_{11})-CH_3 \longrightarrow$

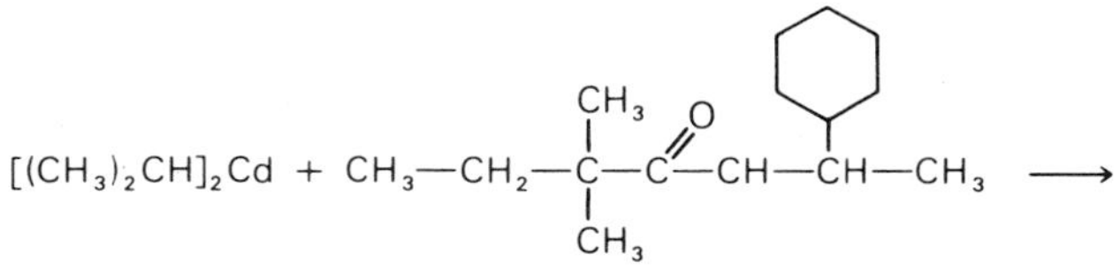

★(*k*) p-dinitrobenzene ($NO_2$, $NO_2$) + succinic anhydride $\xrightarrow[2.\ H_3O]{1.\ 2.1\ \text{equiv}\ AlCl_3\ \text{in}\ CS_2}$

★(*l*) $Br-C_6H_4-NH-NH_2$ (xs) + $CH_3-\overset{O}{\overset{\|}{C}}-CH_2-\underset{H}{C}(C_6H_5)-\underset{O}{\underset{\|}{C}}-CH_2-CH(C_4H_7)-CO-CH_3 \longrightarrow$

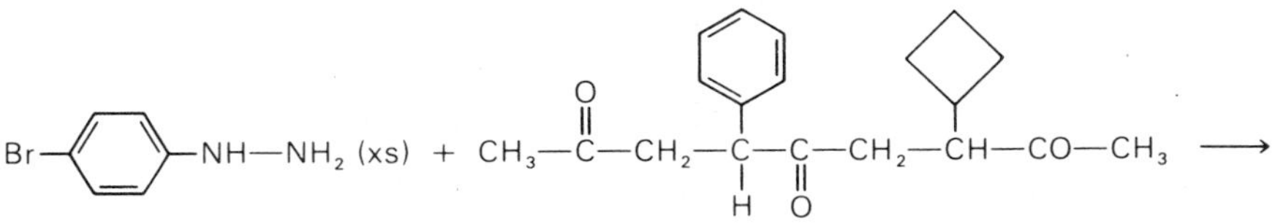

**3.** Indicate a synthesis of the following compounds from the given starting materials and any necessary solvents and inorganic reagents:

★(*a*) $H-C(=O)-C(CH_3)_2-CH_3$ from coke, C, and limestone, CaO

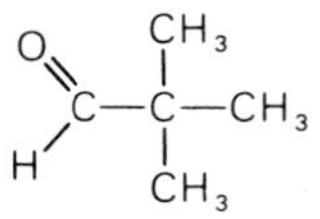

★(*b*) 1-methylcyclopentene ($CH_3$) from phenol and methanol

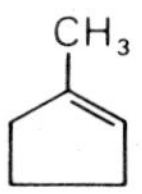

★(*c*) $H_3C{-}C_6H_4{-}CH_2{-}\overset{\displaystyle O}{\overset{\|}{C}}{-}C_6H_4{-}CH_3$ from toluene via an organocadmium compound

★(*d*) $C_6H_5{-}C_6H_4{-}CH_2CH_2CH_2CH{=}N{-}NH_2$ from benzene and succinic acid

★(*e*) spiropentane, from formaldehyde and acetylene

(*f*) $CH_3{-}CH_2{-}\underset{}{\overset{\displaystyle OH}{\overset{|}{C}H}}{-}\underset{\underset{\displaystyle CH_2{-}CH_3}{|}}{CH}{-}\overset{\displaystyle CH_2{-}CH_3}{\overset{|}{C}H}{-}CH_2{-}CH_3$ from any $C_1$ to $C_4$ compounds

(*g*) isobutyraldehyde *n*-butyl hemiacetal from $C_1$ to $C_3$ alcohols

(*h*) cyclopentylidene$=CH{-}CO_2H$ from cyclohexanone via a cyanohydrin

(*i*) $C_7H_{13}{-}\overset{\displaystyle O}{\overset{\|}{C}}{-}C_7H_{13}$ from cycloheptyl bromide

**★4.** When

$$\left[\begin{array}{c} H_3C\quad CH_3 \\ |\qquad | \\ CH_3{-}C{-}C{-}CH_3 \\ |\qquad | \\ HO\quad {}^{+}N_2 \end{array}\right]$$

is formed by treating the corresponding amine with nitrous acid, the final product isolated from solution gives a positive iodoform test and a negative Schiff test and yields an oxime. Give the final product and the mechanism by which it is formed and show clearly the stereochemistry of the oxime.

**★5.** Suggest a reasonable mechanism for the reaction

$$\text{5-chloro-2-pentanone} \xrightarrow[\text{80\% yield}]{\text{NaOH}} \text{methyl cyclopropyl ketone}$$

**6.** Acetals and ketals are useful protecting groups in many syntheses.
(*a*) In the example below, complete the names and structures and calculate the minimum *and* maximum overall yields which might be expected:

$$C_6H_5\text{—}CH{=}CH\text{—}CHO \xrightarrow[\text{95-100\% yield}]{\text{Br}_2\text{ in HOAc}} \left[ C_6H_5\text{—}\underset{\text{Br}}{\underset{|}{CH}}\text{—}\underset{\text{Br}}{\underset{|}{CH}}\text{—}CHO \right] \xrightarrow[\text{75-85\% yield}]{\Delta;\ K_2CO_3}$$

cinnamaldehyde
(cinnamic aldehyde)

$\alpha$-bromocinnamic aldehyde $\xrightarrow[\text{82-86\% yield}]{\text{HC(OEt)}_3\text{ in EtOH; }\Delta}$ $\alpha$-bromocinnamic aldehyde diethylacetal

$\xrightarrow[\text{80-86\% yield}]{\text{alc. KOH; }\Delta}$ phenylpropargyl aldehyde diethylacetal $\xrightarrow[\text{70-81\% yield}]{H_2SO_4}$ $C_6H_5\text{—}C{\equiv}C\text{—}CHO$

phenylpropargyl
aldehyde

(*b*) Predict the product(s) from treatment of $C_6H_5\text{—}CH{=}CBr\text{—}CHO$ directly with alcoholic KOH, a strong base.

# Chapter Fourteen

The chemistry of carboxylic acids and their derivatives is interrelated with, and primarily dependent upon, the electronic charge distribution about the atoms adjacent to the carbonyl group. Organic acids, like alcohols, have relatively high boiling points in relation to their molecular weights because of hydrogen bonding. Both dimeric and polymeric structures contribute to the bonding in the liquid state, causing acids to have a higher effective molecular weight (see Fig. 14-1).

**Figure 14-1 Hydrogen bonding of carboxylic acids**

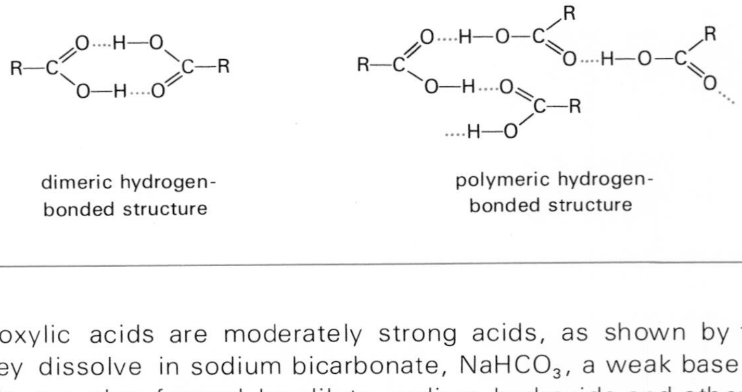

dimeric hydrogen-bonded structure

polymeric hydrogen-bonded structure

Carboxylic acids are moderately strong acids, as shown by the fact that they dissolve in sodium bicarbonate, $NaHCO_3$, a weak base. Salts of acids are also formed by dilute sodium hydroxide and other strong bases; most sodium, potassium, and ammonium salts of the lower-molecular-weight acids are water-soluble.

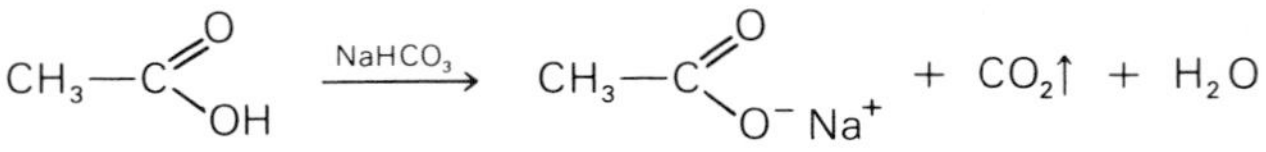

$$CH_3-C(=O)OH \xrightarrow{NaHCO_3} CH_3-C(=O)O^- Na^+ + CO_2\uparrow + H_2O$$

acetic acid — sodium acetate

# Carboxylic Acids

## NOMENCLATURE

Many of the lower members of the saturated-acid homologous series were isolated long ago from natural sources. Most of these compounds are still known by their trivial names, which are based on the natural origin or some characteristic property, e.g., odor, of the compound. In the IUPAC system, the ending *-oic* and the word *acid* are added to the parent name of the hydrocarbon containing the same number of carbon atoms. For example, $CH_3(CH_2)_7CH_2COOH$ is decanoic acid. Additional examples are presented in Table 14-1.

A common functional group, derived from the carboxyl group, is known as the *acyl* or *aroyl* group. The nomenclature of acid halides uses these designations:

*General*: $R{-}C(=O){-}$ acyl group; $R{-}C(=O){-}Cl$ acyl chloride (acid chloride); $Ar{-}C(=O){-}$ aroyl group; $Ar{-}C(=O){-}Br$ aroyl bromide (acid bromide)

*Specific*: $CH_3{-}C(=O){-}$ acetyl group; $C_6H_5{-}C(=O){-}$ benzoyl group

*Example*: $CH_3{-}C(=O){-}Cl$ acetyl chloride; $C_6H_5{-}C(=O){-}Br$ benzoyl bromide

**Table 14-1 Representative carboxylic acids**

| | | |
|---|---|---|
| $H-C(=O)-O-H$<br>formic acid<br>(methanoic acid, IUPAC) | $CH_3-C(=O)-OH$<br>acetic acid<br>(ethanoic acid) | $CH_3-CH_2-C(=O)-OH$<br>propionic acid<br>(propanoic acid) |
| $CH_3(CH_2)_2COOH$<br>*n*-butyric acid<br>(butanoic acid) | $CH_3(CH_2)_3COOH$<br>*n*-valeric acid<br>(pentanoic acid) | $CH_3(CH_2)_4COOH$<br>caproic acid<br>(hexanoic acid) |
| $CH_3(CH_2)_6COOH$<br>caprylic acid<br>(octanoic acid) | $CH_3(CH_2)_8COOH$<br>capric acid<br>(decanoic acid) | $CH_3(CH_2)_{10}COOH$<br>lauric acid<br>(dodecanoic acid) |
| $C_6H_5-COOH$<br>benzoic acid | $C_6H_5-CH_2-COOH$<br>phenylacetic acid | $CH_3-C(CH_3)_2-COOH$<br>trimethylacetic acid<br>(2,2-dimethylpropanoic acid) |

| | | | |
|---|---|---|---|
| $p\text{-}CH_3C_6H_4COOH$<br>*p*-toluic acid | $o\text{-}C_6H_4(COOH)_2$<br>phthalic acid | $m\text{-}C_6H_4(COOH)_2$<br>isophthalic acid | $p\text{-}C_6H_4(COOH)_2$<br>terephthalic acid |

Substitutions other than halogen atoms on an acyl or aroyl group afford classes of compounds which are known by different characteristic names (see Table 14-2). The nomenclature of each of these functional groups will be discussed in the next chapter, although the chemical interrelations of these compounds are discussed later in this chapter (Secs. 14-18 to 14-23).

**Table 14-2 Classes of acid derivatives**

| Structure | Name |
|---|---|
| $R-C(=O)-OH$ | carboxylic acids |
| $R-C(=O)-X$ | acid halides |
| $R-C(=O)-\ddot{N}H_2$ | amides |
| $R-C(=O)-OR'$ | esters |
| $R-C(=O)-O-C(=O)-R'$ | anhydrides |
| $R'-C(=O)-\ddot{N}H-C(=O)-R$ | imides |

## ACIDITY

### 14-1 IONIZATION CONSTANTS, pH AND p$K_a$

Carboxylic acids are considerably stronger acids than phenols, but even *within* these two classes, the relative acidities cover a wide range. How can we put this concept of ''acidity'' on a convenient quantitative scale?

Recall that the mass-action expression for any weak monoprotic acid, HA, in water is

$$HA \rightleftharpoons H^+ + A^-$$

or

$$K_a = \frac{[H^+][A^-]}{[HA]}$$

where $[H^+]$ = equilibrium concentration of proton, moles per liter ($M$)
$[A^-]$ = equilibrium concentration of $A^-$, moles per liter ($M$)
$[HA]$ = equilibrium concentration of HA, moles per liter ($M$)
$K_a$ = equilibrium constant

As a specific example, consider acetic acid, with an ionization constant of approximately $10^{-5}$

$$HOAc \rightleftharpoons H^+ + OAc^- \qquad K = 10^{-5}$$

$$K = \frac{[H^+][OAc^-]}{[HOAc]} = 10^{-5}$$

Similarly for water, $H_2O$,

$$H_2O \rightleftharpoons H^+ + OH^- \qquad K_w = 10^{-14}$$

or

$$K_w = [H^+][OH^-] = 10^{-14}$$

Note that in dilute solutions (0.1 $M$, or less), the concentration of water remains approximately constant, so that its concentration (55 $M$) can be incorporated into the value of $K_w$. Consider another example, phenol:

$$C_6H_5{-}OH \rightleftharpoons C_6H_5{-}O^- + H^+$$

$$K_a = \frac{[C_6H_5{-}O^-][H^+]}{[C_6H_5OH]} = 10^{-10}$$

Since acids dissolve in sodium bicarbonate, a weak base, while phenols require a stronger base such as sodium hydroxide, we may write the order of acidity as $CH_3CO_2H > C_6H_5{-}OH > H_2O$. Quantitatively, the larger the value of the equilibrium constant, the more acidic the compound. Exponentials such as $10^{-14}$ or $10^{-10}$, and especially $1.75 \times 10^{-5}$, are awkward to handle, so that a more convenient scale has been *defined*:

$$pK_a \equiv -\log [K_a]$$

Note that a logarithm is an exponent. For acetic acid,

$$pK_a = -\log (10^{-5}) = -(-5) = +5.$$

Recall the definition of pH,

$$pH \equiv -\log [H^+]$$

and notice the similarity to the definition of $pK_a$. **The smaller the $pK_a$ value, the more acidic the compound.**

| Acid: | $CH_3{-}CO_2H$ > | $C_6H_5{-}OH$ > | $H_2O$ > | $R{-}OH$ |
|---|---|---|---|---|
| $pK_a$: | 5 | 10 | 14 | 16-18 |

A similar definition of $pK_b$ can be made for organic amines, $R{-}NH_2$, which are basic compounds.

## 14-2 RESONANCE EFFECTS ON ACIDITY

You may ask: ***Why*** are organic acids so much stronger acids than other organic molecules containing the —O—H function? The reason for this phenomenon is usually stated: The carboxylate anion which results from removal of the proton has greater resonance stabilization relative to the original acid molecule.

$$CH_3-C(=O)-O-H \longrightarrow H^+ + \left[ CH_3-C(=O)-O^- \longleftrightarrow CH_3-C(-O^-)=O \right]$$

Since there are two equivalent resonance structures for the carboxylate anion but only one for the acid itself, the anion is relatively more stable. Loss of the proton from the acid is facilitated, making these compounds strongly acidic. In addition to the valence-bond description of the anion (two equivalent resonance structures), the anion may also be described in molecular-orbital terms. Here the electronic charge density is delocalized, or spread, over the two oxygen atoms with the $p$ orbital of the carbon atom participating (see Fig. 14-2). Acids have p$K_a$ values of 4 to 6.

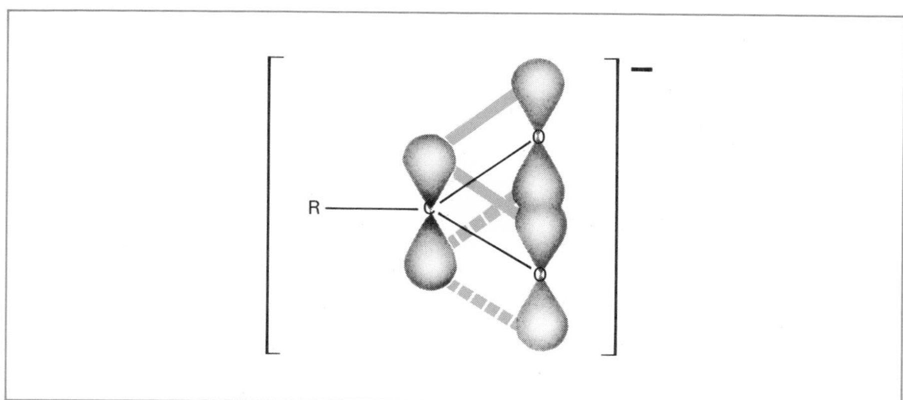


**Figure 14-2 Molecular-orbital representation of the carboxylate anion**

Alcohols, on the other hand, have p$K_a$ values of about 16 to 18, and usually no resonance structures can be written which will contribute significantly to the resonance hybrid. Phenolic anions *are* resonance-stabilized, but the forms which put the charge in the ring are not comparable in energy to the structure with the negative charge on the more electronegative oxygen atom.

$$C_6H_5OH \longrightarrow H^+ + \left[ C_6H_5O^- \longleftrightarrow \text{(ortho carbanion)} \longleftrightarrow \text{(para carbanion)} \longleftrightarrow \text{(ortho carbanion)} \right]$$

Phenols have $pK_a$ values of 9 to 11. Compounds in which resonance and inductive effects play an important role in determining acidity are considered below.

Which of the following would you predict to be the stronger acid?

$CH_3CH_2CO_2H$ or $CH_2{=}CH{-}CO_2H$

propanoic acid — acrylic acid

Considering the resonance stabilization of the anion, the forms which can be written indicate that the $\alpha,\beta$-unsaturated acid anion has the greater resonance stabilization.

$$\left[CH_3{-}CH_2{-}C\overset{\displaystyle O}{\underset{\displaystyle O^-}{\lessgtr}} \longleftrightarrow CH_3{-}CH_2{-}C\overset{\displaystyle O^-}{\underset{\displaystyle O}{\lessgtr}}\right]$$

$$\left[CH_2{=}CH{-}C\overset{\displaystyle O}{\underset{\displaystyle O^-}{\lessgtr}} \longleftrightarrow CH_2{=}CH{-}C\overset{\displaystyle O^-}{\underset{\displaystyle O}{\lessgtr}} \longleftrightarrow \underset{+}{C}H_2{-}CH{=}C\overset{\displaystyle O^-}{\underset{\displaystyle O^-}{\lessgtr}}\right]$$

This can be illustrated by the molecular-orbital picture (Fig. 14-3).

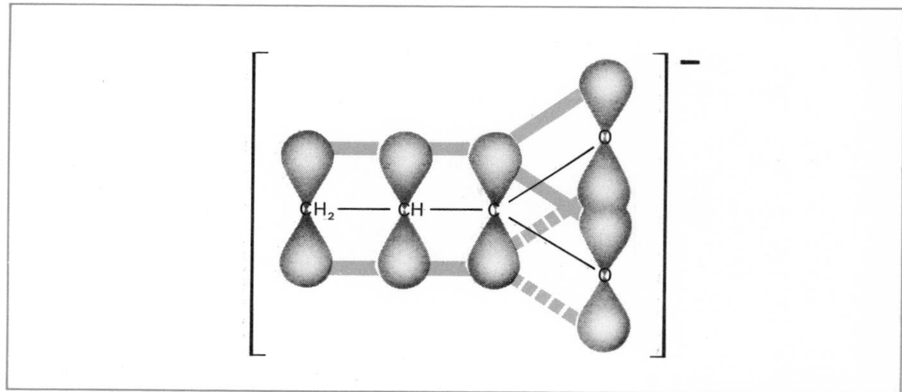


**Figure 14-3 Molecular-orbital representation of acrylate anion**

## 14-3 INDUCTIVE EFFECTS

Substituent groups on the $\alpha$ carbon of a carboxylic acid may either ''loosen'' or ''tighten'' the oxygen-hydrogen bond and affect the acidity.

$$\overset{\delta}{-\overset{|}{\underset{|}{C}}}-\overset{\gamma}{\overset{|}{\underset{|}{C}}}-\overset{\beta}{\overset{|}{\underset{|}{C}}}-\overset{\alpha}{\overset{|}{\underset{|}{C}}}-COOH$$

The following series demonstrates this point:

| $CCl_3—CO_2H$ | $CH_3—CO_2H$ | $(CH_3)_3C—CO_2H$ |
|---|---|---|
| p$K_a$ 0.70 | 4.75 | 5.03 |

Relative to the hydrogen atoms on acetic acid, the chlorine atoms of trichloracetic acid loosen the oxygen-hydrogen bond by withdrawing electrons from oxygen via the inductive effect, which operates through the bonds. The electron density in the oxygen-hydrogen bond is shifted closer to oxygen, weakening that bond and making the proton easier to remove.

$$Cl_3C \leftarrow C(=O) \leftarrow O \leftarrow H \rightleftharpoons Cl_3C—C(=O)O^- + H^+$$

Evidence exists for the operation of this electronic effect directly through space to the center of interest. This is known as a ***field effect***. On the other hand, since methyl groups ***donate*** electrons to the $\alpha$ carbon, the oxygen-hydrogen bond is strengthened, and trimethylacetic acid is a weaker acid than acetic acid itself.

$$(CH_3)_3C \rightarrow C(=O) \rightarrow O \rightarrow H \rightleftharpoons (CH_3)_3C—C(=O)O^- + H^+$$

The increased electron density around the oxygen atom binds the proton more strongly than in acetic acid.

Inductive effects are additive, and the more numerous the electron-withdrawing groups on the $\alpha$ carbon, the stronger the acid. With an increasing number of electron-donating substituents, the acids become progressively weaker. As would be expected, the more electronegative the $\alpha$ substituent, the stronger the acid.

| $CH_3—CO_2H$ | < | $ClCH_2—CO_2H$ | < | $Cl_2CH—CO_2H$ | < | $CCl_3—CO_2H$ |
|---|---|---|---|---|---|---|
| p$K_a$ 4.76 | | 2.81 | | 1.29 | | 0.08 |

| $CH_3—CO_2H$ | < | $ICH_2—CO_2H$ | < | $BrCH_2—CO_2H$ | < | $ClCH_2—CO_2H$ | < | $FCH_2—CO_2H$ |
|---|---|---|---|---|---|---|---|---|
| p$K_a$ 4.76 | | 3.13 | | 2.87 | | 2.81 | | 2.66 |

## 14-4 TRANSMISSION OF INDUCTIVE EFFECTS

The discussion of inductive effects has centered on acetic acid and its $\alpha$-substituted derivatives; this effect falls off rapidly as the substituent is placed further down the carbon chain.

$$\underset{\substack{|\\Cl}}{CH_3CH_2CHCO_2H} > \underset{\substack{|\\Cl}}{CH_3CHCH_2CO_2H} > \underset{\substack{|\\Cl}}{CH_2CH_2CH_2CO_2H} \approx CH_3CH_2CH_2CO_2H$$

$K_a$ $1.4 \times 10^{-3}$ $8.9 \times 10^{-5}$ $3.0 \times 10^{-5}$ $\approx$ $1.5 \times 10^{-5}$

The inductive effect does not operate effectively through more than two or three carbon-carbon bonds unless unsaturation is present in the molecule to aid in the transmission. The role of multiple bonds in transmitting inductive effects can be understood by recalling that $\pi$ electrons are less strongly held than those in $\sigma$ bonds. For example, $ClCH{=}CH{-}CO_2H$ is nearly as strong an acid as $CH_3{-}\underset{\substack{|\\Cl}}{CH}{-}CO_2H$.

$$\underset{\substack{|\\:\ddot{C}l:}}{CH}{=}CH{-}C\begin{matrix}{=}O\\ \diagdown O{-}H\end{matrix} \rightleftharpoons \underset{\substack{|\\:\ddot{C}l:}}{CH}{=}CH{-}C\begin{matrix}{=}O\\ \diagdown O^-\end{matrix} + H^+$$

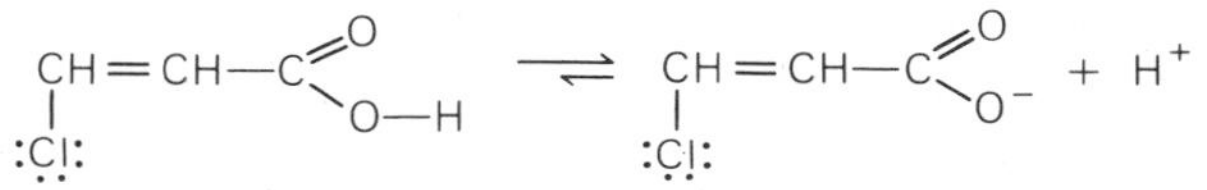

The chlorine atom withdraws electrons from the double bond, leaving the $\alpha$ carbon partially positive, which is very similar to having the chlorine atom attached directly to the $\alpha$ carbon.

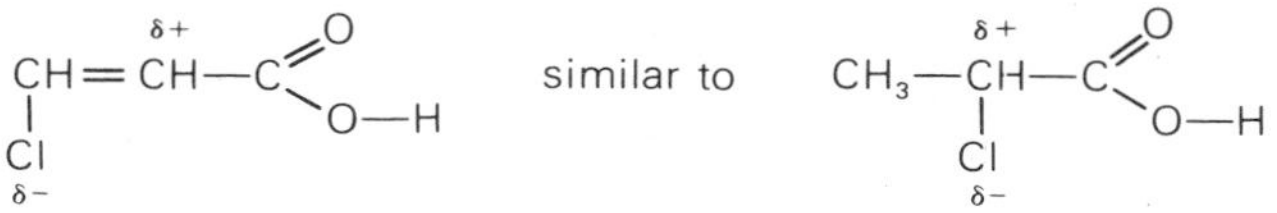

$$\underset{\substack{|\\Cl\\ \delta-}}{CH}{=}\overset{\delta+}{CH}{-}C\begin{matrix}{=}O\\ \diagdown O{-}H\end{matrix} \quad \text{similar to} \quad CH_3{-}\underset{\substack{|\\Cl\\ \delta-}}{\overset{\delta+}{CH}}{-}C\begin{matrix}{=}O\\ \diagdown O{-}H\end{matrix}$$

# PREPARATION

All the methods listed here for the preparation of carboxylic acids have been discussed previously and provide a convenient point for a brief review.

## 14-5 OXIDATION REACTIONS

Reagents such as potassium permanganate, $KMnO_4$, or such sources of Cr(VI) as $CrO_3$, $K_2Cr_2O_7$, and $Na_2CrO_4$ form carboxylic acids by oxidation of primary alcohols (in fair to good yields, Sec. 9-5); alkenes (fair to good, mixtures from unsymmetrical olefins, Sec. 4-6); alkynes (fair, acetylenes are sometimes difficult to obtain, and unsymmetrical ones give mixtures, Sec. 5-6); aldehydes (excellent, but aldehydes usually are more difficult to obtain, and even then an acid derivative may be the convenient starting material, Sec. 13-1); and alkyl arenes (good to excellent, especially Ar—$CH_3$ compounds, Sec. 4-6). Alkenes and alkynes react with ozone, $O_3$, followed by oxidative work-up using $H_2O_2$, affording good to excellent yield of carboxylic acids *on a small scale* (Secs. 4-7 and 5-6).

## 14-6 THE HALOFORM REACTION

In addition to providing a convenient test for certain functional groups, the haloform reaction is an important method of preparing carboxylic acids (review Sec. 13-15). This is *usually* accomplished by treating a methyl ketone with sodium hypochlorite, NaOCl, obtained from chlorine and sodium hydroxide. The reaction may be carried out in a beaker (in the hood!), and the chloroform is lost to the atmosphere at the boiling point of the mixture. Note that a carbon atom is lost in this degradative process.

$$CH_3-C_6H_4-CO-CH_3 \xrightarrow[2.\ H_3O^+]{1.\ NaOH;\ Cl_2;\ \Delta} CH_3-C_6H_4-CO_2H + CHCl_3\uparrow$$

*p*-methylacetophenone → *p*-toluic acid (*p*-methylbenzoic acid)

## 14-7 CARBONATION OF GRIGNARD REAGENTS

Review the formation and reactions of Grignard reagents under halides (Chap. 8) and alcohols (Chap. 9). Pay particular attention to the functional groups which are incompatible because they react with the *incipient* organomagnesium halide.

The carbonation of Grignard reagents and organolithium reagents is an *excellent* synthetic method for obtaining both aliphatic and aromatic carboxylic acids.

$$Br-C_6H_4-Cl \xrightarrow[2.\ CO_2\ (\text{pour onto Dry Ice})\quad 3.\ H_3O^+]{1.\ Mg\ \text{in dry ether}} HO_2C-C_6H_4-Cl$$

*p*-bromochlorobenzene → *p*-chlorobenzoic acid

$$C_{10}H_7Cl \xrightarrow[2.\ CO_2\ (\text{Dry Ice})\quad 3.\ H_3O^+]{1.\ Mg\ \text{in dry THF}} C_{10}H_7CO_2H$$

1-chloronaphthalene ($\alpha$-chloronaphthalene) → 1-naphthalenecarboxylic acid ($\alpha$-naphthoic acid)

### 14-8 HYDROLYSIS OF NITRILES

Aromatic halides containing strongly withdrawing substituents, for example, $—NO_2$ or —CN, and aliphatic halides can be converted to nitriles, via an $S_N2$ mechanism, by refluxing with an alkali metal cyanide in aqueous ethanol. Unactivated aromatic halides can undergo displacement by cyanide ion, using KCN-$Cu_2(CN)_2$-pyridine.

Hydrolysis of a nitrile by a base or by prolonged refluxing in acid solution produces ammonia and the acid salt (or acid itself).

$$CH_2{=}CH{-}CH_2Cl \xrightarrow[EtOH]{Cu_2(CN)_2} CH_2{=}CH{-}CH_2CN \xrightarrow[H_2O]{HCl} CH_2{=}CH{-}CH_2COOH$$

80% yield (first step); 80% yield (second step)

allyl chloride — allyl cyanide — vinylacetic acid (3-butenoic acid)

The intermediate amide, R—CO—$NH_2$, can be isolated if a cold solution of the nitrile in concentrated sulfuric acid is poured into ice water.

$$p\text{-}Cl{-}C_6H_4{-}CH_2CN \xrightarrow[\Delta]{H_2SO_4\text{-}H_2O} p\text{-}Cl{-}C_6H_4{-}CH_2COOH$$

*p*-chlorobenzyl cyanide
*p*-chlorophenylacetonitrile

*p*-chlorophenylacetic acid

> Formulate a reasonable mechanism for the reaction
>
> $$R{-}C{\equiv}N \xrightarrow[2.\ H_2O]{1.\ H_2SO_4} R{-}CO{-}NH_2$$

## SYNTHESES USING ACTIVE METHYLENE COMPOUNDS

### 14-9 MALONIC ESTER SYNTHESES

Compounds such as diethyl malonate, phenylacetonitrile, and cyanoacetone

$$Et{-}O{-}\overset{O}{\overset{\|}{C}}{-}CH_2{-}\overset{O}{\overset{\|}{C}}{-}O{-}Et \qquad C_6H_5{-}CH_2{-}CN \qquad CH_3{-}\overset{O}{\overset{\|}{C}}{-}CH_2{-}CN$$

diethyl malonate — phenylacetonitrile — cyanoacetone

that contain a methylene group flanked by two strongly electron-withdrawing substituents are called ***active methylene compounds*** because of the ease with which the anion (—CH—)$^-$ is formed on treatment with base. Resonance structures can be written for the anion in which the negative charge is placed on the electron-withdrawing substituents.

Primary and secondary alkyl halides can be converted in good yield to carboxylic acids containing two additional carbons

$$R—X \longrightarrow R—CH_2—COOH$$

by $S_N2$ displacement of the halide ion by the malonate anion. Diethyl malonate reacts with sodium ethoxide (from Na + EtOH) to form the anion, which causes an $S_N2$ displacement on an alkyl halide.

$$\underset{\text{diethyl malonate}}{CH_2(CO_2Et)_2} \xrightarrow[\text{in EtOH}]{\text{NaOEt}} \underset{\text{sodium diethyl malonate}}{Na^+\bar{C}H(CO_2Et)_2} + EtOH$$

$$\bar{C}H(CO_2Et)_2 + \underset{n\text{-propyl bromide}}{CH_3CH_2CH_2—Br} \longrightarrow \underset{\text{diethyl } n\text{-propylmalonate}}{CH_3CH_2CH_2—CH(CO_2Et)_2} + Br^-$$

Since the monoalkylated malonic ester, e.g., diethyl *n*-propylmalonate, has an additional acidic hydrogen atom, the compound can be alkylated again with the same halide or with another halide in a separate reaction. Some unreacted malonic ester and some dialkylated product *always* result, even when the monoalkylated compound is the main product.

$$CH_3CH_2CH_2—CH(CO_2Et)_2 \xrightarrow{\text{NaOEt}} CH_3CH_2CH_2—\bar{C}(CO_2Et)_2Na^+$$

$$CH_3CH_2CH_2—\bar{C}(CO_2Et)_2 \xrightarrow{CH_3CH_2CH_2Br} \underset{\text{diethyl di}(n\text{-propyl})\text{malonate}}{(CH_3CH_2CH_2)_2C(CO_2Et)_2}$$

$$CH_3CH_2CH_2—\bar{C}(CO_2Et)_2 \xrightarrow{CH_3I} \underset{\text{diethyl methyl-}n\text{-propylmalonate}}{(H_3C)(CH_3CH_2CH_2)C(CO_2Et)_2}$$

Alkylated compounds, like those in the above examples, can be converted to diacids by hydrolysis and then to the monoacids by thermal decarboxylation.

*Example*: $CH_3CH_2CH_2—CH(CO_2Et)_2 \xrightarrow[2.\ H_3O^+]{1.\ OH^-} CH_3CH_2CH_2—CH(COOH)_2$

$$\underset{n\text{-propylmalonic acid}}{CH_3CH_2CH_2—CH(COOH)_2} \xrightarrow[\Delta \text{ at } 180° \text{ dry, } -CO_2]{\Delta \text{ at } 100° \text{ in } H^+ \text{ or}} \underset{\text{pentanoic acid}}{CH_3CH_2CH_2CH_2COOH}$$

1. Write the corresponding equations for the hydrolysis and subsequent decarboxylation of the two dialkylated malonic esters in the previous examples. Name all compounds.

2. Indicate a reasonable synthesis of octanoic acid from pentanoic acid. (*Hint*: Use a Grignard reaction before the malonic ester synthesis.)

This discussion has described the essential features of the malonic ester synthesis, but we shall discuss in detail four aspects of the method which may be stated as questions:

1. Why does the malonate anion form so readily?

2. Which halides can be used in this synthesis?

3. What special methods are used for the preparation of monomethyl- and monophenylmalonic esters?

4. How is the malonic ester synthesis related to the alkylation of acetoacetic ester and of cyanoacetic ester, which were also mentioned with malonic ester in Sec. 8-7?

## 14-10 WHY DOES THE MALONATE ANION FORM SO READILY?

The acidity of diethyl malonate can be explained in terms of resonance stabilization of the anion formed from the ester and a strong base. Three forms can be written:

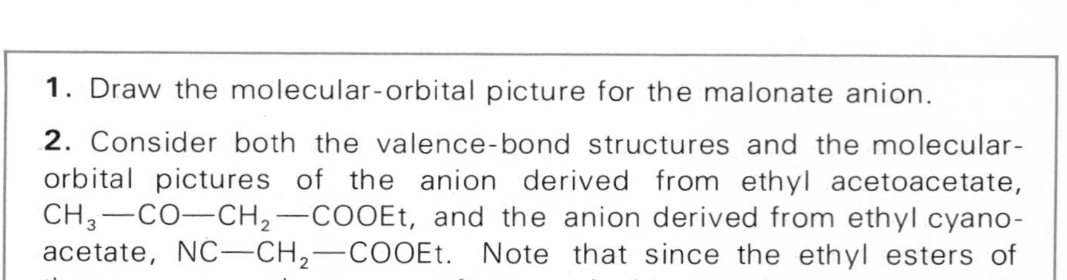

$$\left[ EtO-\overset{\overset{\displaystyle O}{\|}}{C}-\underline{C}H-\overset{\overset{\displaystyle O}{\|}}{C}-OEt \longleftrightarrow EtO-\overset{\overset{\displaystyle O^-}{|}}{C}=CH-\overset{\overset{\displaystyle O}{\|}}{C}-OEt \longleftrightarrow EtO-\overset{\overset{\displaystyle O}{\|}}{C}-CH=\overset{\overset{\displaystyle O^-}{|}}{C}-OEt \right]$$

1. Draw the molecular-orbital picture for the malonate anion.

2. Consider both the valence-bond structures and the molecular-orbital pictures of the anion derived from ethyl acetoacetate, $CH_3—CO—CH_2—COOEt$, and the anion derived from ethyl cyanoacetate, $NC—CH_2—COOEt$. Note that since the ethyl esters of these compounds are so often used, the compounds are usually referred to as simply malonic ester, acetoacetic ester, and cyanoacetic ester.

### 14-11 WHICH HALIDES CAN BE USED?

Since these alkylations are generally $S_N2$ displacements, primary and secondary halides are often used. Although allyl and benzyl halides can be used, the competing $S_N1$ solvolysis (ethanolysis) is an important reaction. The conditions of the reaction are usually arranged so that this side reaction of allyl and benzyl halides is minimized and these halides can be used.

$$C_6H_5{-}CH_2{-}Br \xrightarrow{S_N1} [C_6H_5{-}CH_2^+] \xrightarrow[-H^+]{EtOH} C_6H_5{-}CH_2{-}OEt$$

$$C_6H_5{-}CH_2{-}Br \xrightarrow[^-CH(COOEt)_2]{S_N2} C_6H_5{-}CH_2{-}CH(COOEt)_2$$

$$\text{3-chlorocyclopentene} + CH_2(CO_2Et)_2 \xrightarrow[60\%\ \text{yield}]{NaOEt} \text{diethyl 2-cyclopentene-1-malonate } (CH(CO_2Et)_2 \text{ on cyclopentene})$$

3-chlorocyclopentene — diethyl 2-cyclopentene-1-malonate

Tertiary halides, on the other hand, are a different story. Since the alkylation is carried out in the presence of strong base, NaOEt, the principal reaction with tertiary halides is an $E_2$ elimination. For example, with *tert*-butyl bromide

$$EtO^- + CH_3{-}C(CH_3)(CH_3){-}Br \longrightarrow EtOH + (H_3C)_2C{=}CH_2 + Br^-$$

*t*-butyl bromide — isobutylene

You might suggest adjusting the reaction conditions to minimize the concentration of ethoxide ion and to maximize the malonate ion concentration. This is possible to do; but remember that **the malonate anion itself is a strong base.** Thus, the elimination again predominates:

$$(EtO_2C)_2\bar{C}H + CH_3{-}C(CH_3)(CH_3){-}Br \longrightarrow CH_2(CO_2Et)_2 + CH_2{=}C(CH_3)_2 + Br^-$$

Compounds derived from tertiary halides must be prepared by other methods, which will not be discussed in this text.

Certain dihalides can be used in this reaction, which leads to the formation of cyclic compounds. This represents a moderately good method of forming four-, five-, and six-membered ring compounds.

$$CH_2(CO_2Et)_2 + \underset{Br}{CH_2}-CH_2-\underset{Cl}{CH_2} \xrightarrow[50\%\ \text{yield}]{NaOEt} \text{(cyclobutane with } CO_2Et, CO_2Et) \xrightarrow[\substack{2.\ H_3O^+ \\ 3.\ \Delta\ 80\%\ \text{yield}}]{1.\ OH^-} \text{(cyclobutane with } COOH)$$

1-bromo-3-chloropropane

diethyl 1,1-cyclobutanedicarboxylate

cyclobutanecarboxylic acid

1. Calculate the overall yield of the monoacid in the above synthesis.

2. Cyclobutanecarboxylic acid can be prepared from diethyl malonate and 1,3-dibromopropane (trimethylene bromide) in 20% yield. Formulate all the steps in this synthesis. The ***diacid*** in this sequence can be prepared in 21 to 23% yield from diethyl malonate and the dibromide. Calculate the ***range*** of yields in the decarboxylation step.

3. Why do you suppose the overall yield in part 1 is so much greater than that in part 2?

The use of a particular halide is dictated by many of the same considerations encountered in Grignard reactions (review Sec. 9-10); however, **diethyl methylmalonate, $CH_3$—$CH(COOEt)_2$, cannot be prepared directly** (see Sec. 14-12).

Finally, although certain activated nitrohalobenzenes and cyanohalobenzenes undergo an $S_N2$ displacement, simple aryl halides do not. The synthesis of simple phenylmalonic esters is discussed below.

### 14-12 WHAT SPECIAL METHODS ARE USED FOR THE SYNTHESIS OF METHYLMALONIC AND PHENYLMALONIC ESTERS?

In an attempt to form diethyl methylmalonate, $CH_3$—$CH(COOEt)_2$, it is found that unreacted diethyl malonate, $CH_2(COOEt)_2$, and the dialkylated product, diethyl dimethylmalonate, $(CH_3)_2C(COOEt)_2$, are also present. Because of their boiling points, it is virtually impossible to separate these compounds by fractional distillation, the usual method of purification.

$$CH_2(COOEt)_2 \xrightarrow[CH_3I]{NaOEt} CH_3{-}CH(COOEt)_2 \xrightarrow[CH_3I]{NaOEt} (CH_3)_2C(COOEt)_2$$

b.p. 198° 199° 196°

These three diesters undergo hydrolysis at different rates, and this fact can be used as a method of separation based on kinetic, rather than equilibrium, considerations. Over a long period of time (equilibrium), all these esters would be hydrolyzed; however, the fewer the substituents, the faster the hydrolysis (kinetic). The dimethyl compound, $(CH_3)_2C(COOEt)_2$, can be obtained, of course, by using a large excess of methyl iodide so that the dialkylation is the main reaction.

The synthesis of diethyl methylmalonate, which can undergo alkylation, can be accomplished by the following route. This sequence will be discussed again with reference to the reactions of acids (Sec. 14-17).

$$CH_3{-}CH_2{-}CO_2H \xrightarrow[Br_2]{P} CH_3{-}\underset{\displaystyle Br}{\underset{|}{CH}}{-}CO_2H \xrightarrow[KCN]{alc.} CH_3{-}\underset{\displaystyle CN}{\underset{|}{CH}}{-}CO_2H$$

$$\downarrow H_3O^+$$

$$CH_3{-}CH(CO_2Et)_2 \xleftarrow[H^+]{EtOH} CH_3{-}\underset{\displaystyle CO_2H}{\underset{|}{CH}}{-}CO_2H$$

Diethyl phenylmalonate, $C_6H_5{-}CH(COOEt)_2$, can be prepared in two steps: (1) a base-catalyzed condensation, followed by (2) a decarbonylation reaction, a loss of CO. The first step is the alkylation of ethyl phenylacetate, $C_6H_5{-}CH_2{-}COOEt$, an active methylene compound, using diethyl oxalate, EtOOC—COOEt.

*Overall*:

$$C_6H_5{-}CH_2{-}\overset{\displaystyle O}{\overset{\|}{C}}{-}OEt + EtO{-}\overset{\displaystyle O}{\overset{\|}{C}}{-}\overset{\displaystyle O}{\overset{\|}{C}}{-}OEt \xrightarrow{NaOEt} C_6H_5{-}\overset{\displaystyle COOEt}{\overset{|}{CH}}{-}\overset{\displaystyle O}{\overset{\|}{C}}{-}COOEt$$

*Mechanism*:

$$C_6H_5{-}CH_2{-}COOEt \xrightarrow{NaOEt} \left[C_6H_5{-}\bar{C}H{-}COOEt\right] + O{=}C(OEt){-}C({=}O)OEt \longrightarrow$$

$$C_6H_5{-}\overset{\displaystyle COOEt}{\overset{|}{CH}}{-}\overset{\displaystyle O}{\overset{\|}{C}}{-}COOEt$$

The intermediate $\alpha$ keto ester, $-\overset{\displaystyle O}{\overset{\|}{C}}{-}COOEt$, undergoes a ready loss of CO by the catalytic action of finely divided soft-glass powder at elevated temperatures.

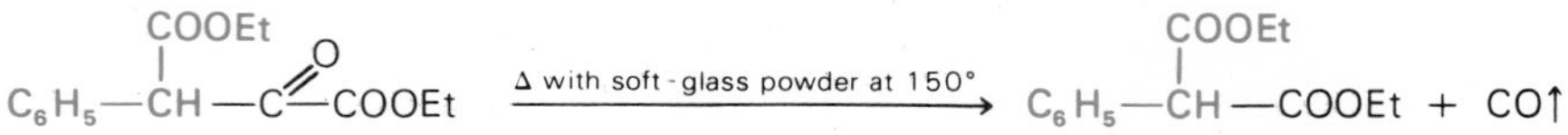

$$C_6H_5-\underset{|}{\overset{COOEt}{CH}}-\overset{O}{\overset{\|}{C}}-COOEt \xrightarrow{\Delta \text{ with soft-glass powder at } 150°} C_6H_5-\underset{|}{\overset{COOEt}{CH}}-COOEt + CO\uparrow$$

Both diethyl phenylmalonate and diethyl methylmalonate can subsequently be alkylated, hydrolyzed, and decarboxylated.

**1.** Employing alkylation reactions, formulate two methods of synthesis of the compound $CH_3CH_2CH_2CH_2CH(CH_3)COOH$.

**2.** Formulate a method of preparing

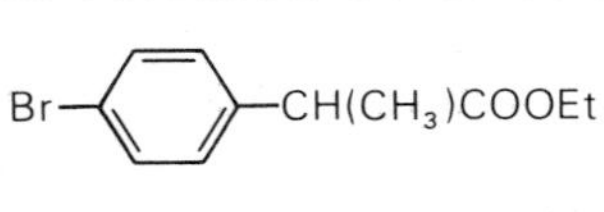

$$Br-C_6H_4-CH(CH_3)COOEt$$

**3.** For the same reasons that diethyl phenylmalonate cannot be prepared directly from an aryl halide and diethyl malonate, ethyl phenylcyanoacetate, $C_6H_5-CH(CN)-COOEt$, cannot be prepared from an aryl halide and ethyl cyanoacetate, $NC-CH_2-COOEt$. Ethyl phenylcyanoacetate can, however, be prepared from phenylacetonitrile, $C_6H_5-CH_2-CN$, an active methylene compound, and diethyl carbonate $EtO-COOEt$ in one step with sodium ethoxide (75% yield). Formulate the overall reaction and indicate a reasonable mechanism for this reaction.

## 14-13 HOW ARE OTHER ACTIVE METHYLENE COMPOUNDS SIMILARLY EMPLOYED?

In general, other active methylene compounds such as acetoacetic ester, $CH_3COCH_2COOEt$, and cyanoacetic ester, $CNCH_2COOEt$, can be used in the same manner as malonic ester; similar cautions and restrictions apply. The base and solvent to be used are dictated by the structure of the active methylene compound; the more acidic ones, such as nitromethane, may use only dilute sodium hydroxide, but very slightly acidic compounds, like phenylacetonitrile, require strong base in an inert solvent, such as $NaNH_2$ in benzene or toluene. These variations should be noted, but these subtleties will not be amplified in this text or considered in the problems.

Alkylated acetoacetic esters

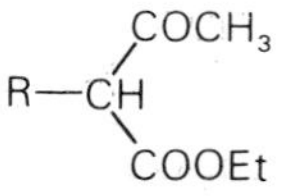

$$R-CH\begin{matrix} \diagup COCH_3 \\ \diagdown COOEt \end{matrix}$$

can be converted either to ***methyl ketones*** or ***carboxylic acids***, depending on the base concentration used in the reaction sequence. With ***dilute*** *base*, the ester carbonyl is attacked, yielding the methyl ketone; however, ***concentrated base*** leads to the ***carboxylic acid*** by attack at the ketone carbonyl.

$$\text{Dilute base: } R\text{—}CH(COCH_3)(COOEt) \xrightarrow[\text{2. } H^+]{\text{1. dil. } OH^-} R\text{—}CH(COCH_3)(COOH) \xrightarrow[-CO_2]{\Delta} R\text{—}CH_2\text{—}\overset{O}{\overset{\|}{C}}\text{—}CH_3$$

$$\text{Strong base: } R\text{—}CH(COCH_3)(COOEt) \xrightarrow[\text{cleavage}]{OH^-} \left[\underset{\text{strong base}}{R\text{—}\bar{C}H\text{—}COOEt} + \underset{\text{weak acid}}{CH_3\text{—}\overset{O}{\overset{\|}{C}}\text{—}OH}\right] \longrightarrow$$

$$[R\text{—}CH_2\text{—}COOEt + CH_3COO^-] \longrightarrow R\text{—}CH_2\text{—}COO^- \xrightarrow[H_3O^+]{\text{dil.}} R\text{—}CH_2\text{—}COOH$$

Note that the use of strong base leads to the same diacid as that obtained from a malonic ester synthesis.

Alkylated cyanoacetic esters can be hydrolyzed to the corresponding malonic acid and subsequently decarboxylated.

$$R\text{—}CH(COOEt)(CN) \xrightarrow[\text{2. } H_3O^+]{\text{1. dil. } OH^-} R\text{—}CH(COOH)(CN) \xrightarrow[-CO_2]{\Delta} R\text{—}CH_2\text{—}CN$$

**1.** Indicate three syntheses of $CH_3CH_2CH_2CH_2COOH$ using 1-bromopropane and (*a*) malonic ester, (*b*) acetoacetic ester, and (*c*) cyanoacetic ester.

**2.** Using ethanol and acetoacetic ester as the only organic compounds, write syntheses of 2-pentanone, butanoic acid, 3-ethyl-2-pentanone, and 2-ethylbutanoic acid.

## REACTIONS

### 14-14 SALT FORMATION AND PYROLYSIS

The formation of salts from carboxylic acids and dilute $NaHCO_3$, with evolution of $CO_2$, is a characteristic reaction of water-soluble carboxylic acids which constitutes a qualitative test. Several examples of acid salt decarboxylation have been cited in earlier chapters (see Secs.

2-12 and 7-17), namely, pyrolysis of salts with soda lime, NaOH-CaO, to form hydrocarbons

$$3,4\text{-}F_2C_6H_3COO^-Na^+ \xrightarrow[\Delta]{\text{CaO-NaOH}} o\text{-}F_2C_6H_4$$

sodium 3,4-difluorobenzoate → *o*-difluorobenzene

and the facile decarboxylation of aromatic acid salts containing electron-withdrawing substituents; e.g., with heat, sodium 2,4,6-trinitrobenzoate yields 1,3,5-trinitrobenzene. Copper chromite and quinoline are commonly used for the direct decarboxylation of an *acid* (rather than the salt). Note that in the following example the geometrical configuration is largely preserved; only about 5% *trans*-stilbene is obtained.

$$\underset{trans\text{-}\alpha\text{-phenylcinnamic acid}}{(H_5C_6)(H)C{=}C(C_6H_5)(COOH)} \xrightarrow[\text{60\% yield}]{\text{copper chromite in quinoline at 200°}} \underset{cis\text{-stilbene}}{(H_5C_6)(H)C{=}C(C_6H_5)(H)} + CO_2\uparrow$$

### 14-15 HUNSDIECKER REACTION

Salts of carboxylic acids can also be formed by treating acids with the moist oxide or hydroxide of heavy metals. A common reaction is that with moist silver oxide.

**Table 14-3 Examples of the Hunsdiecker reaction**

$$CH_3CH_2CH(CH_2CH_3)COO^-Ag^+ \text{ (dry!)} \xrightarrow[\text{75\% yield}]{Br_2 \text{ in dry } CCl_4} CH_3CH_2CH(CH_2CH_3)Br + CO_2\uparrow + AgBr\downarrow$$

$$n\text{-}C_{15}H_{31}COO^-Ag^+ \xrightarrow[\text{20\% yield}]{Cl_2 \text{ in dry } CCl_4} n\text{-}C_{15}H_{31}Cl$$

$$O_2N\text{-}C_6H_4\text{-}CH_2COO^-Ag^+ \xrightarrow[\text{85\% yield}]{Br_2 \text{ in dry } CCl_4} O_2N\text{-}C_6H_4\text{-}CH_2Br$$

$$C_6H_5\text{-}C{\equiv}C\text{-}COO^-Ag^+ \xrightarrow[\text{95\% yield}]{I_2 \text{ in dry } C_6H_6} C_6H_5\text{-}C{\equiv}C\text{-}I$$

$$HOOC(CH_2)_5COOH \xrightarrow[\text{3. } Br_2 \text{ in dry } CCl_4 \text{; 45\% yield}]{\text{1. moist } Ag_2O \text{; 2. dry the salt}} Br(CH_2)_5Br$$

pentamethylene dibromide

$$CH_3CH_2CH_2CO_2H \xrightarrow[Ag_2O]{\text{moist}} CH_3CH_2CH_2CO_2^- Ag^+$$

butanoic acid — silver butanoate

Refluxing a suspension of the ***dry*** silver salt of an aliphatic carboxylic acid in carbon tetrachloride, to which halogen ($Br_2$) is slowly added, produces the ***next lower alkyl halide (bromide)***.

$$R\text{—}COO^- Ag^+ \xrightarrow{X_2} R\text{—}X + AgX + CO_2$$

Yields are considerably lower in the aromatic series, and the reaction finds only limited use there. The examples in Table 14-3 suggest the scope of this reaction.

> Name the starting acids and halide products in the example in Table 14-3.

## 14-16 REDUCTION WITH LITHIUM ALUMINUM HYDRIDE

Carboxylic acids are reduced to primary alcohols in high yield by $LiAlH_4$ (*not* $NaBH_4$) in dry ether or tetrahydrofuran. Since acids contain an active hydrogen atom, R—COOH, 1 mole of $H_2$ is evolved for every acid group being reduced; this wastes one-fourth of the $LiAlH_4$.

$$R\text{—}\overset{\overset{\displaystyle O}{\|}}{C}\text{—}OH + LiAlH_4 \longrightarrow \left[ R\text{—}\overset{\overset{\displaystyle O}{\|}}{C}\text{—}O\ LiAlH_3 \right] + H_2\uparrow$$

The reaction, however, is commonly employed on a small scale with valuable acids.

$$(CH_3)_3C\text{—}COOH \xrightarrow[\text{2. } H_3O^+]{\text{1. } LiAlH_4} (CH_3)_3C\text{—}CH_2OH$$

90% yield

trimethylacetic acid — neopentyl alcohol

cyclopropane carboxylic acid (cyclopropyl—COOH) $\xrightarrow[\text{2. } H_3O^+]{\text{1. } LiAlH_4}$ cyclopropylmethanol (cyclopropyl—$CH_2OH$)

95% yield

cyclopropane carboxylic acid — cyclopropylmethanol

*m*-chlorobenzoic acid (COOH, Cl) $\xrightarrow[\text{2. } H_3O^+]{\text{1. } LiAlH_4}$ *m*-chlorobenzyl alcohol ($CH_2OH$, Cl)

*m*-chlorobenzoic acid — *m*-chlorobenzyl alcohol

Esters, prepared directly from acids or their derivatives, consume no extra hydride ion and are often reduced with $LiAlH_4$. Furthermore, methyl or ethyl esters are generally more soluble than the corresponding acids in ether or tetrahydrofuran, the solvents used in these reductions.

$$R{-}COOH + R'OH \xrightarrow{H^+} R{-}COOR' \xrightarrow[2.\ H_3O^+]{1.\ LiAlH_4} R{-}CH_2OH + R'OH$$

### 14-17 HELL-VOLHARD-ZELINSKY REACTION

Hydrogen atoms on a carbon adjacent to a carboxyl group can be replaced with bromine or chlorine in the presence of phosphorus. Only these $\alpha$ hydrogen atoms are reactive, but all the $\alpha$ hydrogens present can be replaced successively. This reaction can be employed as an aid to structural determinations.

$$CH_3CH_2COOH \xrightarrow[P]{Br_2} CH_3\underset{\substack{|\\ Br}}{C}H{-}COOH \xrightarrow[P]{Br_2} CH_3{-}\overset{\substack{Br\\ |}}{\underset{\substack{|\\ Br}}{C}}{-}COOH$$

$$CH_3{-}\overset{\substack{CH_3\\ |}}{\underset{\substack{|\\ CH_3}}{C}}{-}COOH \xrightarrow[P]{Br_2} \text{N.R.}$$

This reaction has been extensively used in the synthesis of amino acids, where the $\alpha$ bromo acid can be converted to an amino acid by treatment with excess ammonia.

$$R{-}CH_2{-}COOH \xrightarrow[P]{Br_2} R{-}\underset{\substack{|\\ Br}}{C}H{-}COOH \xrightarrow{NH_3} R{-}\underset{\substack{|\\ NH_2}}{C}H{-}COOH$$

an $\alpha$-amino acid

## REACTIONS YIELDING ACID DERIVATIVES: A SURVEY

This section is a preview of the entire next chapter, which will amplify the reactions of carboxylic acids discussed here. This brief presentation is intended to place the wide range of interrelated reactions in proper perspective; only the essence of Chap. 15 appears here.

### 14-18 ESTERS

The Fischer esterification is a simple method of obtaining esters by the reversible reaction of primary or secondary alcohols (*not* tertiary alcohols or phenols) with a carboxylic acid in the presence of a trace of mineral acid, such as HCl or $H_2SO_4$.

*General*: $$R{-}\overset{\overset{\large O}{\|}}{C}{-}OH + R'{-}OH \xrightarrow{H^+} R{-}\overset{\overset{\large O}{\|}}{C}{-}O{-}R' + H_2O$$

*Specific*: $$\underset{\text{acetylenedicarboxylic acid}}{HOOC{-}C{\equiv}C{-}COOH} \xrightarrow[\substack{H_2SO_4\text{ trace}\\ 85\%\text{ yield}}]{CH_3OH(xs)} \underset{\text{dimethyl acetylenedicarboxylate}}{H_3CO_2C{-}C{\equiv}C{-}CO_2CH_3}$$

The equilibrium usually lies on the side of the ester and can be shifted further to the right by simultaneous distillation of the water with benzene or toluene. Phenols react too slowly, and the equilibrium lies far to the left.

### 14-19 ACID CHLORIDES

Of the acyl halides, the chlorides are most commonly employed in synthetic work. They are prepared by the direct reaction of an acid with thionyl chloride, $SOCl_2$, or phosphorus pentachloride, $PCl_5$.

*General*: $$R{-}\overset{\overset{\large O}{\|}}{C}{-}OH \xrightarrow{SOCl_2} R{-}\overset{\overset{\large O}{\|}}{C}{-}Cl + SO_2\uparrow + HCl\uparrow$$

*Specific*: $$\underset{\alpha\text{-naphthoic acid}}{C_{10}H_7{-}COOH} \xrightarrow{SOCl_2} \underset{\alpha\text{-naphthoyl chloride}}{C_{10}H_7{-}COCl} + SO_2\uparrow + HCl\uparrow$$

Acid chlorides give esters on treatment with an alcohol or an alkoxide ion; both reactions are irreversible, affording an excellent method of esterifying valuable or unreactive acids. The hydrolysis of acid chlorides is also irreversible.

$$R{-}\overset{\overset{\large O}{\|}}{C}{-}Cl + R'{-}OH \longrightarrow R{-}\overset{\overset{\large O}{\|}}{C}{-}O{-}R' + HCl$$

$$R{-}\overset{\overset{\large O}{\|}}{C}{-}Cl + R'O^-Na^+ \longrightarrow R{-}\overset{\overset{\large O}{\|}}{C}{-}O{-}R' + Na^+Cl^-$$

### 14-20 ANHYDRIDES

The method of synthesis of anhydrides takes into account the type desired:

$$R{-}\overset{\overset{\displaystyle O}{\|}}{C}{-}O{-}\overset{\overset{\displaystyle O}{\|}}{C}{-}R \qquad R{-}\overset{\overset{\displaystyle O}{\|}}{C}{-}O{-}\overset{\overset{\displaystyle O}{\|}}{C}{-}R'$$

symmetrical unsymmetrical

Acetic anhydride, $CH_3{-}\overset{\overset{\displaystyle O}{\|}}{C}{-}O{-}\overset{\overset{\displaystyle O}{\|}}{C}{-}CH_3$, is useful in the preparation of other anhydrides and is usually prepared by a special method. Ketene, $CH_2{=}C{=}O$, is a very reactive molecule, which can be prepared by the pyrolysis of acetone; it will readily undergo Markownikoff addition to the $C{=}C$ bond. The addition of acetic acid (abbreviated HOAc) yields acetic anhydride, $Ac_2O$.

$$CH_3{-}\underset{\underset{\displaystyle O}{\|}}{C}{-}CH_3 \xrightarrow[\text{Fe wire heating element}]{700\text{-}750^\circ} CH_2{=}C{=}O + CH_4\uparrow$$

$$CH_2{=}C{=}O + CH_3{-}\overset{\overset{\displaystyle O}{\|}}{C}{-}OH \longrightarrow (CH_3CO)_2O$$

Write the expected product from the following:

1. ketene and water
2. ketene and ethanol

Other symmetrical anhydrides can be prepared from acetic anhydride and a carboxylic acid. If a desired anhydride and its acid boil higher than acetic acid, continuous removal of acetic acid from the refluxing reaction mixture containing these compounds will shift the equilibrium to the right.

$$\underset{\text{b.p. }186^\circ}{2CH_3(CH_2)_3COOH} + \underset{140^\circ}{CH_3\overset{\overset{\displaystyle O}{\|}}{C}{-}O{-}\overset{\overset{\displaystyle O}{\|}}{C}{-}CH_3} \overset{\Delta}{\rightleftharpoons} \underset{218^\circ}{CH_3{-}(CH_2)_3{-}\overset{\overset{\displaystyle O}{\|}}{C}{-}O{-}\overset{\overset{\displaystyle O}{\|}}{C}{-}(CH_2)_3CH_3} + \underset{118^\circ}{2CH_3COOH}$$

Unsymmetrical anhydrides can be formed irreversibly by the action of an acid chloride on the sodium salt of an acid.

$$R{-}\overset{\overset{\displaystyle O}{\|}}{C}{-}Cl + R'{-}\overset{\overset{\displaystyle O}{\|}}{C}{-}O^-Na^+ \longrightarrow R{-}\overset{\overset{\displaystyle O}{\|}}{C}{-}O{-}\overset{\overset{\displaystyle O}{\|}}{C}{-}R' + Na^+Cl^-$$

Cyclic anhydrides, especially those containing five- or six-membered rings, form readily when heat is applied to the corresponding diacid, which loses water.

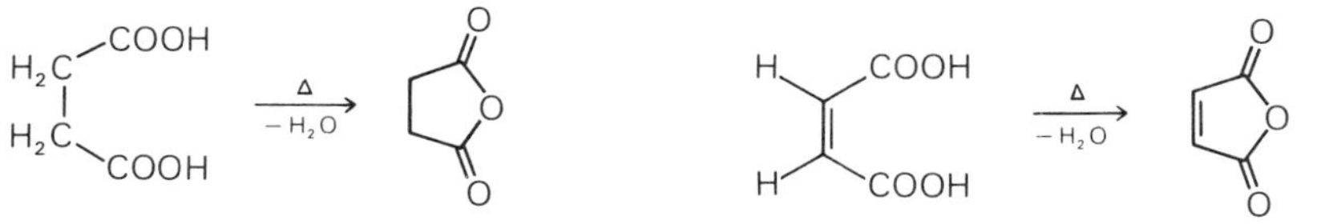

$$H_2C(COOH)-H_2C(COOH) \xrightarrow[-H_2O]{\Delta} \text{succinic anhydride} \qquad HC(COOH)=HC(COOH) \xrightarrow[-H_2O]{\Delta} \text{maleic anhydride}$$

succinic acid — succinic anhydride — maleic acid — maleic anhydride

> Recall the use of succinic anhydride in the Friedel-Crafts reaction (Sec. 7-9) and of maleic anhydride in the Diels-Alder reaction (Chap. 6). Give an example of each of these uses.

### 14-21 AMIDES

Amides can be formed by the action of ammonia, $NH_3$, primary amines, $R—NH_2$, and secondary amines, $R_2NH$, on the three acid derivatives discussed above, esters, acid chlorides, and anhydrides (see Table 14-4).

**Table 14-4 Examples of amide formation**

$$CH_3—\overset{O}{\overset{\|}{C}}—OCH_3 + NH_3 \longrightarrow CH_3—\overset{O}{\overset{\|}{C}}—NH_2 + CH_3OH$$

methyl acetate — acetamide

$$CH_3—\overset{O}{\overset{\|}{C}}—Cl + 2CH_3NH_2 \longrightarrow CH_3—\overset{O}{\overset{\|}{C}}—NH—CH_3 + HCl \xrightarrow{CH_3NH_2} CH_3\overset{+}{N}H_3Cl^-$$

acetyl chloride — methylamine — *N*-methylacetamide

$$CH_3—\overset{O}{\overset{\|}{C}}—O—\overset{O}{\overset{\|}{C}}—CH_3 + 2NH_3 \longrightarrow CH_3—\overset{O}{\overset{\|}{C}}—NH_2 + CH_3—\overset{O}{\overset{\|}{C}}—O^-NH_4^+$$

acetic anhydride — ammonium acetate

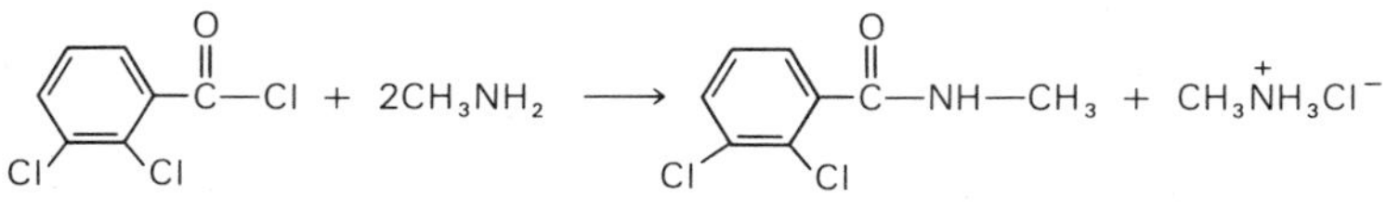

$$\text{2,3-}Cl_2C_6H_3—\overset{O}{\overset{\|}{C}}—Cl + 2CH_3NH_2 \longrightarrow \text{2,3-}Cl_2C_6H_3—\overset{O}{\overset{\|}{C}}—NH—CH_3 + CH_3\overset{+}{N}H_3Cl^-$$

2,3-dichlorobenzoyl chloride — 2,3-dichloro-*N*-methylbenzamide

Ammonium salts of carboxylic acids, $R—COO^-NH_4^+$, are converted to amides on pyrolysis.

$$R\text{—}COOH \xrightarrow{NH_4OH} R\text{—}COO^- NH_4^+ \xrightarrow{\Delta} R\text{—}\overset{O}{\overset{\|}{C}}\text{—}NH_2 + H_2O$$

## 14-22 IMIDES

Cyclic imides, which are nitrogen analogs of anhydrides,

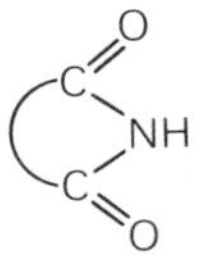

are the only ones discussed in this text. A few familiar examples are given here.

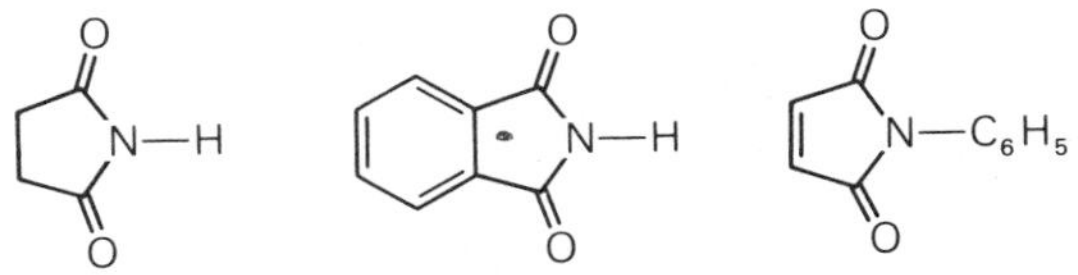

succinimide
recall NBS brominations

phthalimide
useful in amino acid syntheses

*N*-phenylmaleimide
used in Diels-Alder reactions

In order to avoid confusion concerning nomenclature, note the difference between acet*amide* and acet*imide* and between succin*amide* (a diamide) and succin*imide* (an imide).

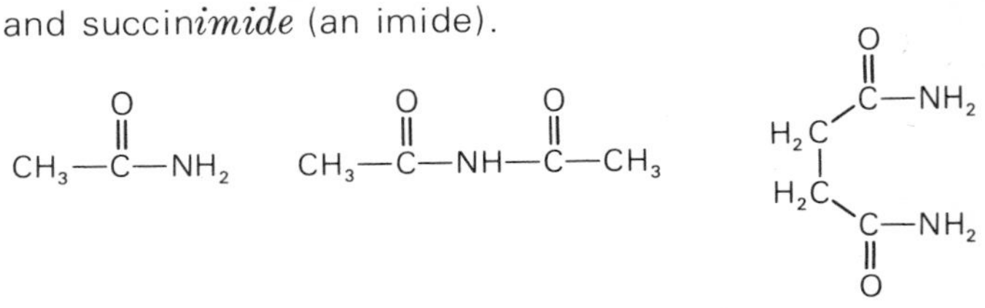

$$CH_3\text{—}\overset{O}{\overset{\|}{C}}\text{—}NH_2 \qquad CH_3\text{—}\overset{O}{\overset{\|}{C}}\text{—}NH\text{—}\overset{O}{\overset{\|}{C}}\text{—}CH_3$$

acet*amide* acet*imide* succin*amide*

## 14-23 NITRILES (CYANIDES)

Strictly speaking, nitriles are not directly related to the acid derivatives discussed above; i.e., they have no carbonyl group. In fact, since the cyanide ion reacts very much like a halide ion in inorganic reactions, it is called a ***pseudohalide***; nitriles might properly be discussed with organic halides. In addition to the hydrolysis of nitriles to amides and acids, nitriles can be prepared by the dehydration of amides with $P_2O_5$ or $SOCl_2$.

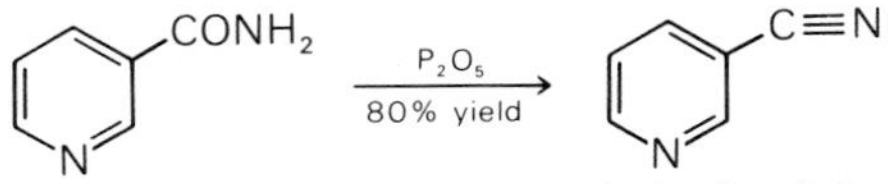

nicotinamide $\xrightarrow[\text{80\% yield}]{P_2O_5}$ nicotinonitrile

$$\underset{\text{diethyl fumarate}}{\overset{CH_3CH_2O_2C}{}\!\!\!\!\!\!\!\!\!\underset{H}{}C{=}C\overset{H}{\underset{CO_2CH_2CH_3}{}}} \xrightarrow[86\%\ \text{yield}]{NH_4OH} \underset{\text{fumaramide}}{\overset{H_2N{-}C(=O)}{}\!\!\!\!\!\!\underset{H}{}C{=}C\overset{H}{\underset{C(=O){-}NH_2}{}}}$$

fumaramide

$$\downarrow 80\%\ \text{yield},\ P_2O_5\ 200°$$

$$N{\equiv}C{-}CH{=}CH{-}C{\equiv}N$$

fumaronitrile

$$3\,CH_2(Cl){-}C(=O){-}NH_2 + P_2O_5 \xrightarrow[\text{in aromatic hydrocarbon solvent, 70\% yield}]{\Delta \text{ at } 170°} Cl{-}CH_2{-}C{\equiv}N + 2H_3PO_4$$

chloroacetonitrile

## SUGGESTED READINGS

Brown, H.C.: New Selective Reducing Agents, *J. Chem. Educ.*, **38**, 173 (1961).

Gibson, D.M.: The Biosynthesis of Fatty Acids, *J. Chem. Educ.*, **42**, 236 (1965).

Green, D. E.: The Synthesis of Fat, *Sci. Am.*, **202** (2), 46 (1960). Demonstrates the role of coenzyme A in forming fats in the body.

Hoogenboom, B.E.: Homolytic, Cationotropic, and Anionotropic Reactions, *J. Chem. Educ.*, **41**, 639 (1964). Includes a discussion of the ionization of various types of acids.

## PROBLEMS

**1.** (*a*) Give the structural formula and name of the 18 esters which can be made from the following starting materials ***and*** indicate a method of preparation other than simple Fischer esterification:

Alcohols: $CH_3OH$ $CH_3CH_2OH$ cyclohexanol (cyclohexyl–OH) benzyl alcohol ($C_6H_5CH_2OH$)

Phenols: phenol ($C_6H_5OH$) 2-naphthol (naphthyl–OH)

Acids: $CH_3CO_2H$ cyclopentanecarboxylic acid (cyclopentyl–$CO_2H$) benzoic acid ($C_6H_5CO_2H$)

(*b*) Indicate the synthesis of these three acids, using a different method of preparation for each.

(*c*) Indicate a synthesis of the acyl chloride derived from each acid.

(*d*) Indicate a synthesis for each anhydride which can be prepared from these three acids (nine anhydrides).

**2.** Indicate the preparation of the following compounds employing the alkylation of malonic ester, acetoacetic ester, cyanoacetic ester, or other active methylene compound at some point in the scheme.

★(*a*) $CH_3-CH_2-CH_2-CH(CH_3)-CONH_2$

★(*b*) $CH_3-CH_2-CH_2-CH(CH_2-CH_3)-CO-O-CO-CH(CH_2-CH_3)-CH_2-CH_2-CH_3$

(*c*) $(CH_3)_2CH-CO_2CH_3$

(*d*) Br–$C_6H_4$–$CH(CH_3)CO_2H$

★(*e*) $CH_3CH_2CH_2C(=N-NH-C_6H_5)-CH_3$

(*f*) $CH_3-C(Br)(CH_2-C_4H_7)-CO_2H$ (cyclobutylmethyl)

★(*g*) $CH_3-C_6H_4-CH_2-CH(CO_2CH_2CH_3)-C_6H_4-CH_3$

★**3.** Arrange the following compounds in order of decreasing acidity and justify your answer:

(*a*) cyclohexanol (OH); phenol (OH); $O_2N$–$C_6H_4$–$CO_2H$; $CH_3O$–$C_6H_4$–OH

(*b*) 1-chlorocyclopentanecarboxylic acid ($CO_2H$, Cl); 3,3-dichlorocyclopentanecarboxylic acid (Cl, Cl, $CO_2H$); 4-chlorocyclohexanecarboxylic acid (Cl, $CO_2H$)

(*c*) $C_6H_5-CH=CH-CO_2H$; NC–$C_6H_3$(CN)–$CH=CH-CO_2H$

$C_6H_5-CH=CH-C(CH_3)_2-CO_2H$

**4.** Give the structural formula and name of the starting material and structural formula of the product(s). If no reaction occurs, write N.R.

(*a*) diethyl diethylmalonate $\xrightarrow[\substack{2.\ H_3O^+ \\ 3.\ \Delta}]{1.\ OH^-}$

(*b*) *p*-bromobenzyl bromide + diethyl malonate (xs) $\xrightarrow[NaOEt]{1\ equiv}$

(*c*) diethyl sodiomalonate + 2-bromo-2-methylbutane $\longrightarrow$

★(*d*) *n*-heptanoic acid $\xrightarrow[\substack{3.\ H_3O^+ \\ 4.\ SOCl_2 \\ 5.\ NH_3}]{\substack{1.\ P;\ Br_2 \\ 2.\ alc.\ KCN}}$

(*e*) methyl cyanoacetate (xs) + *n*-butyl bromide $\xrightarrow{1\ equiv\ NaOEt}$

★(*f*) product in (*e*) + 3-phenyl-1-bromopropane $\xrightarrow{1\ equiv\ NaOEt}$

(*g*) product in (*f*) $\xrightarrow[2.\ H_3O^+]{1.\ conc.\ base}$

★(*h*) product in (*f*) $\xrightarrow[\substack{2.\ H_3O^+ \\ 3.\ \Delta}]{1.\ dil.\ OH^-}$

(*i*) silver cyclopentylcarboxylate $\xrightarrow{Br_2\ in\ dry\ CCl_4}$

(*j*) product in (*i*) $\xrightarrow[KCN]{alc.}$

★(*k*) 2,6-dimethylbenzoic acid $\xrightarrow[H^+]{CH_3OH}$

(*l*) acetone $\xrightarrow[Fe\ wire]{700°}$

(*m*) product in (*l*) + isobutyric acid

★(*n*) ammonium phenylacetate $\xrightarrow{\Delta}$

(*o*) product in (*n*) $\xrightarrow{P_2O_5}$

(*p*) potassium *O*-acetylsalicylate $\xrightarrow{KHCO_3}$

★(*q*) 2,6-dichlorotoluene $\xrightarrow{KMnO_4}$

★(*r*) 4,5-dimethyl-1-acetonaphthalene $\xrightarrow[2.\ H_3O^+]{1.\ I_2;\ KOH}$

★(*s*) 3,5-dimethylbromobenzene $\xrightarrow[\substack{3.\ H_3O^+ \\ 4.\ SOCl_2 \\ 5.\ NH_3 \\ 6.\ P_2O_5}]{\substack{1.\ Mg\ in\ dry\ THF \\ 2.\ Dry\ Ice}}$

# Chapter Fifteen

Simple relationships between carboxylic acids and their derivatives were presented in Chap. 14. This chapter examines each of these classes of organic compounds in greater detail. The occurrence in nature of esters (flavors and odors) and amides (proteins) increases the importance of these functional groups in our study. The more reactive functional groups, such as acid halides and anhydrides, enable the chemist to achieve certain chemical transformations of acid derivatives in the laboratory which do not readily occur with acids themselves.

Esters often have pleasing, well-defined odors which make them desirable as synthetic additives to certain foods and beverages.

$CH_3CO_2CH_2CH_2CH(CH_3)_2$
isopentyl acetate
odor of bananas

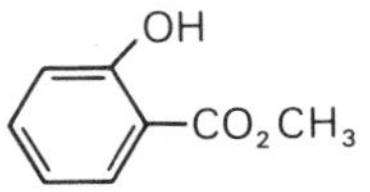

$o\text{-}HOC_6H_4CO_2CH_3$
methyl salicylate
odor of wintergreen

$CH_3CH_2CO_2CH_2CH(CH_3)_2$
isobutyl propionate
odor of rum

## ESTERS

All esters may be considered formally as being derived from the reaction of a carboxylic acid with an alcohol or phenol. In practice, certain esters must be prepared by a less direct route.

$$R\text{—}\overset{\overset{\displaystyle O}{\|}}{C}\text{—}OH + R'\text{—}OH \rightleftharpoons R\text{—}\overset{\overset{\displaystyle O}{\|}}{C}\text{—}O\text{—}R' + H_2O$$

The electronic distribution around the carbonyl group of acids is con-

# Derivatives of Carboxylic Acids: Esters, Acid Halides, Anhydrides, Amides, Nitriles

siderably different from that in aldehydes and ketones because of the participation of the unshared electrons on the adjacent oxygen atom.

Aldehydes and ketones: $\left[ -\overset{\overset{\displaystyle O}{\|}}{C}- \longleftrightarrow -\overset{\overset{\displaystyle O^-}{|}}{\underset{+}{C}}- \right]$

Esters: $\left[ -\overset{\overset{\displaystyle O}{\|}}{C}-\ddot{\underset{..}{O}}- \longleftrightarrow -\overset{\overset{\displaystyle O^-}{|}}{C}=\underset{\underset{+}{..}}{O}- \right]$

The carbonyl carbon in esters is not nearly as susceptible to nucleophilic attack, although strong nucleophiles can achieve displacements. Resonance structures like those for the ester group can be written for other acid derivatives with unshared electrons on the atom adjacent to the carbonyl group, such as acid halides R—CO—$\ddot{\underset{..}{Cl}}$: and amides R—CO—$\ddot{N}H_2$.

## NOMENCLATURE OF ESTERS

The names of esters are written as two words. The first is derived from the alcohol or phenol portion (naming this as an ***alkyl*** alcohol or ***phenyl*** alcohol); the second is taken from the acid name, from which the suffix -***ic*** is dropped and -***ate*** is added. For example, $CH_3CO_2CH_3$ is named methyl acetate. See Table 15-1.

**Table 15-1 Examples of ester nomenclature**

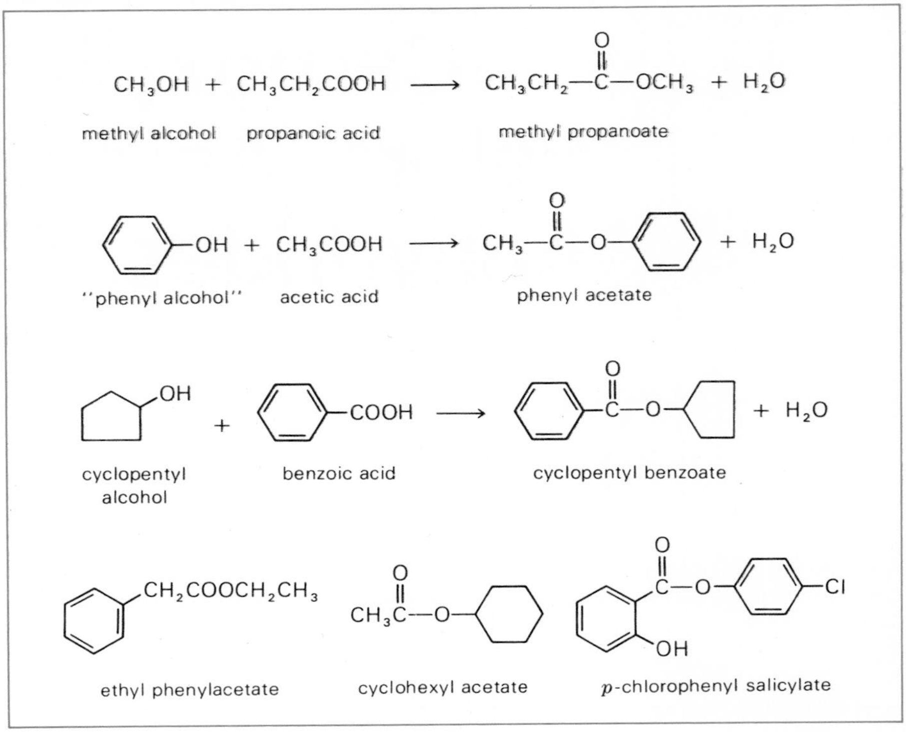

$$CH_3OH + CH_3CH_2COOH \longrightarrow CH_3CH_2-\overset{O}{\overset{\|}{C}}-OCH_3 + H_2O$$

methyl alcohol — propanoic acid — methyl propanoate

$$C_6H_5-OH + CH_3COOH \longrightarrow CH_3-\overset{O}{\overset{\|}{C}}-O-C_6H_5 + H_2O$$

"phenyl alcohol" — acetic acid — phenyl acetate

$$C_5H_9OH + C_6H_5COOH \longrightarrow C_6H_5-\overset{O}{\overset{\|}{C}}-O-C_5H_9 + H_2O$$

cyclopentyl alcohol — benzoic acid — cyclopentyl benzoate

$$C_6H_5CH_2COOCH_2CH_3 \qquad CH_3\overset{O}{\overset{\|}{C}}-O-C_6H_{11} \qquad o\text{-}HOC_6H_4\overset{O}{\overset{\|}{C}}-O-C_6H_4Cl$$

ethyl phenylacetate — cyclohexyl acetate — *p*-chlorophenyl salicylate

## PREPARATION OF ESTERS

### 15-1 FISCHER ESTERIFICATION

The simple, direct esterification of an acid with a primary or secondary alcohol usually proceeds satisfactorily by refluxing an excess of the alcohol as the reactant and solvent with the carboxylic acid in the presence of a few drops of concentrated sulfuric acid or hydrochloric acid.

$$R-COOH + R'-OH \overset{H^+}{\rightleftharpoons} R-COOR' + H_2O$$

This ***equilibrium*** reaction is known as a ***Fischer esterification***. Tertiary alcohols, in the presence of warm acid, undergo a ready dehydration; phenols react so slowly that other methods are preferable. Sterically hindered acids require another technique (Sec. 15-2).

Since the mechanism of Fischer esterification is reversible at every step in the process, devices which will shift the equilibrium to the side of the ester, e.g., the use of excess alcohol and removal of the water as it is formed, are used to maximize the yield.

*General*: $R{-}\overset{\displaystyle O}{\overset{\|}{C}}{-}OH + R'{-}OH \overset{H^+}{\rightleftharpoons} R{-}\overset{\displaystyle O}{\overset{\|}{C}}{-}OR' + H_2O$

*Overall*: $C_6H_5{-}COOH + CH_3OH \overset{H^+}{\rightleftharpoons} C_6H_5{-}COOCH_3 + H_2O$

*Mechanism*: $C_6H_5{-}\overset{\displaystyle O}{\overset{\|}{C}}{-}OH \overset{H^+}{\rightleftharpoons} \left[C_6H_5{-}\overset{+}{C}(OH){-}OH\right] \underset{CH_3\ddot{O}H}{\rightleftharpoons}$

$$\left[C_6H_5{-}C(OH)(OH){-}\overset{+}{O}(H)CH_3\right] \overset{-H^+}{\rightleftharpoons} \left[C_6H_5{-}C(OH)(OH){-}OCH_3\right] \overset{+H^+}{\rightleftharpoons}$$

$$\left[C_6H_5{-}C(\overset{+}{O}H_2)(OH){-}OCH_3\right] \xrightarrow[-H_2O]{-H^+} C_6H_5{-}\overset{\displaystyle O}{\overset{\|}{C}}{-}OCH_3$$

The formulation of this mechanism has been aided by the use of $CH_3{}^{18}OH$. Note that the ***alkyl oxygen atom of the alcohol*** is the one to which the acyl group is bonded in the ester.

$$C_6H_5{-}COOH + CH_3{}^{18}OH \overset{H^+}{\rightleftharpoons} C_6H_5{-}\overset{\displaystyle O}{\overset{\|}{C}}{-}{}^{18}OCH_3 + H_2O$$

> Suppose the starting benzoic acid had been prepared (via the Grignard reaction) from $C^{18}O_2$, in which both oxygen atoms were labeled. What percent of the original $^{18}O$ would be present in the methyl benzoate after esterification with $CH_3OH$?

## 15-2 ESTERIFICATION OF STERICALLY HINDERED ACIDS

A simple esterification method has been devised which is exceptionally suitable for sterically hindered carboxylic acids like ortho disubstituted benzoic acids. The organic acid is dissolved in concentrated sulfuric acid, and the resulting solution is poured slowly into cold anhydrous alcohol. Hindered acids do not undergo simple Fischer esterification because the required intermediate with a tetrahedral geometry cannot be readily formed. In the mechanism note that the formation of the acyl carbonium ion, which is resonance-stabilized, relieves steric strain in the starting acid.

*Overall*: 2,6-dimethylbenzoic acid $\xrightarrow[\text{2. dry cold } CH_3OH]{\text{1. cold conc. } H_2SO_4}$ methyl 2,6-dimethylbenzoate

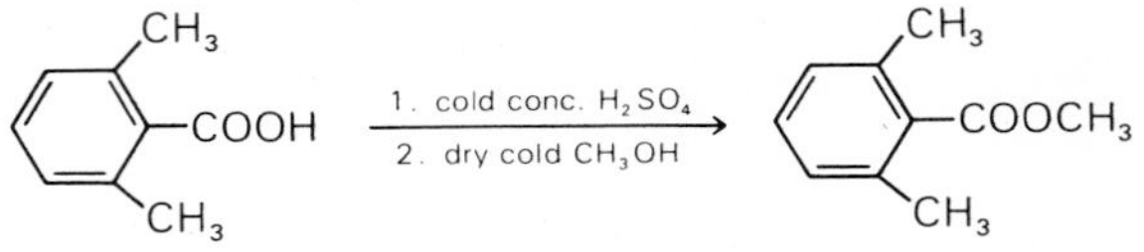

2,6-dimethylbenzoic acid — methyl 2,6-dimethylbenzoate

*Mechanism*

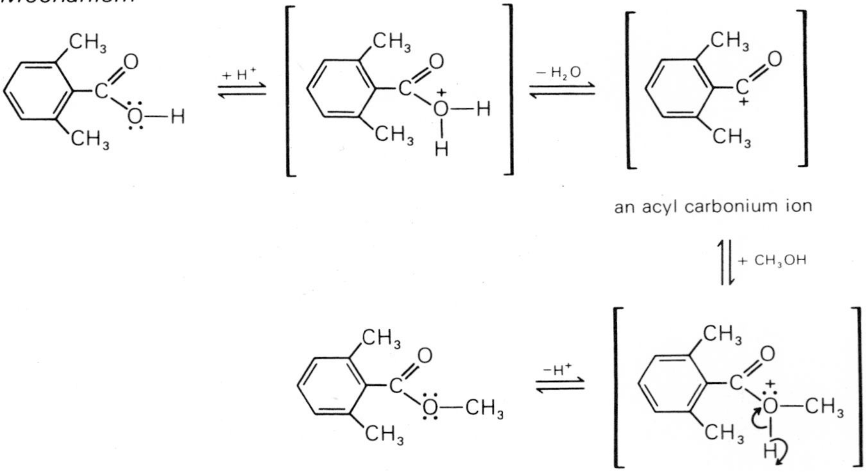

2,6-dimethylbenzoic acid $\underset{}{\overset{+H^+}{\rightleftharpoons}}$ [protonated acid, $C(=O)\overset{+}{O}H_2$] $\overset{-H_2O}{\rightleftharpoons}$ [acyl cation, $\overset{+}{C}=O$]

an acyl carbonium ion

$\Big\Updownarrow + CH_3OH$

methyl 2,6-dimethylbenzoate $\overset{-H^+}{\rightleftharpoons}$ [$C(=O)\overset{+}{O}(H)-CH_3$]

All the steps in this mechanism are reversible, and thus the hydrolysis of these hindered esters can be carried out by dissolving the ester in cold concentrated sulfuric acid and pouring the mixture into ice water.

## 15-3 ESTERIFICATION OF PHENOLS

The direct reaction of a phenol with a carboxylic acid in the presence of mineral acid proceeds ***very slowly*** to give the ester, and, furthermore, the equilibrium usually lies far to the side of the starting materials. More reactive acid derivatives, such as acid chlorides or anhydrides, must be employed. Alcohols also undergo esterification with acid chlorides and anhydrides (Secs. 15-16 and 15-21).

*Overall*

$$R-\overset{O}{\overset{\|}{C}}-Cl + Ar-OH \longrightarrow R-\overset{O}{\overset{\|}{C}}-O-Ar + HCl$$

*Mechanism*: $R-\overset{O}{\overset{\|}{C}}-Cl + Ar-\ddot{O}-H \rightleftharpoons \left[ R-\overset{O^-}{\overset{|}{C}}(-Cl)-\overset{+}{O}(H)Ar \right]$

$\rightleftharpoons -H^+$

$R-\overset{O}{\overset{\|}{C}}-O-Ar + Cl^- \xleftarrow[\text{step}]{\text{irreversible}} \left[ R-\overset{O^-}{\overset{|}{C}}(-Cl)-O-Ar \right]$

The equilibrium in this case lies far to the side of the ester and is not reversed by the addition of hydrogen chloride to the ester. Chloride ion, a poor nucleophile, will not readily attack the ester carbonyl group.

The use of cyclic anhydrides and ***alcohols*** leads first to the half ester, which is converted to the diester on further reaction with alcohol. The usefulness of this reaction is shown in the following example, in which the anhydride is converted to the half ester acid chloride, which can be used in Friedel-Crafts acylation reactions.

$$\text{succinic anhydride} \xrightarrow[\text{95\% yield}]{\text{1 equiv } CH_3OH} \begin{array}{l} CH_2-\overset{O}{\overset{\|}{C}}-OCH_3 \\ | \\ CH_2-\underset{O}{\underset{\|}{C}}-OH \end{array} \xrightarrow[\text{90\% yield}]{SOCl_2} \begin{array}{l} CH_2-\overset{O}{\overset{\|}{C}}-OCH_3 \\ | \\ CH_2-\underset{O}{\underset{\|}{C}}-Cl \end{array}$$

succinic anhydride — methyl hydrogen succinate — β-carbomethoxypropionyl chloride

Phenols, on the other hand, react with anhydrides, affording only the monoester; the diester is not obtained even on treatment with excess phenol.

## 15-4 ESTERS FROM ACID SALTS AND ALKYL HALIDES

The carboxylate anion, like other anions discussed in Sec. 8-7, can cause an $S_N2$ displacement with primary or secondary alkyl halides. Tertiary halides cannot be used because of competing elimination and substitution reactions. When the silver carboxylates are used, there is an additional driving force for the esterification, namely, the formation of an insoluble silver halide.

$$\text{R—COOH} \xrightarrow[\text{Ag}_2\text{O}]{\text{moist}} \text{R—COO}^-\,\text{Ag}^+ \xrightarrow[S_N2]{\text{R'—X}} \text{R—}\overset{\text{O}}{\overset{\|}{\text{C}}}\text{—O—R'} + \text{AgX}\downarrow$$

## 15-5 METHYL ESTERS VIA DIAZOMETHANE

Unlike the reversible equilibrium conditions employed in the Fischer esterification, the use of diazomethane, $CH_2N_2$, to form the methyl ester is an ***irreversible reaction*** because nitrogen gas is evolved.

$$m\text{-}CH_3O\text{—}C_6H_4\text{—COOH} \xrightarrow{CH_2N_2} m\text{-}CH_3O\text{—}C_6H_4\text{—COOCH}_3 + N_2\uparrow$$

*m*-methoxybenzoic acid — methyl *m*-methoxybenzoate

The ester is often obtained directly in a highly pure state and in excellent yield. Other related diazo alkyl compounds have not been extensively used for the formation of higher alkyl esters because of numerous competing reactions of the larger diazo compounds.

It should be noted that the effectiveness of diazomethane in forming a methyl ester lies in the acidity of the carboxyl hydrogen atom. Other compounds containing an acidic proton will also undergo reaction. Phenols, for instance, afford the corresponding methyl ether. Alcohols, although they generally require an acid catalyst, such as $BF_3$, to enhance the acidity of the —OH proton, will undergo reaction with diazomethane, to give the methyl ether.

# REACTIONS OF ESTERS

## 15-6 HYDROLYSIS (REVERSE OF ESTERIFICATION) AND SAPONIFICATION

The acid-catalyzed hydrolysis of an ester is a reversible reaction; the mechanism is the reverse of the simple Fischer esterification, starting with water, mineral acid, and the ester (Sec. 15-1).

On the other hand, when base is used, the reaction is not reversible, and the carboxylate salt formation requires a full equivalent of the base. This reaction is known as ***saponification***, the process of making soap, since the salts of higher carboxylic acids are, indeed, soaps. In the saponification reaction a separate acidification step (mineral acid) is necessary in order to obtain the carboxylic acid itself from the reaction mixture.

*Overall*: $CH_3COOCH_3 \xrightarrow{Na^+\ OH^-} CH_3COO^-Na^+ + CH_3OH$

methyl acetate — sodium acetate — methanol

*Mechanism*: $CH_3{-}\overset{\overset{O}{\|}}{C}{-}OCH_3 + OH^- \rightleftharpoons \left[ CH_3{-}\overset{\overset{O^-}{|}}{\underset{\underset{OCH_3}{|}}{C}}{-}OH \right]$

$$\downarrow$$

$CH_3COO^-Na^+ + CH_3OH \longleftarrow [CH_3O^- + CH_3COOH]$

strong base — weak acid

### 15-7 AMMONOLYSIS: AMIDE FORMATION

The reaction of compounds with ammonia is called ***ammonolysis*** (compare with hydrolysis). In the case of esters, this leads to amides; primary and secondary amines, $R{-}NH_2$ and $R_2NH$, can also be used.

$CH_3COOCH_3 + \ddot{N}H_3\ (xs) \longrightarrow CH_3CONH_2 + CH_3OH$

> Considering the mechanisms previously described in this chapter, formulate a reasonable mechanism for ammonolysis of esters.

### 15-8 TRANSESTERIFICATION

Treatment of an ester with an alcohol (different from that in the starting ester) may cause an ester exchange to take place; this is called ***trans-esterification***. Since the simple Fischer esterification of acids with alcohols is a reversible reaction, it is possible to cause transesterification by heating the ester with an excess of another alcohol.

*General*: $R{-}\overset{\overset{O}{\|}}{C}{-}OR' + R''{-}OH \overset{H^+}{\rightleftharpoons} R{-}\overset{\overset{O}{\|}}{C}{-}OR'' + R'{-}OH$

*Specific*: $o\text{-}CH_3C_6H_4{-}COOC(CH_3)_3 + CH_3OH \overset{H^+}{\rightleftharpoons} o\text{-}CH_3C_6H_4{-}COOCH_3 + (CH_3)_3COH$

*tert*-butyl *o*-toluate — methyl *o*-toluate

Since transesterification is an equilibrium reaction, some strong driving force is necessary in order to allow the reaction to proceed mainly to the right; otherwise, a mixture of compounds will result. The necessary shift in equilibrium can be obtained by the formation of a more stable ester (because of less steric hinderance in the above example), by the use of an excess of the alcohol, or by the removal of the ester or alcohol as it is formed. In the following example the methanol-methyl acrylate mixture is the lowest-boiling component (b.p. 62-63°).

$$CH_2{=}CHCOOCH_3 + CH_3CH_2CH_2CH_2OH \xrightleftharpoons[\text{90\% yield}]{\text{trace } H^+} CH_2{=}CHCOOCH_2CH_2CH_2CH_3 + CH_3OH$$

methyl acrylate b.p. 80° — *n*-butyl alcohol 117° — *n*-butyl acrylate 145° — methanol 65°, b.p. of mixture 62-63°

> The transesterification of methyl acrylate has been carried out in high yields using other alcohols. Formulate these reactions and name the ester formed.
>
> **1.** 2-ethylhexyl alcohol, 95%
>
> **2.** furfuryl alcohol, 86%
>
> **3.** allyl alcohol, 70%
>
> **4.** benzyl alchol, 81%

## 15-9 REDUCTION TO ALCOHOLS

One of the best methods for reducing esters to pure primary alcohols in high yield is the treatment of the ester in ether or THF with lithium aluminum hydride, followed by dilute acid hydrolysis. The stoichiometry is such that 1 mole of the reagent will reduce two ester groups. A further advantage of this reaction is that the intermediate salts, which must be hydrolyzed in a separate step, are usually soluble in these ester solvents.

$$C_6H_5{-}COOCH_2CH_3 \xrightarrow[\text{2. } H_3O^+ \text{ 90\% yield}]{\text{1. } LiAlH_4} C_6H_5{-}CH_2OH + CH_3CH_2OH$$

ethyl benzoate — benzyl alcohol

$$CH_3CH_2OOC{-}(CH_2)_4{-}COOCH_2CH_3 \xrightarrow[\text{2. } H_3O^+ \text{ 80\% yield}]{\text{1. } LiAlH_4} HOCH_2{-}(CH_2)_4{-}CH_2OH$$

diethyl adipate — 1,6-hexanediol

There are other useful methods of reduction, but often they are less reliable or convenient than the use of lithium aluminum hydride. For example, sodium metal in alcohol or catalytic reduction ($CuCr_2O_4$ catalyst at 250° and 3,000 to 4,000 psi of hydrogen) involve cheaper reagents and are often used in industrial processes. The catalytic reduction of diethyl adipate also affords an 80% yield of 1,6-hexanediol, but the hydride reduction is much more convenient on a small scale.

$$CH_3(CH_2)_7CH{=}CH(CH_2)_7COOCH_2CH_3 + 4Na + 3CH_3CH_2OH \xrightarrow{50\%\ yield}$$

ethyl oleate

$$CH_3(CH_2)_7CH{=}CH(CH_2)_7CH_2OH + 4CH_3CH_2ONa$$

9-octadecen-1-ol
(oleyl alcohol)

### 15-10 THE GRIGNARD REACTION

Treatment of an ester with two equivalents of a Grignard reagent gives tertiary alcohols in which at least two of the alkyl or aryl groups *must* be alike. Review this reaction in Sec. 9-16.

## ACID HALIDES: NOMENCLATURE AND PREPARATION

### 15-11 NOMENCLATURE OF ACID HALIDES

Acid halides, R—CO—X, are also known as *acyl halides*. (The following sections will be restricted mainly to the acid chlorides because they are the most commonly used.) These compounds are named as halide derivatives of the acyl group from which they are derived. Examples are shown in Table 15-2.

**Table 15-2 Examples of acid chloride nomenclature**

| Structure | Name |
|---|---|
| $CH_3—C(=O)—Cl$ | acetyl chloride |
| $C_6H_5—C(=O)—Cl$ | benzoyl chloride |
| $3,5-(O_2N)_2C_6H_3—C(=O)—Cl$ | 3,5-dinitrobenzoyl chloride |
| $CH_3CH_2CH_2C(=O)—Cl$ | butanoyl chloride |
| $C_{10}H_7—C(=O)—Cl$ | α-naphthoyl chloride |

### 15-12 PREPARATION OF ACID CHLORIDES

Acid chlorides are widely used in syntheses where the acid itself is not sufficiently reactive. Acids are converted to acid chlorides on treatment with thionyl chloride, $SOCl_2$. This is a very good method since the gaseous products (HCl and $SO_2$) are removed from the reaction mixture, thereby shifting the equilibrium. Excess thionyl chloride (b.p. 77°) is readily removed, giving the acid chloride in such a high state of purity that it often is used without further purification.

$$C_6H_5COOH + SOCl_2\ (xs) \xrightarrow{\Delta} C_6H_5COCl + SO_2\uparrow + HCl\uparrow$$

m.p. 122° b.p. 77° b.p. 197°

## REACTIONS OF ACID CHLORIDES

### 15-13 HYDROLYSIS

The hydrolysis of acid chlorides gives acids in high yield but is seldom used as a preparation of acids. (Why?) The hydrolysis is an irreversible reaction which can be carried out with water or aqueous hydroxide, the latter giving the carboxylate salt; the acid itself is obtained on acidification.

*Overall*: $$CH_3{-}\overset{O}{\overset{\|}{C}}{-}Cl + H_2O \xrightarrow[\text{fast}]{\text{usually}} CH_3{-}\overset{O}{\overset{\|}{C}}{-}OH + HCl$$

*Mechanism*: $$CH_3{-}\overset{O}{\overset{\|}{C}}{-}Cl + \ddot{O}H_2 \rightleftharpoons \left[CH_3{-}\underset{{}^{+}OH_2}{\overset{O^-}{\overset{|}{\underset{|}{C}}}}{-}Cl\right] \underset{}{\overset{-H^+}{\rightleftharpoons}} \left[CH_3{-}\underset{OH}{\overset{O^-}{\overset{|}{\underset{|}{C}}}}{-}Cl\right] \longrightarrow CH_3COOH + Cl^-$$

### 15-14 ANHYDRIDE FORMATION

Salts of carboxylic acids react irreversibly with acid halides to give anhydrides.

$$R{-}COO^-Na^+ + R'{-}CO{-}Cl \longrightarrow (R{-}CO){-}O{-}(CO{-}R') + Na^+Cl^-$$

Recall that acetic anhydride can be prepared from ketene and acetic acid; symmetrical anhydrides, in turn, are prepared from acetic anhydride and higher carboxylic acids (see Secs. 7-10 and 14-20).

This irreversible reaction of acid salts with acid halides is an excellent method for preparing mixed or unsymmetrical carboxylic anhydrides.

$$CH_3CH_2COO^-Na^+ + CH_3COCl \longrightarrow CH_3CH_2\overset{O}{\overset{\|}{C}}{-}O{-}\overset{O}{\overset{\|}{C}}CH_3 + Na^+Cl^-$$

sodium propionate — acetyl chloride — acetic propanoic anhydride

### 15-15 AMIDE FORMATION

Amides can be prepared by the reaction of ammonia, primary amines, or secondary amines with an acid chloride or with an ester. Tertiary amines form salts with acid chlorides but do not give amides. Two equivalents of ammonia or of the amine are required; the second equivalent reacts with the liberated HCl.

$$CH_3CH_2COCl + 2NH_3 \longrightarrow CH_3CH_2CONH_2 + NH_4Cl$$

propanoyl chloride — propanamide

$$C_6H_5{-}COCl + 2CH_3NH_2 \longrightarrow C_6H_5{-}CONH{-}CH_3 + CH_3NH_3{}^+Cl^-$$

benzoyl chloride — methylamine — *N*-methylbenzamide

### 15-16 ALCOHOLYSIS: ESTER FORMATION

Both alcohols and phenols react with acid chlorides, yielding the corresponding ester.

$$C_6H_5{-}CH{=}CH{-}COCl + C_6H_5{-}OH \xrightarrow[\text{yield}]{70\%} C_6H_5{-}CH{=}CH{-}COO{-}C_6H_5 + HCl$$

cinnamoyl chloride — phenol — phenyl cinnamate

### 15-17 ROSENMUND REDUCTION

The preparation of aldehydes by controlled reduction of acid chlorides is called the Rosenmund reduction (see Sec. 13-3).

$$C_6H_{11}{-}C_6H_4{-}\overset{O}{\overset{\|}{C}}{-}Cl \xrightarrow[\text{sulfur-quinoline poison}]{H_2/\text{Pd on }BaSO_4} C_6H_{11}{-}C_6H_4{-}CHO + HCl$$

*p*-cyclohexylbenzoyl chloride — *p*-cyclohexylbenzaldehyde

### 15-18 KETONES VIA DIALKYL CADMIUM COMPOUNDS

This preparation of ketones by reaction of dialkyl cadmium compounds with acid chlorides was discussed in Sec. 13-10. The organocadmium compounds are less reactive than the corresponding Grignard reagents from which they are prepared.

$$2[CH_3CH_2CH_2CH_2MgBr] + CdCl_2 \longrightarrow [(CH_3CH_2CH_2CH_2)_2Cd]$$

$$[(CH_3CH_2CH_2CH_2)_2Cd] + CH_3COCl \xrightarrow[\text{yield}]{75\%} CH_3COCH_2CH_2CH_2CH_3$$

methyl *n*-butyl ketone

$$(C_6H_5)_2Cd + C_6H_5COCl \xrightarrow[\text{yield}]{60\%} C_6H_5COC_6H_5$$

diphenylcadmium benzoyl chloride benzophenone

### 15-19 FRIEDEL-CRAFTS ACYLATIONS

Review Friedel-Crafts acylations in Sec. 7-9. Both acid chlorides and anhydrides are commonly used. Acid chlorides require 1.1 equiv of $AlCl_3$, whereas anhydrides, containing two carbonyl groups, require 2.1 equiv. Recall that each carbonyl group is complexed with 1 equiv of $AlCl_3$; the 0.1 equiv acts as a catalyst. The reaction with most monosubstituted benzenes gives primarily the para isomer.

$$C_6H_5Br + CH_3CH_2COCl \xrightarrow[\text{2. } H_3O^+]{\text{1. 1.1 equiv } AlCl_3 \text{ in } CS_2 \text{ or } C_6H_5NO_2} CH_3CH_2CO\text{—}C_6H_4\text{—}Br$$

bromobenzene propanoyl chloride *p*-bromophenyl ethyl ketone

### 15-20 QUALITATIVE TESTS

Acid halides usually produce an immediate precipitate of the silver halide with alcoholic silver nitrate, although other active halogen compounds (allyl, benzyl, and tertiary halides) also give a precipitate rapidly.

## ANHYDRIDES

### 15-21 CHEMISTRY OF ANHYDRIDES

Anhydrides are named from the acid or acids from which they are formally derived. Mixed anhydrides bear the name of each acid, the sim-

**Table 15-3 Examples of anhydride nomenclature**

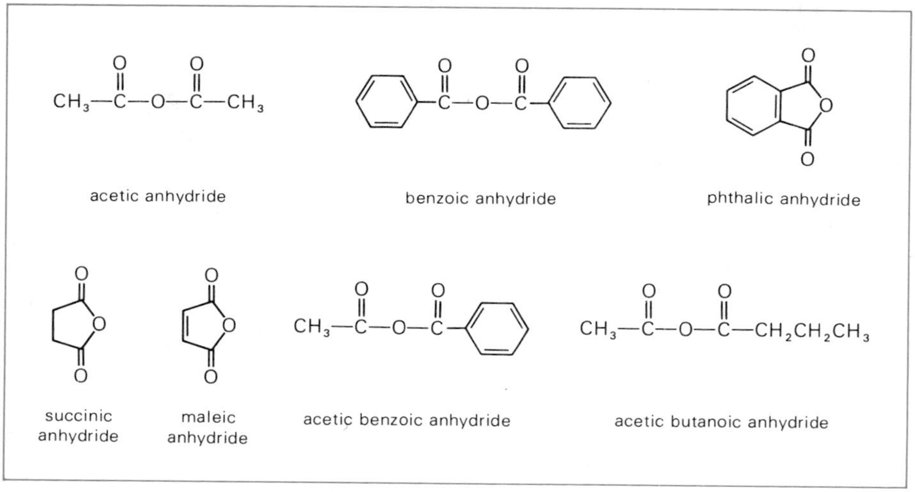

| Structure | Name |
|---|---|
| $CH_3-\overset{O}{\overset{\|}{C}}-O-\overset{O}{\overset{\|}{C}}-CH_3$ | acetic anhydride |
| $C_6H_5-\overset{O}{\overset{\|}{C}}-O-\overset{O}{\overset{\|}{C}}-C_6H_5$ | benzoic anhydride |
| (cyclic, benzene ring fused) | phthalic anhydride |
| (cyclic, saturated five-membered ring) | succinic anhydride |
| (cyclic, five-membered ring with C=C) | maleic anhydride |
| $CH_3-\overset{O}{\overset{\|}{C}}-O-\overset{O}{\overset{\|}{C}}-C_6H_5$ | acetic benzoic anhydride |
| $CH_3-\overset{O}{\overset{\|}{C}}-O-\overset{O}{\overset{\|}{C}}-CH_2CH_2CH_3$ | acetic butanoic anhydride |

> Most of the chemistry of the anhydride pertinent to the following two paragraphs has been covered previously in the sections noted. Write a representative example for each preparation and reaction described below. Write a reasonable mechanism for one of the anhydride reactions.

pler usually being written first. Examples are shown in Table 15-3.

Acetic and mixed acetic anhydrides can be prepared from ketene (Sec. 14-20); higher symmetrical anhdrides can be prepared from acetic anhydride (Sec. 7-10). In general, mixed anhydrides can be prepared from acyl halides and salts of organic acids (Sec. 15-14).

Anhydrides, like acid chlorides, readily undergo hydrolysis (Sec. 15-13), alcoholysis (Sec. 15-16), and ammonolysis with ammonia, primary amines, and secondary amines (Sec. 15-15).

## 15-22 NAPHTHALENE SYNTHESES USING SUCCINIC ANHYDRIDE

The Friedel-Crafts acylation of benzene and its derivatives with succinic anhydride, followed by other transformations including ring closure, affords an excellent synthetic procedure for naphthalene derivatives which cannot be prepared by direct substitution of naphthalene or its derivatives. The basic five-step scheme is illustrated by the preparation of 1-methyl-7-bromonaphthalene; however, the scope of this synthesis is much greater, as shown by a consideration of possible variations.

step 1: succinoylation
1. 2.1 equiv $AlCl_3$
2. $H_3O^+$

step 2: reduction
Zn(Hg)/HCl

step 3: ring closure liquid anhyd. HF or polyphosphoric acid

step 4: Grignard elaboration
1. $CH_3MgI$
2. $H_3O^+$

$\Delta$, $-H_2O$

step 5: aromatization
S or Se

may spontaneously dehydrate during isolation

## Variations in the naphthalene synthesis

*Step* 1: Any aromatic compound, including higher polycyclic aromatic compounds, which will undergo Friedel-Crafts acylation can be used in the initial succinoylation. The position taken by the incoming succinoyl group is determined by the substitution pattern of the aromatic system. The yields are generally fair to good; in the above case, the product is obtained in 75% yield by using excess bromobenzene as the solvent.

*Step* 2: The Clemmenson reduction (Sec. 13-12), as shown above, is commonly used in this step. Instead of reducing this carbonyl function, the succinoylated aromatic compound (keto acid) can be treated with an ***excess*** of a Grignard reagent, dehydrated, and subsequently hydrogenated. The excess quantity of the Grignard reagent is necessary because of the presence of the active hydrogen atom of the carboxyl group, —COOH. For example, suppose we carry through such a variation with $C_6H_5MgBr$ on the case cited above. After such a variation, the next step is ring closure.

$C_6H_5MgBr$ (xs)

$+ C_6H_6$

$H_3O^+$ (xs)
$\Delta$; $-H_2O$

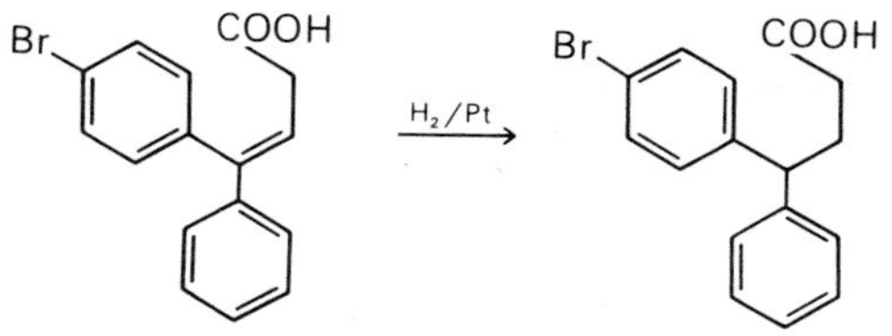

Br COOH $\xrightarrow{H_2/Pt}$ Br COOH

*Step* 3: At least three different methods are used to achieve this ring closure. One of the best is to dissolve the acid in liquid anhydrous hydrogen fluoride (in the hood!). One difficulty is the danger involved in handling hydrogen fluoride, which must be used in platinum, copper, or plastic flasks or beakers since it reacts with glass ($HF + SiO_2 \longrightarrow SiF_4 + H_2O$). Nevertheless, yields are usually in the range of 80 to 90%; side reactions are few.

Probably the best method is to dissolve the organic acid in polyphosphoric acid (PPA), i.e., phosphoric acid to which additional phosphorus pentoxide has been added. This is an excellent dehydrating agent, and the procedure is readily carried out in a beaker at steam-bath temperatures.

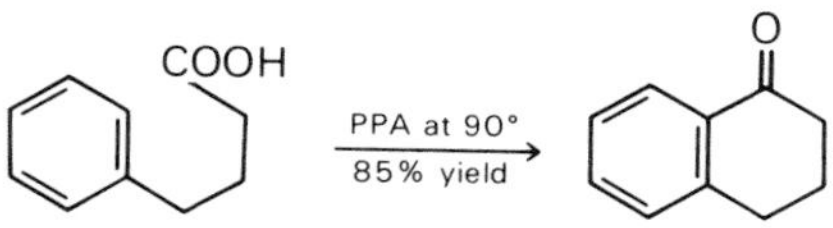

COOH $\xrightarrow[\text{85\% yield}]{\text{PPA at 90°}}$ O

$\gamma$-phenylbutyric acid $\qquad$ $\alpha$-tetralone

A third method, used in the past, is an internal Friedel-Crafts reaction. The acid is converted to the acid chloride with $SOCl_2$; this is then treated with $AlCl_3$; and finally the reaction mixture is hydrolyzed with dilute mineral acid. This rather tedious three-step procedure has been replaced, for the most part, by the two methods discussed above.

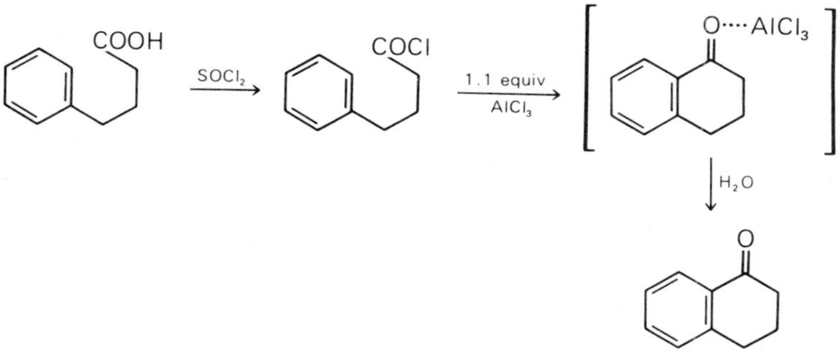

COOH $\xrightarrow{SOCl_2}$ COCl $\xrightarrow[AlCl_3]{\text{1.1 equiv}}$ [O····$AlCl_3$] $\xrightarrow{H_2O}$ O

*Step* 4: This step, of course, can be omitted. In the first example it gives rise to 2-bromonaphthalene after reduction and aromatization, thus affording a method of introducing a substituent into the $\alpha$ position of the newly formed naphthalene.

α-tetralone + [$C_6H_5$MgBr] $\xrightarrow[H_2O]{then}$ (HO, $C_6H_5$) $\xrightarrow[-H_2O]{acetic\ anhydride}$ ($C_6H_5$) $\xrightarrow{S;\ \Delta,\ -H_2S}$

1-phenylnaphthalene
40% overall yield
based on α-tetralone

*Step* 5: This dehydrogenation or aromatization step using sulfur or selenium is a standard one, although other dehydrogenating agents or hydrogen acceptors have been used.

In attempting to devise syntheses of naphthalenes by the above method, do not be misled by the way in which the naphthalene is oriented on the page. First, ascertain what benzene aromatic substrate is needed as a starting material by noting that Grignard elaborations (at steps 2 and 4) place substituents *only* in α positions of the final naphthalene. With this scheme, β substituents must come from the original aromatic compounds, although (final) α substituents of naptha-lene can also be present in the starting benzene derivative. Finally, note that a functional group which has been carried through this entire scheme may then undergo further reactions. For example, a final elaboration of the first case cited above might be carried out on the bromine atom.

(Br, $CH_3$) $\xrightarrow[2.\ CO_2\quad 3.\ H_3O^+]{1.\ Mg\ in\ dry\ ether}$ (HOOC, $CH_3$)

Devise reasonable syntheses of the following compounds:

(*a*) ($H_3C$, $CH_2CH_3$) (*b*) ($CH_3$, $H_3C$) (*c*) ($CH_3$)

# AMIDES

## 15-23 AMIDE NOMENCLATURE

The amide nomenclature is based on the name of the acid from which it is formally derived. The *-oic* acid ending is dropped, and the *-amide* is added. Substituents on the amide nitrogen atom are often denoted by $N$ (see Table 15-4).

**Table 15-4 Examples of amide nomenclature**

| Structure | Name |
|---|---|
| $H—C(=O)—NH_2$ | formamide |
| $H—C(=O)—N(CH_3)_2$ | $N,N$-dimethylformamide (DMF) |
| $CH_3—C(=O)—NH_2$ | acetamide |
| $CH_3CH_2CH_2CH_2CONH_2$ | pentanamide |
| $C_6H_{11}—CO—NH—CH_2CH_3$ | $N$-ethylcyclohexanecarboxamide |
| $H_2N—C(=O)—CH_2—CH_2—C(=O)—NH_2$ | succinamide |
| $C_6H_4(CONH_2)_2$ | phthalamide |
| $O_2N—C_6H_4—CONH_2$ | $p$-nitrobenzamide |
| $C_6H_5—NH—CO—CH_3$ | acetanilide |

# PREPARATION OF AMIDES

## 15-24 FROM ACID DERIVATIVES

Amides can be prepared from the reaction of esters, acid halides, and anhydrides with ammonia and with primary or secondary amines (Secs. 15-7, 15-15, and 15-21). The pyrolysis of dry ammonium salts, from the reaction of carboxylic acids with ammonium hydroxide, is a convenient method of amide formation.

$$CH_3CH_2COOH \xrightarrow{NH_4OH} CH_3CH_2COO^-NH_4^+ \xrightarrow{\Delta;\ \text{dry salt}} CH_3CH_2CONH_2$$

> Illustrate each of the above nine ammonolysis reactions with a specific example. Name the starting material and product.

### 15-25 HYDROLYSIS OF NITRILES

Although the total hydrolysis of nitriles (cyanides) gives carboxylic acids, the intermediate amide can often be isolated in excellent yield. The nitrile is dissolved in concentrated sulfuric or hydrochloric acid, the solution is allowed to stand at room (or slightly higher) temperature, and finally the mixture is poured onto crushed ice.

$$C_6H_5-CH_2CN \xrightarrow[\text{40°; 1 hr. 80\% yield}]{HCl;\ H_2O} C_6H_5-CH_2CONH_2$$

benzyl cyanide — phenylacetamide

### 15-26 BECKMANN REARRANGEMENT OF OXIMES

Hydroxylamine, $H_2N—OH$, reacts with ketones to give oximes. Two stereoisomers are possible, but the major product is usually the oxime in which the larger alkyl (or aryl) group is anti to the —OH (see Sec. 13-14).

$$RR'C=O + H_2\ddot{N}—OH \longrightarrow RR'C=\ddot{N}—OH + H_2O$$

R'— larger than R- — ketoxime

Ketoximes give amides on treatment either with concentrated sulfuric acid or $PCl_5$; this reaction is known as the ***Beckmann rearrangement.***

$$RR'C=\ddot{N}—OH \xrightarrow[\text{rearrangement}]{PCl_5 \text{ or } H_2SO_4} R—\overset{O}{\overset{\|}{C}}—NH—R'$$

Although the formation of two amides is possible, one is usually obtained as the major product; this is the amide derived from migration of the group anti to the —OH in the oxime. Although a variety of side products may be formed, the rearrangement of an aliphatic-aromatic ketoxime generally affords 80 to 90% yields of the amide expected from anti migration.

The acid-catalyzed mechanism follows.

$$R'RC=N—OH \underset{}{\overset{H^+}{\rightleftharpoons}} \left[R'RC=N—\overset{+}{O}H_2\right] \rightleftharpoons \left[R'\cdots C=N\cdots OH_2\right]^+ \longrightarrow$$

R' larger than R

$$\left[\begin{matrix} {}^{+}\mathrm{C}{=}\ddot{\mathrm{N}}\mathrm{-R'} \\ \mathrm{R}\ \ \ \ddot{\mathrm{O}}\mathrm{H_2} \end{matrix}\right] \longrightarrow \left[\begin{matrix} \mathrm{R}\diagdown\mathrm{C}{=}\ddot{\mathrm{N}}\diagup\mathrm{R'} \\ \mathrm{H_2}\overset{+}{\mathrm{O}} \end{matrix}\right] \xrightleftharpoons{-\mathrm{H^+}} \left[\begin{matrix} \mathrm{R}\diagdown\mathrm{C}{=}\ddot{\mathrm{N}}\diagup\mathrm{R'} \\ \mathrm{H{-}O} \end{matrix}\right]$$

amide
enol form

$$\rightleftharpoons$$

$$\mathrm{R{-}\overset{O}{\overset{\|}{C}}{-}NH{-}R'}$$

keto form

*Example*:

$$\mathrm{C_6H_5{-}\overset{*}{C}H(CH_3){-}\overset{\ddot{N}{-}OH}{\overset{\|}{C}}{-}CH_3} \xrightarrow{H_2SO_4} \mathrm{C_6H_5{-}\overset{*}{C}H(CH_3){-}NH{-}\overset{O}{\overset{\|}{C}}{-}CH_3}$$

L isomer L isomer

Note that there is a simultaneous migration of the larger group from carbon to nitrogen and loss of water. This leads to ***retention*** of configuration in the migration of an optically active carbon atom.

> Formulate the Beckmann rearrangement of the major ketoxime derived from each of these ketones:
>
> **1.** methyl ethyl ketone ⟶ *N*-ethylacetamide (80% yield with $PCl_5$)
>
> **2.** benzophenone ⟶ benzanilide (99% yield with HI)
>
> **3.** cyclohexanone ⟶ ϵ-caprolactam (90% yield with $H_2SO_4$)

## REACTIONS OF AMIDES

### 15-27 HYDROLYSIS

The hydrolysis of amides can be effected with either acid or base. With acid, the products are the carboxylic acid and the ammonium salt; with base, the products are the carboxylate salt and ammonia or the organic amine. Basic hydrolysis requires a separate acidification step in order to obtain the carboxylic acid itself. Similarly, amines are obtained from acid hydrolyses by making the solution basic.

$$R{-}\overset{\overset{\displaystyle O}{\|}}{C}{-}NHR' \xrightarrow{H_3O^+} R{-}COOH + R'{-}\overset{+}{N}H_3$$

$$R{-}\overset{\overset{\displaystyle O}{\|}}{C}{-}NHR' \xrightarrow[H_2O]{OH^-} R{-}CO\bar{O} + R{-}NH_2$$

### 15-28 NITRILES FROM DEHYDRATION

Phosphorus pentoxide, $P_2O_5$, is a strong dehydrating agent which is capable of converting amides to nitriles. The examples cited in Table 15-5 serve to illustrate the usefulness of this reaction. Recall that nitriles can also be prepared by treating halides with $CN^-$ (Sec. 8-7).

**Table 15-5 Examples of nitrile formation via amide dehydration**

General:

$$3R{-}\overset{\overset{\displaystyle O}{\|}}{C}{-}NH_2 + P_2O_5 \longrightarrow 3R{-}C{\equiv}N + 3H_3PO_4$$

Specific:

$$(CH_3)_2CHCOOH \xrightarrow[90\%\ yield]{SOCl_2} (CH_3)_2CHCOCl \xrightarrow[80\%\ yield]{NH_3} (CH_3)_2CHCONH_2$$

isobutyric acid → isobutyryl chloride → isobutyramide

$$\downarrow P_2O_5;\ 200° \quad (70\text{–}85\%\ yield)$$

$$(CH_3)_2CH{-}CN$$

isobutyronitrile

$$HOOC{-}(CH_2)_7{-}COOH \xrightarrow[\Delta]{NH_3} \left[ H_2N{-}\overset{\overset{\displaystyle O}{\|}}{C}{-}(CH_2)_7{-}\overset{\overset{\displaystyle O}{\|}}{C}{-}NH_2 \right]$$

azelaic acid → azelamide

$$\downarrow P_2O_5 \text{ or silica gel; } \Delta$$

$$NC{-}(CH_2)_7{-}CN$$

azelanitrile

65% yield overall (compare with the halide displacement reaction below)

$$Br{-}(CH_2)_7{-}Br \xrightarrow[80\%\ yield]{KCN} NC{-}(CH_2)_7{-}CN$$

1,7-dibromoheptane

## 15-29 REDUCTION TO AMINES

Excellent yields of primary, secondary, and tertiary amines are obtained by the reduction of amides with $LiAlH_4$.

$$C_6H_{11}CON(CH_3)_2 \xrightarrow[\text{2. } H_2O \text{ 90\% yield}]{\text{1. } LiAlH_4} C_6H_{11}CH_2N(CH_3)_2$$

*N,N*-dimethylcyclohexane-carboxamide — *N,N*-dimethylcyclohexylmethylamine

## 15-30 HOFMANN REACTION: PURE PRIMARY AMINES FROM AMIDES

The conversion of an unsubstituted amide to the next lower primary amine by means of hypohalite ion, $OX^-$, is called the ***Hofmann reaction***. Two common sources of the requisite hypohalite ion are strong base and halogen, such as NaOH-$Br_2$ or KOH-$Cl_2$, and *N*-bromosuccinimide (NBS) in aqueous base.

$$Br_2 + 2OH^- \longrightarrow Br^- + BrO^- + H_2O$$

$$\text{(succinimide)N—Br} + OH^- \longrightarrow \text{(succinimide)N—H} + OBr^-$$

The multistep mechanism contains several new mechanistic features which deserve further comment.

*Overall*:

$$C_6H_5—\overset{O}{\overset{\|}{C}}—NH_2 + OBr^- \xrightarrow[\text{yield}]{95\%} C_6H_5—NH_2 + CO_2 + Br^-$$

benzamide — aniline

*Mechanism*

Step 1:

$$C_6H_5—\overset{O}{\overset{\|}{C}}—NH_2 \xrightarrow{OBr^-} \left[C_6H_5—\overset{O}{\overset{\|}{C}}—NH—Br\right] + OH^-$$

*N*-bromobenzamide

Step 2:

$$\left[C_6H_5—\overset{O}{\overset{\|}{C}}—\ddot{N}(Br)H\right] + {}^-OH \longrightarrow \left[C_6H_5—\overset{O}{\overset{\|}{C}}—\ddot{N}:\right]$$

$$\downarrow$$

$$[O{=}C{=}\ddot{N}—C_6H_5] + H_2O$$

phenyl isocyanate

$$\text{Step 3:} \quad \left[ C_6H_5 \overset{\delta-}{-N} = \overset{\delta+}{C} = O \right] + H{-}OH \longrightarrow \left[ C_6H_5{-}NH{-}C\begin{matrix} {}^{\nearrow O} \\ {}_{\searrow OH} \end{matrix} \right]$$

unstable

$$\text{Step 4:} \quad \left[ C_6H_5{-}\ddot{N}(H){-}C(=O){-}O{-}H \right] + {}^{-}OH \longrightarrow \left[ C_6H_5{-}\ddot{N}H^{-} \right] + CO_2 \xrightarrow{H_2O} C_6H_5NH_2 + OH^{-}$$

*Step* 1: *N*-Haloamides are a well-known class of compounds formed by the action of halogen and base on amides.

$$\underset{\text{acetamide}}{CH_3CONH_2} \xrightarrow[\text{50\% yield}]{Br_2;\ KOH} \underset{N\text{-bromoacetamide}}{CH_3CONHBr}$$

Many of these compounds are used as free-radical halogenating agents in much the same way that NBS is (Sec. 8-3). The Hofmann reaction is often carried out without isolating and purifying the *N*-haloamide.

*Step* 2: Note that the intermediate involved in the isocyanate formation contains an uncharged but electron-deficient nitrogen atom with only six electrons around it. This intermediate rapidly rearranges by the shift of an alkyl or aryl group ***with its pair of electrons***.

*Step* 3: Isocyanates readily add water or alcohol forming carbamic acids, $>N{-}COOH$, or their esters, known as ***urethanes***. Polymers derived from these esters are plastics known as ***polyurethanes***.

*Step* 4: Although the *N*-carboxylic acid group (carbamic acids) is unstable with respect to carbon dioxide and the amine, the corresponding esters, urethanes, are stable. This base-catalyzed decarboxylation gives the amine anion, which reacts with water to give the amine.

Another example of the reaction is:

$$H_2N{-}CO{-}\overset{\alpha}{C}H_2{-}\overset{\beta}{C}H(CH_3){-}CH_2{-}CH_2{-}CO{-}NH_2$$

$\beta$-methyladipamide

$$\Big\downarrow \text{NaOBr} \quad 70\% \text{ yield}$$

$$H_2N{-}CH_2{-}CH(CH_3){-}CH_2{-}CH_2{-}NH_2$$

2-methyl-1,4-diaminobutane

### 15-31 SAPONIFICATION AND REACTIONS WITH NITROUS ACID

Amides are detected qualitatively by saponification, which liberates ammonia or the amine.

$$R{-}CONH_2 \xrightarrow{H_2O} R{-}COOH + NH_3$$

Amides also react with nitrous acid in a characteristic way; amides of primary amines liberate nitrogen, whereas monosubstituted amides afford the corresponding *N*-nitroso derivative.

$$R{-}CO{-}NH_2 + HONO \longrightarrow R{-}COOH + N_2\uparrow + H_2O$$

$$R{-}CO{-}NHR' + HONO \longrightarrow R{-}CO{-}N(NO){-}R' + H_2O$$

## NITRILES

### 15-32 NOMENCLATURE

Nitriles, also known as cyanides, are not direct derivatives of carboxylic acids since they do not contain the carboxyl group found in the other functional groups discussed in this chapter. However, their conversion to carboxylic acids and derivatives, discussed in this chapter and the previous one, justifies their inclusion here. Two systems of nomenclature are commonly used. Named as ***nitriles***, the compounds are denoted by the acid to which they can be hydrolyzed. Named as ***cyanides***, the alkyl or aryl name precedes the separate word cyanide (see Table 15-6).

**Table 15-6 Examples of nitrile nomenclature**

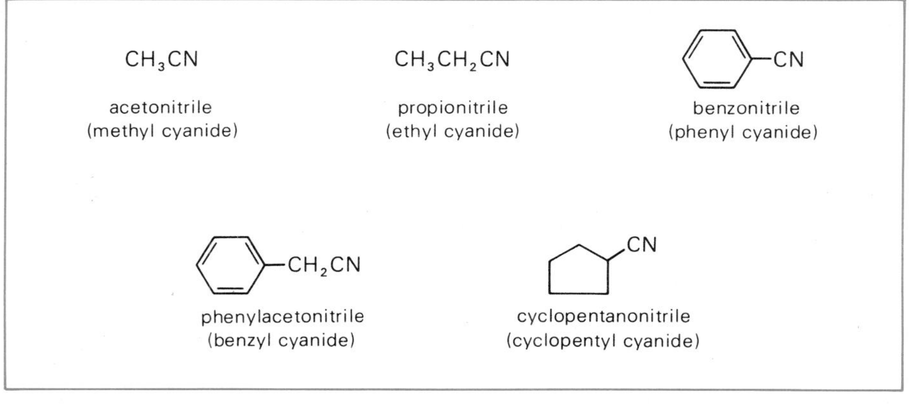

## PREPARATIONS AND REACTIONS OF NITRILES

The preparations and reactions of nitriles in the next two sections have been previously described where noted. Write a specific example illustrating each.

### 15-33 PREPARATION OF NITRILES

Primary and secondary alkyl halides and ***activated*** aromatic halides undergo $S_N2$ displacement by cyanide ion in alcohol (Secs. 8-7 and 8-10). Tertiary halides undergo elimination. Ordinary aromatic halides are unreactive toward simple displacement, but the conversion can be effected by using KCN and $Cu_2(CN)_2$ in pyridine (Sec. 8-9). Dehydration of unsubstituted amides gives nitriles (Sec. 15-28).

### 15-34 REACTIONS OF NITRILES

Nitriles undergo acid-catalyzed hydrolysis and basic saponification, yielding the acid or its salt (Sec. 14-8). The acid-catalyzed reaction can be stopped short of total hydrolysis and the amide can be isolated (Sec. 15-25). Reduction of nitriles with lithium aluminum hydride gives primary amines (Sec. 16-5). Nitriles undergo reaction with the Grignard reagent, but the reaction proceeds best when an aryl nitrile is treated with $CH_3MgX$; an aryl methyl ketone is formed after hydrolysis (Sec. 13-9).

## SUGGESTED READINGS

Amoore, J.E, J.W. Johnston, Jr., and M. Rubin: The Stereochemical Theory of Odor, *Sci. Am.*, **210** (2), 42 (1964). Suggests that there are seven basic odors based on geometries of the olfactory receptor nerve endings.

Caserio, M.C.: Reaction Mechanisms in Organic Chemistry, I. The Experimental Approach; II. The Reaction Intermediate, *J. Chem. Educ.*, **42**, 570, 627 (1965). An excellent presentation of the role of mechanisms in organic chemistry illustrated with many interesting examples.

Cash, R.V.: Nucleophilic Reactions at Trigonally Bonded Carbon, *J. Chem. Educ.*, **41**, 108 (1964).

Collier, H.O.J.: Aspirin, *Sci. Am.*, **209** (5), 96 (1963). Reviews the chemistry and effects of this widely used drug.

Hurd, C.D.: Acid Anhydride Functionality, *J. Chem. Educ.*, **44**, 454 (1967). Discusses the general concept of an anhydride, E═C(─)─E─C(─)═E, where E = O, S, N, and sometimes carbon.

Jacobson, M., and M. Beroza: Insect Attractants, *Sci. Am.*, **211** (2), 20 (1964). The chemical structure of some sex attractants and how they have been isolated.

Leisten, J.A.: Homogeneous Catalysis, *J. Chem. Educ.*, **41**, 23 (1964).

Roderick, W.R.: Current Ideas on the Chemical Basis of Olfaction, *J. Chem. Educ.*, **43**, 510 (1966). Discusses the relationship of size and structure to odors.

Rose, A.H.: New Penicillins, *Sci. Am.*, **204** (3), 66 (1961). Outlines the synthesis of penicillins with various side chains.

Sterrett, F.S.: The Nature of Essential Oils, I. Production; II. Chemical Constituents, Analysis, *J. Chem. Educ.*, **39**, 203, 246 (1962).

## PROBLEMS

**1.** Give the name or structural formula of each of the following esters and acid halides:

(*a*) cyclopropyl benzoate

★(*b*) *n*-hexyl hexanoate

(*c*) 3-ethyloctyl acetate

★(*d*) $CH_3—C_6H_4—CO_2CH_2CH_2—C_6H_5$

(*e*) [cyclobutyl]—O—CO—$C(CH_3)_3$

★(*f*) [benzene ring bearing $CO_2CH_3$, with $H_3C$, $CH_3$, $H_3C$, $CH_3$, $CH_3$ substituents]

(*g*) $C_6H_5CO_2C_6H_5$

(*h*) $CH_3O_2C(CH_2)_2CO_2CH_2CH_3$

★(*i*) $CH_3—C_6H_4COCl$

(*j*) $CH_3(CH_2)_8COBr$

(*k*) [naphthalene ring]—COCl

★(*l*) 3-methylhexanoyl chloride

(*m*) *p*-fluorobenzoyl fluoride

★(*n*) 2,4-dibromo-1-naphthoyl bromide

**2.** Give the name or structural formula of each of the following anhydrides and amides:

(*a*) $CH_3COOCOCH_2CH_2CH_3$

★(*b*) [phthalic anhydride ring with $O_2N$ substituent]

(*c*) [cyclic anhydride ring with two $H_3C$ substituents on C=C, two C=O and ring O]

★(*d*) propanoic para-*n*-propylbenzoic anhydride

(*e*) butanoic anhydride

(*f*) *α*-naphthoic *β*-naphthoic anhydride

★(*g*) Cl—[benzene ring]—$NHCOCH_3$

★(*h*) [benzene ring]—N(Cl)—CO—$CH_3$

(*i*) $C_6H_5$—NH—CO—$CH_2Cl$

★(*j*) 4,5-dichloro-1,2-benzenedicarboxamide ring structure: Cl, Cl, $CONH_2$, $CONH_2$

(*k*) *N,N*-dimethylhexanamide

(*l*) 2,3-dicyanobenzamide

★(*m*) 2,2-dimethylsuccinamide

(*n*) *N*-cyclohexylacetamide

**3.** Give the name or structural formula of each of the following imides and nitriles:

★(*a*) $CH_3CH_2CONHCOCH_2CH_3$

(*b*) $CH_3CH_2CH_2CH(OH)CH_2CN$

★(*c*) ring structure: $H_3C$–benzene fused to C(=O)–N–$CH_3$–C(=O) imide ring

(*d*) 2,3-dimethylsuccinimide

★(*e*) *p*-cyanobenzyl cyanide

(*f*) $\alpha$-cyanotoluene

★(*g*) heptanimide

(*h*) *N*-bromomaleimide

**4.** Give the structural formula (or name) of the starting material(s) and the structural formula and name of the product(s). If no reaction occurs, write N.R.

★(*a*) $C_6H_5CH_2COOH + CH_3CH_2CH_2CH_2OH \xrightarrow{H^+}$

(*b*) pentanoic acid $\xrightarrow{Ag_2O}$

(*c*) product in (*b*) + $CH_3CH_2CH_2CH{=}CH{-}CH_2Br \longrightarrow$

★(*d*) cyclopentane–COOH + $CH_2N_2 \longrightarrow$

(*e*) cyclopentanol + $CH_2N_2 \xrightarrow{H^+}$

(*f*) benzene ring with $CH_2COOCH_2CH_3$ and Cl (ortho) $\xrightarrow[H_2O]{NaOH}$

★(*g*) naphthalene with $CH_3$, Cl, $COOCH_3$ $\xrightarrow[2.\ H_3O^+]{1.\ LiAlH_4}$

(*h*) $(CH_3CH_2)_2CHCOOH + SOCl_2 \longrightarrow$

(*i*) product in (*h*) + $(CH_3)_2NH \longrightarrow$

(*j*) product in (*h*) + $CH_3CH(OH)CH_3 \longrightarrow$

★(*k*) $C_6H_5COO^-K^+$ + $CH_3COBr \longrightarrow$

(*l*) sodium phenoxide + $CH_3COBr \longrightarrow$

(*m*) $C_6H_5COCl$ + $C_6H_5COO^-Na^+ \longrightarrow$

★(*n*) $(CH_3)_2CH-C(=N-OH)-CH_3 \xrightarrow{H_2SO_4}$

(*o*) *N,N*-diethylcyclopentanecarboxamide $\xrightarrow[2.\ H_3O^+]{1.\ LiAlH_4}$

(*p*) succinimide $\xrightarrow[NaOH]{Br_2}$

**★5.** A student unfamiliar with organic mechanisms might attempt to carry out the following reactions. Explain why these are poor synthetic procedures and suggest a feasible route to the compound.

(*a*) 8-methyl-2-methyl-1-naphthalenecarboxylic acid (CH$_3$, COOH, CH$_3$ on naphthalene) $+ CH_3CH_2OH \xrightarrow{H^+}$ (CH$_3$, $COOCH_2CH_3$, CH$_3$ on naphthalene) $+ H_2O$

(*b*) $CH_3-C_6H_4-OH + CH_3COOH \xrightarrow{H^+} CH_3-C_6H_4-O-CO-CH_3 + H_2O$

(*c*) cyclopropyl$-COOH + NH_3 \longrightarrow$ cyclopropyl$-CONH_2 + H_2O$

(*d*) $CH_3CH_2CH_2CN \xrightarrow[H_2O;\ \Delta]{NaOH} CH_3CH_2CH_2CONH_2$

(*e*) $C_6H_5Br \xrightarrow{\text{KCN in alcohol}}$

**★6.** Show how the following compounds can be prepared starting with naphthalene, benzene, methanol, and succinic anhydride:

(*a*) [phenyl-substituted phenanthrene]

(*b*) [$H_3C$-substituted phenanthrene]

(*c*) [1-ethylnaphthalene, $CH_2CH_3$]

(*d*) [chrysene]

# Chapter Sixteen

This chapter brings to a close the detailed discussion of single functional groups usually found on aliphatic, aromatic, and heterocyclic systems. This does not mean that all the possible organic functional groups have been explored here; many have been omitted, others have been mentioned only briefly, and new ones are continually being synthesized.
compounds, which can be reduced to aromatic amines, (2) preparations and reactions of aliphatic, aromatic, and heterocyclic amines, and (3) the transformations of diazonium salts, $Ar—N_2^+X^-$, prepared from primary aromatic amines, $Ar—NH_2$.

## AROMATIC NITRO COMPOUNDS: IMPORTANT BUILDING BLOCKS OF SYNTHETIC AROMATIC CHEMISTRY

Recall that the nitro group is a polar, electron-attracting substituent; two resonance structures can be written

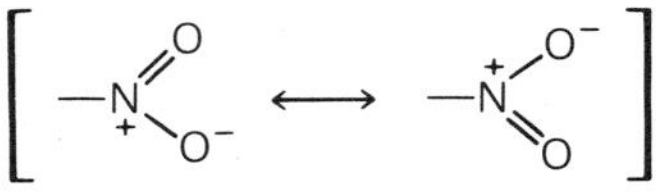

$$\left[ -\overset{+}{N}\begin{smallmatrix} \nearrow O \\ \searrow O^- \end{smallmatrix} \longleftrightarrow -\overset{+}{N}\begin{smallmatrix} \nearrow O^- \\ \searrow O \end{smallmatrix} \right]$$

In electrophilic aromatic substitution the nitro group is a strongly deactivating, meta-directing substituent. Many functional groups $Y$ can be introduced into an aromatic hydrocarbon by the following sequence:

$$Ar—H \longrightarrow Ar—NO_2 \longrightarrow Ar—NH_2 \longrightarrow \left[ Ar—N_2^+ \right] \longrightarrow Ar—Y$$

In this synthetic scheme, the aromatic nitro compounds are important intermediates.

# Amines and Diazonium Compounds

## 16-1 PREPARATION

Nearly all aromatic hydrocarbons, many of which are available directly from coal tar, can be nitrated by the action of nitric and sulfuric acids; however, the position taken by the incoming group depends on the individual substitution pattern of the hydrocarbon (Sec. 7-11).

$$\text{Ar—H} \xrightarrow[H_2SO_4]{HNO_3} \text{Ar—NO}_2$$

Because of the deactivating effect of one nitro group, dinitration is usually not a serious side reaction. Nitro isomers of many hydrocarbons are readily separated by fractional distillation, steam distillation, or fractional crystallization.

## 16-2 REACTIONS

Reduction of nitro compounds can produce a variety of products, depending on the reaction conditions and reducing agent employed; for example,

$$C_6H_5\text{—}NO_2 \xrightarrow{2[H]} C_6H_5\text{—}N{=}O \xrightarrow{2[H]} C_6H_5\text{—}N(H)\text{—}OH \xrightarrow{2[H]} C_6H_5\text{—}NH_2$$

nitrobenzene nitrosobenzene *N*-phenylhydroxylamine aniline

Here we shall discuss only the total reduction of nitro compounds in acid solution, which gives the amino functional group. The usual reagent is a metal-acid system such as Fe or Sn and HCl or $H_2SO_4$; $SnCl_2$ and $FeSO_4$ can also be used.

$$C_6H_5NO_2 \xrightarrow{Sn/HCl} C_6H_5NH_2$$

Catalytic reduction using hydrogen and Raney nickel is effective.

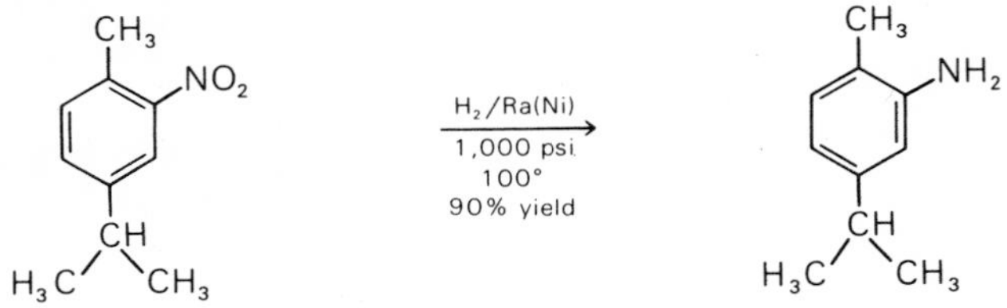

$H_2$/Ra(Ni), 1,000 psi, 100°, 90% yield

3-nitro-4-methylisopropylbenzene → 3-amino-4-methylisopropylbenzene

## 16-3 DONOR-ACCEPTOR COMPLEXES

Since nitro groups strongly withdraw electrons from the $\pi$ aromatic system, the $\pi$-electron density in the rings of polynitroaromatic compounds is lower than that found in unsubstituted aromatic hydrocarbons or those containing electron-donating substituents. These nitro and cyano compounds are called ***acceptors***, common examples are:

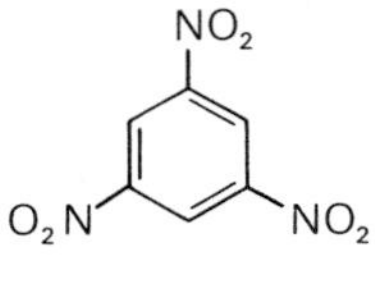

1,3,5-trinitrobenzene 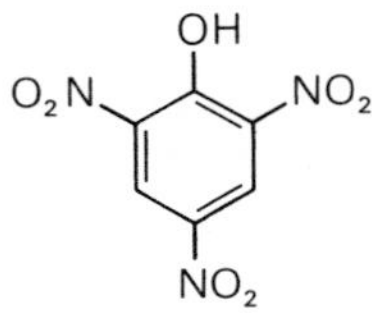 picric acid 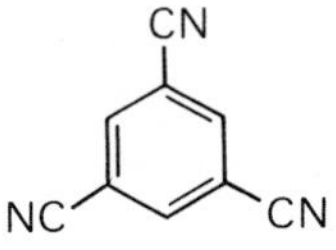 1,3,5-tricyanobenzene

These electron-rich and electron-poor aromatics sometimes form compounds known as ***donor-acceptor complexes***. Donor molecules are such familiar aromatic compounds as benzene, methyl-substituted benzenes, and polynuclear aromatic hydrocarbons (naphthalene, anthracene, phenanthrene) and their derivatives. Acceptor molecules are those containing such strongly electron-withdrawing groups as —$NO_2$ or—CN. Combinations of these donors and acceptors give rise to new complexes held together by fairly strong electrostatic interactions of the $\pi$-electron system. For instance, treatment of naphthalene with picric acid gives rise to a new solid compound. Many of these complexes have well-defined melting points.

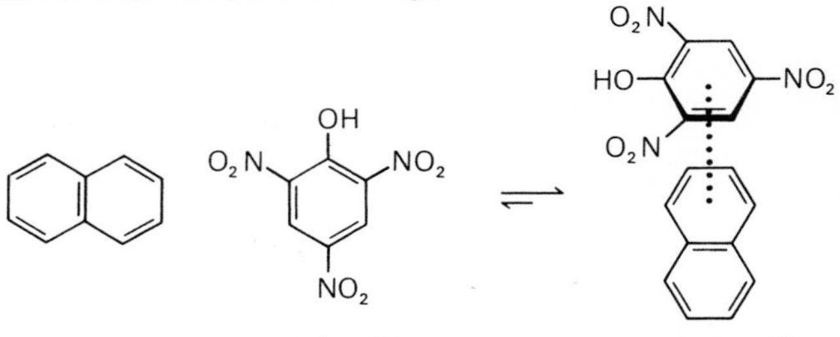

naphthalene "donor" + picric acid "acceptor" ⇌ $\pi$-complex or adduct

## AMINE NOMENCLATURE

Amines are denoted as ***primary***, R—$NH_2$, secondary, $R_2NH$, or tertiary, $R_3N$, according to whether the nitrogen atom bears one, two, or three alkyl or aryl groups, respectively. These amines have a pyramidal structure similar to that of ammonia and are free to undergo ammonia-like inversion. A nitrogen atom with four groups attached is positively charged and is known as a ***quaternary ammonium salt***:

$$(CH_3)_4N^+ \; Cl^-$$

tetramethylammonium chloride

These salts cannot invert. The names of amines are written as one word, which consists of the alkyl or aryl groups attached to the nitrogen and the suffix-*amine*. Table 16-1 shows some examples.

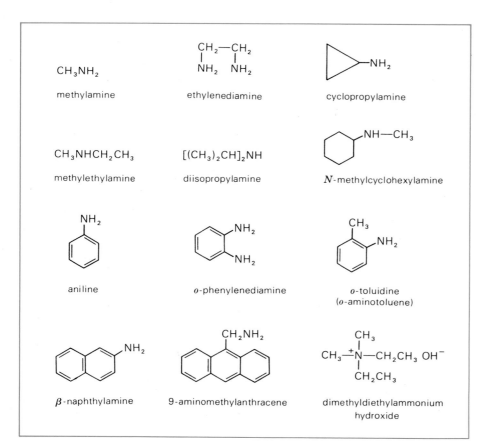

**Table 16-1 Representative organic amines**

| | | |
|---|---|---|
| $CH_3NH_2$<br>methylamine | $CH_2(NH_2)$—$CH_2(NH_2)$<br>ethylenediamine | cyclopropyl—$NH_2$<br>cyclopropylamine |
| $CH_3NHCH_2CH_3$<br>methylethylamine | $[(CH_3)_2CH]_2NH$<br>diisopropylamine | cyclohexyl—NH—$CH_3$<br>*N*-methylcyclohexylamine |
| $C_6H_5NH_2$<br>aniline | $C_6H_4(NH_2)_2$<br>*o*-phenylenediamine | $CH_3C_6H_4NH_2$<br>*o*-toluidine<br>(*o*-aminotoluene) |
| $C_{10}H_7NH_2$<br>*β*-naphthylamine | $C_{14}H_9CH_2NH_2$<br>9-aminomethylanthracene | $(CH_3)_2N^+(CH_2CH_3)_2 \; OH^-$<br>dimethyldiethylammonium hydroxide |

## BASICITY OF AMINES

Since amines contain a nitrogen atom with an unshared pair of electrons which may accept a proton, amines are Lewis bases. For example,

$$CH_3CH_2\ddot{N}H_2 \xrightarrow{HCl} CH_3CH_2\overset{+}{N}H_3\ Cl^-$$

ethylamine ethylamine hydrochloride

Even in aqueous solution the amine is partially protonated.

$$R\text{—}\ddot{N}H_2 + H_2O \rightleftharpoons R\text{—}\overset{+}{N}H_3 + OH^-$$

As with acids, the equilibrium constant is determined by the molar concentration of each species involved. Thus,

$$K_b = \frac{[R\overset{+}{N}H_3][OH^-]}{[RNH_2]}$$

where the concentration of water (55 $M$) has already been incorporated in the numerical value of $K_b$. The p$K_b$, defined as

$$pK_b \equiv -\log K_b$$

enables us to express the strengths of these bases in convenient numbers. As with the p$K_a$, the smaller the p$K_b$, the stronger the base. Consider the p$K_b$'s of some simple aliphatic amines.

| | $(CH_3)_2\ddot{N}H$ > | $CH_3\ddot{N}H_2$ > | $(CH_3)_3\ddot{N}$ > | $\ddot{N}H_3$ |
|---|---|---|---|---|
| $K_b$ | $5.2 \times 10^{-4}$ | $4.4 \times 10^{-4}$ | $5.4 \times 10^{-5}$ | $1.8 \times 10^{-5}$ |
| p$K_b$ | 3.28 | 3.36 | 4.26 | 4.75 |

Compared to ammonia, most primary and secondary aliphatic amines are stronger bases, because the alkyl groups increase the electron density at the nitrogen atom by the inductive effect. Tertiary aliphatic amines, however, are usually stronger bases than ammonia but weaker than comparable secondary amines. In tertiary amines the steric bulk of the groups prevents, to some extent, the compression of these alkyl groups in the transition from the three-coordinated amines to the four-coordinated ammonium salt.

$$(CH_3)_3\ddot{N} \xrightarrow{H^+} (CH_3)_3\overset{+}{N}\text{—}H$$

There is less alkyl-alkyl repulsive interaction in the tertiary amines than in the salts. Quaternary ammonium hydroxides are very strong bases and are highly ionized in aqueous solution.

$$(CH_3)_4N^+\ {}^-OH \rightleftharpoons (CH_3)_4N^+ + {}^-OH$$

Water molecules solvate and thus help disperse the charge of the separate ions.

Most *aromatic amines* are considerably weaker bases than ammonia. The resonance effect of the phenyl group on the unshared pair of electrons decreases the electron density at the nitrogen atom.

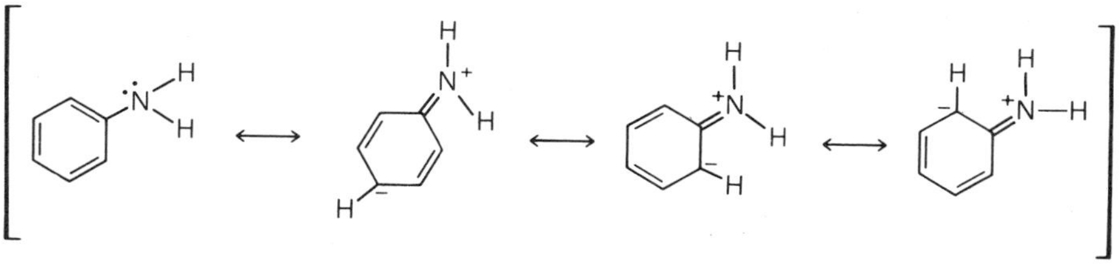

$$\left[ C_6H_5\ddot{N}H_2 \longleftrightarrow \cdots \longleftrightarrow \cdots \longleftrightarrow \cdots \right]$$

Tertiary aromatic amines have the added steric effects described above, and many of these compounds are very weakly basic.

$$C_6H_5{-}NH_2 > (C_6H_5)_2NH > (C_6H_5)_3N$$

| | $C_6H_5{-}NH_2$ | $(C_6H_5)_2NH$ | $(C_6H_5)_3N$ |
|---|---|---|---|
| $K_b$ | $4.6 \times 10^{-10}$ | $10^{-14}$ | basicity constant cannot be measured in $H_2O$ |

Substituents on the aromatic ring have predictable effects on the basicity: electron-donating substituents increase the basicity, whereas electron-withdrawing ones decrease it.

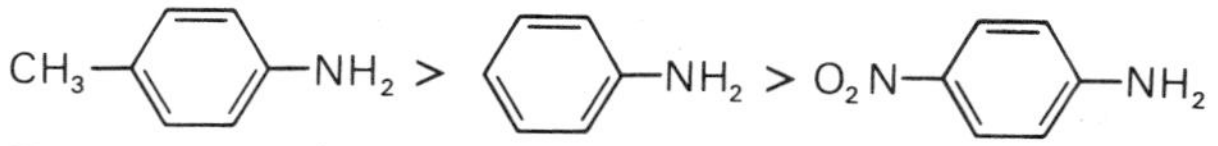

$$CH_3{-}C_6H_4{-}NH_2 > C_6H_5{-}NH_2 > O_2N{-}C_6H_4{-}NH_2$$

| | $CH_3{-}C_6H_4{-}NH_2$ | $C_6H_5{-}NH_2$ | $O_2N{-}C_6H_4{-}NH_2$ |
|---|---|---|---|
| $K_b$ | $1.2 \times 10^{-9}$ | $3.8 \times 10^{-10}$ | $1.1 \times 10^{-12}$ |
| $pK_b$ | 8.92 | 9.42 | 11.96 |

***Amides***, $R{-}\overset{O}{\overset{\|}{C}}{-}\ddot{N}H_2$, are not basic compounds because the resonance effect lowers the electron density around the nitrogen atom.

***Imides***, $R{-}\overset{O}{\overset{\|}{C}}{-}\ddot{N}H{-}\overset{O}{\overset{\|}{C}}{-}R$, on the other hand, are considerably more acidic than amides because of resonance stabilization of the anion.

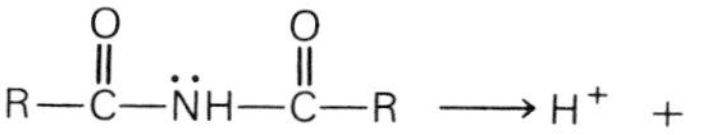

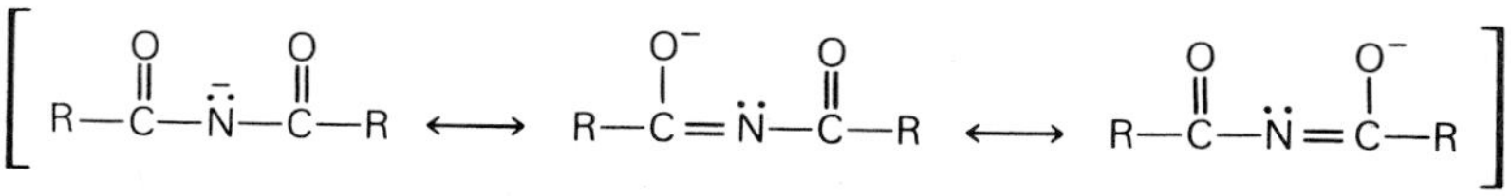

$$\left[ R{-}\overset{O}{\overset{\|}{C}}{-}\ddot{N}H_2 \longleftrightarrow R{-}\overset{O^-}{\overset{|}{C}}{=}\overset{+}{N}H_2 \right]$$

$$R{-}\overset{O}{\overset{\|}{C}}{-}\ddot{N}H{-}\overset{O}{\overset{\|}{C}}{-}R \longrightarrow H^+ +$$

$$\left[ R{-}\overset{O}{\overset{\|}{C}}{-}\overset{-}{\ddot{N}}{-}\overset{O}{\overset{\|}{C}}{-}R \longleftrightarrow R{-}\overset{O^-}{\overset{|}{C}}{=}\ddot{N}{-}\overset{O}{\overset{\|}{C}}{-}R \longleftrightarrow R{-}\overset{O}{\overset{\|}{C}}{-}\ddot{N}{=}\overset{O^-}{\overset{|}{C}}{-}R \right]$$

*Amine salts* are formed by the reaction of either inorganic or organic acids with an amine. This reaction is used in the resolution of racemic acids by naturally occurring amines. The free base and the salt of the acid can be obtained by treatment of the amine salt with a stronger base, such as sodium hydroxide. [The resolved acid is then obtained in a separate acidification step (see Chap. 12).] Inorganic acids usually give water-soluble salts.

$$o\text{-toluidine} \underset{NaOH}{\overset{HCl}{\rightleftharpoons}} o\text{-toluidine hydrochloride } (\overset{+}{N}H_3\ Cl^-)$$

*o*-toluidine *o*-toluidine hydrochloride

Many strongly basic amines form the carbonate salt on exposure to the moist atmosphere.

$$2CH_3CH_2\ddot{N}H_2 + CO_2 + H_2O \longrightarrow 2CH_3CH_2\overset{+}{N}H_3\ CO_3^{--}$$

ethylamine ethylamine carbonate

## PREPARATION OF AMINES

### 16-4 REDUCTION OF NITRO COMPOUNDS

Catalytic hydrogenation (hydrogen with Raney nickel), metal-acid systems (HCl or $H_2SO_4$ with Fe, Sn, or Zn), or ammonium polysulfide, $NH_4S_xH$, can be used in the reduction of aromatic nitro compounds. A special advantage of ammonium polysulfide is its ability to reduce only one nitro group at a time in the presence of several others; in unsymmetrical cases, it is not always possible to predict which of the nitro groups will be reduced.

$$\text{dimethyl 5-nitroisophthalate} \xrightarrow[25°;\ 40\ psi]{H_2/Ra(Ni)} \text{dimethyl 5-aminoisophthalate}$$

dimethyl 5-nitroisophthalate dimethyl 5-aminoisophthalate

$$m\text{-dinitrobenzene} \xrightarrow[\Delta \text{ in alcohol}]{H_2S + NH_4OH} m\text{-nitroaniline}$$

*m*-dinitrobenzene *m*-nitroaniline

$$\text{2,4-dinitroaniline} \xrightarrow[\text{NH}_4\text{OH 55\% yield}]{\text{H}_2\text{S}} \text{4-nitrophenylenediamine (1,2-diamino-4-nitrobenzene)}$$

2,4-dinitroaniline

4-nitrophenylenediamine
(1,2-diamino-4-nitrobenzene)

## 16-5 REDUCTION OF NITRILES AND AMIDES

Primary amines, R—$CH_2NH_2$, are formed by the reduction of nitriles, R—C≡N, and of unsubstituted amides, R—$CONH_2$, with $LiAlH_4$. Substituted amides give the corresponding amine. Note that although the carbonyl group of aldehydes, R—CHO, and ketones, R—CO—R, are reduced with $LiAlH_4$ to the corresponding alcohols, R—$CH_2OH$ and R—CHOH—R', amides are reduced directly to the amine. Examples are shown in Table 16-2.

**Table 16-2 Examples of amine preparation using $LiAlH_4$**

| Starting material | Conditions | Product |
|---|---|---|
| $CH_3CH_2CH_2CN$ <br> *n*-butyronitrile | 1. $LiAlH_4$ 2. $H_2O$ 60% yield | $CH_3CH_2CH_2CH_2NH_2$ <br> *n*-butylamine |
| $C_6H_5$—$CONH_2$ <br> benzamide | 1. $LiAlH_4$ 2. $H_2O$ 85% yield | $C_6H_5$—$CH_2NH_2$ <br> benzylamine |
| $CH_3CH_2CONHCH_2CH_3$ <br> *N*-ethylpropionamide | 1. $LiAlH_4$ 2. $H_2O$ 50% yield | $CH_3CH_2CH_2NHCH_2CH_3$ <br> ethylpropylamine |
| $CH_3CON(CH_2CH_3)_2$ <br> *N,N*-diethylacetamide | 1. $LiAlH_4$ 2. $H_2O$ 50% yield | $(CH_3CH_2)_3N$ <br> triethylamine |

Nitriles can also be reduced catalytically (often in the presence of $NH_3$) to the corresponding primary amine.

$$C_6H_5\text{—}CH_2CN \xrightarrow[\text{125°; 2,000 psi; 85\% yield}]{H_2/\text{Ra(Ni)}} C_6H_5\text{—}\overset{\beta}{C}H_2\overset{\alpha}{C}H_2NH_2$$

benzyl cyanide → *β*-phenylethylamine

$$N{\equiv}C\text{—}(CH_2)_8\text{—}C{\equiv}N \xrightarrow[\text{NH}_3\text{; 125°; 1,500 psi; 80\% yield}]{H_2/\text{Ra(Ni)}} H_2N\text{—}(CH_2)_{10}\text{—}NH_2$$

sebaconitrile → 1,10-decanediamine (decamethylenediamine)

## 16-6 REDUCTIVE AMINATION OF ALDEHYDES AND KETONES

Catalytic reduction of aldehydes and ketones in the presence of ammonia yields primary amines. Examples are shown in Table 16-3.

**Table 16-3 Examples of amines from aldehydes and ketones**

| Reactant | Conditions | Product |
|---|---|---|
| $C_6H_5$—CO—$CH_3$ (acetophenone) | $H_2$/Ra(Ni), $NH_3$; 150°, 3,500-5,000 psi, 50% yield | $C_6H_5$—CH($NH_2$)—$CH_3$ (α-phenylethylamine) |
| $CH_3$—C(=O)—$CH_2CH_2CH_2CH_2CH_3$ (methyl pentyl ketone) | $H_2$/Ra(Ni), $NH_3$; 150°, 3,500-5,000 psi, 50% yield | $CH_3$—CH($NH_2$)—$CH_2CH_2CH_2CH_2CH_3$ (2-aminoheptane) |
| $CH_3(CH_2)_4CH_2CHO$ (*n*-heptaldehyde) | $H_2$/Ra(Ni), $NH_3$; 150°, 3,500-5,000 psi, 60% yield | $CH_3(CH_2)_4CH_2CH_2NH_2$ (*n*-heptylamine) |
| 2-furyl—CHO (furfural) | $H_2$/Ra(Ni), $NH_3$; 150°, 3,500-5,000 psi, 50% yield | 2-furyl—$CH_2NH_2$ (furfurylamine) |

## 16-7 ALKYLATION OF AMMONIA OR AMINES WITH HALIDES

The nucleophilic displacement of the halide ion from alkyl halides by ammonia or primary or secondary amines affords a salt which, by loss of a proton, gives a new amine. The newly formed amine is more basic than ammonia and competes favorably with it in further displacement reactions.

$$H_3\ddot{N} + CH_3{-}I \xrightarrow{S_N2} H_3\overset{+}{N}{-}CH_3\ I^- \rightleftharpoons CH_3\ddot{N}H_2 + HI$$

$$CH_3\ddot{N}H_2 + CH_3{-}I \xrightarrow{S_N2} (CH_3)_2\overset{+}{N}H_2\ I^- \rightleftharpoons (CH_3)_2\ddot{N}H + HI$$

Such displacements continue in competition until a quaternary ammonium salt is formed which can undergo no further reactions.

$$(CH_3)_2\ddot{N}H + CH_3{-}I \longrightarrow (CH_3)_3\overset{+}{N}H\ I^- \rightleftharpoons (CH_3)_3\ddot{N} + HI$$

$$(CH_3)_3\ddot{N} + CH_3{-}I \longrightarrow (CH_3)_4\overset{+}{N}\ I^-$$

Consequently the reaction of ammonia with alkyl halides gives rise to a mixture of products which are chemically similar. Although secondary and tertiary amines are usually not prepared by this method, primary amines can be obtained in reasonable yield and purity by using a very large *excess* of ammonia. Quaternary ammonium salts are obtained by using an excess of the halide. The reaction has been used to prepare amino acids from $\alpha$ halo acids.

$$\underset{\substack{|\\ Br}}{R—CH—COOH} \xrightarrow{NH_3(xs)} \underset{\substack{|\\ NH_2}}{R—CH—COOH}$$

Although aryl halides, which do not generally undergo $S_N2$ displacement, cannot be used, aryl halides containing ortho and para nitro groups give the corresponding nitroanilines.

$$p\text{-}ClC_6H_4NO_2 \xrightarrow{NH_3} p\text{-}H_2NC_6H_4NO_2$$

*p*-chloronitrobenzene *p*-nitroaniline

A compound which has been used successfully in amino acid determinations is 2,4-dinitrofluorobenzene (2,4-DNFB), which reacts with single amino acids or the free-amino end of a protein (see also Chap. 17).

$$2,4\text{-}(NO_2)_2C_6H_3F + \underset{\substack{|\\ NH_2}}{R—CH—COOH} \longrightarrow 2,4\text{-}(NO_2)_2C_6H_3—NH—CH(R)—COOH + HF$$

## 16-8 GABRIEL PHTHALIMIDE SYNTHESIS OF PRIMARY AMINES

Pure primary alkylamines can be obtained by the alkylation of phthalimide; there is no possibility of contamination by secondary and tertiary amines or quaternary ammonium salts. This synthesis takes advantage of the acidic proton in imides; the anion causes a backside displacement ($S_N2$ reaction) of a primary or secondary alkyl halide.

$$C_6H_4(CO)_2N—H \xrightarrow{KOH} C_6H_4(CO)_2N^- K^+ + H_2O$$

phthalimide

$$\text{C}_6\text{H}_4(\text{CO})_2\text{N}^- + \text{CH}_3\text{CH}_2\text{—I} \longrightarrow \text{C}_6\text{H}_4(\text{CO})_2\text{N—CH}_2\text{CH}_3 + \text{I}^-$$

*N*-ethylphthalimide

The free amine is then obtained by saponification of the *N*-alkylphthalimide. This reaction has often been used in the synthesis of amino acids.

$$\text{C}_6\text{H}_4(\text{CO})_2\text{N—CH}_2\text{CH}_3 \xrightarrow[\text{H}_2\text{O}]{\text{K}^+\text{OH}^-} \text{C}_6\text{H}_4(\text{COO}^-\text{K}^+)_2 + \text{CH}_3\text{CH}_2\text{NH}_2$$

potassium phthalate

$$\text{C}_6\text{H}_4(\text{CO})_2\text{N}^- + \text{R—}\underset{\text{Br}}{\text{CH}}\text{—COOH} \longrightarrow \text{C}_6\text{H}_4(\text{CO})_2\text{N—CH(R)COOH} \quad \text{then hydrolysis}$$

## 16-9 THE HOFMANN REACTION

This reaction was presented in Sec. 15-30, but, because of its synthetic usefulness, the rearrangement mechanism is presented here with additional examples (Table 16-4).

*Overall*

$$\text{C}_6\text{H}_5\text{—CH}_2\text{—}\overset{\text{O}}{\overset{\|}{\text{C}}}\text{—NH}_2 \xrightarrow[\text{60-85\% yield}]{\text{KOBr}} \text{C}_6\text{H}_5\text{—CH}_2\text{NH}_2 + \text{CO}_2 + \text{K}^+\text{Br}^-$$

phenylacetamide      benzylamine

*Mechanism*

$$\text{C}_6\text{H}_5\text{—CH}_2\text{—}\overset{\text{O}}{\overset{\|}{\text{C}}}\text{—NH}_2 \xrightarrow{\text{KOBr}} \left[\text{C}_6\text{H}_5\text{—CH}_2\text{—}\overset{\text{O}}{\overset{\|}{\text{C}}}\text{—}\underset{\text{Br}}{\text{N}}\text{—H}\right] \xrightarrow{^-\text{OH}}$$

*N*-bromophenylacetamide

$$\left[\text{C}_6\text{H}_5\text{—CH}_2\text{—C}(\text{=O})\text{—}\ddot{\text{N}}\text{:}\right] \longrightarrow [\text{O=C=N—CH}_2\text{—C}_6\text{H}_5] \xrightarrow{\text{H}_2\text{O}} [\text{C}_6\text{H}_5\text{CH}_2\text{NH—CO}_2\text{H}]$$

benzylisocyanate      unstable

$$\downarrow -\text{CO}_2$$

$$\text{C}_6\text{H}_5\text{CH}_2\text{NH}_2 + \text{CO}_2$$

**Table 16-4 Examples of the Hofmann rearrangement**

nicotinamide (pyridine with $CONH_2$) $\xrightarrow[\text{70\% yield}]{\text{NaOBr or KOBr}}$ 3-aminopyridine (pyridine with $NH_2$)

cycloheptylacetamide (cycloheptane–$CH_2CONH_2$) $\xrightarrow[\text{40\% yield}]{\text{KOBr}}$ aminomethylcycloheptane (cycloheptane–$CH_2NH_2$)

The Hofmann reaction also takes place with some imides under similar conditions:

phthalimide (benzene fused to C(=O)–N–H–C(=O)) $\xrightarrow[\text{75-85\% yield}]{\text{KOBr or NaOBr}}$ anthranilic acid (benzene with COOH and $NH_2$)

## REACTIONS OF AMINES

The following reactions of amines have already been presented in the section indicated: (1) salt formation with acids (this chapter, Basicity of Amines), (2) amide formation by reaction of ammonia, primary amines, or secondary amines with acyl halides (Sec. 15-24) or anhydrides (Sec. 15-21), (3) alkylation with primary or secondary halides or activated aromatic halides (Sec. 16-7).

Write a specific example to illustrate each of the above reactions and name the starting materials and products.

### 16-10 REACTION WITH NITROUS ACID

The reactions of aliphatic amines with nitrous acid are different enough to be used in distinguishing between primary, secondary, and tertiary amines.

Primary: $R—\ddot{N}H_2 \xrightarrow{\text{HONO}} R—OH + N_2\uparrow$ observe $N_2$ evolution

Secondary: $R_2\ddot{N}H \xrightarrow{HONO} R_2N{-}NO$ observe *N*-nitrosoamine formation

Tertiary: $R_3\ddot{N} \xrightarrow{HONO}$ N.R. under these conditions; may observe salt formation

Primary amines react with nitrous acid to give an unstable alkyl diazonium salt, $R{-}\overset{+}{N}_2$, which readily loses nitrogen, giving the reactive carbonium ion intermediate, $R^+$. In the presence of water the carbonium ion may give the alcohol, R—OH, although this is generally not a good preparative method for alcohols. The carbonium ion may undergo other characteristic reactions, such as loss of a proton to give an olefin. Often these primary carbonium ions first rearrange to a more stable secondary or tertiary carbonium ion, which subsequently undergoes reaction.

$$R{-}NH_2 \xrightarrow{HONO} [R{-}N_2^+] \xrightarrow{-N_2} [R^+] \longrightarrow [R'^+]$$

$$[R^+] \begin{cases} \xrightarrow{-H^+} \text{olefin} \\ \xrightarrow{H_2O} \text{alcohol} \end{cases} \quad \text{and} \quad [R'^+] \begin{cases} \xrightarrow{-H^+} \text{olefin} \\ \xrightarrow{H_2O} \text{alcohol} \end{cases}$$

A reaction similar to the pinacolone rearrangement (Sec. 13-16) takes place when an α amino alcohol is treated with nitrous acid. Formulate a reasonable mechanism for the reaction of each of the following and predict the products:

**1.** $(CH_3)_2C(OH){-}C(NH_2)(CH_3)_2$

**2.** 2-aminocyclohexanol (cyclohexane ring bearing OH and $NH_2$ on adjacent carbons) Consider both cis and trans isomers.

Secondary alkyl amines give a relatively stable, water-insoluble *N*-nitrosoamine, probably by attack of the unshared pair of electrons on the nitrosonium ion, $NO^+$, followed by loss of a proton.

$$R_2\ddot{N}{-}H + [\overset{+}{N}O] \longrightarrow \left[ R_2{-}\overset{+}{N}(N{=}O){-}H \right] \xrightarrow{-H^+} R_2\ddot{N}{-}\ddot{N}{=}O + H^+$$

***Aromatic amines*** also give characteristic test reactions with nitrous acid, but they differ somewhat from those observed with alkyl amines.

Primary: $Ar{-}NH_2 \xrightarrow{HONO} [Ar{-}\overset{+}{N}_2]$ observe colored coupling products with Ar—OH

Secondary: $Ar{-}NHR \xrightarrow{HONO} Ar{-}N(NO){-}R$ observe water-insoluble *N*-nitrosoamine layer

Tertiary: $Ar{-}NR_2 \xrightarrow{HONO}$ *p*-O=N—Ar—$NR_2$ observe *C*-nitrosation by product identification

Primary aromatic amines, unlike aliphatic primary amines, afford relatively stable diazonium salts in aqueous solution at 0 to 5°. These salts are useful, important chemical intermediates, and their further transformations are discussed in the last sections of this chapter. These salts may couple with very reactive aromatic compounds such as phenols and *N,N*-dialkyl aromatic amines, giving rise to azo compounds, Ar—N=N—Ar, many of which are important dyes.

$$C_6H_5NH_2 \xrightarrow[+\ NaNO_2\ \text{at}\ 0\text{-}5^\circ]{\text{HONO from HCl}} \left[C_6H_5\overset{+}{N}_2\ Cl^-\right] \xrightarrow{C_6H_5{-}OH} C_6H_5{-}N{=}N{-}C_6H_4{-}OH$$

aniline — benzenediazonium chloride — *p*-hydroxyazobenzene

> Write a reasonable mechanism for the reaction of a diazonium salt with phenol. Consider previous discussions of electrophilic aromatic substitution.

Secondary aromatic amines, like the aliphatic ones, give *N*-nitroso compounds with nitrous acid.

$$C_6H_5N(CH_3)H \xrightarrow[0\text{-}5^\circ]{HONO} C_6H_5N(CH_3)NO$$

*N*-methylaniline — *N*-nitroso-*N*-methylaniline

Tertiary aromatic amines give no reaction with nitrous acid except when the aromatic nucleus contains a strong electron-releasing substituent, such as a dialkylamino group. In these cases the product is a *C*-nitroso compound, which results from electrophilic attack of the ***nitrosonium ion***, $NO^+$, a very weak electrophile. If the para position is blocked, attack may occur at the ortho position; little or no meta substitution is observed.

$$C_6H_5N(CH_3)_2 \xrightarrow{HONO} p\text{-}ON\text{-}C_6H_4N(CH_3)_2$$

*N,N*-dimethylaniline — *p*-nitroso-*N*, *N*-dimethylaniline

## 16-11 HOFMANN ELIMINATION (DEGRADATION) OF QUATERNARY AMMONIUM HYDROXIDES

Treatment of a tertiary amine with an alkyl halide (often methyl iodide) gives the corresponding quaternary ammonium halide (iodide). These salts can be converted to the hydroxide by treatment with moist silver oxide, $Ag_2O$.

$$CH_3{-}CH_2{-}\ddot{N}(CH_3)_2 \xrightarrow{CH_3I} CH_3{-}CH_2{-}\overset{+}{N}(CH_3)_3\ I^- \xrightarrow[Ag_2O]{moist} CH_3{-}CH_2{-}\overset{+}{N}(CH_3)_3\ {}^-OH$$

dimethylethylamine — trimethylethylammonium iodide — trimethylethylammonium hydroxide

Pyrolysis of these quaternary ammonium hydroxides (at about 140°) proceeds smoothly, affording an olefin and the tertiary amine. This is known as a Hofmann elimination or degradation. The reaction proceeds by an $E_2$ elimination; the hydroxide ion attacks a $\beta$ hydrogen.

*Overall*: $$CH_3{-}CH_2{-}\overset{+}{N}(CH_3)_3\ OH^- \xrightarrow{\Delta} CH_2{=}CH_2 + N(CH_3)_3 + H_2O$$

*Mechanism*: $$\overset{\beta}{C}H_2(H){-}\overset{\alpha}{C}H_2{-}\overset{+}{N}(CH_3)_3 \ \ {}^-OH \xrightarrow{E_2} CH_2{=}CH_2 + N(CH_3)_3 + H_2O$$

The newly formed tertiary amine is an excellent leaving group. In those cases where several possible alkenes can be formed, the least-substituted olefin, that is, $CH_2{=}CH_2$, is usually the major product except when one of the possible olefins has the added stability of conjugation.

Contrast this with the basic dehydrohalogenation of alkyl halides, where the most highly substituted olefin is formed (Sec. 4-2).

$$CH_3{-}CH_2{-}\underset{\displaystyle Br}{\underset{|}{C}H}{-}CH_3 \xrightarrow{\text{NaOEt}} \underset{80\%}{CH_3CH{=}CHCH_3} + \underset{20\%}{CH_3CH_2CH{=}CH_2}$$

$$\overset{\gamma}{C}H_3\overset{\beta}{C}H_2{-}\overset{\alpha}{\underset{\displaystyle {}^{+}N(CH_3)_3\ {}^{-}OH}{\underset{|}{C}H}}{-}\overset{\beta'}{C}H_3 \xrightarrow{\Delta} \underset{5\%}{CH_3CH{=}CHCH_3} + \underset{95\%}{CH_3CH_2CH{=}CH_2} + H_2O + N(CH_3)_3$$

Three factors are important to the course of this reaction (1) the stability of the olefin, (2) the acidity of the $\beta$ hydrogen which is removed, and (3) the steric interactions in the transition state. The preferential elimination of ethylene is probably due to the steric effect rather than to the inductive effect on the acidity of the $\beta$ hydrogen. In the following example, conjugation of the double bond with the aromatic ring stabilizes both the transition state and the product; there is also increased acidity of the $\beta$ proton.

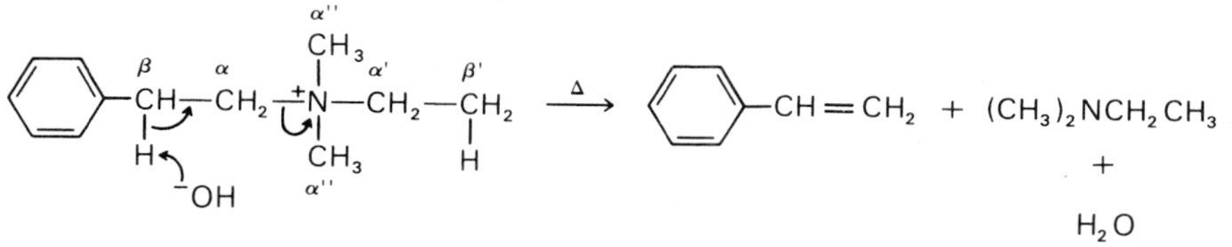

$$C_6H_5{-}\overset{\beta}{C}H_2{-}\overset{\alpha}{C}H_2{-}\overset{+}{N}(\overset{\alpha''}{C}H_3)_2{-}\overset{\alpha'}{C}H_2{-}\overset{\beta'}{C}H_3\ \ {}^{-}OH \xrightarrow{\Delta} C_6H_5{-}CH{=}CH_2 + (CH_3)_2NCH_2CH_3 + H_2O$$

The trans nature of the reaction can be demonstrated by many examples; two follow.

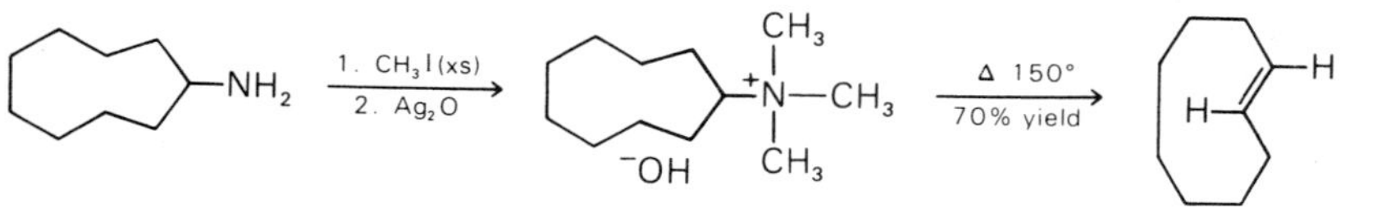

$$\text{cyclononyl}{-}NH_2 \xrightarrow[\text{2. } Ag_2O]{\text{1. } CH_3I\text{(xs)}} \text{cyclononyl}{-}\overset{+}{N}(CH_3)_3\ {}^{-}OH \xrightarrow[\text{70\% yield}]{\Delta\ 150°} \textit{trans}\text{-cyclononene}$$

cyclononylamine — trimethylcyclononylammonium hydroxide — *trans*-cyclononene

The reaction is concerted; it takes place in one step. Under conditions which do not isomerize either the starting materials or products, the reaction proceeds by a trans elimination. Hence cyclononylamine gives *trans*-cyclononene, and the erythro isomer gives the *cis*-$\alpha$-methylstilbene whereas the threo gives the trans form.

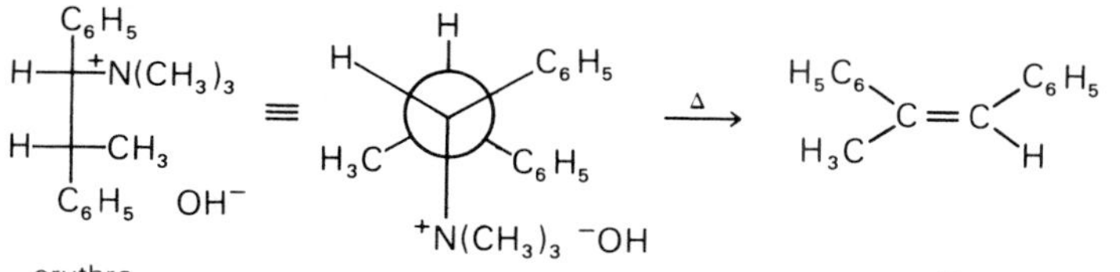

Erythro (Fischer projection: top $C_6H_5$; H—C—$\overset{+}{N}(CH_3)_3$; H—C—$CH_3$; bottom $C_6H_5$, $OH^-$) ≡ Newman projection (front: H, $C_6H_5$, $^{+}N(CH_3)_3\ {}^{-}OH$; back: H, $H_3C$, $C_6H_5$) $\xrightarrow{\Delta}$ cis: $(H_5C_6)(H_3C)C{=}C(C_6H_5)(H)$

erythro — cis

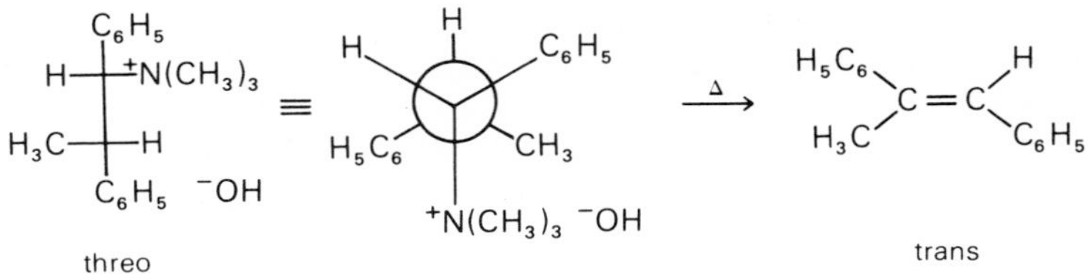

threo

trans

Since many natural products contain a nitrogen atom as an amino function, the results of successive Hofmann degradations can provide information about the structure of the original compound. Many alkaloids, including the following, have been subjected to such a series of reactions:

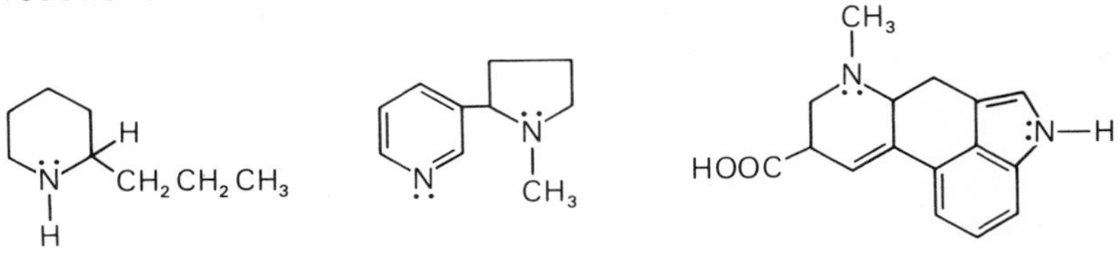

coniine
hemlock poison

nicotine
tobacco alkaloid

lysergic acid
from cereal fungus
(LSD, not a natural product, is the diethylamide.)

**1.** 1,11-Dodecadiene can be prepared in 65% yield from 1,12-diaminododecane. Outline the steps for this synthesis.

**2.** Show the expected result of successive Hofmann elimination on coniine.

**3.** Trimethylcyclopropylammonium hydroxide gives 1,2-dibromopropane when heated at 325° and the resulting vapor is absorbed in bromine. What is the significance of this experiment?

## 16-12 ELECTROPHILIC AROMATIC SUBSTITUTION

The unshared pair of electrons on the nitrogen atom of an aromatic amine greatly increases the electron density of the aromatic ring, especially at the ortho and para positions, because of the resonance effects. The dimethylamino group, $—N(CH_3)_2$, is one of the strongest activating substituents toward electrophilic aromatic substitution. Even weak electrophiles such as the nitrosonium ion, $NO^+$, and aromatic diazonium ions, $Ar—N_2^+$, will react with aromatic amines.

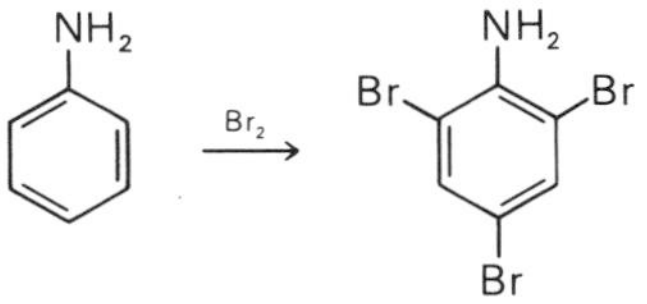

Aromatic compounds with a high $\pi$-electron density, such as phenols and primary amines, are particularly susceptible to oxidation by reactants such as Cr(VI) and $HNO_3$. The resulting products are known as ***quinones***:

$$\text{4-amino-3-chlorophenol} \xrightarrow[\text{Na}_2\text{Cr}_2\text{O}_7;\ 25°;\ 60\%\ \text{yield}]{H_2SO_4} \text{chloro-}p\text{-benzoquinone}$$

4-amino-3-chlorophenol chloro-*p*-benzoquinone

Protection of the —OH and $—NH_2$ functions permits transformations, such as nitration:

$$p\text{-anisidine} \xrightarrow[0\text{-}5°]{(CH_3CO)_2O} [\text{4-methoxyacetanilide}] \xrightarrow[75\%\ \text{yield}]{HNO_3;\ 60°}$$

*p*-anisidine 4-methoxyacetanilide

$$\text{2-nitro-4-methoxyacetanilide} \xrightarrow[95\%\ \text{yield}]{KOH;\ H_2O} \text{2-nitro-}p\text{-anisidine}$$

2-nitro-4-methoxyacetanilide 2-nitro-*p*-anisidine

## QUALITATIVE ANALYSIS

### 16-13 THE HINSBERG TEST

Primary and secondary amines react with benzenesulfonyl chlorides, $Ar—SO_2Cl$, to give $Ar—SO_2—NHR$ or $Ar—SO_2—NR_2$, benzenesulfonamides, in a reaction similar to that observed with carboxylic acid chlorides ($R—NH_2 + Ar—CO—Cl \longrightarrow Ar—CO—NHR$), which gives amides of carboxylic acids. The reaction is carried out in basic solution in order to neutralize the HCl formed in the reaction.

Primary amines: $R—\ddot{N}H_2 \xrightarrow[OH^-]{C_6H_5SO_2Cl} C_6H_5SO_2\bar{N}—R\ Na^+ \xrightarrow{H^+} C_6H_5SO_2NHR\downarrow$

soluble in base insoluble in acid

Secondary amines: $R_2\ddot{N}H \xrightarrow[OH^-]{C_6H_5SO_2Cl} C_6H_5SO_2NR_2\downarrow$

insoluble in base

Tertiary amines: $R_3\ddot{N} \xrightarrow[OH^-]{C_6H_5SO_2Cl}$ N.R., but salt formation is sometimes observed; neutralization yields the amine

Treatment of an unknown amine with benzenesulfonyl chloride in basic solution affords the *soluble* benzenesulfonamide of primary amines or the *insoluble* benzenesulfonamide derivative of secondary amines; tertiary amines give no derivative, but the salt of a tertiary amine is sometimes formed. Unlike carboxamides, the proton on primary benzenesulfonamides is relatively acidic because of the adjacent electron-withdrawing sulfur and oxygen atoms, which stabilize the anion.

$$C_6H_5-SO_2-NH-R \xrightarrow{-H^+} \left[ C_6H_5-SO_2-\bar{N}-R \longleftrightarrow C_6H_5-S(O^-)(=O)=N-R \longleftrightarrow C_6H_5-S(=O)(O^-)=N-R \right]$$

Acidification of the homogeneous reaction mixture from primary amines gives the insoluble primary amine benzenesulfonamide. The Hinsberg test can be used for qualitative determination of the type of amine and to separate primary, secondary, and tertiary amines. The amine is regenerated by basic hydrolysis of the benzenesulfonamide.

## AROMATIC DIAZONIUM SALTS

### 16-14 INTRODUCTION OF FUNCTIONAL GROUPS INTO AN AROMATIC SYSTEM

Many of the syntheses previously discussed involve the direct reaction between an aromatic substrate and reactants to form an aromatic system with a new functional group. Consider the entire class of electrophilic aromatic substitution reactions (Chap. 7). In many cases, however, the conditions required for such a direct reaction cause serious side reactions with other functional groups already present; in other cases, the groups already present do not direct the incoming substituent to the desired position. Sometimes the directing influence or deactivation prevents the attack from occurring at all. These difficulties can often be overcome by introducing a nitro group, reducing it to the amino function, carrying out other transformations on the molecule, and then removing the amino group or replacing it by another functional group via the diazonium salts. Diazonium salts are important synthetic intermediates in organic synthesis and find wide use in the preparation of a class of compounds known as azo dyes (see Sec. 16-15). Aromatic diazonium salts, $Ar—N_2^+$, with one notable exception, are not isolated, because they detonate violently when dry. Benzenediazonium chloride can be prepared from benzene:

$$C_6H_6 \xrightarrow[H_2SO_4]{HNO_3} C_6H_5NO_2 \xrightarrow{Sn/HCl} C_6H_5NH_2 \xrightarrow[0\text{-}5^\circ]{HONO\ (HCl + NaNO_2)} [C_6H_5\overset{+}{N_2}Cl^-]$$

Table 16-5 lists representative transformations of these diazonium salts which will be discussed in succeeding paragraphs.

**Hydrogen, —H:** Often an amino (or nitro) group is used in a molecule to obtain an activating (or deactivating) effect and the desired position of substitution. After serving this purpose, the amino group can be diazotized and then treated with aqueous hypophosphorus acid, $H_3PO_2$, which replaces the diazonium group with a hydrogen atom. An excellent example of this synthetic approach is the preparation of *m*-bromotoluene from toluene. Direct bromination of toluene leads almost exclusively to a mixture of the ortho and para bromo isomers. A diazonium salt reaction, however, allows the amino group to be used as a directing influence and then removed.

$$\underset{\text{toluene}}{C_6H_5CH_3} \xrightarrow[H_2SO_4]{HNO_3} \underset{\text{liquid}}{o\text{-}CH_3C_6H_4NO_2} + \underset{\text{m.p. } 54^\circ}{p\text{-}CH_3C_6H_4NO_2} \quad \text{(easily separated)}$$

$$\underset{p\text{-nitrotoluene}}{p\text{-}CH_3C_6H_4NO_2} \xrightarrow{Sn/HCl} \underset{p\text{-toluidine}}{p\text{-}CH_3C_6H_4NH_2} \xrightarrow{Br_2} \underset{\text{3-bromo-4-aminotoluene}}{CH_3C_6H_3(Br)NH_2} \xrightarrow[0\text{-}5^\circ]{HONO} [CH_3C_6H_3(Br)N_2^+] \xrightarrow[H_2O]{H_3PO_2}$$

**Table 16-5 Reactions of diazonium salts**

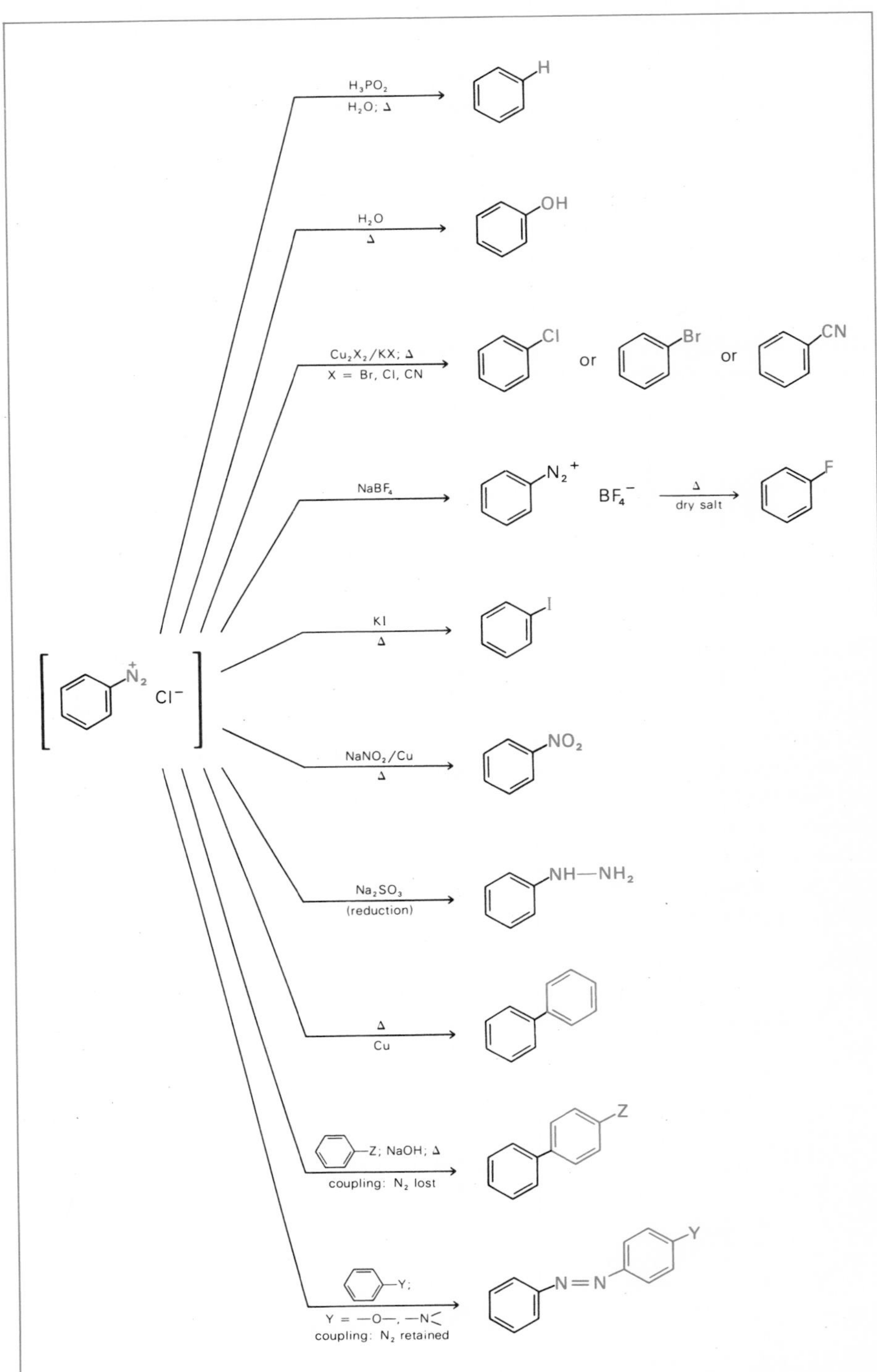

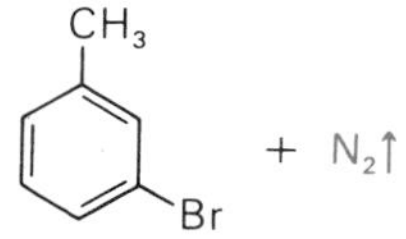

*m*-bromotoluene

Another example, from the biphenyl series, is

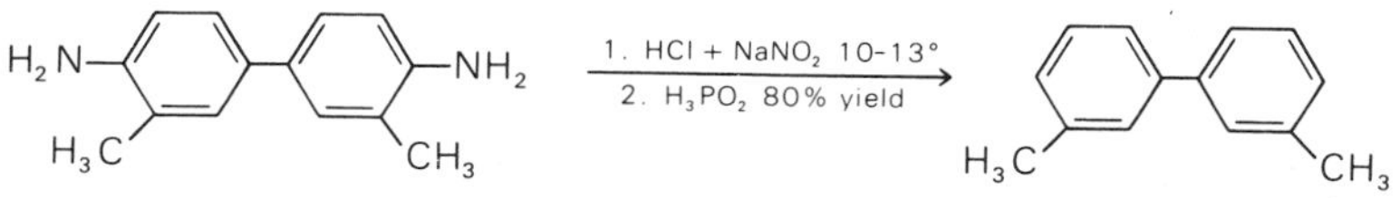

*o*-tolidine 3,3'-dimethylbiphenyl

> Suggest a method of synthesizing 2,4,6-tribromobenzoic acid from *m*-aminobenzoic acid.

**Hydroxyl group, —OH:** The conversion of diazonium salts to phenols occurs simply on boiling the salt in water. Contrast this synthesis of phenols with two others previously discussed: (1) the fusion of sulfonic acid salts, which occurs under drastic conditions, and (2) the nucleophilic displacement of aromatic halides by hydroxide ion, which requires a particular substitution pattern.

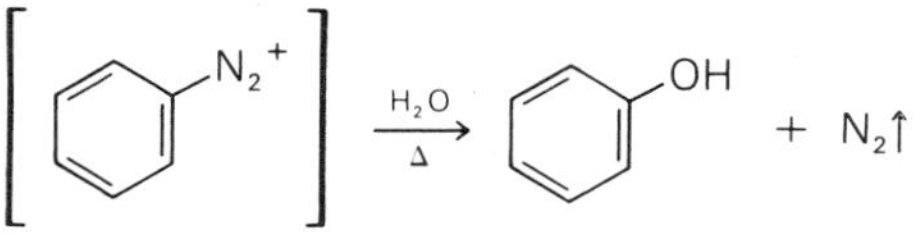

**—Cl, —Br, —CN:** Chloro, bromo, and cyano groups can be introduced via the diazonium salt reaction by heating the salt with the appropriate cuprous salt and either the alkali metal salts or the corresponding HX. The iodo and fluoro groups require other reagents, which are discussed in the following sections.

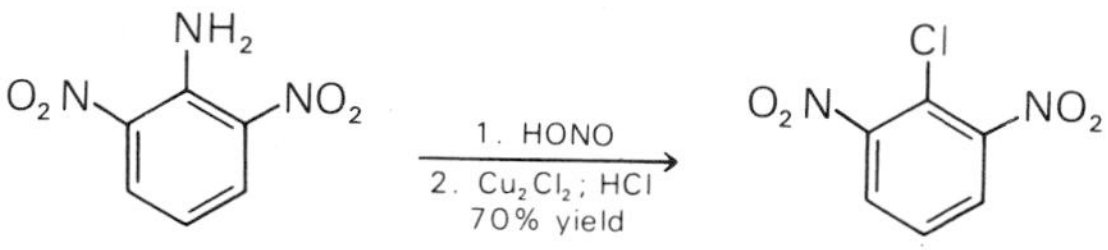

2,6-dinitroaniline 2,6-dinitrochlorobenzene

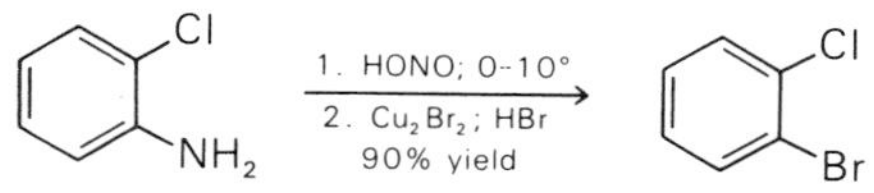

*o*-chloroaniline *o*-chlorobromobenzene

Formulate the following reactions:

**1.** *m*-chlorobromobenzene from *m*-chloroaniline, 91 to 94% yield

**2.** *m*-bromobenzene from *m*-bromoaniline, 80 to 87% yield

**3.** *o*-bromophenol from *o*-anisidine in 88 to 93% yield

**Fluorine, —F.** In general, diazonium salts are water-soluble compounds that decompose violently when dry. The fluoroborate salt, $ArN_2^+BF_4^-$, is exceptional in that it is water-insoluble and usually can be isolated safely. The diazonium salt, such as the chloride, is prepared in the usual manner by treating the amine in hydrochloric acid solution with a cold solution of sodium nitrite. The fluoroborate salt is obtained as a precipitate by the addition of sodium fluoroborate. It can then be isolated, purified by recrystallization to a constant decomposition point, dried, and thermally decomposed. The nitrogen and boron trifluoride are evolved as gases; the latter may be recycled.

$$[C_6H_5N_2^+Cl^-] \xrightarrow{NaBF_4} C_6H_5N_2^+BF_4^- \xrightarrow{\Delta} C_6H_5F + N_2\uparrow + BF_3\uparrow$$

benzenediazonium chloride — benzenediazonium fluoborate — fluorobenzene

$$BF_3 + NaF \longrightarrow NaBF_4$$

When nitro groups are present on the aromatic ring, the thermal decomposition is often explosive; sand or some other inert material is often used as a moderator which "dilutes" the diazonium salt.

$$m\text{-}CH_3C_6H_4NH_2 \xrightarrow[\text{3. }\Delta\text{; dry salt; 90\% yield}]{\text{1. HONO; 2. }NaBF_4} m\text{-}CH_3C_6H_4F$$

*m*-toluidine — *m*-fluorotoluene

$$\text{7-aminoquinoline} \xrightarrow[\text{3. }\Delta\text{ at 120°; 30\% yield}]{\text{1. HONO; 2. }NaBF_4} \text{7-fluoroquinoline}$$

7-aminoquinoline — 7-fluoroquinoline

1. HONO
2. $NaBF_4$
3. Δ 60% yield

3-aminobiphenyl → 3-fluorobiphenyl

**Iodine, —I:** The iodo group can be introduced by treating the diazonium salt solution with potassium iodide.

$$\left[ C_6H_5N_2^+\,Cl^- \right] \xrightarrow[\Delta]{KI} C_6H_5I + N_2\uparrow + KCl$$

**Nitro group, —$NO_2$:** Even the nitro group itself can be introduced by a diazonium salt reaction; but **direct nitration is usually a better method when feasible.** An example from the naphthalene series illustrates these methods.

naphthalene —direct nitration→ 1,8-dinitronaphthalene + 1,5-dinitronaphthalene

4-nitro-1-naphthylamine —1. HONO; 2; $NaNO_2$; Cu, 55% yield→ 1,4-dinitronaphthalene

The finely divided copper in this reaction is prepared by reduction of cupric sulfate with sodium sulfite.

$$CuSO_4 + SO_3^{--} + H_2O \longrightarrow Cu\downarrow + 2SO_4^{--} + 2H^+$$

> Suggest a method of synthesizing 4-nitro-1-naphthylamine from naphthalene. *Caution*: Direct nitration of α-naphthylamine might be expected to lead to naphthoquinone formation.

**—NH—NH$_2$:** Sodium sulfite will also reduce diazonium salts directly, giving the corresponding phenylhydrazine.

$$[C_6H_5\overset{+}{N}\equiv N\ Cl^-] \xrightarrow[H_2O]{Na_2SO_3} C_6H_5NH—NH_2$$

**Phenyl group:** Symmetrical biphenyls, which can also be prepared by heating aryl halides with finely divided copper metal (Ullmann reaction), are obtained when diazonium salts are heated with finely divided copper. Another common preparation of copper for diazonium salt decomposition is the reduction of cupric sulfate by hydroxylamine.

$$Cu^{++} + 2H_2H—OH \longrightarrow Cu\downarrow + N_2\uparrow + 2H_2O + 2H^+$$

$$\text{anthranilic acid} \xrightarrow[75\%\ \text{yield}]{Cl_2;\ 25°} \text{3,5-dichloro-2-aminobenzoic acid} \xrightarrow[\substack{2.\ Cu;\ NH_4OH;\ \Delta \\ 50\%\ \text{yield}}]{1.\ HCl + NaNO_2;\ 10°} \text{D,L-4,4',6,6'-tetrachlorodiphenic acid}$$

anthranilic acid — 3,5-dichloro-2-aminobenzoic acid — D,L-4,4',6,6'-tetrachlorodiphenic acid

**Para substituted biphenyls:** Para substituted biphenyls result from the decomposition of diazonium salts in the presence of substituted benzenes. This copper-catalyzed coupling, which takes place in basic solution, occurs with the *loss* of nitrogen.

$$[C_6H_5—N_2^+] + C_6H_5Z \xrightarrow[NaOH]{Cu} C_6H_5—C_6H_4—Z + N_2\uparrow$$

$$[Z—C_6H_4—N_2^+] + C_6H_6 \xrightarrow[NaOH]{Cu} C_6H_5—C_6H_4—Z + N_2\uparrow$$

### 16-15 COUPLING REACTIONS OF DIAZONIUM IONS

Compounds containing the azo linkage, —N=N—, can be formed by coupling diazonium salts to aromatic molecules containing strongly electron-donating substituents such as —NR$_2$, —OH, or —O$^-$. The commercial importance of this reaction lies in the preparation of dyes and other coloring agents. Note the possibility of cis-trans isomerism about the nitrogen-nitrogen double bond.

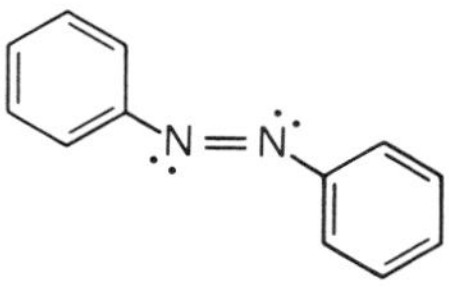

*trans*-azobenzene

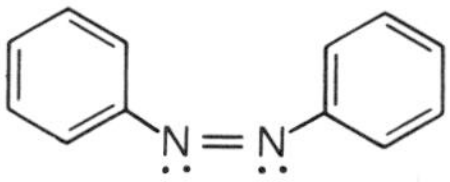

*cis*-azobenzene

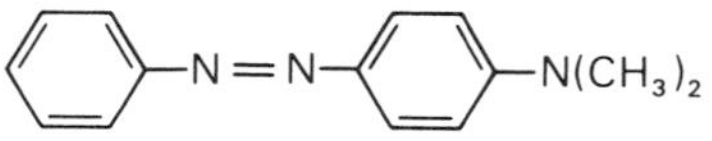

*p*-dimethylaminoazobenzene (Butter yellow) carcinogenic

The acidity of the solution in which coupling of diazonium ions with amines or phenols takes place is critical. ***Amines*** are usually coupled in weakly acidic solution (pH 6 to 7), where a significant concentration of the amine, $—NR_2$, rather than the ammonium ion, $—\overset{+}{N}R_2H$, exists. ***Phenols***, on the other hand, are usually coupled in weakly basic solution (pH 7 to 8), where the phenoxide ion, $—O^-$, rather than the phenol itself, —OH, undergoes reaction.

Another factor to be considered is the nature of the diazonium species. In aqueous solution there exist equilibria between the ion, the corresponding hydroxide, and its anion.

$$[ArN_2^+] \rightleftharpoons [ArN{=}N{-}OH] \rightleftharpoons [Ar{-}N{=}N{-}O^-]$$

diazonium ion diazohydroxide diazotate ion

Since the diazonium ion alone is the most electrophilic species, an appreciable concentration must be present to effect the coupling.

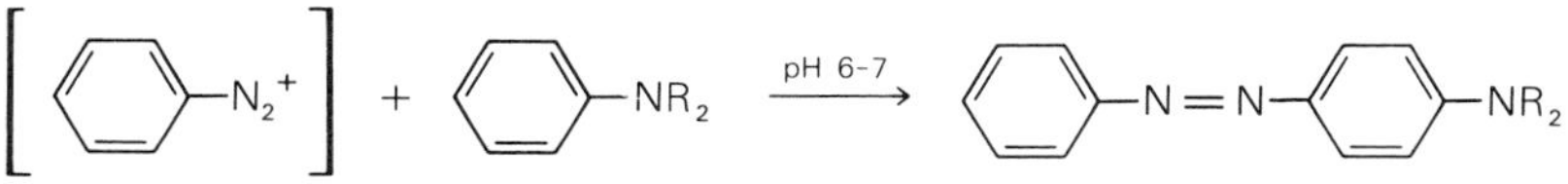

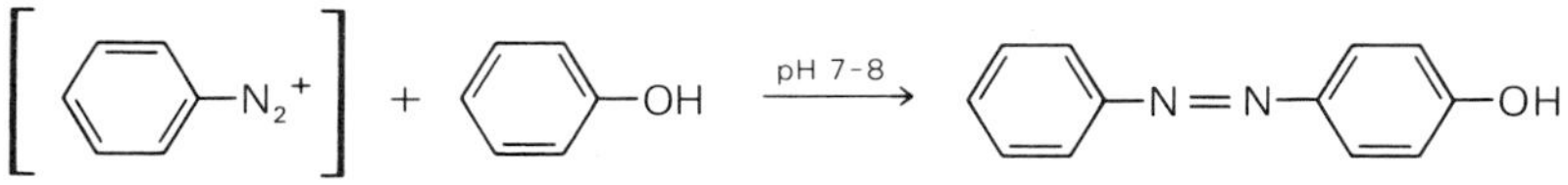

$$[C_6H_5{-}N_2^+] + C_6H_5{-}NR_2 \xrightarrow{\text{pH 6-7}} C_6H_5{-}N{=}N{-}C_6H_4{-}NR_2$$

$$[C_6H_5{-}N_2^+] + C_6H_5{-}OH \xrightarrow{\text{pH 7-8}} C_6H_5{-}N{=}N{-}C_6H_4{-}OH$$

## SUGGESTED READINGS

### Qualitative tests and reactions

Baumgarten, R.J.: Aliphatic Deaminations in Organic Synthesis, *J. Chem. Educ.*, **43**, 398 (1966). Discusses reactions of the $R{-}NH_2 \longrightarrow R{-}Y$ type.

Fanta, P.E., and C.S. Wang: Limitation of the Hinsberg Method for Primary Amines, *J. Chem. Educ.*, **41**, 280 (1964).

Frigerio, N.A.: The Coupling of Diazonium Salts, *J. Chem. Educ.*, **43**, 142 (1966).

Hein, G.E.: The Reaction of Tertiary Amines with Nitrous Acid, *J. Chem. Educ.*, **40**, 181 (1963).

Valentine, J.L., J.B. Entriken, and M.W. Hanson: A Test for the Subclasses of Aliphatic Amines, *J. Chem. Educ.*, **41**, 569 (1964).

Weiss, H.M.: Selective Reduction of Dinitro Compounds, *J. Chem. Educ.*, **43**, 384 (1966). Discusses the reduction of aromatic nitro compounds with ammonium sulfide.

### Others

Brown, H.C.: The Chemistry of Molecular Shapes, *J. Chem. Educ.*, **36**, 424 (1959). Relates steric effects to observed basicities of amines.

Idoux, J.P.: Conformational Analysis and Chemical Reactivity, *J. Chem. Educ.*, **44**, 495 (1967). Stereochemical predictions of products from elimination reactions of amines.

Plummer, A.J., and F.F. Yonkman: Antihypertensive and Diuretic Agents: Past, Present and Future, *J. Chem. Educ.*, **37**, 179 (1960). Discusses the clinical use of some nitrogen-containing compounds.

## PROBLEMS

**1.** Explain why each of the following reactions is not a feasible method of preparation of the given product and show how the given product can be synthesized in good yield and high purity. Use any necessary starting materials.

★(*a*) $C_6H_5Cl \xrightarrow{NH_3} C_6H_5NH_2 + HCl$

★(*b*) $2\,C_6H_5-CH_2-CH_2-Br + 2NH_3 \longrightarrow (C_6H_5-CH_2-CH_2)_2N-H + 2HBr$

(*c*) $CH_3-CH_2-C(CH_3)_2-CH_2-NH_2 \xrightarrow{HONO} CH_3-CH_2-C(CH_3)_2-CH_2OH + N_2\uparrow + H_2O$

★(*d*) $C_6H_5NH_2 \xrightarrow{Br_2}$ *m*-$BrC_6H_4NH_2$ $+ HBr$

(*e*) $CH_3$-benzene $\xrightarrow{F_2}$ p-fluorotoluene ($CH_3$, F) + HF

★(*f*) p-dinitrobenzene ($NO_2$, $NO_2$) $\xrightarrow[HCl]{Sn}$ p-nitroaniline ($NH_2$, $NO_2$)

(*g*) bromobenzene (Br) $\xrightarrow{NH_2—NH_2}$ phenylhydrazine (NH—$NH_2$) + HBr

★(*h*) iodobenzene (—I) + p-iodotoluene (I, $H_3C$) $\xrightarrow[\Delta]{Cu}$ 4-methylbiphenyl (—$CH_3$) + $CuI_2$

**2.** Arrange the following compounds in order of decreasing basicity.

(*a*) toluene, benzylamine, ammonia, acetimide

★(*b*) *n*-propylamine, triphenylamine, *p*-toluidine, ammonia, acetimide, acetamide

★(*c*) *o*-cresol, *o*-toluidine, *o*-methylbenzoic acid, phthalimide, *o*-methylbenzyl alcohol

(*d*) tetramethylammonium hydroxide, sodium hydroxide, *n*-butylamine, aniline

**3.** Name the starting material(s) and give the name and structural formula for the product(s). If no reaction occurs, write N.R. If a reaction does occur, show the mechanism and describe it by a phrase or a few words.

(*a*) benzene ring with $CH_3$, I, $NO_2$ $\xrightarrow{NH_3}$

★(*b*) benzene ring with $CH_3$ and $CH_2$—Br (para) $\xrightarrow{NH_3\ (xs)}$

(*c*) five-membered ring imide with two C=O (O), N—H, two $H_3C$ and two $CH_3$ groups $\xrightarrow[25°]{dil.\ Na^+OH^-}$

★(*d*) $CH_3CH_2CH_2CH_2CH_2\overset{O}{\overset{\|}{C}}NH_2$ $\xrightarrow[Br_2]{NaOH}$

★(*e*) $CH_3—\overset{+}{N}(CH_2CH_3)(CH_2—CH_2—CH=CH_2)—CH_3$ $OH^-$ $\xrightarrow{\Delta}$

(*f*) N,N-dimethyl-m-toluidine [benzene ring bearing $N(CH_3)_2$ and $CH_3$ meta] $\xrightarrow[NaNO_2]{HCl}$

★(*g*) $C_6H_5-SO_2Cl + (CH_3)_2CH-CH_2NH_2 \xrightarrow{OH^-}$

## REVIEW PROBLEM SET FOR CHAPS. 9 TO 16

**1.** Name the following compounds and show a simple chemical method, based on differences in acidity and basicity, for separating each of the following mixtures and recovering each of the compounds in pure form:

(*a*) $C_6H_5OH$ $C_6H_5CH_2OH$ $C_6H_5CO_2H$

(*b*) $C_6H_5OH$ $p\text{-}CH_3C_6H_4CH_3$ $C_6H_5NH_2$

(*c*) $C_6H_5OH$ $C_6H_5OCH_3$ $p\text{-}H_2NC_6H_4CO_2H$ $C_6H_5CO_2H$

**2.** Formulate the following transformations by the use of projection formulas:

$$\begin{array}{c} OH \\ | \\ H-C-H \\ | \\ H-\overset{*}{C}-CH_3 \\ | \\ CH_2 \\ | \\ CH_3 \end{array} \xrightarrow{KMnO_4} C_5H_{10}O_2 \xrightarrow{SOCl_2} C_5H_9OCl \xrightarrow[Pd\text{-}BaSO_4]{H_2}$$

$$C_5H_{10}O \xrightarrow[CH_2O]{Ca(OH)_2} C_6H_{14}O_2 \text{ (not resolvable)}$$

$$\downarrow KMnO_4$$

$$C_6H_{10}O_4 \text{ (acid, not resolvable)} \xleftarrow{KMnO_4} \text{racemic } C_6H_{12}O_3 \text{ (acidic, resolvable)}$$

**3.** Write the formula of the simplest optically active hydroxy acid $C_nH_{2n}O_3$ which upon oxidation would give:

(*a*) a meso-dicarboxylic acid, $C_nH_{2n-2}O_4$
(*b*) an optically active dicarboxylic acid
(*c*) an inactive dicarboxylic acid, $C_nH_{2n-2}O_4$, having no optical isomers

**4.** A person unfamiliar with the mechanism of organic reactions might attempt to carry out the chemical reactions shown below. Point out and justify an alternative or accompanying pathway which you would expect each reaction to take:

(*a*) $(CH_3)_3CBr + NaNH_2 \xrightarrow{\text{toluene}} (CH_3)_3C{-}NH_2 + NaBr$

(*b*) $(CH_3)_2\underset{\diagdown O \diagup}{C{-}CH_2} + EtOH \xrightarrow{H_2SO_4} (CH_3)_2{-}\underset{\large OH}{\underset{|}{C}}{-}CH_2OEt$

(*c*) *trans*-2-bromocyclohexanol $\xrightarrow{\text{HBr}}$ *cis*-1,2-dibromocyclohexane

**5.** Which substrate reacts more rapidly with silver acetate in acetic acid? Give a reason for each choice.

(*a*) $CH_3CH_2CH_2{-}Br$ or $CH_3{-}\overset{\large Br}{\overset{|}{C}H}{-}CH_3$
(*b*) $C_6H_5{-}CH_2{-}Cl$ or $C_6H_5{-}CH_2CH_2Cl$
(*c*) $CH_3{-}\ddot{\underset{..}{O}}{-}CH_2Cl$ or $CH_3CH_2CH_2{-}Cl$
(*d*) $CH_3{-}\overset{\large Cl}{\overset{|}{C}H}{-}CH_3$ or $CH_3{-}\overset{\large I}{\overset{|}{C}H}{-}CH_3$

**6.** Arrange the following series of compounds in order of increasing acidity giving a theoretical explanation of the place of each acid in the series:

(*a*) $H_2O$, $CH_3CH_2CH_2CH_2OH$, $Cl_3CCO_2H$, $CH_3CH_2CH_2CO_2H$, $CH_3CH_2\underset{\large Br}{\underset{|}{C}H}CO_2H$, $BrCH_2CH_2CH_2CO_2H$

(*b*) $CH_3CO_2H$, $ICH_2CO_2H$, $ClCH_2CO_2H$, $FCH_2CO_2H$

(*c*) phenol ($C_6H_5OH$), $H_3C{-}C_6H_4{-}CO_2H$ (para), $Cl{-}C_6H_4{-}CO_2H$ (para), 2,4,6-trinitrophenol (OH with $O_2N$, $NO_2$, $NO_2$)

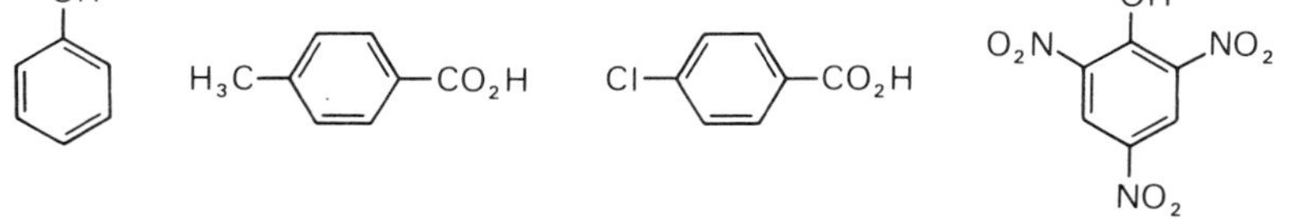

**7.** Give the structure of (*a*) and (*b*):

1,2-dimethylenecyclohexane + $H{-}C{\equiv}C{-}COOEt \longrightarrow C_{13}H_{18}O_2$ (*a*) $\xrightarrow[300°]{Pd, C}$ $C_{13}H_{12}O_2$ (*b*) $\xrightarrow{H_3O^+}$ β-naphthoic acid

**8.** Arrange the following series of compounds in order of increasing basicity and explain:

(*a*) $CH_3C(=O){-}NH_2$ $\quad NH_3 \quad C_6H_5{-}NH_2 \quad C_6H_{11}{-}N(CH_3){-}CH_3$

(*b*) $CH_3NH_2 \quad CH_3C(=O){-}N(H){-}C(=O){-}CH_3 \quad$ m-$O_2N{-}C_6H_4{-}NH_2 \quad$ p-$O_2N{-}C_6H_4{-}NH_2$

(*c*) $NH_3 \quad NH_4^+OH^- \quad H_2O \quad NO_2{-}C_6H_4{-}NH_2$ (para)

**9.** Synthesize the following compounds from readily available starting materials:

(*a*) *m*-cresol

(*b*) benzoic acid from nitrobenzene

(*c*) 1-bromo-1-methylcyclohexane ($C_6H_{10}(CH_3)Br$) from cyclohexanol

(*d*) p-$CH_3{-}C_6H_4{-}CO_2H$

(*e*) $OCHCH_2CH_2CH_2CH_2CHO$ from cyclohexanol

(*f*) m-$O_2N{-}C_6H_4{-}CHO$

(*g*) $C_6H_5{-}CH_2CH_2CH_2CH_3$

(*h*) p-$O_2N{-}C_6H_4{-}C(=O){-}CH_3$

(*i*) $CH_3{-}CH_2{-}C(H)(CH_3){-}C(CH_3)(H){-}CHO$

(*j*) $CH_3-C(=O)-CH(CH_2CH(CH_3)CH_3)-CH_2-CH(CH_3)-CH_3$

(*k*) cyclopentanecarboxylic acid ($CO_2H$) from cyclohexanol (OH)

(*l*) 1,8-octanediol from adipic acid

(*m*) 5-bromopentanoic acid from adipic acid

(*n*) m-nitrobenzylamine ($CH_2NH_2$, $NO_2$) from *m*-dinitrobenzene

(*o*) $C_6H_5-N=N-C_6H_4-N(CH_3)_2$

(*p*) m-toluidine ($H_3C$, $NH_2$) from benzoic acid

(*q*) m-dibromobenzene (Br, Br) from benzene

**10.** Name the starting materials and give the structure and name of the products. If no reaction, write N.R. A starred carbon indicates a single optical isomer. Indicate whether the reaction is stereospecific.

(*a*) 2,6-dimethylphenyl allyl ether ($OCH_2-CH=CH_2$; $H_3C$, $CH_3$) $\xrightarrow{\Delta}$

(*b*) phenol (OH) $\xrightarrow[\text{2. HI; }\Delta]{\text{1. NaOH; }(CH_3)_2SO_4}$

(*c*) 2,4,6-trinitrophenol (OH; $O_2N$, $NO_2$, $NO_2$) $\xrightarrow{KHCO_3}$

(*d*) 3-methylcyclopentene ($CH_3$, starred carbon) $\xrightarrow{\text{NBS in dry } CCl_4;\ \Delta}$

(*e*) $H-\overset{*}{C}(CH_3)(CH_2CH_3)-Br$ $\xrightarrow{NH_3}$

(*f*) $CH_3-C(CH_3)_2-O^-Na^+$ $\xrightarrow{CH_3Br}$

(g) [structure: $C_6H_5$–CH(OH)–CH(Br)–$C_6H_5$, with OH and Br shown] $\xrightarrow[\text{internal } S_N2]{\text{OH}^-}$ ? $\xrightarrow[\text{2. } H_3O^+]{\text{1. } CH_3MgBr}$ ?

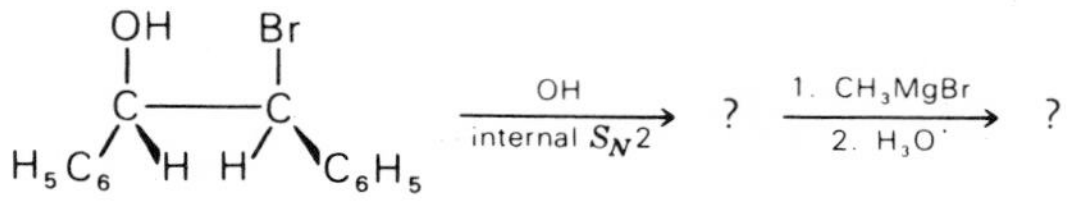

(h) $CH_3Br + (C_6H_5)_3P \xrightarrow{\text{strong base}}$

(i) product in (h) + $CH_3$—C(=O)—$C_6H_5$ ⟶

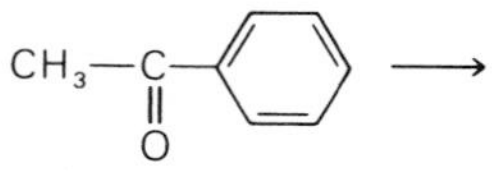

(j) p-chloronitrobenzene (Cl, $NO_2$) $\xrightarrow{\text{OH}^-}$

(k) biphenyl $\xrightarrow[\text{2. } H_3O^+ \quad \text{3. } H_2N\text{—}NH_2\text{; KOH; } \Delta]{\text{1. } C_6H_5COCl \text{, 1.1 equiv } AlCl_3}$

(l) o-methylacetophenone (C(=O)—$CH_3$, $CH_3$) $\xrightarrow[\text{4. } H_2/\text{Pd-}BaSO_4 \text{, sulfur-quinoline} \quad \text{5. } H_2C{=}O \text{ (xs); OH}^-]{\text{1. } Cl_2\text{, NaOH} \quad \text{2. } H_3O^+ \quad \text{3. } SOCl_2}$

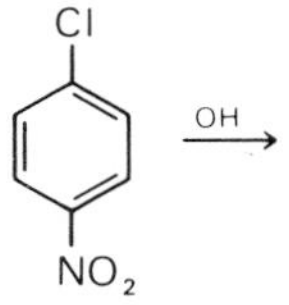

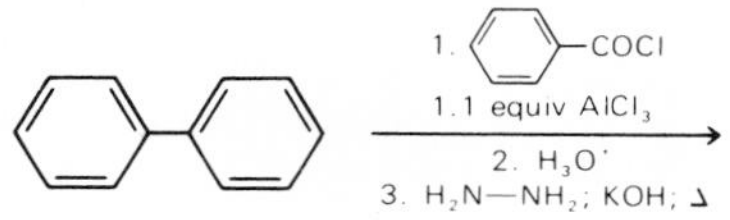

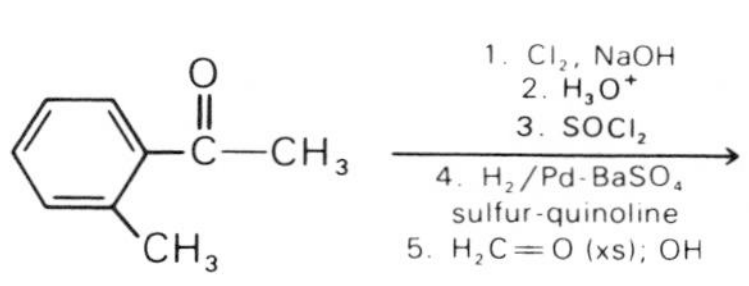

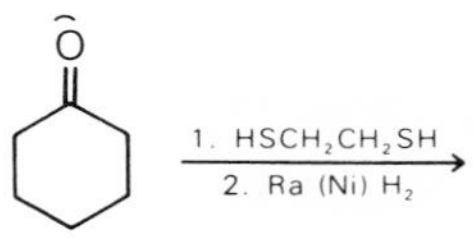

(m) cyclohexanone $\xrightarrow[\text{2. Ra (Ni) } H_2]{\text{1. } HSCH_2CH_2SH}$

(n) $H_3C$—$C_6H_4$—Br $\xrightarrow[\text{DMF}]{\text{KCN; } Cu(CN)_2}$ $\xrightarrow{H_3O^+}$

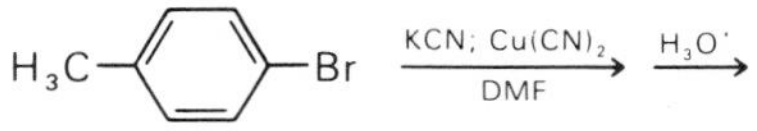

(o) $BrCH_2CH_2Br \xrightarrow{\text{Mg}}$

(p) $CH_3CH_2CH_2CH_2CO_2H \xrightarrow{CH_2N_2}$

(q) cyclohexyl—Br + $CH_3C(=O)$—$CH_2CO_2Et$ $\xrightarrow[\text{3. } \Delta\text{; } -CO_2]{\text{1. NaOEt} \quad \text{2. } H_3O^+}$

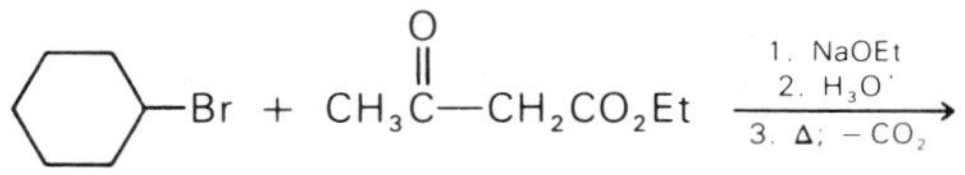

(r) [cyclic barium dicarboxylate: C(=O)—O—Ba—O—C(=O)] $\xrightarrow{\Delta}$

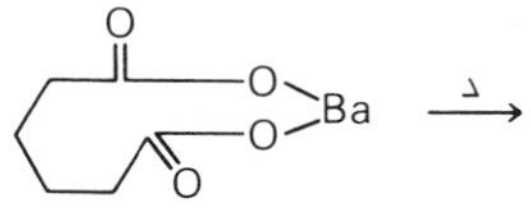

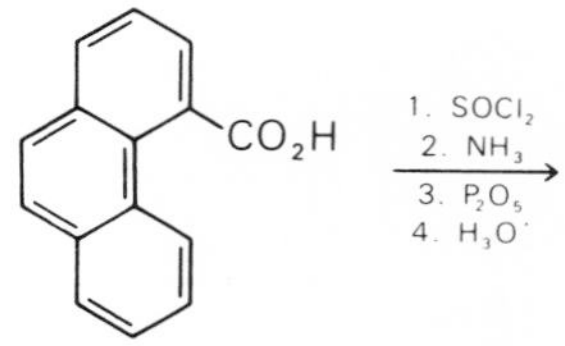

(s) phenanthrene—$CO_2H$ $\xrightarrow[\text{3. } P_2O_5 \quad \text{4. } H_3O^+]{\text{1. } SOCl_2 \quad \text{2. } NH_3}$

(t) cyclohexyl—C(=O)—Cl + $CH_3CO_2^-Na^+$ ⟶

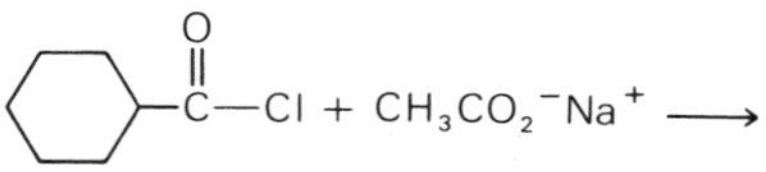

(u) $(CH_3)_3C$—C(=O)—$NH_2$ $\xrightarrow[\text{HCl}]{NaNO_2}$

(*v*) $CH_3-\overset{O}{\overset{\|}{C}}-NH-C_6H_5 \xrightarrow{LiAlH_4}$

(*w*) $CH_3CH_2CO_2H \xrightarrow[\text{3. } H_2O;\ OH^-]{\text{1. P; }Br_2}$

2. phthalimide (N—H) + $OH^-$

(*x*) 2-methylcyclohexyl-$\overset{+}{N}(CH_3)_3$ $OH^-$ $\xrightarrow{\Delta}$

(*y*) $H_3C-C_6H_4-NH_2$ (para) $\xrightarrow[\text{2. } NaBF_4 \text{; 3. } \Delta]{\text{1. HONO}}$

(*z*) $C_6H_5-O-CH_3$ $\xrightarrow[25°]{\text{dil. HCl}}$

# Part Three:
# Organic Compounds of Biological Interest

# Chapter Seventeen

While it is true that any organic compound which contains both an amino group, $—NH_2$, and a carboxyl group, —COOH, is an amino acid, here we shall restrict the discussion to $\alpha$-amino acids

$$\mathrm{R{-}\underset{\underset{NH_2}{|}}{CH}{-}COOH}$$

and, in particular, to those which have been obtained from the hydrolysis of natural proteins. Proteins are large organic molecules composed of many amino acid units joined by an amide linkage, also called a ***peptide bond***. A molecule composed of two amino acids is called a ***dipeptide***, of three amino acids is a ***tripeptide***, and so on until many amino acid units are joined to form a ***polypeptide***, or ***protein***.

$$\underset{\text{glycine}}{\mathrm{\underset{\underset{NH_2}{|}}{CH_2}{-}COOH}} + \underset{\text{glycine}}{\mathrm{\underset{\underset{NH_2}{|}}{CH_2}COOH}} \longrightarrow \underset{\text{glycylglycine (a dipeptide)}}{\mathrm{\underset{\underset{NH_2}{|}}{CH_2}{-}\overset{\overset{O}{\|}}{C}{-}NH{-}CH_2{-}COOH}}$$

By convention, the free-amino end of a peptide is written on the left-hand side and the free-carboxyl end on the right.

$$\underset{\text{alanine (Ala)}}{\mathrm{CH_3{-}\underset{\underset{NH_2}{|}}{CH}{-}COOH}} + \underset{\text{glycine (Gly)}}{\mathrm{\underset{\underset{NH_2}{|}}{CH_2}{-}COOH}} \longrightarrow \underset{\text{alanylglycine (Ala-Gly)}}{\mathrm{CH_3{-}\underset{\underset{NH_2}{|}}{CH}{-}\overset{\overset{O}{\|}}{C}{-}NH{-}CH_2{-}COOH}}$$

$$\underset{\text{glycine}}{\mathrm{\underset{\underset{NH_2}{|}}{CH_2}{-}COOH}} + \underset{\text{alanine}}{\mathrm{CH_3{-}\underset{\underset{NH_2}{|}}{CH}{-}COOH}} \longrightarrow \underset{\text{glycylalanine (Gly-Ala)}}{\mathrm{\underset{\underset{NH_2}{|}}{CH_2}{-}\overset{\overset{O}{\|}}{C}{-}NH{-}\underset{\underset{CH_3}{|}}{CH}{-}COOH}}$$

# Amino Acids and Proteins

Table 17-1 lists the naturally occurring $\alpha$-amino acids which have been isolated by the hydrolysis of proteins from such diverse sources as gelatin, muscle fiber, wool, thyroid tissue, and coral. Well-known examples of proteins are oxytocin (a hormonal protein), insulin, and ACTH.

**Table 17-1**
**$\alpha$-Amino acids from proteins**

Aliphatic neutral amino acids:

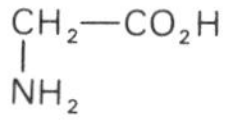

$\underset{NH_2}{CH_2}—CO_2H$ glycine (Gly)

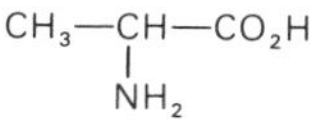

$CH_3—\underset{NH_2}{CH}—CO_2H$ alanine (Ala)

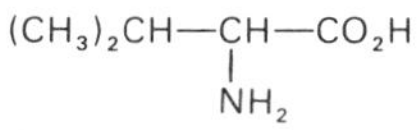

$(CH_3)_2CH—\underset{NH_2}{CH}—CO_2H$ valine (Val)

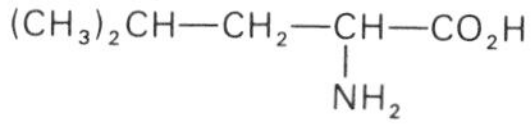

$(CH_3)_2CH—CH_2—\underset{NH_2}{CH}—CO_2H$ leucine (Leu)

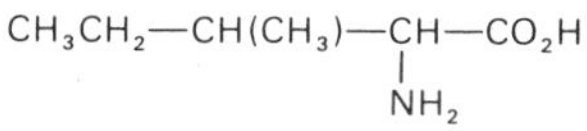

$CH_3CH_2—CH(CH_3)—\underset{NH_2}{CH}—CO_2H$ isoleucine (Ileu)

$\underset{OH}{CH_2}\underset{NH_2}{CH}—CO_2H$ serine (Ser)

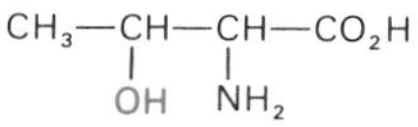

$CH_3—\underset{OH}{CH}—\underset{NH_2}{CH}—CO_2H$ threonine (Thr)

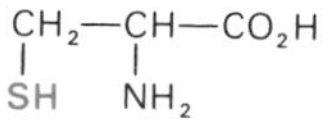

$\underset{SH}{CH_2}—\underset{NH_2}{CH}—CO_2H$ cysteine (CySH)

$\underset{S}{CH_2}—\underset{NH_2}{CH}—CO_2H$
$\underset{S}{|}$
$CH_2\underset{NH_2}{CH}—CO_2H$
cystine (CyS-SCy)

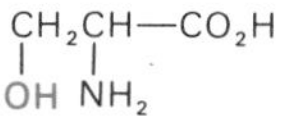

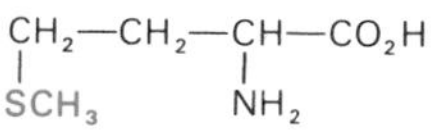

$\underset{SCH_3}{CH_2}—CH_2—\underset{NH_2}{CH}—CO_2H$ methionine (Met)

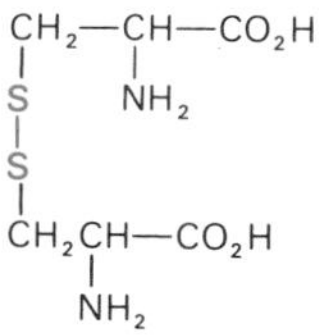

Aliphatic basic amino acids:

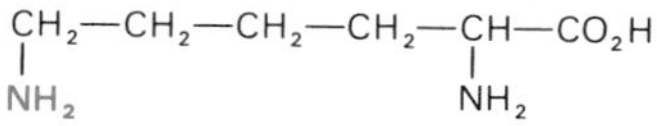

$\underset{NH_2}{CH_2}—CH_2—CH_2—CH_2—\underset{NH_2}{CH}—CO_2H$ lysine (Lys)

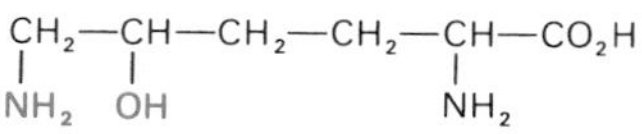

$\underset{NH_2}{CH_2}—\underset{OH}{CH}—CH_2—CH_2—\underset{NH_2}{CH}—CO_2H$ $\delta$-hydroxylysine (Lys-OH)

**Table 17-1 (continued)**

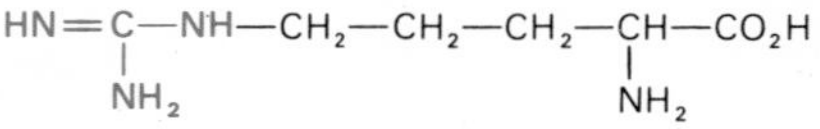

$HN{=}C(NH_2){-}NH{-}CH_2{-}CH_2{-}CH_2{-}CH(NH_2){-}CO_2H$

arginine (Arg)

Aliphatic acidic amino acids:

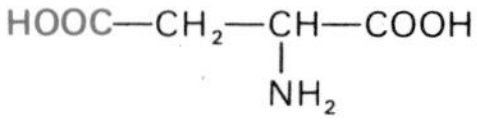

$HOOC{-}CH_2{-}CH(NH_2){-}COOH$

aspartic acid (Asp)

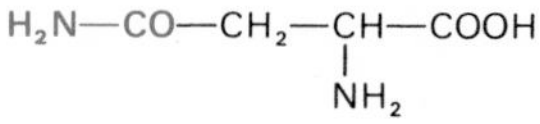

$H_2N{-}CO{-}CH_2{-}CH(NH_2){-}COOH$

asparagine (Asp-$NH_2$)

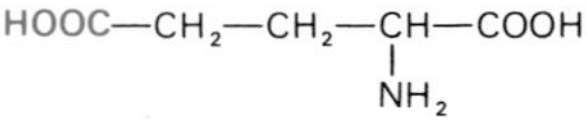

$HOOC{-}CH_2{-}CH_2{-}CH(NH_2){-}COOH$

glutamic acid (Glu)

$H_2N{-}CO{-}CH_2{-}CH_2{-}CH(NH_2){-}COOH$

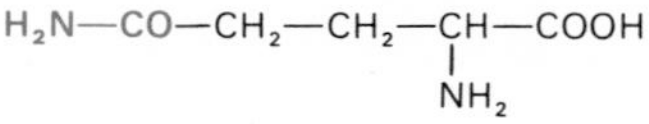

glutamine (Glu-$NH_2$)

Aromatic neutral amino acids:

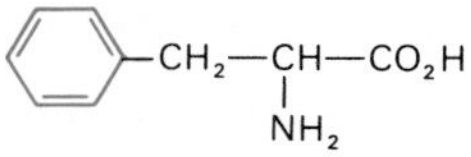

$C_6H_5{-}CH_2{-}CH(NH_2){-}CO_2H$

phenylalanine (Phe)

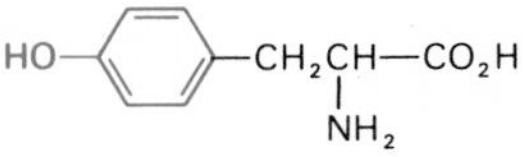

$HO{-}C_6H_4{-}CH_2CH(NH_2){-}CO_2H$

tyrosine (Tyr)

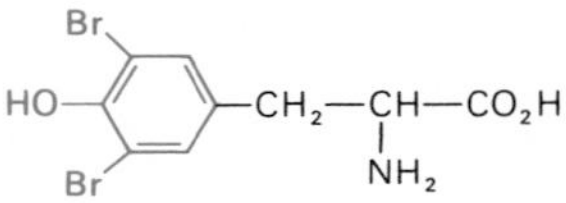

HO–C₆H₂(Br)₂–CH₂–CH(NH₂)–CO₂H

3,5-dibromotyrosine

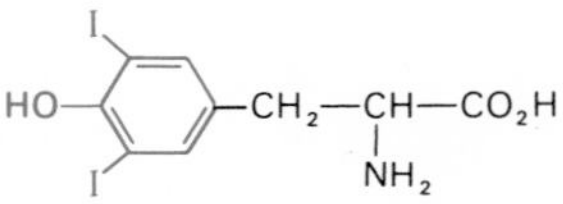

HO–C₆H₂(I)₂–CH₂–CH(NH₂)–CO₂H

3,5-diiodotyrosine

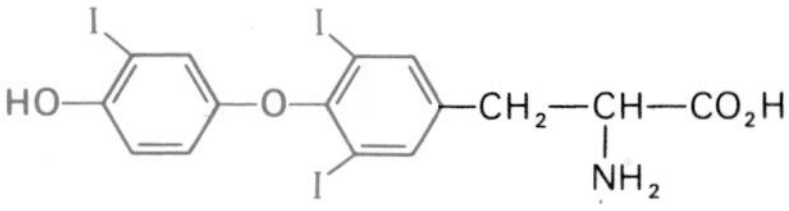

HO–C₆H₃(I)–O–C₆H₂(I)₂–CH₂–CH(NH₂)–CO₂H

3,3',5-triiodothyroxine

HO–C₆H₂(I)₂–O–C₆H₂(I)₂–CH₂–CH(NH₂)–CO₂H

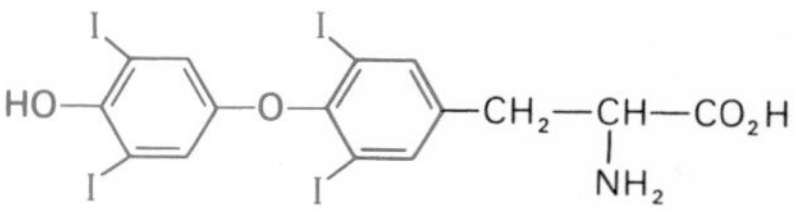

thyroxine

Heterocyclic neutral amino acids:

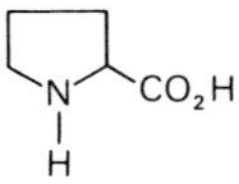

proline (Pro)

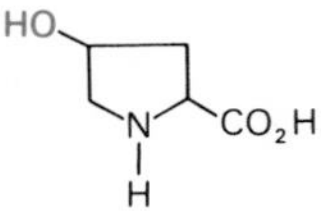

hydroxyproline (Hypro)

Heterocyclic basic amino acids:

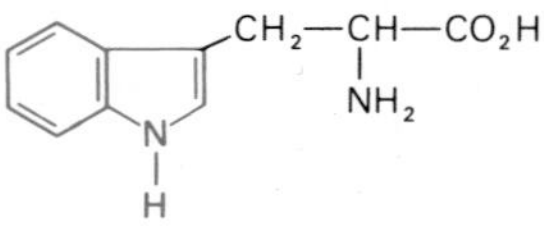

tryptophane (Try)

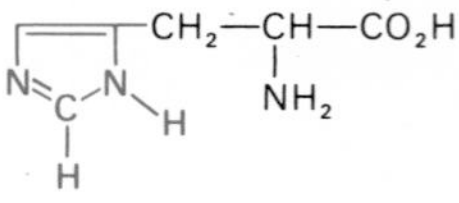

histidine (His)

## NOMENCLATURE AND STRUCTURE

Although the compounds listed in Table 17-1 can be named by the IUPAC system, many of the amino acids, like most other natural products, have trivial names which reflect the source of the material, its properties, or some other circumstance surrounding the isolation. These early names are in general use, and for simplicity each has been given a standard abbreviation. These abbreviations can be used to designate the ***general structure*** by separating the abbreviations with ***commas*** or the ***specific*** structure by using ***hyphens***. For instance, in an early tripeptide structural determination it was known that the compound contained glycine, alanine, and valine (gly, ala, val); further work showed that the specific order is alanine (amino terminus), valine, glycine (carboxyl terminus), which is designated ala-val-gly.

Amino acids with an equal number of amino and carboxyl groups are called ***neutral amino acids***, whereas those with a greater number of mino groups, e.g., lysine, $CH_2(NH_2)CH_2CH_2CH_2CH(NH_2)COOH$, are called basic and those with a greater number of carboxyl groups, e.g., aspartic acid, $HOOCCH_2CH(NH_2)COOH$, are called ***acidic***. This is the arrangement followed in Table 17-1, which also takes note of whether the acids are aromatic or heterocyclic.

All the amino acids shown in Table 17-1 are related in optical configuration to L-glyceraldehyde; however, the sign of rotation of an amino groups e.g., lysine, $CH_2(NH_2)CH_2CH_2CH_2CH(NH_2)COOH$, are called acids from natural sources have the L configuration, the D amino acids can be synthesized. Some naturally occurring D amino acids have been isolated, but the sources are usually metabolic products of lower organisms. For example, D-alanine, D-valine, and D-phenylalanine have been isolated and identified from polypeptide hydrolysates of certain compounds produced by bacteria. Table 17-2 shows the structures of some amino acids (and their source) which have been isolated from nonprotein materials.

Most amino acids are nonvolatile, crystalline organic compounds with high melting (or decomposition) points. They are generally soluble in water but rather insoluble in the common organic solvents. The aqueous solutions have a high dielectric constant, and the structure of the solvated amino acid is predominantly dipolar rather than the implied covalent structure we have been writing. This dipolar structure is also called the ***zwitterion*** form.

$$CH_3—\underset{\substack{|\\NH_2}}{CH}—COOH \qquad CH_3—\underset{\substack{|\\{}^{+}NH_3}}{CH}—COO^-$$

alanine — dipolar form (zwitterion)

Since all amino acids incorporate at least one acidic, —COOH, and one basic, $—NH_2$, group, the principal species in solution depends on

**Table 17-2 Amino acids from nonprotein sources**

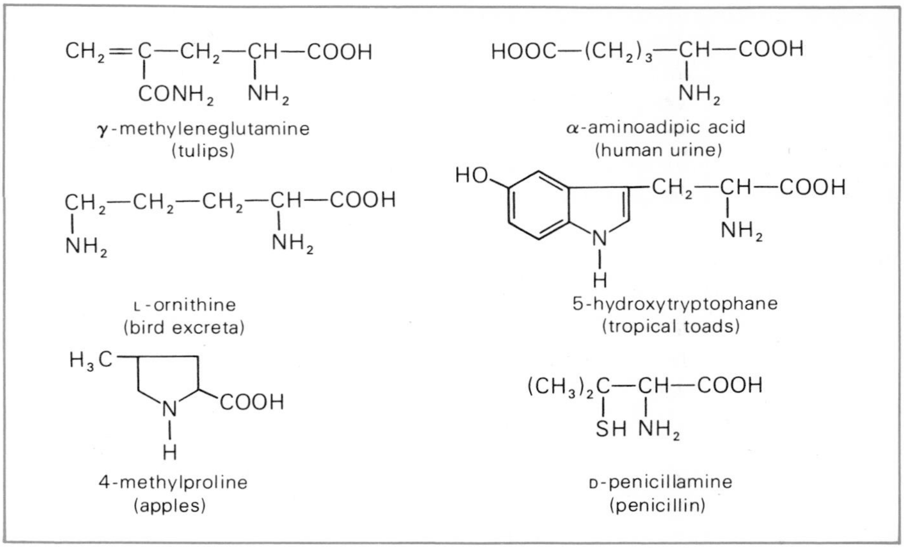

| Structure | Name (source) | Structure | Name (source) |
|---|---|---|---|
| $CH_2{=}C(CONH_2){-}CH_2{-}CH(NH_2){-}COOH$ | γ-methyleneglutamine (tulips) | $HOOC{-}(CH_2)_3{-}CH(NH_2){-}COOH$ | α-aminoadipic acid (human urine) |
| $CH_2(NH_2){-}CH_2{-}CH_2{-}CH(NH_2){-}COOH$ | L-ornithine (bird excreta) | HO-indole(N–H)–$CH_2{-}CH(NH_2){-}COOH$ | 5-hydroxytryptophane (tropical toads) |
| $H_3C$-pyrrolidine(N–H)-COOH | 4-methylproline (apples) | $(CH_3)_2C(SH){-}CH(NH_2){-}COOH$ | D-penicillamine (penicillin) |

the acid-base equilibria established and, thus, on the pH. As would be expected, the cation is the predominant form in acid solution (low pH), the dipolar form occurs near pH 6, and the anion is the important form in base (high pH).

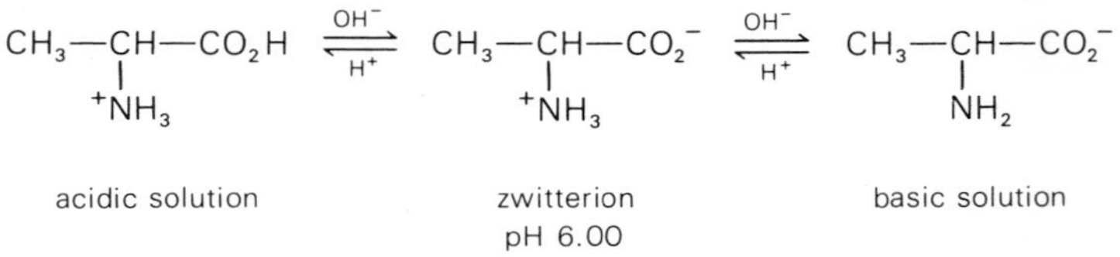

$$\underset{\text{acidic solution}}{CH_3{-}\underset{{}^{+}NH_3}{CH}{-}CO_2H} \underset{H^+}{\overset{OH^-}{\rightleftharpoons}} \underset{\substack{\text{zwitterion}\\ \text{pH 6.00}}}{CH_3{-}\underset{{}^{+}NH_3}{CH}{-}CO_2^-} \underset{H^+}{\overset{OH^-}{\rightleftharpoons}} \underset{\text{basic solution}}{CH_3{-}\underset{NH_2}{CH}{-}CO_2^-}$$

Under the influence of an electric field the amino acid cation (in acid solution) migrates to the negative pole (cathode); under basic conditions the anion migrates to the positive pole (anode). The ***isoelectric point*** is the pH at which the zwitterion predominates; it does not migrate under the influence of an electric field. The isoelectric point of most neutral amino acids is in the range of pH 5 to 6; for the acidic ones pH 2 to 3 and for the basic ones pH 9 to 11. Since the isoelectric point is characteristic for a particular amino acid, it is one means of identification.

## SYNTHESIS OF AMINO ACIDS

### 17-1 AMMONOLYSIS OF α-HALO ACIDS

Treatment of a carboxylic acid (containing at least one α hydrogen atom) with bromine and a catalytic amount of red phosphorus (or $PCl_3$) gives the α-bromo acid in good yield. Subsequent treatment of this bromo acid with a ***large excess*** of ammonia, to avoid dialkylation, gives the racemic amino acid.

$$CH_3CH_2CO_2H \xrightarrow[\text{red P cat.}]{Br_2} CH_3-\underset{Br}{CH}-CO_2H \xrightarrow[\text{70\% yield}]{NH_3\,(xs)} CH_3-\underset{NH_2}{CH}-CO_2H$$

propanoic acid — D, L-2-bromopropanoic acid — D, L-alanine

$$(CH_3)_2CHCH_2COOH \xrightarrow[\text{88\% yield}]{Br_2,\ PCl_3\ cat.} (CH_3)_2CH\underset{Br}{CH}COOH \xrightarrow[\text{50\% yield}]{NH_3\,(xs)} (CH_3)_2CH\underset{NH_2}{CH}COOH$$

isovaleric acid — α-bromoisovaleric acid — D, L-valine

## 17-2 GABRIEL PHTHALIMIDE SYNTHESIS

The synthesis of amino acids using phthalimide is similar to that described in Sec. 16-8 for the preparation of pure primary amines from halides.

$$\text{phthalimide (N—H)} \xrightarrow[2.\ \underset{Cl}{CH_2}-CO_2Et]{1.\ KOH} \text{phthalimide-N}-CH_2-CO_2Et \xrightarrow[\Delta]{H_3O^+} \underset{NH_2}{CH_2}-CO_2H + C_6H_4(CO_2H)_2$$

phthalimide — 90% yield

## 17-3 USE OF HEXAMETHYLENETETRAMINE

In addition to being a useful reagent for the conversion of halides to aldehydes (Sec. 13-4), hexamethylenetetramine (HMTA) can be used to synthesize amines (from halides) and amino acids (from α-halo acids). The intermediate quaternary ammonium salt is formed in good yield and is readily cleaved with acid.

$$CH_3-\underset{Br}{CH}-CO_2H + \text{HMTA} \longrightarrow [\text{salt}] \xrightarrow[HCl]{EtOH} CH_3-\underset{NH_2\cdot HCl}{CH}-CO_2CH_2CH_3$$

α-bromopropanoic acid — HMTA — ethyl alanine hydrochloride, 93% yield

$$(CH_3)_2CH-CH_2-\underset{Br}{CH}-CO_2H + C_6H_{12}N_4 \longrightarrow [\text{salt}] \xrightarrow[HCl]{EtOH} (CH_3)_2CH-CH_2-\underset{NH_2\cdot HCl}{CH}-CO_2CH_2CH_3$$

α-bromoisovaleric acid — HMTA — ethyl leucine hydrochloride, 91% yield

### 17-4 STRECKER SYNTHESIS

Cyanohydrins, prepared from aldehydes and hydrogen cyanide, can be converted to $\alpha$-amino nitriles and subsequently hydrolyzed to $\alpha$-amino acids.

$$C_6H_5-CH_2-CHO \xrightarrow{HCN} C_6H_5-CH_2-\underset{OH}{\overset{H}{C}}-CN \xrightarrow{NH_3} C_6H_5-CH_2-\underset{NH_2}{\overset{H}{C}}-CN \xrightarrow{1.\ OH^-\ 2.\ H_3O^+} C_6H_5-CH_2-\underset{NH_2}{CH}-CO_2H$$

phenylacetaldehyde

phenylalanine
74% yield

A modification of this reaction avoids the handling of toxic liquid hydrogen cyanide by the direct conversion of the aldehyde to the $\alpha$-amino nitrile using ammonium cyanide. A radioactive carbon can be introduced by this method:

$$C_6H_5-CH_2-CHO \xrightarrow[2.\ H_3O^+]{1.\ NH_4{}^{14}CN} C_6H_5-CH_2-\underset{NH_2}{CH}-{}^{14}CO_2H$$

29% yield

### 17-5 MALONIC ESTER SYNTHESIS

Malonic ester, a useful reagent for the preparation of carboxylic acids from halides ($RCH_2-X \longrightarrow RCH_2-CH_2COOH$, Sec. 14.9), can be employed directly or converted to one of its nitrogen-containing derivatives. The direct synthesis of a racemic $\alpha$ amino acid from the related halide is illustrated by the preparation of leucine, in which two carbons are added via malonic ester and the amino function is introduced by ammonolysis of the $\alpha$-bromo acid.

$$(CH_3)_2CH-CH_2Br + H_2C(CO_2Et)_2 \xrightarrow{NaOEt} (CH_3)_2CH-CH_2-CH(CO_2Et)_2 \xrightarrow[\Delta]{H^+}$$

isobutyl bromide — diethyl isobutylmalonate

$$(CH_3)_2CH-CH_2-CH_2-CO_2H \xrightarrow[P\ (cat.)]{Br_2} (CH_3)_2CH-CH_2-\underset{Br}{CH}-CO_2H \xrightarrow{NH_3\ (xs)}$$

4-methylpentanoic acid — 2-bromo-4-methylpentanoic acid

$$(CH_3)_2CH-CH_2-\underset{NH_2}{CH}-CO_2H$$

leucine in 30% yield
based on 4-methylpentanoic acid

A similar series of reactions, starting with diethyl malonate and benzyl chloride, gives phenylalanine in 60% yield. Formulate the steps and name the compounds in this sequence.

Diethyl aminomalonate, $H_2N—CH(CO_2Et)_2$, and its acyl derivatives, $R—CO—NH—CH(CO_2Et)_2$, have been used in the synthesis of $\alpha$-amino acids. These reagents, which can be alkylated at the carbon atom in color, are prepared from malonic ester and nitrous acid followed by reduction and acylation.

$$\underset{\text{diethyl malonate}}{CH_2(CO_2Et)_2} \xrightarrow{HONO} \underset{\text{diethyl nitrosomalonate}}{O{=}N—CH(CO_2Et)_2} \xrightarrow{H_2/Ni} \underset{\text{diethyl aminomalonate}}{\underset{NH_2}{\overset{|}{CH}}(CO_2Et)_2} \xrightarrow{C_6H_5COCl} \underset{\text{diethyl } N\text{-benzoylaminomalonate}}{\underset{NH—CO—C_6H_5}{\overset{|}{CH}}(CO_2Et)_2}$$

$$\underset{NH_2}{\overset{|}{CH}}(CO_2Et)_2 \xrightarrow{(CH_3CO)_2O} \underset{\text{diethyl } N\text{-acetylaminomalonate}}{\underset{NH—CO—CH_3}{\overset{|}{CH}}(CO_2Et)_2}$$

The advantage of using these compounds is that since the (protected) amino group is already present in the decarboxylated product, fewer steps are required for the overall synthesis of a particular optical isomer.

$$\underset{NH—CO—R}{\overset{|}{CH}}(CO_2Et)_2 \xrightarrow[\substack{3.\ H_3O^+\ \text{(form diacid and remove RCO— group)}\\ 4.\ \Delta;\ -CO_2}]{\substack{1.\ \text{NaOEt (remove } H^+ \text{ from } \alpha \text{ carbon)}\\ 2.\ R—X\ \text{(introduce the alkyl group)}}} R—\underset{NH_2}{\overset{}{CH}}—COOH$$

Formulate the synthesis of leucine from diethyl malonate via the $N$-benzoyl derivative. The overall yield is 30% based on malonic ester.

## 17-6 RESOLUTION OF AMINO ACIDS

The synthetic methods described in the previous sections lead to the formation of a racemic mixture of the amino acid; this mixture must be resolved in order to obtain the pure optical isomer. The common methods of resolution were described in Chap. 12. Although enzymatic resolution is sometimes possible, the formation of diastereomeric salts is frequently used to resolve either the *N*-substituted amino acid or the free-amino amide or ester of the amino acid. For example, treatment of DL-*N*-benzoylphenylalanine with cinchonine gives an insoluble salt containing the D isomer.

> Formulate the equations for the above resolution.

## THE SYNTHESIS OF PEPTIDES (PROTEINS)

We now turn to a discussion of the synthesis of peptides from amino acids. For example, suppose we wish to achieve the following transformation:

$$\underset{\displaystyle NH_2}{\underset{|}{A}}\text{—COOH} + \underset{\displaystyle NH_2}{\underset{|}{B}}\text{—COOH} \longrightarrow \underset{\displaystyle NH_2}{\underset{|}{A}}\text{—CO—NH—B—COOH}$$

where A and B may represent either simple amino acids or a peptide.

Peptide syntheses require special precautions and relatively mild conditions in order to avoid racemization of the component amino acids (or peptides) and to achieve high yields of pure peptide products. Classically, five steps are employed for the synthesis of a general peptide of the type shown above: (1) protection of the A—$NH_2$ group, (2) protection of the B—COOH group, (3) activation of the A—COOH group, (4) formation of the peptide bond (amide linkage), and (5) removal of the A—$NH_2$ protective group. It will be seen below that the removal of the B—COOH protective groups needs no special attention. It is clear that without the protection in steps 1 and 2, the reaction which follows (step 4) would also give the peptide containing the amino acids in reverse order.

### 17-7 PROTECTION OF THE AMINO GROUP

Because of its easy removal from the newly formed peptide under mild conditions, the carbobenzoxy group, $C_6H_5$—$CH_2$—O—CO—, abbreviated Cbz—, is commonly employed. The reagent, carbobenzoxy chloride, can be prepared from benzyl alcohol and phosgene.

$$C_6H_5CH_2OH + Cl\text{—}\overset{\displaystyle O}{\overset{\|}{C}}\text{—}Cl \xrightarrow[\text{yield}]{95\%} C_6H_5CH_2O\text{—}\overset{\displaystyle O}{\overset{\|}{C}}\text{—}Cl + HCl$$

The reaction of this chloride with amines is analogous to the reaction of ordinary carboxylic acid chlorides.

$$\underset{\substack{|\\ NH_2}}{CH_2COOH} \xrightarrow[\text{2. } H_3O^+]{\text{1. } C_6H_5-CH_2OCOCl;\ OH^-} \underset{\substack{|\\ NH-COOCH_2C_6H_5}}{CH_2COOH}$$

glycine carbobenzoxyglycine

The phthalyl group, abbreviated Phth—, which is also easy to remove later, can be introduced by heating the amino acid with phthalic anhydride, which prevents the amino group from forming a peptide bond.

$$C_6H_5-CH_2-\underset{\substack{|\\ NH_2}}{CH}-COOH + \text{phthalic anhydride} \xrightarrow[\text{88\% yield}]{\Delta;\ 150°} \text{Phth}N-\underset{\substack{|\\ CH_2-C_6H_5}}{CH}-COOH$$

L-phenylalanine phthalic anhydride phthalyl-L-phenylalanine

### 17-8 PROTECTION OF THE CARBOXYL GROUP

The carboxylic acid function is usually protected during a peptide synthesis by conversion to its sodium salt (with base) or to an unreactive ester (with alcohol and a trace of mineral acid). The ester is removed later by hydrolysis under mild conditions.

### 17-9 ACTIVATION OF THE CARBOXYL GROUP OF THE *N*-PROTECTED AMINO ACID OR PEPTIDE

Activation of the carboxyl group is accomplished by conversion to the acid chloride (with thionyl chloride) or to a very reactive ester, such as the *p*-nitrophenyl ester. A dehydrating agent, *N,N*-dicyclohexylcarbodiimide, $C_6H_{11}-N{=}C{=}N-C_6H_{11}$, can be used to promote the esterification under mild conditions.

$$\underset{\substack{|\\ NH-CO-R}}{CH_2}-COOH + HO-C_6H_4-NO_2 \xrightarrow[\text{(soluble in THF)}]{C_6H_{11}-N=C=N-C_6H_{11}}$$

$$\underset{\substack{|\\ NH-CO-R}}{CH_2}-\overset{\overset{O}{\|}}{C}-O-C_6H_4-NO_2 + C_6H_{11}-NH-\overset{\overset{O}{\|}}{C}-NH-C_6H_{11}$$

*N, N*-dicyclohexylurea (insoluble inTHF)

### 17-10 PEPTIDE-BOND FORMATION

When both a carboxyl group and an amino group have been protected, a peptide bond can form between the two amino acids in only one way.

Since the formation of an amide bond from an amine and an acid formally involves the removal of water,

$$—NH_2 + HOOC— \longrightarrow —NH—CO— + H_2O$$

*N,N*-dicyclohexylcarbodiimide can be used here too. Although simple heating of the two components would achieve the desired peptide-bond formation, using the carbodiimide in THF gives a more controlled reaction under milder conditions.

$$\underset{\displaystyle \text{NH—CO—R}}{\text{A—COOH}} + \underset{\displaystyle NH_2}{\text{B—COOR}} + C_6H_{11}\text{—N=C=N—}C_6H_{11} \xrightarrow[\text{in}]{\text{THF}}$$

$$\underset{\text{insoluble in THF}}{C_6H_{11}\text{—NH—}\overset{O}{\overset{\|}{C}}\text{—NH—}C_6H_{11}} + \underset{\displaystyle \text{NH—CO—R}}{\text{A—CO—NH—B—COOR}}$$

### 17-11 REMOVAL OF THE AMINO PROTECTIVE GROUP

The final step is the removal of the carbobenzoxy or phthalyl protective group. The former can be removed by hydrogenolysis with hydrogen and palladium under mild conditions. The intermediate *N*-carboxyl group is unstable and undergoes spontaneous decarboxylation.

$$\underset{\displaystyle NH\text{—COO—}CH_2\text{—}C_6H_5}{\text{A—CO—NH—B—COOR}} \xrightarrow{H_2/Pd} \left[\underset{\displaystyle \text{NH—COOH}}{\text{A—CO—NH—B—COOR}}\right] + C_6H_5CH_3 \longrightarrow$$

$$\underset{\displaystyle NH_2}{\text{A—CO—NH—B—COOR}} + CO_2$$

The phthalyl group is removed by treating the *N*-protected peptide with hydrazine in alcohol; phthalhydrazide is formed.

$$\text{(phthalimido)N—A—CO—NH—B—COOR} \xrightarrow[\text{alcohol; }\Delta]{H_2N\text{—}NH_2 \text{ in}} \text{phthalhydrazide } (C_6H_4(CO)_2N_2H_2) + H_2N\text{—A—CO—NH—B—COOR}$$

### 17-12 AUTOMATED PEPTIDE SYNTHESIS

A synthetic procedure has been recently developed by which optically pure peptides can be prepared in high yield; amino acids can be incorporated into a peptide in a given sequence. Since the entire procedure can be carried out in a single reaction vessel by using automatic addition and filtration operations, this has been called a ***peptide-synthesis machine***.

The key to this method is the use of an insoluble polymer to which the newly formed peptide is attached. A polystyrene polymer containing chloromethyl groups, $—CH_2Cl$, is treated with an $N$-protected amino acid salt; the protective group is removed, and other amino acids are incorporated by variations of the methods previously described. At all times the reactions are taking place at the surface of the insoluble polymer containing the amino acid or peptide. Finally, after the desired number of amino acids have been incorporated, the peptide is cleaved from the polymer. Shown in Table 17-3 is an example of the chemical process.

**Table 17-3 Representative chemical reactions used in automated peptide syntheses**

**Polystyrene polymer containing chloromethyl groups:**

$$\sim CH_2—CH(C_6H_5)—CH_2—CH(C_6H_5)—CH_2—CH(C_6H_4CH_2Cl)—CH_2—CH(C_6H_5)\sim \quad \text{or polymer}—CH_2Cl$$

↓ protect—NH—CH(R)—COO⁻

$$\text{polymer}—CH_2—O—C(=O)—CH(R)—NH—\text{protect}$$

↓ remove protective group

$$\text{polymer}—CH_2—O—C(=O)—CH(R)—NH_2$$

↓ $N$-protected amino acid: protect—NH—CH(R')—COOH and $N,N'$-dicyclohexylcarbodiimide

$$\text{polymer}—CH_2—O—C(=O)—CH(R)—NH—C(=O)—CH(R')—NH—\text{protect}$$

↓ repeated as many times as desired

$$\text{polymer}—CH_2—O—C(=O)—CH(R)—NH—C(=O)—CH(R')—NH—C(=O)—CH(R'')—NH—\text{protect}$$

↓ HBr in $CF_3COOH$: cleaves the C—O polymer bond and removes the protective group.

$$\text{polymer}—CH_2Br + HO—C(=O)—CH(R)—NH—C(=O)—CH(R')—NH—C(=O)—CH(R'')—NH_2 + \text{protective group}$$

## PHYSICAL STRUCTURE OF PROTEINS

The synthesis and chemical constitution of peptides have been described in the previous sections, but there remains the question of the physical nature and configuration of proteins.

Proteins, which are polymers composed of many amino acid residues, often have molecular weights greater than 10,000. The backbone of these molecules are the amide linkages (peptide bond), and other functional groups which occur in amino acids are attached to this structure; for example,

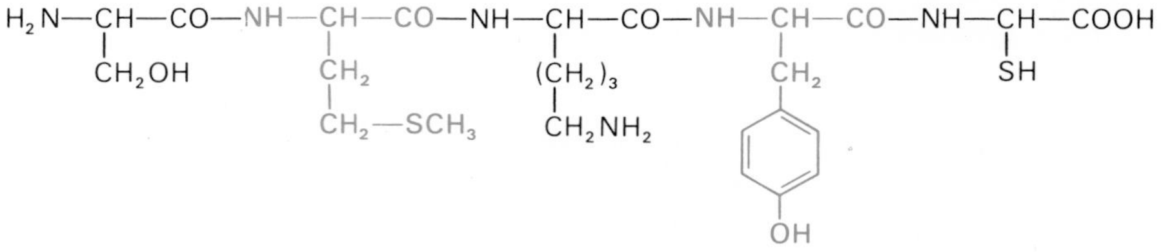

$$H_2N\text{—}\underset{\underset{CH_2OH}{|}}{CH}\text{—}CO\text{—}NH\text{—}\underset{\underset{\underset{CH_2\text{—}SCH_3}{|}}{CH_2}}{\underset{|}{CH}}\text{—}CO\text{—}NH\text{—}\underset{\underset{\underset{CH_2NH_2}{|}}{(CH_2)_3}}{\underset{|}{CH}}\text{—}CO\text{—}NH\text{—}\underset{\underset{\underset{C_6H_4OH}{|}}{CH_2}}{\underset{|}{CH}}\text{—}CO\text{—}NH\text{—}\underset{\underset{SH}{|}}{CH}\text{—}COOH$$

serylthreonyllysyltyrosylcysteine

These functional groups can interact to hold the molecule in a particular conformation. Further, two chains can be cross-linked, commonly by a disulfide, —S—S—, linkage.

There are two main types of proteins: the ***fibrous***, e.g., fibroin of silk, collagen of connective tissue, and keratin of horn, feathers, and nails, and the ***globular***, e.g., egg albumin, casein, and blood-plasma proteins. Fibrous proteins are generally water-insoluble; they tend to be rather elongated in structure and capable of being stretched. Globular proteins, on the other hand, are water-soluble substances; they are more spherically shaped and are cross-linked by side-chain interactions.

Peptides can interact with each other (and with other peptide chains), affording the observed configurations and conformations, in several important ways. The first of these is by hydrogen bonding, particularly between the amide nitrogen and the amide carbonyl.

$$>N\text{—}H\cdots O{=}C<$$

Hydrogen bonding allows some protein molecules to assume a helical conformation and attain a lower energy than is found in the non-hydrogen-bonded molecule. Further, each amide linkage is somewhat flattened into a conformation which allows the maximum overlap of the nitrogen $p$-electrons with the carbonyl $\pi$ bond.

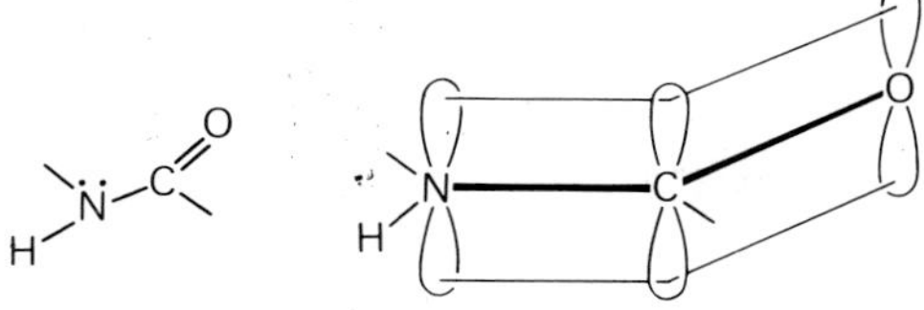


A second type of bonding which occurs both within and between protein molecules is the covalent disulfide linkage, —S—S—. For example, oxidation of a sulfhydryl group, —SH, like that in cysteine

```
CH₂—CH—COOH
|    |
SH   NH₂
```

leads to the disulfide linkage, like that in cystine

```
CH₂—CH—COOH
|    |
S    NH₂
|
S
|
CH₂—CH—COOH
     |
     NH₂
```

Disulfide linkages can be broken by reduction.

The exact geometry of peptides, which is based on such features as hydrogen bonding and disulfide linkages, is a key factor in determining their physical, chemical, and physiological properties. Any process which changes these secondary features is said to ***denaturate*** the protein. Common methods of protein denaturation are treatment with acid, base, some organic solvents, x-rays, or even simple mechanical agitation. The denatured protein is typically less soluble and less physiologically active; often it has been fragmented. Although the details of the denaturing process are not always clearly understood, it is known that most crystalline proteins cannot be induced to crystallize after such treatment.

## STRUCTURAL DETERMINATION

In order to synthesize a naturally occurring peptide or protein it is necessary to know which amino acids comprise the protein and the *order* in which they occur in the molecule. This information can be acquired by a combination of many methods which have been developed for structural determination. Several of the chemical methods are discussed in the following sections.

### 17-13 PARTIAL AND TOTAL HYDROLYSIS

A complex peptide can be hydrolyzed into its constituent amino acids by prolonged refluxing with either 20% hydrochloric acid or 20% sulfuric acid. The total hydrolysis, followed by the quantitative isolation and identification of the individual amino acids, indicates both the specific amino acids present and their relative abundance. This is a tedious manual operation, but automatic amino acid analyzers have been developed which determine the quantity of each amino acid present in a period of about 2 hr using less than 1 g of protein!

If the acid hydrolysis is stopped short of total reaction, the resulting solution contains, in addition to some single amino acids, small peptide fragments such as di-, tri-, tetra-, and pentapeptides. By the stepwise analysis of these fragments and knowing the total amino acid content, it is possible to deduce the *order* of the amino acids in the original protein. The use of base in total or partial hydrolyses causes extensive racemization of the optically active $\alpha$ carbon.

### 17-14 AMINO END-GROUP ANALYSES

Any peptide which is not totally cyclic will have both a free-amino and a free-carboxyl end. Information concerning these terminal amino acids aids in determining the order of amide linkages in the molecule. The following procedures can be carried out on either the original peptide or on the smaller peptide fragments obtained from partial hydrolysis.

Treatment of a peptide with nitrous acid, followed by hydrolysis, will lead to the formation of an $\alpha$ hydroxy acid derived from the amino terminal group.

$$\underset{\text{glycylalanine}}{\underset{NH_2}{\underset{|}{CH_2}}—CO—NH—\underset{CH_3}{\underset{|}{CH}}—COOH} \xrightarrow[2.\ H_3O^+]{1.\ HONO} \underset{\text{lactic acid}}{\underset{OH}{\underset{|}{CH_2}}—COOH} + \underset{\text{alanine}}{CH_3—\underset{NH_2}{\underset{|}{CH}}—COOH}$$

This reaction is similar to the treatment of primary aliphatic amines with nitrous acid (Sec. 16-10). The hydrolysis in the second step of this procedure releases not only the hydroxy acid but also single amino acids and small peptides.

Another frequently used determination of the amino end group involves aromatic nucleophilic displacement of the fluorine atom from 2,4-dinitrofluorobenzene (2,4-DNFB). Recall that nitro groups ortho and para to an aromatic halogen atom activate that atom toward nucleophilic displacement (see Sec. 8-10).

$$O_2N\text{-}C_6H_3(NO_2)\text{-}F + H_2N\text{—}\underset{}{\overset{R}{CH}}\text{—CO—NH—}\overset{R'}{CH}\text{—CO—}$$

$$\downarrow$$

$$O_2N\text{-}C_6H_3(NO_2)\text{-}NH\text{—}\overset{R}{CH}\text{—CO—NH—}\overset{R'}{CH}\text{—CO—} + HF$$

Subsequent hydrolysis of the *N*-substituted original protein or peptide yields the *N*-2,4-dinitrophenylamino acid, together with amino acids and small peptides.

$$O_2N\text{-}C_6H_3(NO_2)\text{-}NH\text{—}\overset{R}{CH}\text{—CO—NH—}\overset{R'}{CH}\text{—CO—}$$

$$\downarrow H_3O^+$$

$$O_2N\text{-}C_6H_3(NO_2)\text{-}NH\text{—}\overset{R}{CH}\text{—COOH} + \underset{NH_2}{\overset{R'}{CH}}\text{—CO—}$$

All these dinitrophenyl derivatives of the common pure amino acids have been prepared, and thus a comparison of the properties of the unknown derivative with those of the known compounds is possible.

## 17-15 CARBOXYL END-GROUP ANALYSIS

The free-carboxyl end of a protein or peptide can be determined chemically by treatment of the molecule with excess hydrazine. All the *amide* linkages are converted to hydrazides, —CO—NHNH$_2$, but the carboxyl group itself remains unaltered. Treatment of the reaction mixture with excess benzaldehyde converts all these amino acid hydrazides to neutral benzal derivatives, —CO—NH—N=CH—C$_6$H$_5$, and the amino acid, containing the free carboxyl group, can readily be separated. The separation is facilitated by the increased molecular weight of the benzal derivative of the hydrazides; the amino acid is of relatively low molecular weight.

$$\underset{\substack{|\\ NH_2}}{CH_2}CO{-}NH{-}\underset{\substack{|\\ CH_3}}{CH}{-}CO{-}NH{-}CH_2{-}COOH \xrightarrow{H_2N{-}NH_2\ (xs)}$$

glycylalanylglycine

$$\left[\underset{\substack{|\\ NH_2}}{CH_2}{-}CO{-}NHNH_2 + CH_3{-}\underset{\substack{|\\ NH_2}}{CH}{-}CO{-}NHNH_2 + \underset{\substack{|\\ NH_2}}{CH_2}{-}COOH\right] \xrightarrow[\Delta]{C_6H_5CHO\ (xs)}$$

$$\underset{\substack{|\\ NH_2}}{CH_2}{-}CONHN{=}CHC_6H_5 + CH_3{-}\underset{\substack{|\\ NH_2}}{CH}CONHN{=}CHC_6H_5 + \underset{\substack{|\\ NH_2}}{CH_2}COOH$$

easily separated

## 17-16 ENZYMATIC HYDROLYSIS

In addition to the purely chemical methods described in previous sections for the structural determination of peptides, it has been found that certain enzymes, which themselves are polypeptides, catalyze the hydrolysis of peptides at certain amide linkages.

Digestive enzymes produced by the pancreas, e.g., trypsin, chymotrypsin, and carboxypeptidases A and B, have been extensively investigated. A brief description of their action will serve to illustrate their usefulness in peptide analyses. Trypsin hydrolyzes only bonds whose carbonyl group is on an amino acid with a positively charged side chain, such as lysine or arginine. Chymotrypsin-catalyzed hydrolysis requires the carbonyl group to be adjacent to an amino acid with an aromatic ring, such as phenylalanine or tyrosine. Trypsin and chymotrypsin catalyze the hydrolysis of internal peptide bonds and are thus known as *endopeptidases*.

$$H_2N{-}CH_2{-}CO{-}NH{-}CH(CH_2CH_2CH_2CH_2NH_2){-}CO{\uparrow}NH{-}CH(CH_3){-}CO{\uparrow}NH{-}CH(CH_2C_6H_5){-}CO{-}NH{-}CH_2{-}COOH$$

HO—H + trypsin (first arrow); HO—H + chymotrypsin (second arrow)

glycyllysylalanylphenylalanylglycine

Carboxypeptidases A and B both catalyze the hydrolysis of terminal peptide bonds and are called ***exopeptidases***. The requirement for carboxypeptidase A is that the terminal amino acid residue contain a benzene ring, whereas carboxypeptidase B operates on those amino acid linkages next to terminal basic residues, e.g., lysine or arginine. Consequently, the judicious use of enzymes can afford preferential hydrolysis of a polypeptide.

$$H_2N{-}CH(C_6H_4OH){-}CO{\uparrow}NH{-}CH_2{-}CO{-}NH{-}CH(CH_2C_6H_5){-}CO{\uparrow}NH{-}CH[(CH_2)_3NH{-}C(NH_2){=}NH]{-}COOH$$

HO—H + carboxypeptidase A (first arrow); HO—H + carboxypeptidase B (second arrow)

tyrosylglycylphenylalanylarganine

**1.** An optically active peptide, $C_{18}H_{23}O_5N_5$, on partial hydrolysis gave the following compounds in unspecified quantity: Gly, Gly-Gly, Gly-Ala, Gly-Ala-Gly, and tripeptide **X**. No satisfactory end-group analyses could be obtained for the original compound, despite numerous attempts with nitrous acid, 2,4-DNFB, and hydrazine (followed by benzaldehyde). These reactions were attempted under many sets of conditions.

Tripeptide **X** was defined by the following observations. Treatment of **X** with nitrous acid (followed by hydrolysis) gave $\alpha$-hydroxy-$\beta$-phenylpropanoic acid and dipeptide **Y**. Treatment of dipeptide **Y** with 2,4-DNFB (followed by acid hydrolysis) gave an optically inactive *N*-2,4-dinitrophenyl derivative and an amino acid which was converted to lactic acid on treatment with nitrous acid.

Write a structure for the original compound. How many possible stereoisomers exist for the original unknown?

**2.** An unknown hexapeptide, on total hydrolysis, gave equal moles of glycine and alanine. Partial hydrolysis of the unknown gave the following compounds in unspecified quantity: Gly, Ala, Gly-Gly, Gly-Gly-Ala, and tripeptide **A**. Treatment of **A** with nitrous acid (followed by hydrolysis) gave lactic acid. Treatment of **A** with hydrazine (then benzaldehyde) gave alanine. Treatment of **A** with 2,4-DNFB (then hydrolysis) gave *N*-2,4-dinitrophenylglycine and dipeptide **B**, which on treatment with 2,4-DNFB (then hydrolysis) gave *N*-2,4-dinitrophenylalanine.

The original hexapeptide was treated with hydrazine (then benzaldehyde) yielding alanine. The end-group analysis of the hexapeptide (using 2,4-DNFB) showed glycine present in the terminal position.

Using the data given above, write a structure for the original hexapeptide. From the information given, is the structure uniquely determined? If not, how many additional structures can be written which are consistent with the data?

## SUGGESTED READINGS

Alexander, P.: Radiation-imitating Chemicals, *Sci. Am.*, **202** (1), 99 (1960). Shows the interaction of various nitrogen mustards [R—$N(CH_2CH_2Cl)_2$] with proteins.

Gally, J.H.: Bence-Jones Proteins and Antibodies, *J. Chem. Educ.*, **44**, 56 (1967). Review of studies on unusual proteins which occur in the urine of patients suffering from a rare disease, multiple myeloma.

Kendrew, J.C.: The Three-dimensional Structure of a Protein Molecule, *Sci. Am.*, **205** (6), 96 (1961). Extensive discussion of the x-ray determination of myoglobin, which consists of about 150 amino acid units (2,600 atoms), and how the protein is wrapped around the iron atom.

Li, C.H.: The ACTH Molecule, *Sci. Am.*, **209** (1), 46 (1963). Discusses the role of this adrenocortitropic protein in terms of structure and function.

Neurath, N.: Protein-digesting Enzymes, *Sci. Am.*, **211** (6), 68 (1964). Discusses the hydrolytic action of trypsin, chymotrypsin, and carboxypeptidase.

Perutz, M.F.: The Hemoglobin Molecule, *Sci. Am.*, **211** (5), 64 (1964). Discusses the structure determination of hemoglobin by x-ray analysis.

Stein, W.H., and S. Moore: The Chemical Structure of Proteins, *Sci. Am.*, **204** (2), 81 (1961). Describes the structure determination of insulin and ribonuclease with emphasis on the use of the automatic amino acid analyzer.

Zuckerkandl, E.: The Evolution of Hemoglobin, *Sci. Am.*, **212** (5), 110 (1965). Compares human hemoglobin chains with those from the gorilla, pig, horse, and whale myoglobin.

# Chapter Eighteen

Polyhydroxy aldehydes (aldoses) and polyhydroxy ketones (ketoses) are the principal compounds of the class known as sugars or ***saccharides***. Since the composition in most cases corresponds to the general formula $C_x(H_2O)_x$, sugars belong to a larger class known as ***carbohydrates***, which are often polymers of simple sugars.

***Monosaccharides*** are simple sugars which do not undergo hydrolysis, ***disaccharides*** are hydrolyzed either to two different sugars or to two equivalents of one sugar, trisaccharides give three equivalents of sugar, and so on until high-molecular-weight saccharides, ***polysaccharides***, are hydrolyzed either to many different sugars or to many equivalents of a given sugar. The term ***oligosaccharides*** is sometimes used for saccharides containing two to six simple-sugar residues.

The discussion in this text will be confined mainly to the reactions, synthesis, and structural determination of naturally occurring simple sugars which have been isolated from blood, urine, honey, milk, wood, and a variety of other natural substances. Common examples of carbohydrates are glucose, a monosaccharide; sucrose, table sugar, a disaccharide; lactose, a disaccharide found in milk; and cellulose, a polysaccharide. Sugars in which the hydroxyl group is replaced by an amino group (amino sugars) and those in which the hydroxyl group is removed (deoxy sugars) are among those found in nature.

## NOMENCLATURE AND STRUCTURE

### 18-1 GENERAL STRUCTURAL FEATURES

Sugars commonly have three to seven carbon atoms and are known generally as ***aldoses*** or ketoses depending on the form of the carbonyl group. The number of carbon atoms can be indicated in the general

# Sugars and Carbohydrates

name; e.g., six-carbon sugars are called ***aldohexoses*** or ***ketohexoses***. Ketoses are also named by the insertion of *-ul* into the aldose name: ketohexoses are also called **hexuloses** (see Table 18-1).

**Table 18-1 General nomenclature of the sugars**

| *Number of carbons* | *Functional group* | |
|---|---|---|
| | *Aldehydes (aldoses)* | *Ketones (ketoses)* |
| 3 | a triose (aldotriose)<br>CHO—CHOH—$CH_2OH$ | a triulose (a ketotriose)<br>$CH_2OH$—CO—$CH_2OH$ |
| 4 | a tetrose (aldotetrose)<br>CHO—$(CHOH)_2$—$CH_2OH$ | a tetrulose (ketotetrose)<br>$CH_2OH$—CO—CHOH—$CH_2OH$ |
| 5 | a pentose (aldopentose)<br>CHO—$(CHOH)_3$—$CH_2OH$ | a pentulose (ketopentose)<br>$CH_2OH$—CO—$(CHOH)_2$—$CH_2OH$ |
| 6 | a hexose (aldohexose)<br>CHO—$(CHOH)_4$—$CH_2OH$ | a hexulose (ketohexose)<br>$CH_2OH$—CO—$(CHOH)_3$—$CH_2OH$ |
| 7 | a heptose (aldoheptose)<br>CHO—$(CHOH)_5$—$CH_2OH$ | a heptulose (ketoheptose)<br>$CH_2OH$—CO—$(CHOH)_4$—$CH_2OH$ |

### 18-2 ABSOLUTE CONFIGURATION

Most of the naturally occurring sugars contain at least one asymmetric carbon and have an absolute stereochemical configuration **at the highest numbered asymmetric carbon atom** which is related to D(+)-glyceraldehyde. A few sugars isolated from natural products belong to the L series.

The optical series is defined by the stereochemistry **at the highest asymmetric carbon.**

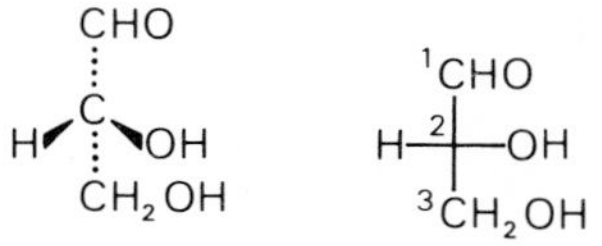

CHO / H–C–OH / $CH_2OH$ (wedge projection) ; $^{1}$CHO / H–$^{2}$C–OH / $^{3}CH_2OH$ (Fischer projection)

D-glyceraldehyde

CHO / HO–C–H / $CH_2OH$ (wedge projection) ; CHO / HO–C–H / $CH_2OH$ (Fischer projection)

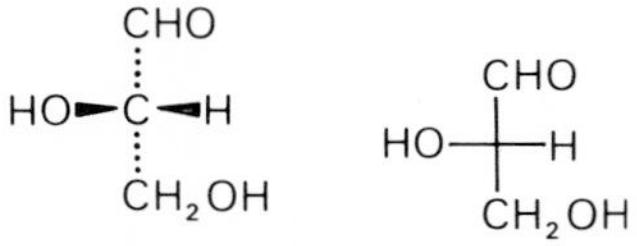

L-glyceraldehyde

| | | |
|---|---|---|
| $^{1}$CHO | | CHO |
| H–$^{2}$C–OH | | HO–C–H |
| HO–$^{3}$C–H | | H–C–OH |
| H–$^{4}$C–OH | | HO–C–H |
| H–$^{5}$C–OH | | HO–C–H |
| $^{6}CH_2OH$ | | $CH_2OH$ |

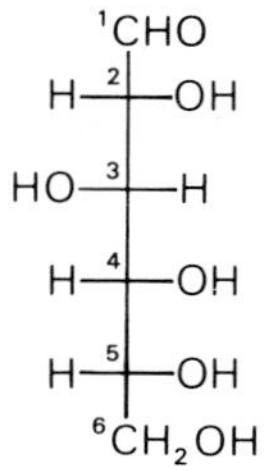

D-glucose 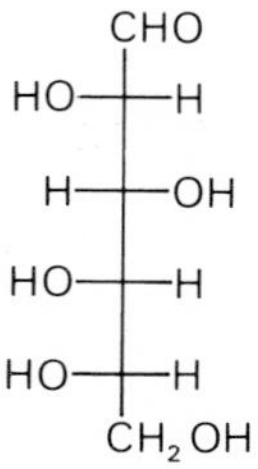 L-glucose

Sugars, like other natural products isolated and studied in the early years of chemistry, were assigned trivial names, which have been retained. Tables 18-2 and 18-3 show the D-series aldoses and ketoses. The mirror images of the projections shown in these tables represent the corresponding L-series.

## 18-3 CYCLIC-ETHER FORMATION

Aldehydes and ketones react with 1 equiv of an alcohol, yielding hemiacetals and hemiketals (Sec. 13-13).

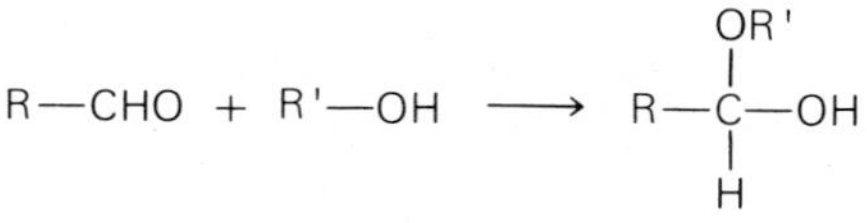

$$R\text{—}CHO + R'\text{—}OH \longrightarrow R\text{—}\underset{H}{\overset{OR'}{C}}\text{—}OH$$

an aldehyde a hemiacetal

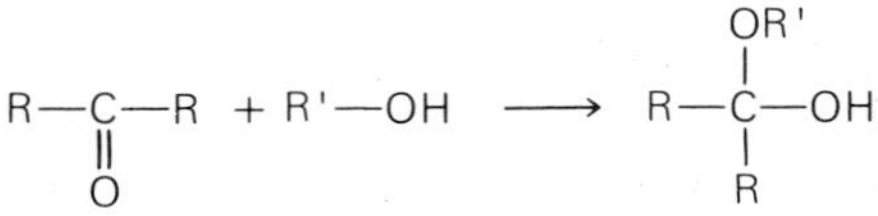

$$R\text{—}\underset{\|\atop O}{C}\text{—}R + R'\text{—}OH \longrightarrow R\text{—}\underset{R}{\overset{OR'}{C}}\text{—}OH$$

a ketone a hemiketal

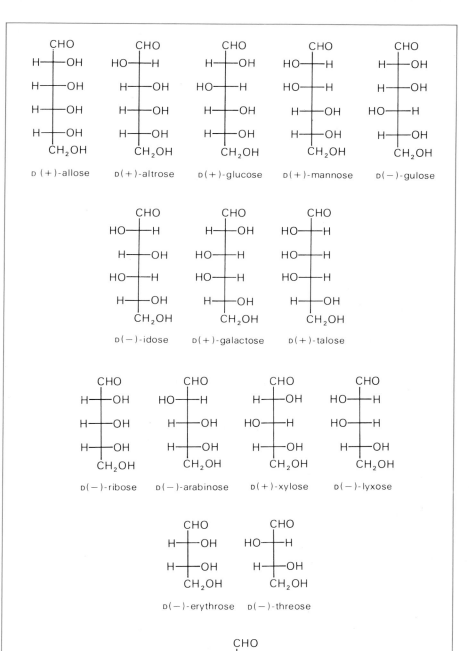

**Table 18-2**
**Three- to six-carbon D-aldoses**

CHO
H—OH
H—OH
H—OH
H—OH
$CH_2OH$
D(+)-allose

CHO
HO—H
H—OH
H—OH
H—OH
$CH_2OH$
D(+)-altrose

CHO
H—OH
HO—H
H—OH
H—OH
$CH_2OH$
D(+)-glucose

CHO
HO—H
HO—H
H—OH
H—OH
$CH_2OH$
D(+)-mannose

CHO
H—OH
H—OH
HO—H
H—OH
$CH_2OH$
D(−)-gulose

CHO
HO—H
H—OH
HO—H
H—OH
$CH_2OH$
D(−)-idose

CHO
H—OH
HO—H
HO—H
H—OH
$CH_2OH$
D(+)-galactose

CHO
HO—H
HO—H
HO—H
H—OH
$CH_2OH$
D(+)-talose

CHO
H—OH
H—OH
H—OH
$CH_2OH$
D(−)-ribose

CHO
HO—H
H—OH
H—OH
$CH_2OH$
D(−)-arabinose

CHO
H—OH
HO—H
H—OH
$CH_2OH$
D(+)-xylose

CHO
HO—H
HO—H
H—OH
$CH_2OH$
D(−)-lyxose

CHO
H—OH
H—OH
$CH_2OH$
D(−)-erythrose

CHO
HO—H
H—OH
$CH_2OH$
D(−)-threose

CHO
H—OH
$CH_2OH$
D(+)-glyceraldehyde

**Table 18-3 Three- to six-carbon D-ketoses**

| | | | |
|---|---|---|---|
| $CH_2OH$, C=O, H–C–OH, H–C–OH, H–C–OH, $CH_2OH$ | $CH_2OH$, C=O, HO–C–H, H–C–OH, H–C–OH, $CH_2OH$ | $CH_2OH$, C=O, H–C–OH, HO–C–H, H–C–OH, $CH_2OH$ | $CH_2OH$, C=O, HO–C–H, HO–C–H, H–C–OH, $CH_2OH$ |
| D-allose (D-psicose) | D-fructose (levulose) | D-sorbose | D-tagatose |
| | $CH_2OH$, C=O, H–C–OH, H–C–OH, $CH_2OH$ | $CH_2OH$, C=O, HO–C–H, H–C–OH, $CH_2OH$ | |
| | D-ribulose (adonose) | D-xylulose (D-lyxulose) | |

$CH_2OH$, C=O, H–C–OH, $CH_2OH$

D-erythrulose (D-threulose)

$CH_2OH$, C=O, $CH_2OH$

dihydroxyacetone

If the carbonyl and hydroxyl groups are properly situated in the same molecule, five- and six-membered cyclic hemiacetals readily form.

$^{1}CHO$–$^{2}CH_2$–$^{3}CH_2$–$^{4}CHOH$–$^{5}CH_2$–$^{6}CH_3$ ⟶ (HO)(H)C in five-membered ring with O, ring carbon bearing $CH_2CH_3$

a γ-hydroxy aldehyde

furanose
a five-membered
cyclic hemiacetal

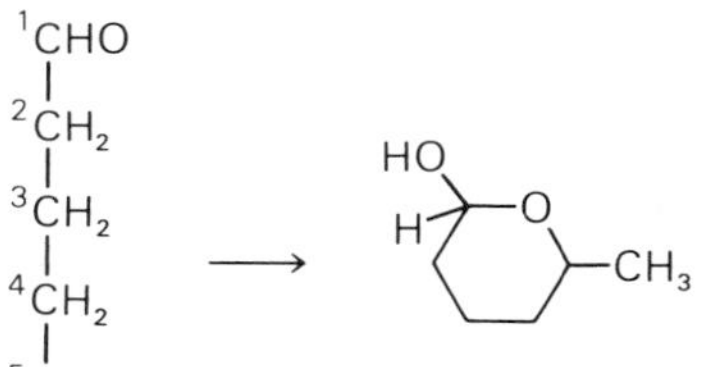

$^{1}CHO-{}^{2}CH_2-{}^{3}CH_2-{}^{4}CH_2-{}^{5}CHOH-{}^{6}CH_3$ ⟶ pyranose

a δ-hydroxy aldehyde

pyranose
a six-membered
cyclic hemiacetal

These structures resemble furan and pyran, and the cyclic hemiacetal sugars are known as ***furanoses*** (five-membered ring) or ***pyranoses*** (six-membered ring), depending upon the ring size.

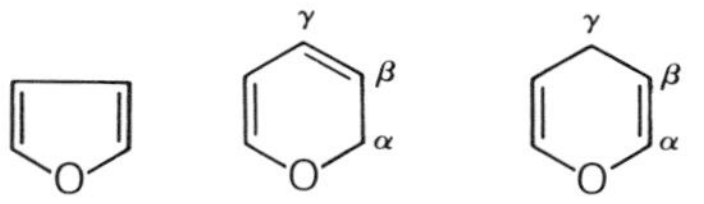

furan α-pyran γ-pyran

Cyclic hemiacetal or hemiketal formation in sugars creates a new asymmetric center at the carbonyl carbon in a molecule which is already optically active. Since the new center is adjacent to one of specific configuration, the two possible optical configurations will not be created with equal probability. This represents an example of internal asymmetric induction (Sec. 12-19).

In solution these two cyclic hemiacetals are in equilibrium via the open form, the aldehyde or ketone. When either pure hemiacetal is placed in solution, the optical rotation changes until the two forms are in equilibrium with each other and with the aldehyde or ketone; such a change in configuration is called ***mutarotation***.

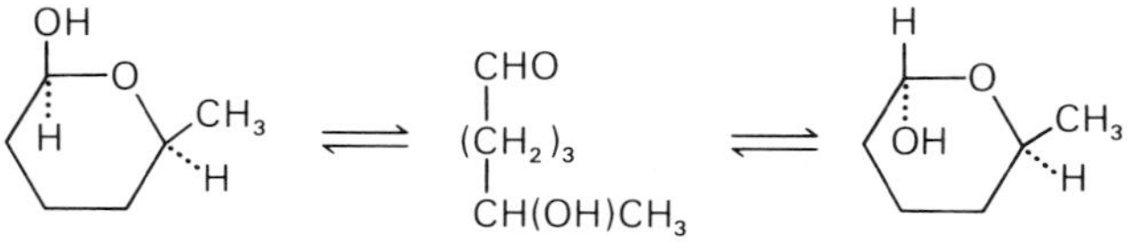

β-isomer ⇌ $CHO-(CH_2)_3-CH(OH)CH_3$ ⇌ α-isomer

β-isomer open aldehyde form α-isomer

A convention has been adopted which allows the isomers formed to be drawn and named unambiguously either with projection formulas or with three-dimensional representations. If the hydroxyl group of the newly created asymmetric center is placed on the right-hand side of a projection formula or placed down in a three-dimensional representation, the compound is denoted as the α isomer. Placing the —OH on the left-hand side (or up) represents the β isomer. These sugar epimers are known also as ***anomers***. See Table 18-4 for examples using D-glucose and D-fructose.

**Table 18-4**
**Hemiacetal formation of D-glucose and D-fructose**
Asterisks denote the new asymmetric center

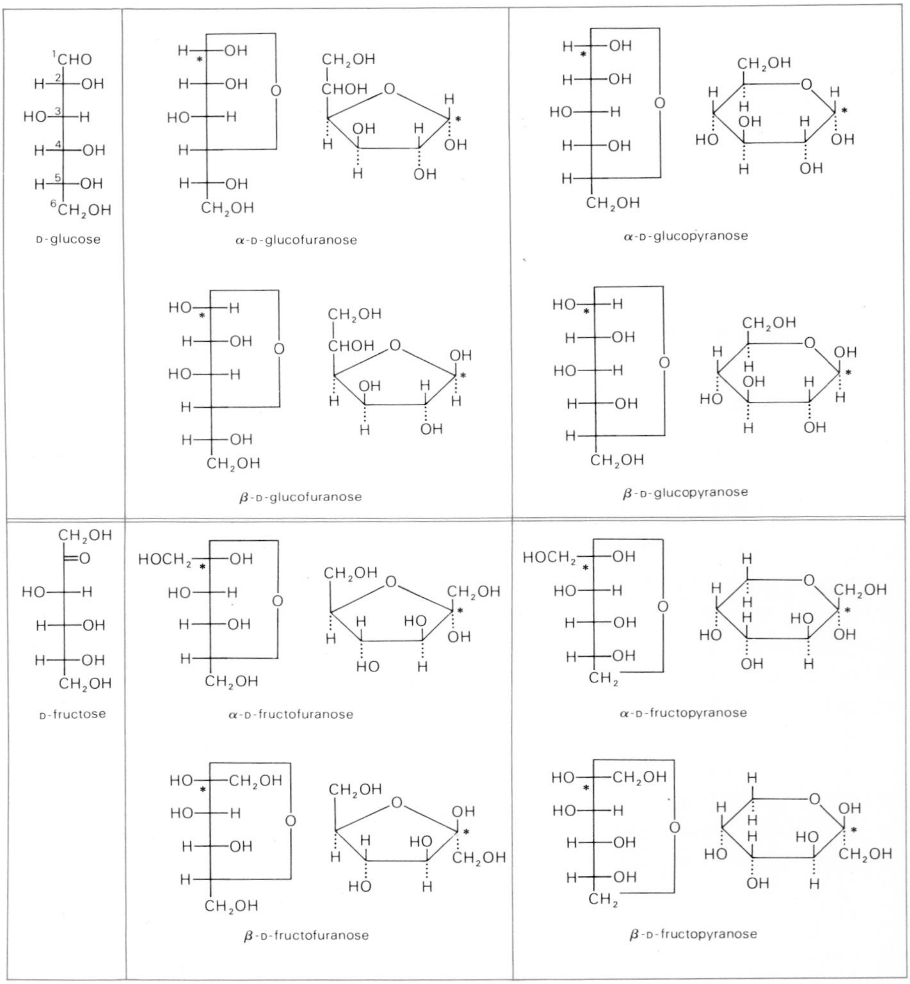

| | | |
|---|---|---|
| D-glucose | α-D-glucofuranose | α-D-glucopyranose |
| | β-D-glucofuranose | β-D-glucopyranose |
| D-fructose | α-D-fructofuranose | α-D-fructopyranose |
| | β-D-fructofuranose | β-D-fructopyranose |

## 18-4 GLUCOSIDES

Ether formation at the newly created asymmetric center of a furanose or pyranose gives rise to compounds known as ***furanosides*** or ***pyranosides***; the general name being ***glucosides***. Since many sugars exist in solution as the hemiacetal or hemiketal, rather than as the free aldehyde or ketone, treatment of a sugar with methanolic or ethanolic hydrochloric acid serves to transform the sugar to a mixture of the two epimeric methyl or ethyl esters and methyl or ethyl glucosides.

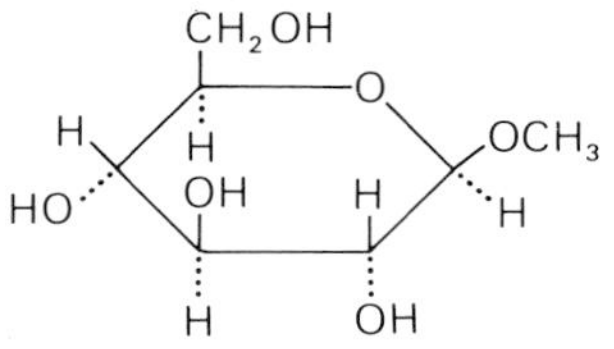

methyl β-D-glucopyranoside

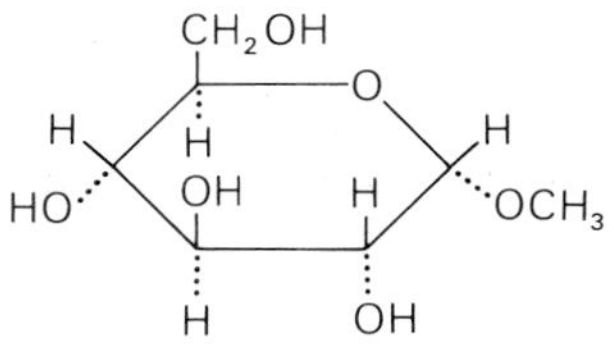

methyl α-D-glucopyranoside

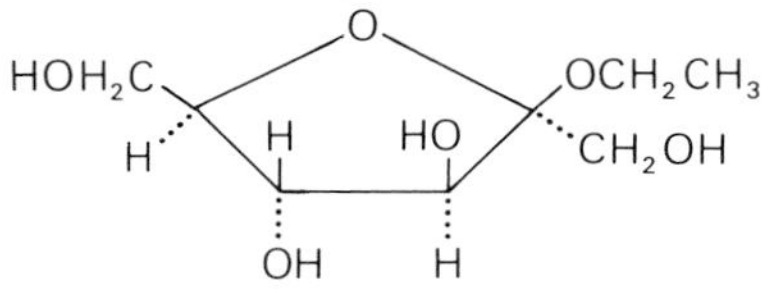

ethyl β-D-fructofuranoside

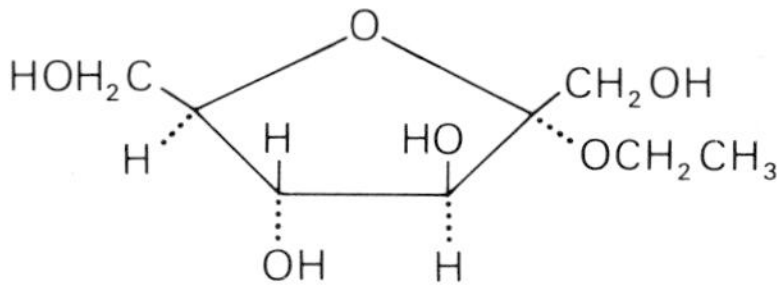

ethyl α-D-fructofuranoside

### 18-5 CONFORMATIONAL ANALYSIS

The pyranose ring, like that of cyclohexane, is subject to conformational changes. Although substitution of an oxygen atom in pyranoses for a carbon atom of cyclohexanes slightly modifies the geometry of the ring, **the preferred conformation of pyranoses is the chair form**. Taking methyl α-D-glucopyranoside as an example, the preferred conformation can be determined by a consideration of the 1,3 diaxial interactions. As in the cyclohexanes, the conformation with the fewer 1,3 diaxial interactions, and thus the maximum number of equatorial substituents, is the preferred conformation.

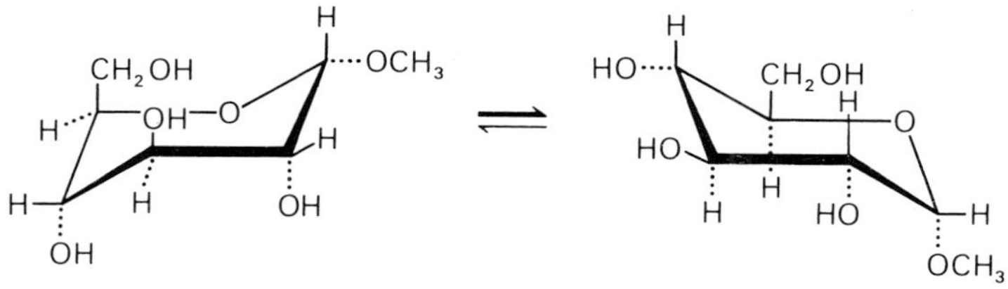

methyl α-D-glucopyranoside

## REACTIONS OF SUGARS

### 18-6 REDUCTION OF SUGARS

The structural determination of a new sugar may begin by ascertaining the number of carbons it contains and whether or not the chain is branched. Two reactions which lead to the reduction of sugars, yet retain all the carbon atoms, are the treatment with hydriodic acid, HI, and phosphorus, P, and the reduction of an aldehyde, —CHO, to the hydroxymethyl group, $—CH_2OH$, with sodium amalgam.

Sugars are completely reduced to the corresponding alkane on treatment with HI and P.

$$\begin{array}{c} CHO \\ H-\!\!\!\!-\!\!\!+\!\!\!\!-OH \\ H-\!\!\!\!-\!\!\!+\!\!\!\!-OH \\ CH_2OH \\ \text{D-erythrose} \end{array} \xrightarrow[\Delta]{HI/P} \begin{array}{c} CH_3—CH_2—CH_2—CH_3 \\ \text{butane} \end{array}$$

The hydroxyl groups are first converted to iodo functions, which are subsequently reduced with phosphorus (Sec. 2-8). This reaction was commonly used in the early work on the structural determination of sugars.

Additional information about the structure of sugars, particularly ketoses, can be obtained if the carbonyl group of the sugar is first converted to the cyanohydrin and hydrolyzed to the hydroxy acid before reduction. Because the carboxyl group is not reduced by HI and P, aldoses yield straight-chain acids and ketoses give branched acids, whose structure depends on the position of the carbonyl group in the sugars.

$$\begin{array}{l} CHO \\ | \\ CHOH \\ | \\ CHOH \\ | \\ CHOH \\ | \\ CH_2OH \\ \text{an aldopentose} \end{array} \xrightarrow{HCN} \begin{array}{l} CH(OH)CN \\ | \\ CHOH \\ | \\ CHOH \\ | \\ CHOH \\ | \\ CH_2OH \\ \text{a cyanohydrin} \end{array} \xrightarrow{H_3O^+} \begin{array}{l} CH(OH)COOH \\ | \\ CHOH \\ | \\ CHOH \\ | \\ CHOH \\ | \\ CH_2OH \end{array} \xrightarrow[\Delta]{HI/P} \begin{array}{l} CH_2COOH \\ | \\ CH_2 \\ | \\ CH_2 \\ | \\ CH_2 \\ | \\ CH_3 \\ \text{hexanoic acid} \end{array}$$

$$\begin{array}{l} CH_2OH \\ | \\ C{=}O \\ | \\ CHOH \\ | \\ CHOH \\ | \\ CH_2OH \\ \text{a 2-ketopentose} \end{array} \xrightarrow{HCN} \begin{array}{l} CH_2OH \\ | \\ C(OH)CN \\ | \\ CHOH \\ | \\ CHOH \\ | \\ CH_2OH \end{array} \xrightarrow{H_3O^+} \begin{array}{l} CH_2OH \\ | \\ C(OH)COOH \\ | \\ CHOH \\ | \\ CHOH \\ | \\ CH_2OH \end{array} \xrightarrow[\Delta]{HI/P} \begin{array}{l} CH_3 \\ | \\ CH—COOH \\ | \\ CH_2 \\ | \\ CH_2 \\ | \\ CH_3 \\ \text{2-methylpentanoic acid} \end{array}$$

$$\begin{array}{l} CH_2OH \\ | \\ CHOH \\ | \\ C{=}O \\ | \\ CHOH \\ | \\ CH_2OH \\ \text{a 3-ketopentose} \end{array} \xrightarrow{HCN} \begin{array}{l} CH_2OH \\ | \\ CHOH \\ | \\ C(OH)CN \\ | \\ CHOH \\ | \\ CH_2OH \end{array} \xrightarrow{H_3O^+} \begin{array}{l} CH_2OH \\ | \\ CHOH \\ | \\ C(OH)COOH \\ | \\ CHOH \\ | \\ CH_2OH \end{array} \xrightarrow[\Delta]{HI/P} \begin{array}{l} CH_3 \\ | \\ CH_2 \\ | \\ CH—COOH \\ | \\ CH_2 \\ | \\ CH_3 \\ \text{2-ethylbutanoic acid} \end{array}$$

This reaction sequence produces acids with one more carbon (from HCN) than those found in the starting sugar.

> Formulate the reaction sequence shown above for:
>
> **1.** glucose
>
> **2.** fructose
>
> **3.** glyceraldehyde
>
> **4.** dihydroxyacetone

The simple reduction of an aldehyde to a hydroxymethyl group can be accomplished under mild conditions by treating a sugar with sodium amalgam, Na(Hg), in water. Although sodium itself reacts with water with near-explosive violence, hydrogen is liberated from water much more slowly with sodium amalgam. Application of this reaction in the sugar series may give some indication of the stereochemistry of the starting material. Compare the optical activity of the reduction products derived from D(−)-erythrose and D(−)-threose; the former gives an optically active product, the latter gives an inactive (meso) product.

| CHO | | $CH_2OH$ | CHO | | $CH_2OH$ |
|---|---|---|---|---|---|
| H—C—OH | $\xrightarrow[H_2O]{Na(Hg)}$ | H—C—OH | HO—C—H | $\xrightarrow[H_2O]{Na(Hg)}$ | HO—C—H |
| H—C—OH | | H—C—OH | H—C—OH | | H—C—OH |
| $CH_2OH$ | | $CH_2OH$ | $CH_2OH$ | | $CH_2OH$ |
| D(−)-erythrose | | 1,2,3,4-butanetetraol optically inactive | D(−)-threose | | 1,2,3,4-butanetetraol optically active |

> Given the following pairs of isomers, would you be able to distinguish between them on the basis of optical activity before and after treatment with Na(Hg) and $H_2O$?
>
> **1.** D(−)-ribose and L(+)-ribose
>
> **2.** D(−)-ribose and D(+)-xylose
>
> **3.** D(−)-arabinose and D(+)-xylose
>
> **4.** L(+)-lyxose and D(−)-arabinose

### 18-7 OXIDATION OF SUGARS

Like the Na(Hg) reduction discussed in the previous section, controlled oxidation affords products which are useful in structural determination.

In particular, stereochemical information can be gained by comparing the optical activity before and after oxidation. Of the many reagents which are useful for oxidizing sugars, the discussion here is restricted to three: (1) warm nitric acid, (2) bromine or hypobromous acid, and (3) periodic acid, $HIO_4$.

Terminal hydroxymethyl groups and aldehyde functions are oxidized to carboxylic acids by warm dilute nitric acid. Only aldehydes, not hydroxymethyl groups, are oxidized to acids with bromine or hypobromous acid.

$$\underset{\text{a mono acid}}{\begin{array}{c}COOH\\|\\CHOH\\|\\CHOH\\|\\CH_2OH\end{array}} \xleftarrow[HOBr]{Br_2\ \text{or}} \underset{\text{an aldotetrose}}{\begin{array}{c}CHO\\|\\CHOH\\|\\CHOH\\|\\CH_2OH\end{array}} \xrightarrow[HNO_3]{\text{warm dil.}} \underset{\text{a diacid}}{\begin{array}{c}COOH\\|\\CHOH\\|\\CHOH\\|\\COOH\end{array}}$$

The oxidation by $Br_2$ or HOBr does not change the general asymmetry of sugars, but the use of nitric acid often introduces symmetry into sugar molecules. Compare the stereochemical results of the oxidations of D(−)-erythrose and D(−)-threose.

$$\begin{array}{c}CHO\\H-\!\!\!-\!\!\!-OH\\H-\!\!\!-\!\!\!-OH\\CH_2OH\end{array} \xrightarrow[HNO_3]{\text{warm dil.}} \begin{array}{c}COOH\\H-\!\!\!-\!\!\!-OH\\H-\!\!\!-\!\!\!-OH\\COOH\end{array}$$

D(−)-erythrose

*meso*-tartaric acid
optically inactive

$$\begin{array}{c}CHO\\HO-\!\!\!-\!\!\!-H\\H-\!\!\!-\!\!\!-OH\\CH_2OH\end{array} \xrightarrow[HNO_3]{\text{warm dil.}} \begin{array}{c}COOH\\HO-\!\!\!-\!\!\!-H\\H-\!\!\!-\!\!\!-OH\\COOH\end{array}$$

D(−)-threose

D-tartaric acid
optically active

Which of the D-aldohexoses (Table 18-2) will give the same diacid on treatment with warm dilute nitric acid? Of these diacids, which are optically inactive?

Of the mild oxidizing agents available for the structural determination of sugars and other polyhydroxy compounds, periodic acid, $HIO_4$, is one of the most useful. Simple *vicinal*-glycols, —CH(OH)—CH(OH)—, are cleaved to give aldehydes.

$$\begin{array}{l} CH_3 \\ | \\ CHOH \\ | \\ CHOH \\ | \\ CH_3 \end{array} \xrightarrow{HIO_4} 2CH_3CHO$$

Terminal (primary) hydroxyl groups give formaldehyde, $CH_2O$, but internal hydroxyls flanked by hydroxymethylene groups give formic acid. Formic acid is also one of the products of the oxidation of $\alpha$-hydroxy aldehydes.

$$\begin{array}{l} CHO \\ | \\ CHOH \\ | \\ CHOH \\ | \\ CH_2OH \end{array} \xrightarrow{HIO_4} CH_2O + 3HCOOH$$

$$\begin{array}{l} CH_3 \\ | \\ CHOH \\ | \\ CHOH \\ | \\ CHOH \\ | \\ CH_3 \end{array} \xrightarrow{HIO_4} 2CH_3CHO + HCOOH$$

$$\text{1,2,3-cyclohexanetriol (OH, OH, OH)} \xrightarrow{HIO_4} OHC\text{—}(CH_2)_3\text{—}CHO + HCOOH$$

The application of the method, as discussed here, gives information about the gross structure of sugars but not about the stereochemistry.

Which of the following products would be expected from the periodic oxidation of D-glucose? Which of the other aldohexoses would give the same products under similar conditions?

**1.** $2CH_2O + 4HCOOH$

**2.** $CH_2O + 5HCOOH$

**3.** $3CH_2O + 4HCOOH$

### 18-8 LENGTHENING THE CARBON CHAIN

In both the structural determination and the synthesis of sugars, chemical techniques for lengthening a carbon chain are important. Addition of one carbon atom by the conversion of a sugar to its cyanohydrin and reduction of the corresponding acid to an aldehyde is known as the ***Kiliani synthesis***. The overall reaction combines certain features detailed in Sec. 18-6. This synthesis is accomplished in three steps: sugar $\xrightarrow{HCN}$ epimeric cyanohydrins $\xrightarrow{H_3O^+}$ epimeric $\alpha$-hydroxy acids $\xrightarrow[H_2O]{Na(Hg)}$ epimeric sugars containing an additional carbon atom (see Table 18-5).

**Table 18-5 Example of Kiliani synthesis**

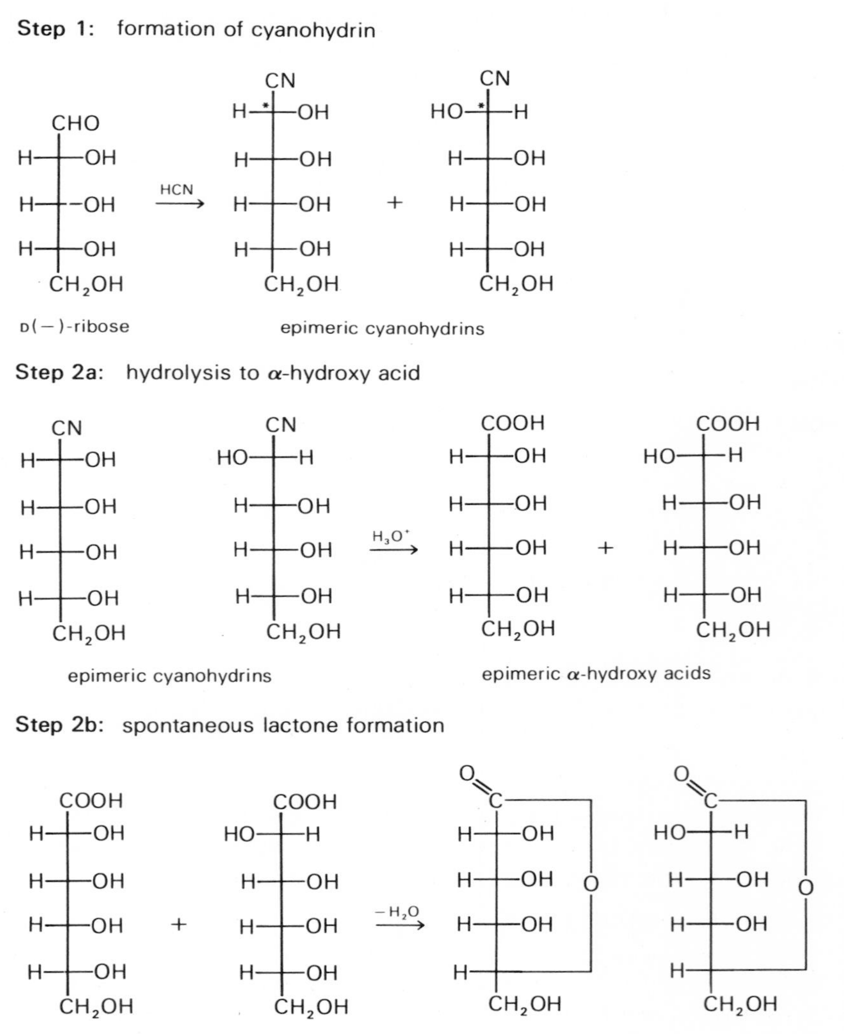

**Table 18-5 (continued)**

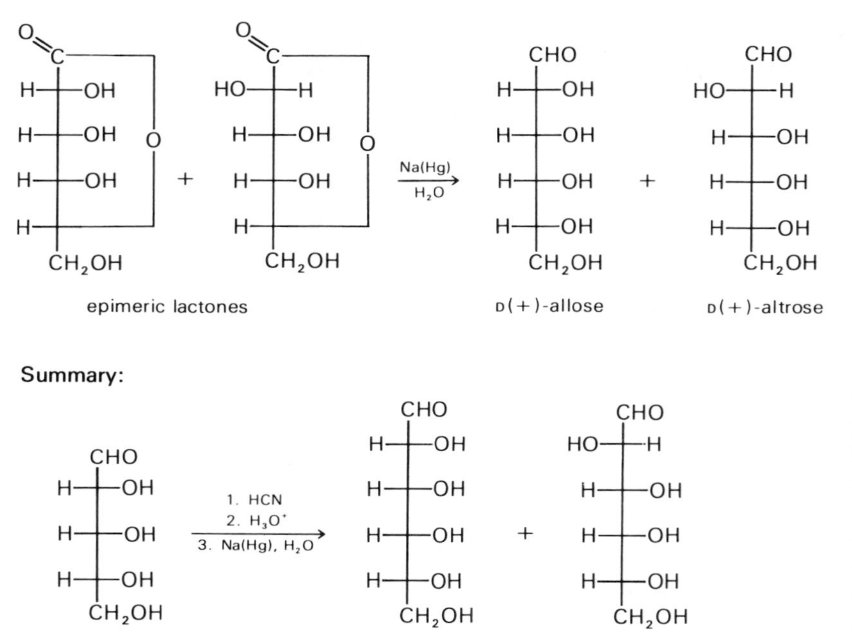


An internal ester is called a ***lactone***. Since lactones are cyclic compounds, they often form spontaneously where esterification yields a five- or six-membered ring. The reduction of lactones to aldehydes can be accomplished with Na(Hg) and $H_2O$, with $NaBH_4$, or with Zn in acetic acid. All these systems are mild reducing agents which allow the formation of the aldehyde with a minimum of further reduction to the alcohol.

What sugars would result by carrying out a Kiliani synthesis with D-glyceraldehyde? Formulate the steps in this sequence.

## 18-9 DECREASING THE CARBON CHAIN

Two well-known schemes for the systematic degradation of sugars are the ***Wohl degradation*** (modified), which is a ''reversal'' of the Kiliani cyanohydrin synthesis, and the ***Ruff degradation***, which uses an oxidizing system of bromine water and then a decarboxylating system of $H_2O_2$ and $Fe^{3+}$.

Step 1. Oxime formation:

$$\begin{array}{c} CHO \\ H-C-OH \\ H-C-OH \\ CH_2OH \end{array} \xrightarrow{H_2N-OH} \begin{array}{c} CH=N-OH \\ H-C-OH \\ H-C-OH \\ CH_2OH \end{array} + H_2O$$

D-erythrose D-erythrose oxime

Step 2. Oxime dehydration:

$$\begin{array}{c} CH=N-OH \\ H-C-OH \\ H-C-OH \\ CH_2OH \end{array} \xrightarrow[NaOAc;\ \Delta]{Ac_2O} \begin{array}{c} C\equiv N \\ H-C-OCOCH_3 \\ H-C-OCOCH_3 \\ CH_2OCOCH_3 \end{array} + H_2O$$

D-erythrose oxime D-glyceraldehyde cyanohydrin triacetate

Step 3. Elimination of the cyano carbon:

$$\begin{array}{c} C\equiv N \\ H-C-OCOCH_3 \\ H-C-OCOCH_3 \\ CH_2OCOCH_3 \end{array} \xrightarrow{NaOCH_2CH_3} \begin{array}{c} CHO \\ H-C-OH \\ CH_2OH \end{array}$$

D-glyceraldehyde cyanohydrin triacetate D-glyceraldehyde

The first step in the Wohl degradation is a simple oxime formation; the second step accomplishes both the dehydration of the oxime and the acetylation of the hydroxyl groups. The final step accomplishes the removal of the cyano carbon and the acetyl groups.

The Ruff degradation is essentially a decarboxylation of the calcium salt of the acid corresponding to the original sugar.

$$\begin{array}{c} CHO \\ H-C-OH \\ H-C-OH \\ CH_2OH \end{array} \xrightarrow{Br_2\text{-}H_2O} \begin{array}{c} COOH \\ H-C-OH \\ H-C-OH \\ CH_2OH \end{array} \xrightarrow{Ca(OH)_2} \begin{array}{c} COO^-Ca^{++}/2 \\ H-C-OH \\ H-C-OH \\ CH_2OH \end{array} \xrightarrow[Fe^{3+}]{H_2O_2} \begin{array}{c} CHO \\ H-C-OH \\ CH_2OH \end{array} + CO_2$$

D-erythrose D-glyceraldehyde

1. Formulate the Ruff degradation of (*a*) D-glucose and (*b*) D-galactose.

2. Which other sugars would give rise to D-arabinose and D-lyxose via the Wohl degradation?

3. Formulate these reactions.

## QUALITATIVE TESTS AND DERIVATIVES

The qualitative tests for sugars are those which will identify the common functional groups: aldehydes, ketones, and alcohols. The derivatives of sugars are formed either from the hydroxyl groups (esters and ethers) or from the carbonyl group (phenylhydrazones).

### 18-10 QUALITATIVE TESTS

Although Fehling's solution, $Cu(tartrate)_2^{--}$ and Tollens' solution, $Ag(NH_3)_2^+$, give positive tests for aldoses and ketoses, these tests are negative for glycosides (ethers of the hemiacetal group) because the open-chain carbonyl form is no longer in equilibrium with the cyclic hemiacetal.

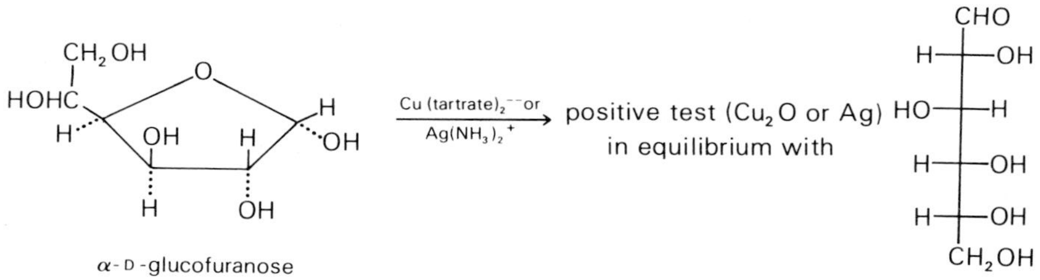

α-D-glucofuranose $\xrightarrow[Ag(NH_3)_2^+]{Cu(tartrate)_2^{--}\text{ or}}$ positive test ($Cu_2O$ or Ag) in equilibrium with CHO, H—C—OH, HO—C—H, H—C—OH, H—C—OH, $CH_2OH$

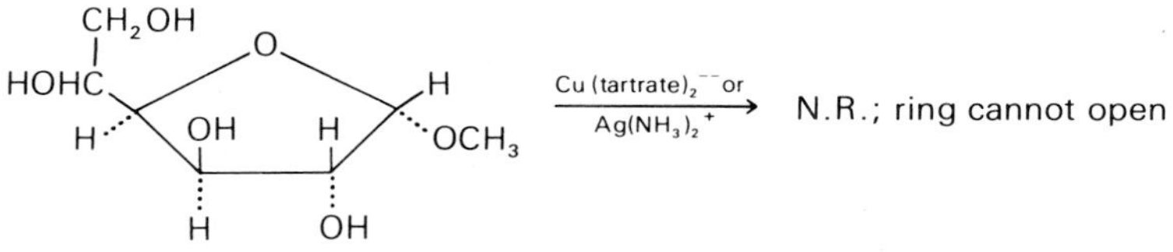

methyl α-D-glucofuranoside $\xrightarrow[Ag(NH_3)_2^+]{Cu(tartrate)_2^{--}\text{ or}}$ N.R.; ring cannot open

Sugars which give a positive test are known as ***reducing sugars***. The Schiff test, although positive for simple aldehydes, is negative for sugars and their glucosides. See Sec. 13-23 for a review of these aldehyde and ketone tests.

### 18-11 ESTERS AND ETHERS

Acetates of sugars, the common ester derivative, are prepared by heating the sugar with acetic acid and sodium acetate or by allowing the sugar to stand at room temperature in an acetic anhydride–pyridine mixture (Sec. 9-19).

Ethers of sugars, commonly methyl or ethyl ethers, can be formed by treating sugars with alcoholic hydrogen chloride or with dimethyl (or diethyl) sulfate and base. It should be noted that the glucosidic ether group (an acetal or ketal) is the one most readily hydrolyzed by dilute acid.

Write chemical equations (including preferred conformations of the compounds) for the following reactions:

**1.** Treatment of methyl $\alpha$-glucopyranoside with dimethyl sulfate and sodium hydroxide yields methyl tetra-$O$-methyl-$\alpha$-D-glucopyranoside.

**2.** The product in part 1, on treatment with 5% HCl, gives tetra-$O$-methyl-$\alpha$-D-glucopyranose.

### 18-12 PHENYLHYDRAZONES AND OSAZONES

Treatment of aldoses and ketoses with a molar equivalent of phenylhydrazine yields the usual phenylhydrazone of the carbonyl group. However, in the presence of excess phenylhydrazine the phenylhydrazone reacts further, to give a bisphenylhydrazone, called an *osazone*. This product results from the oxidation of the hydroxyl adjacent to the aldehyde or ketone. **The asymmetry of $C_2$ in sugars is destroyed by**

**1.** Write the structure of at least one other sugar which gives the same osazone as D-glucose and D-fructose.

**2.** Give the structure of several compounds which, on treatment with phenylhydrazine, yield this osazone:

$$\begin{array}{rcl} & CH{=}NNHC_6H_5 & \\ & | & \\ & C{=}NNHC_6H_5 & \\ HO- & C & -H \\ HO- & C & -H \\ & CH_2OH & \end{array}$$

**Table 18-6**
**Relation of D-glucose to D-fructose**

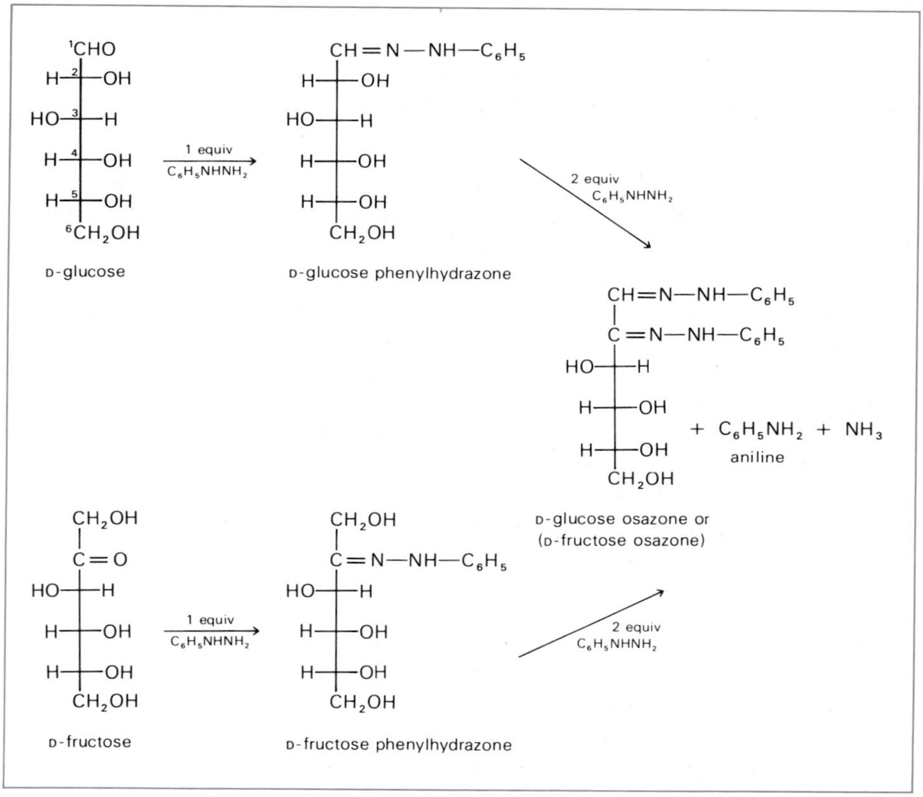

| D-glucose | | D-glucose phenylhydrazone | | |
|---|---|---|---|---|
| $^1$CHO; H–$^2$C–OH; HO–$^3$C–H; H–$^4$C–OH; H–$^5$C–OH; $^6CH_2OH$ | $\xrightarrow[C_6H_5NHNH_2]{\text{1 equiv}}$ | $CH{=}N{-}NH{-}C_6H_5$; H–C–OH; HO–C–H; H–C–OH; H–C–OH; $CH_2OH$ | $\xrightarrow[C_6H_5NHNH_2]{\text{2 equiv}}$ | |

D-glucose osazone or (D-fructose osazone):
$CH{=}N{-}NH{-}C_6H_5$; $C{=}N{-}NH{-}C_6H_5$; HO–C–H; H–C–OH; H–C–OH; $CH_2OH$ + $C_6H_5NH_2$ (aniline) + $NH_3$

| D-fructose | | D-fructose phenylhydrazone | | |
|---|---|---|---|---|
| $CH_2OH$; C=O; HO–C–H; H–C–OH; H–C–OH; $CH_2OH$ | $\xrightarrow[C_6H_5NHNH_2]{\text{1 equiv}}$ | $CH_2OH$; $C{=}N{-}NH{-}C_6H_5$; HO–C–H; H–C–OH; H–C–OH; $CH_2OH$ | $\xrightarrow[C_6H_5NHNH_2]{\text{2 equiv}}$ | D-glucose osazone |

osazone formation; this reaction can be used to establish the structures of compounds which are epimeric at $C_2$ (see Table 18-6).

## 18-13 ACETONIDES

A *cis*-1,2-glycol can be identified by its reaction with acetone in the presence of $ZnCl_2$. The product is a cyclic ketal, called an *acetonide*. Other catalysts such as HCl and $CuSO_4$ have also been effective in this reaction. Since a five-membered ring is formed, trans glycols do not undergo this reaction.

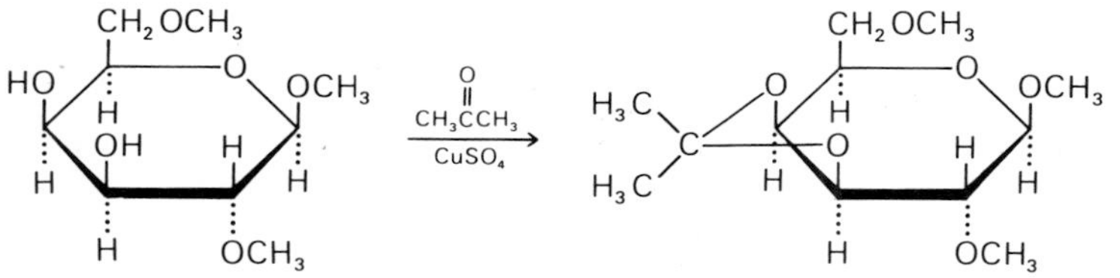

$$\text{methyl-2,6-di-}O\text{-methyl-}\beta\text{-galactoside} \xrightarrow[CuSO_4]{CH_3\overset{O}{\overset{\|}{C}}CH_3} \text{3,4-}O\text{-isopropylidene acetonide }((H_3C)_2C<)$$

methyl-2,6-di-*O*-methyl-
*β*-galactoside

Refer to Tables 18-2 and 18-3 for configurations and rotations.

**1.** Compound A, $C_6H_{12}O_6$, gave a positive test with Fehling's and Tollens' solution but a negative Schiff test. Treatment of A with HI and P gave *n*-hexane; treatment of A with HCN, then $H_3O^+$, and finally HI and P gave *n*-heptanoic acid. Treatment of A with warm dilute nitric acid gave an optically active diacid.

Ruff degradation of compound A yielded aldopentose B (negative rotation), which was oxidized with $HNO_3$ to an optically active diacid X. Ruff degradation of compound B gave aldotetrose C (negative rotation), which was oxidized to an optically active diacid Y. Ruff degradation of C gave compound D, which showed a positive rotation and which was oxidized to an optically inactive acid Z.

(*a*) Write structures for compounds A to D and X to Z. (*b*) Formulate the osazone derived from compound A. Which other sugars would also give this osazone?

**2.** Compound S, $C_6H_{12}O_6$, showed a negative rotation and gave a positive Tollens' test but a negative Schiff test. On treatment with phenylhydrazine it gave first a phenylhydrazone and then an osazone. Treatment of S with HI and P gave *n*-hexane, and treatment of S with HCN, acid, then HI gave *n*-heptanoic acid. Treatment of S with Na(Hg) and $H_2O$ then acetic anhydride afforded a hexaacetate. Nitric acid oxidation of S gave an optically active diacid. The Wohl degradation proceeded as follows:

$$\text{Compound S} \xrightarrow[\text{degradation}]{\text{Wohl}} \underset{\text{(negative rotation)}}{\text{aldopentose}} \xrightarrow{HNO_3} \text{optically active diacid}$$

$$\downarrow \text{Wohl degradation}$$

$$\underset{\text{(positive rotation)}}{\text{aldotetrose}} \xrightarrow{HNO_3} \text{optically inactive diacid}$$

The Kiliani synthesis, HCN, $H_3O^+$, then Na(Hg), afforded two aldoheptoses, one of which was oxidized to an optically inactive diacid.

Give the name and structure of compound S.

## DI- AND POLYSACCHARIDES

Polysaccharides are polymers composed of many sugar units joined by ether linkages. The sugar units usually occur in these polymers in the furanoside or pyranoside form, and the ether linkage is commonly at the anomeric carbon. Polysaccharides occur widely in nature. The following sections discuss the structures of four common disaccharides: sucrose, lactose, maltose, and cellobiose.

### 18-14 SUCROSE

Common table sugar, sucrose, is a disaccharide obtained from the sugar beet and sugar cane. Hydrolysis of sucrose, a nonreducing sugar, gives D-glucose and D-fructose; the nonreducing nature of sucrose shows that these monosaccharides are joined by an ether linkage at their anomeric carbons and hence are not in equilibrium with the open-chain form. Complete methylation of sucrose affords the octamethyl derivative, which gives the corresponding glucopyranose and fructofuranose on hydrolysis. The linkage of the rings ($\alpha$ or $\beta$) is determined by enzymatic reactions. Sucrose is $\alpha$-D-glucopyranosyl-$\beta$-D-fructofuranoside.

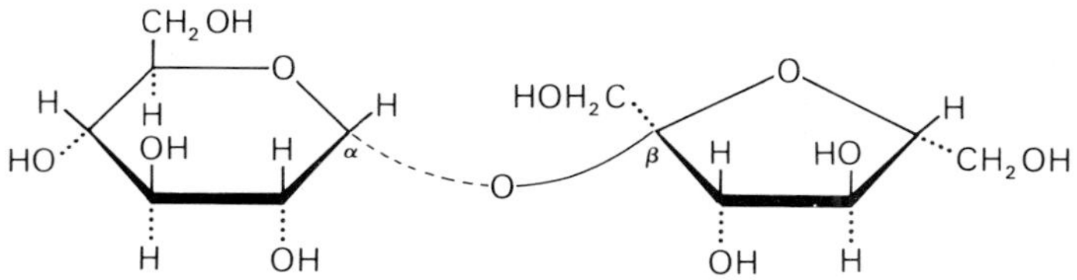

sucrose

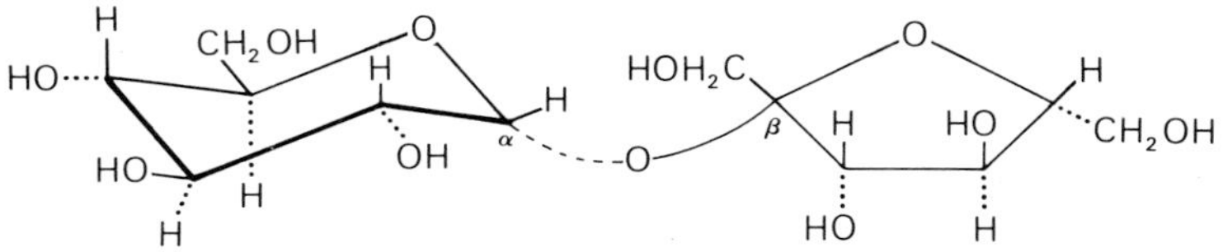

preferred conformation

### 18-15 LACTOSE

Lactose, a reducing sugar, is found in cow's milk and human milk. Hydrolysis of this disaccharide yields only D-glucose and D-galactose; it has been shown to be 4-*O*-$\beta$-D-galactopyranosyl-D-glucopyranose. The 4-*O* denotes the linkage at the 4-position, rather than at the anomeric carbon center.

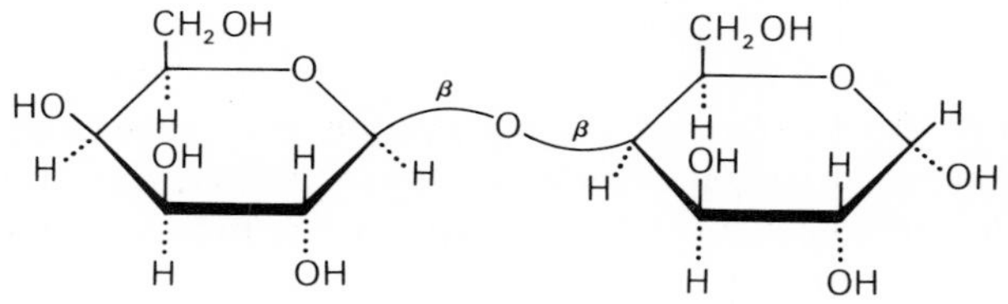

lactose

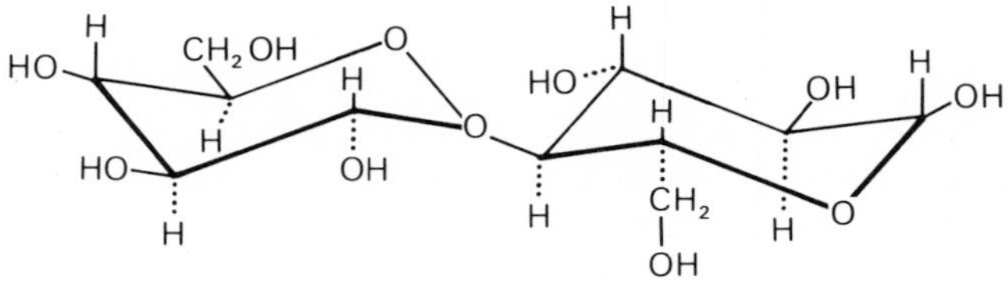

preferred conformation

## 18-16 MALTOSE, STARCH GLYCOGEN

Starch is a complex polysaccharide that serves as a carbohydrate reserve for most plants. Total hydrolysis of starch gives only D-glucose; partial hydrolysis gives maltose, a reducing disaccharide of glucose. There are, of course, many ways in which two such sugar units can be joined. In maltose this is a 1,4 linkage, and the compound is 4-*O*-α-D-glucopyranosyl-D-glucopyranose.

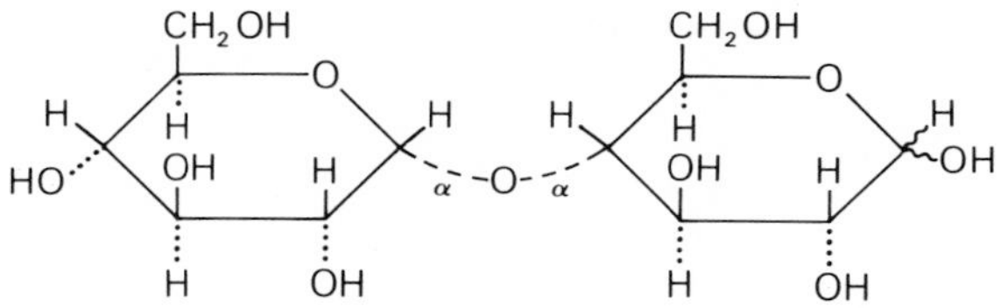

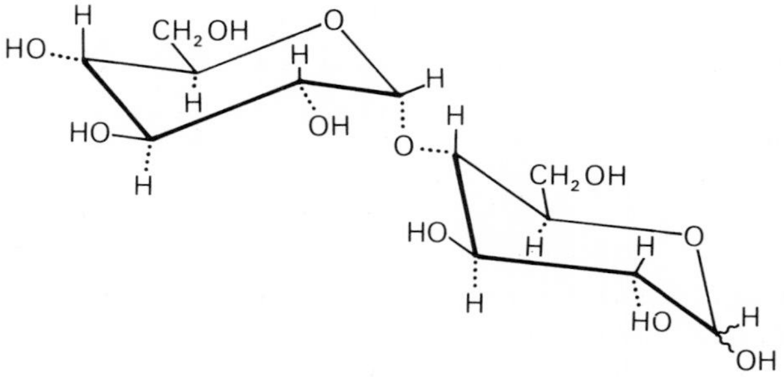

It is interesting to note that glycogen, the carbohydrate reserve for animals, is strikingly similar to starch. The liver and muscles are sources rich in glycogen. The hydrolysis products of glycogen, D-glucose and maltose, are the same as those of starch; however, glycogen appears to be more highly branched. The exact structural nature of these substances remains to be elucidated.

### 18-17 CELLOBIOSE AND CELLULOSE

Cellulose is a major consituent of wood, where it is found in the cell walls, and the principal chemical component of cotton. Cellulose is a linear polymer of cellobiose, a glucose disaccharide identical to maltose except for the position of the glycosidic linkage, which is $\beta$.

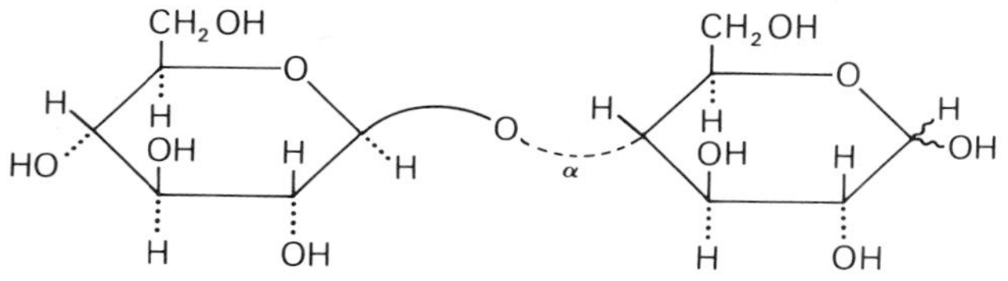

cellobiose

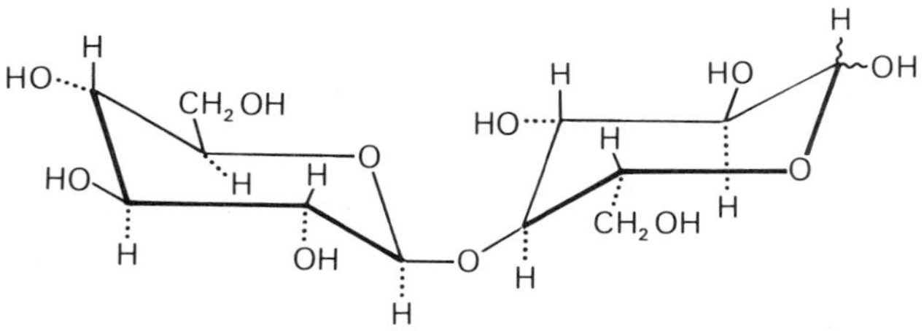

preferred conformation

## SUGGESTED READINGS

Farber, E.: Philosophy and Carbohydrate Chemistry, *J. Chem. Educ.*, **37**, 245 (1960).

Hanson, K.R.: The Configuration of (−)-Shikimic Acid and Certain Biochemically Related Compounds, *J. Chem. Educ.*, **39**, 418 (1962).

Horecker, B.L.: Pathways of Carbohydrate Metabolism and Their Physiological Significance, *J. Chem. Educ.*, **42**, 244 (1965).

Rosenblatt, D.H.: A Panoramic Approach to the Proof of Configuration of Aldohexoses, *J. Chem. Educ.*, **42**, 271 (1965).

Sickels, J.P., and H.P. Schultz: Evidence for the Configuration of $C_1$ of D-Glucose, *J. Chem. Educ.*, **41**, 343 (1964).

Sunderwirth, S.G., and G.G. Olson: Conformational Analysis of the Pyranoside Ring, *J. Chem. Educ.*, **39**, 410 (1962).

# Chapter Nineteen

Steroids are those natural products which contain the cyclopentanoperhydrophenanthrene skeleton.

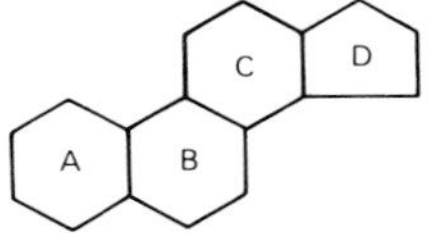


cyclopentanoperhydrophenanthrene

Among them are molecules of the following kind: sterols, such as cholesterol, from animals, plants, yeast, and fungi; bile acids; cardiac aglycones (heart stimulants); male and female sex hormones; adrenal-cortical steroids such as cortisone; toad poisons; and oral contraceptives. In this text the discussion will be restricted to a few categories which are representative of the chemistry of the steroids.

## 19-1 NOMENCLATURE AND STRUCTURE

In addition to the general feature of the cyclopentanoperhydrophenanthrene skeleton, in which the rings are lettered A, B, C, and D, steroids usually contain oxygenated functions (often at $C_3$), and alkyl groups (often methyl groups) are commonly found at $C_{10}$ and $C_{13}$.

steroid numbering
(cholestane)

# Steroids

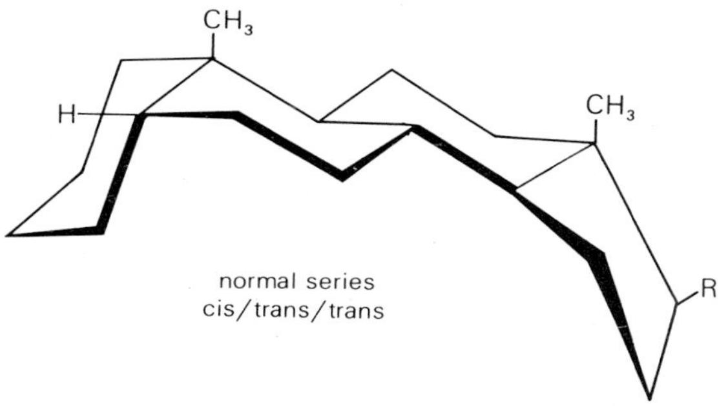

normal series
cis/trans/trans

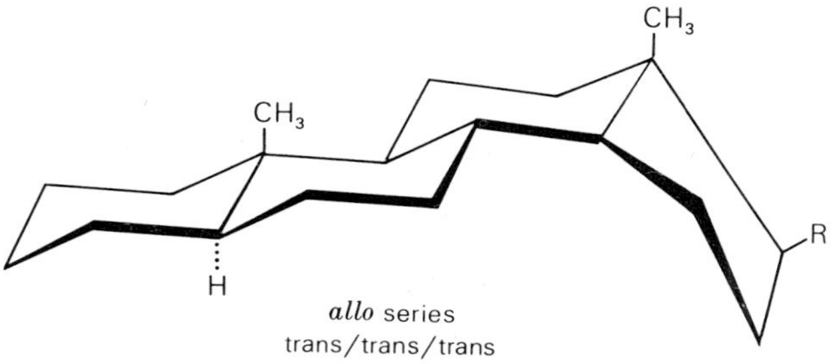

*allo* series
trans/trans/trans

Although the B-C and C-D ring junctions are trans, the A-B ring juncture gives rise to two series of compounds depending on whether the juncture is cis (normal series) or trans (allo series). **Consequently, steroids with known structures are important in the study of mechanisms of chemical reactions in which the conformation of a cyclohexane ring and its substituents must be known.** As seen in the conformational drawings, the steroid nucleus is nearly flat, and consequently substituents are designated as $\alpha$ (dotted line) if they lie below the plane and $\beta$ (solid line) if they lie above; a wavy line is used to denote an unknown or unspecified configuration. In addition to the $\alpha$ and $\beta$ designation, which shows the relationship of the substituents to the flat nucleus, each substituent may be designated, in the usual manner, as axial or equatorial (with respect to the ring to which it is attached).

Like many other natural products, steroids have trivial names, based on their biological occurrence or physiological effects, which are used today. Various prefixes are used to name synthetic compounds related to the natural product (see Table 19-1).

**Table 19-1**
**Some steroid prefixes**

| *Prefix* | *Meaning* |
|---|---|
| nor | elimination of methyl groups, degraded side chain, or ring contraction |
| homo | ring expansion |
| seco | ring fission with the addition of two hydrogen atoms to the cleaved atoms |
| iso | an isomer or closely related structure (a common but vague term) |
| epi | an epimer |
| anhydro | product of dehydration |
| dehydro | product of dehydrogenation of carbon-carbon or carbon-oxygen bonds; that is $-CH-CH- \longrightarrow >C=C<$ or $>CH-OH \longrightarrow >C=O$ |
| deoxo or desoxo | hydrocarbon from carbonyl compound $>C=O \longrightarrow >CH_2$ |
| deoxy or desoxy | hydrocarbon from alcohol $>CH-OH \longrightarrow >CH_2$ |

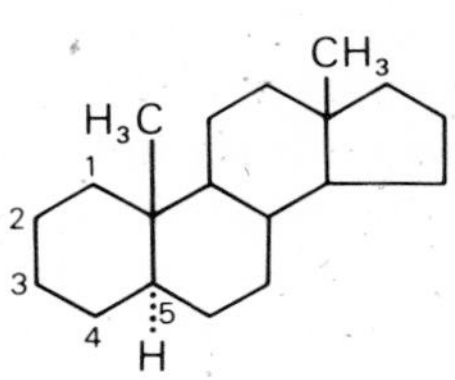

5α-androstane

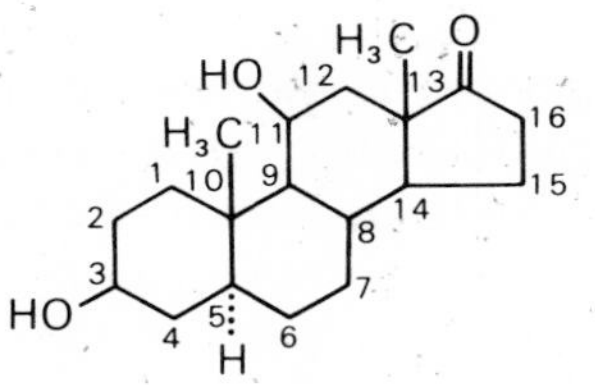

5α-androstane-3β, 11β-diol-17-one (11β-hydroxyepiandrosterone)

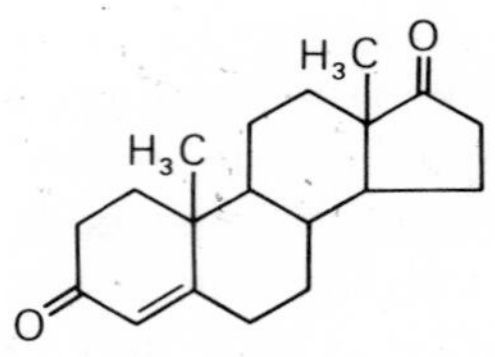

androst-4-ene-3,17-dione

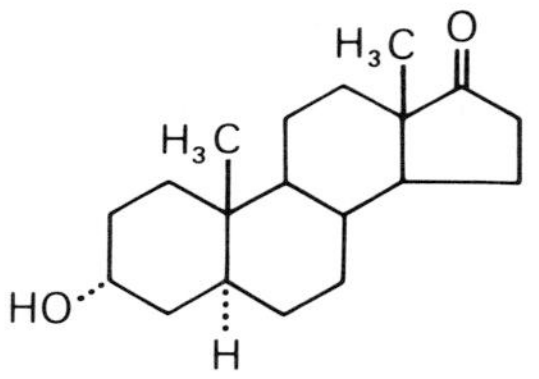

androsterone
($3\alpha$-hydroxy-$5\alpha$-androstane-17-one)

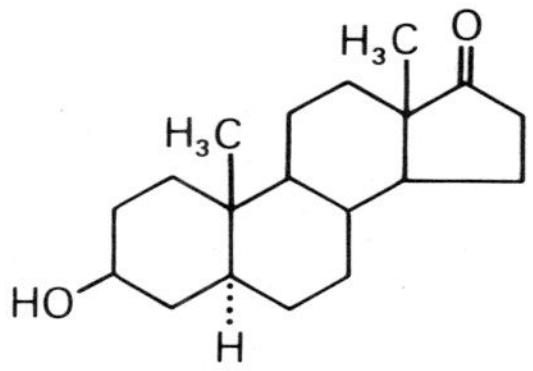

epiandrosterone (epimeric at $C_3$)
($3\beta$-hydroxy-$5\alpha$-androstane-17-one)

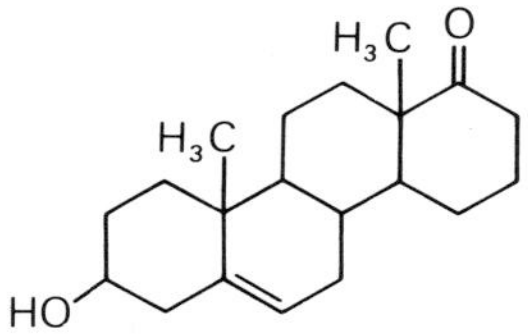

dehydroepiandrosterone
($3\beta$-hydroxyandrost-5-en-17-one)

### 19-2 STEROLS

Sterols, solid steroid alcohols, can be conveniently classified by their sources: ***zoosterols*** from animals, ***phytosterols*** from plants, and ***mycosterols*** from yeast and fungi.

Probably the best-known steroid is cholesterol, a zoosterol found in animal tissues as a structural component of cell membranes. It occurs in all tissues but can be isolated most easily from gallstones, which are composed largely of this steroid. Coprosterol (coprostanol), a related sterol, is found in the feces of human beings and carnivorous animals. These two sterols have been converted, by reduction, to the parent epimeric hydrocarbons, named ***cholestane*** and ***coprostane***.

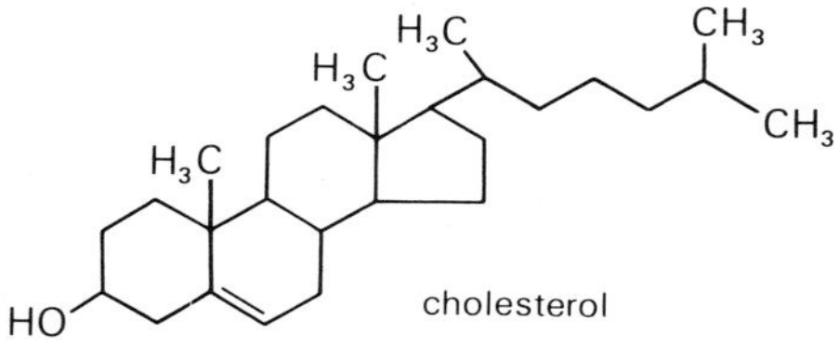

cholesterol

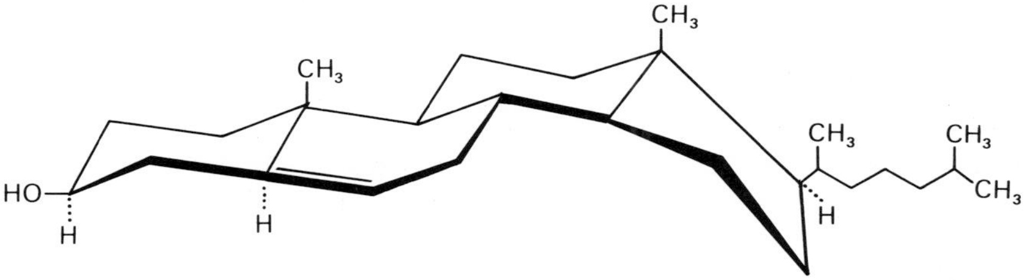

(preferred conformation)

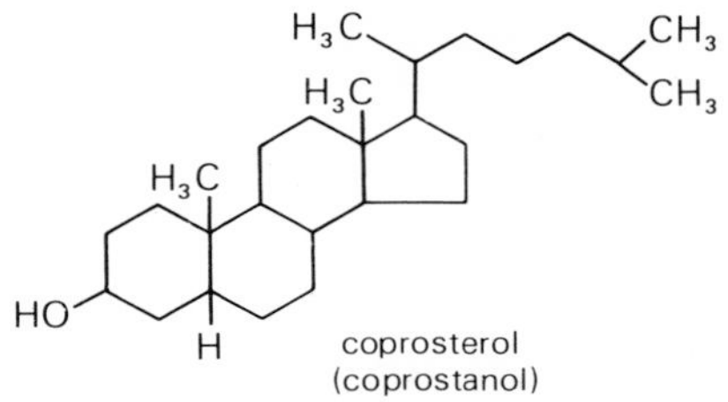

coprosterol (coprostanol)

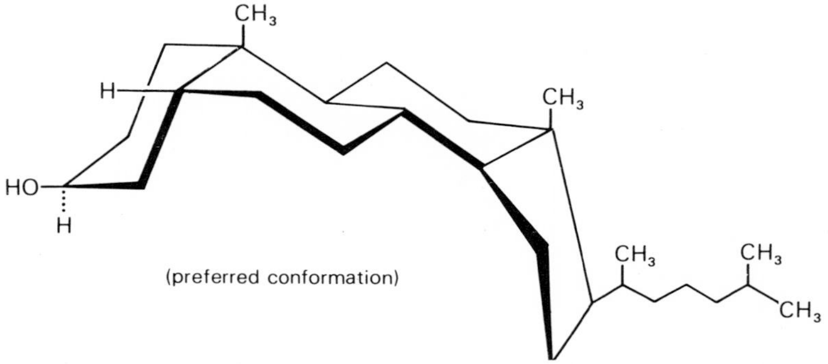

(preferred conformation)

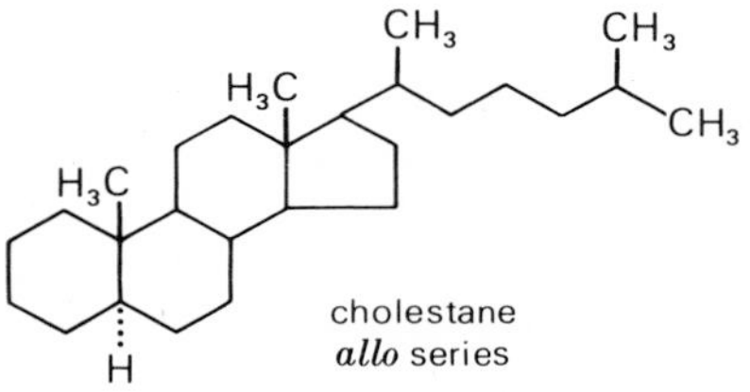

cholestane *allo* series

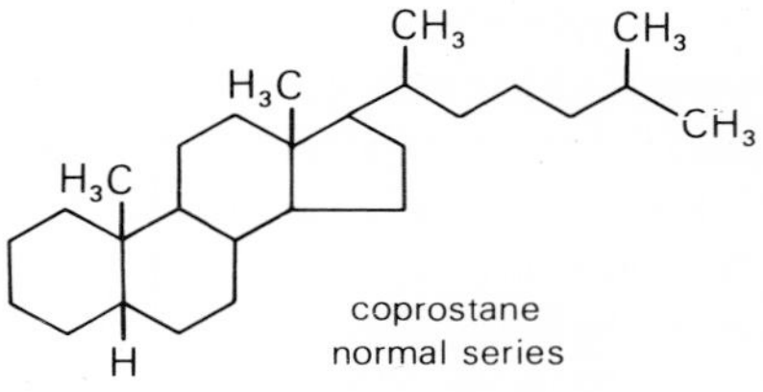

coprostane normal series

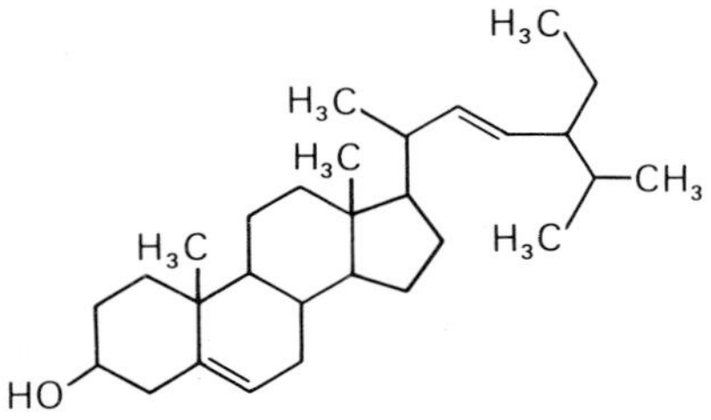

stigmasterol

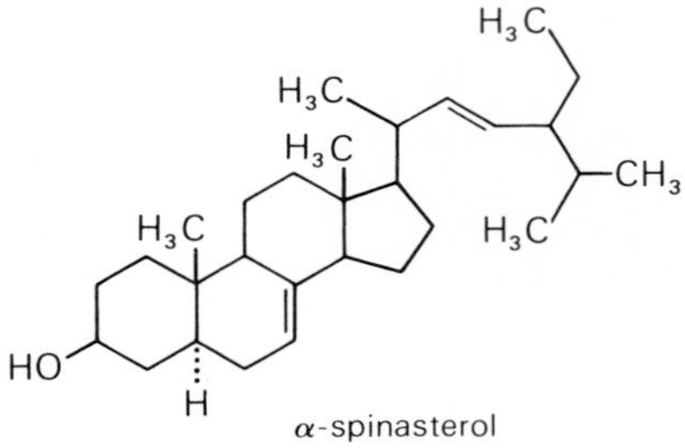

α-spinasterol

Ergosterol, the principal steroid from yeast, is a mycosterol which is converted to vitamin $D_2$ on irradiation. This photochemical transformation aroused much interest in the 1920s and in the 1960s the nature of the electronically excited states involved has received additional attention. Vitamin $D_2$ is not the direct or the only product isolated after ultraviolet irradiation of ergosterol; *cis*-tachysterol is an intermediate.

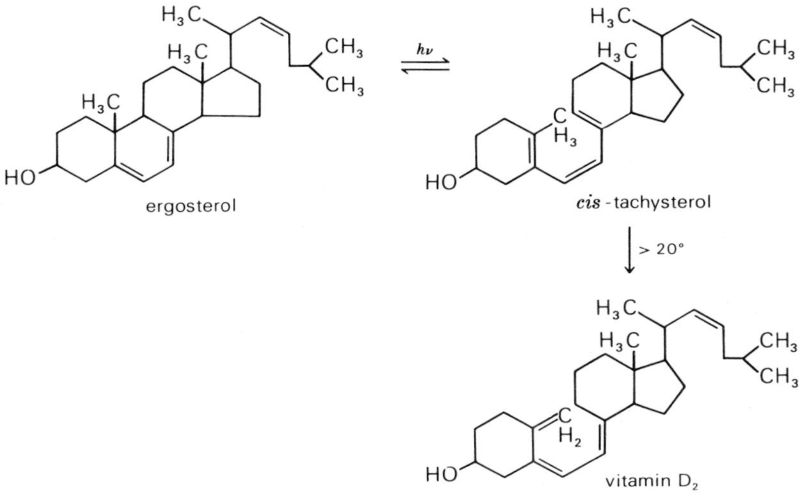


ergosterol ⇌ *cis*-tachysterol → vitamin $D_2$

## 19-3 BILE ACIDS

Bile acids are steroid hydroxy acids occurring in bile salts, which are emulsifying agents promoting hydrolysis and absorption of fats from the intestinal tract. Synthesized in the liver, most bile acids have structures based on either cholanic acid or *allo*cholanic acid.

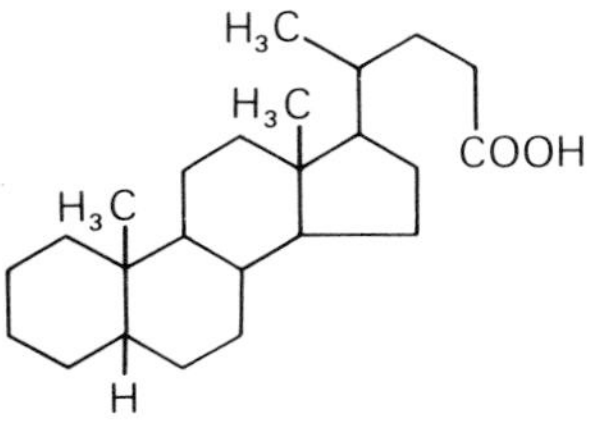


cholanic acid

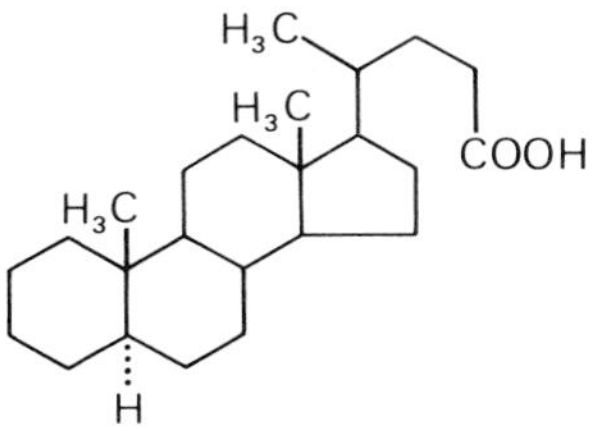


*Allo*cholanic acid

Common positions of hydroxylation are shown by cholic acid, $3\alpha,7\alpha,$ $12\alpha$-trihydroxycholanic acid, which is the major bile acid from human bile.

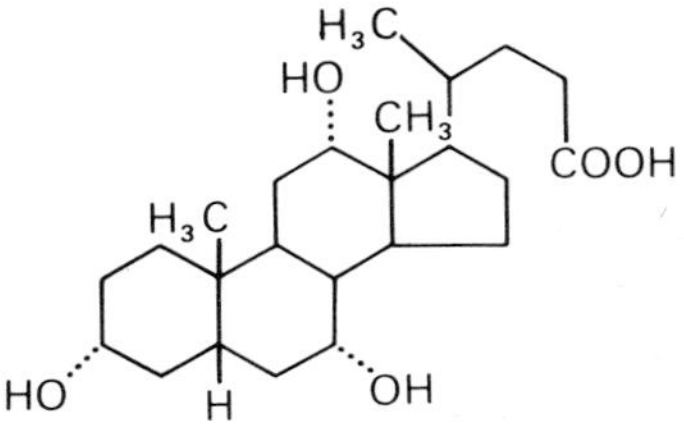


cholic acid

Generally these compounds do not occur as free acids but are usually found as amides of glycine, $H_2N—CH_2—COOH$, in herbivores or taurine, $H_2N—CH_2—CH_2—SO_3H$, in carnivores.

## 19-4 SEX HORMONES

Both male and female sex hormones (androgens and estrogens, respectively) are steroids. These natural hormones occur in the glands of the genital system, are transported by the blood, and have striking physiological effects. The fact that they are produced in the anterior lobe of the pituitary gland has been demonstrated by surgical removal of the gland, and observation of sexually related changes. The original state can be restored in whole or in part by injection of glandular extracts or synthetic hormones. Other than progesterone, a female sex hormone, it is extremely difficult to classify hormones as ***strictly*** male or female. Most of the compounds show at least some physiological activity in both sexes. Studies of the effect of structure on physiological activity (discussed below) have elucidated the important chemical features necessary for a given activity.

Female sex hormones, estrogens, can be assayed by examining vaginal smears of ovarectomized rats; positive reactions are characterized by the onset of estrus, which is accompanied by a distinct change in the appearance of the vaginal lining. Concentrates of urine from pregnant women or mares and extracts of placenta show high activity in such a bioassay. Since the concentration of the active substances is low, many volumes of urine or kilograms of placenta must be processed in order to isolate the pure steroids.

Examples of natural estrogens are estriol, estradiol, estrone, and pregnanediol. The chemical relation of the first three is shown below.

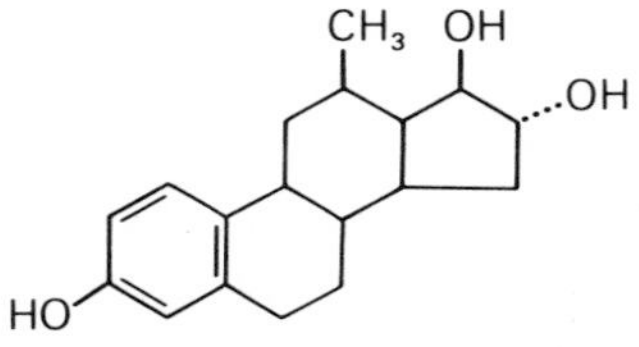

estriol $\xrightarrow{KHSO_4}$ estrone

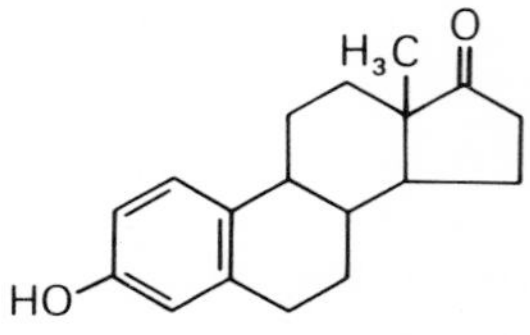

estrone $\xrightarrow{NaBH_4}$ estradiol

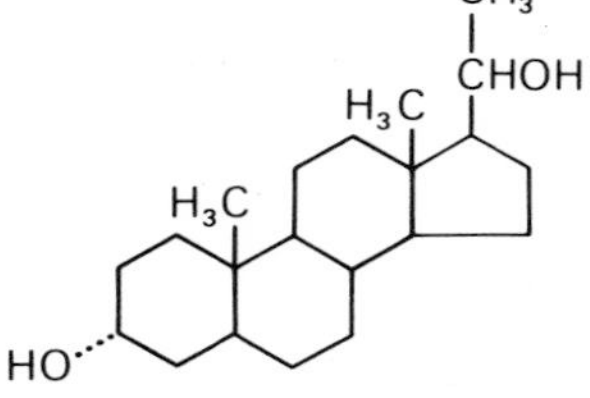

pregnanediol

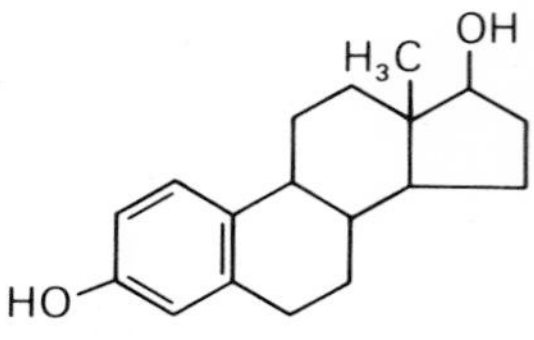

estradiol

Reduction of estrone with metal hydrides produces almost entirely the 17$\beta$-isomer, which is physiologically more reactive than estrone. This diol is used therapeutically as the benzoate of the phenolic hydroxyl.

Formulate the following reactions which establish a relationship of the bile acids to one series of sex hormones. Pregnanediol is oxidized to pregnanedione (with chromic acid), which is reduced to pregnane on treatment with Zn(Hg) and HCl. Methyl bisnorcholanate is treated with phenylmagnesium bromide, followed by an acid work-up, to give an olefin which can be oxidized to a ketone. Reduction of this ketone yields pregnane.

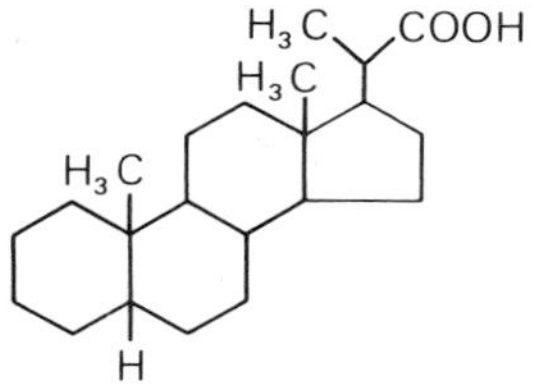

bisnorcholanic acid

Many natural sex hormones have been totally synthesized, and a few have been prepared by several independent routes. In nearly all these schemes the steroid A and B rings are derived from substituted naphthalenes or closely related derivatives which are elaborated in such a way as to form the C and D rings in succession. The key steps in one such synthesis are shown in Table 19-2. Note that although the requisite four rings are formed in the initial reaction, ring D must be formed by oxidation (loss of one carbon atom) and reclosure.

A number of synthetic compounds structurally related to the estrogens have been prepared. Some have been found to exhibit high estrogenic activity, a few being as active as the natural hormones. Some of the most active synthetic compounds are those based on the dihydroxydialkylstilbene structure, called ***stilbestrols***. The double bond is not essential to estrogenic activity; dihydrodiethylstilbestrol (hexesterol) is nearly as effective as diethylstilbestrol.

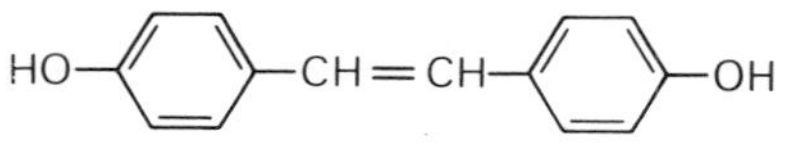

$HO-C_6H_4-CH=CH-C_6H_4-OH$

4,4'-dihydroxystilbene (stilbestrol)

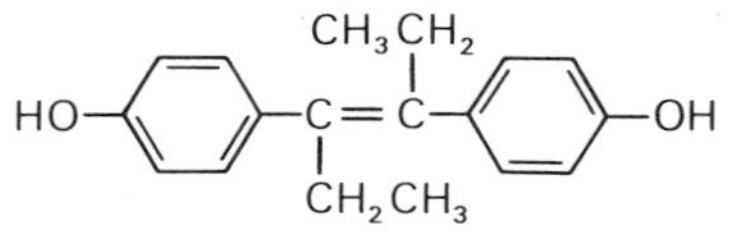

$HO-C_6H_4-C(CH_2CH_3)=C(CH_2CH_3)-C_6H_4-OH$

diethylstilbestrol

$CH_3CH_2$

HO—C₆H₄—CH—CH—C₆H₄—OH

$CH_2CH_3$

dihydrodiethylstilbestrol
(hexestrol)

Progesterone and pregnane derivatives are produced in the corpus luteum, a small yellow body in the ovary.

pregnane

progesterone
(4-pregnene-3,20-dione)

The presence of these compounds creates favorable conditions in the lining of the uterus for a fertilized ovum. If the ovum is fertilized, the hormones continue to be produced, and estrus and further ovulation are suppressed.

**Table 19-2**
**Some steps in an estrone synthesis**

1-vinyl-6-methoxy-3,4-dihydronaphthalene + benzoquinone —Diels-Alder reaction→

several steps to D-ring cleavage, double-bond reduction and methylation at $C_{13}$ →

several steps to ring closure and formation of estrone →

estrone

Study of known natural products continues in an effort to establish a relationship between structure and physiological activity. For instance, it might be asked: Is the carbonyl group at $C_3$ (or at $C_{20}$) of progesterone essential for activity? How do modifications of the side chain of progesterone affect the physiological activity?

The following information has been obtained for progesterone. Show how you would chemically modify the molecule in order to obtain compounds necessary for establishing these results.

**1.** The enol acetate of progesterone shows activity almost as high as that of progesterone itself (see Sec. 14-20).

**2.** Total reduction of the $C_{20}$ carbonyl group destroys activity, but reduction of the $C_{20}$ carbonyl to a hydroxyl group does not.

**3.** 21-Ethyl progesterone is inactive.

**4.** Introduction of a carbonyl group at $C_6$ destroys activity.

**5.** Both the $C_3$ carbonyl and the $C_4$ double bond are essential to the progesterone activity.

A group of synthetic oral contraceptives currently marketed is based on the structure of 19-nortestosterone. The discovery that 19-norprogesterone is as active as progesterone itself set off an extensive survey of other 19-norsteroids which might be useful. The synthetic steroid with the unnatural configuration at $C_{14}$ and $C_{17}$ and without the $C_{19}$ methyl group is eight times as active as progesterone!

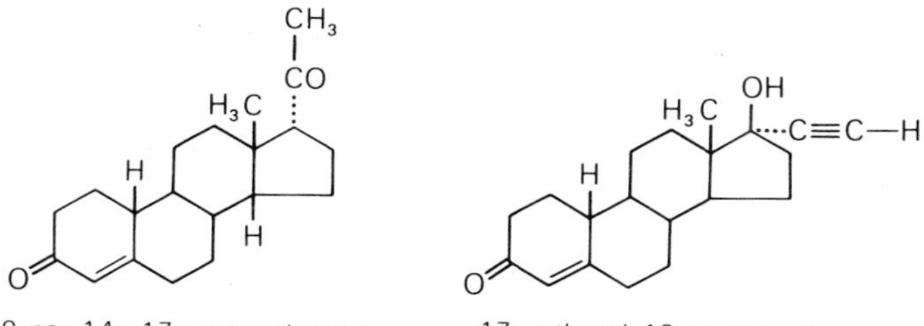

19-nor-14$\alpha$,17$\alpha$-progesterone

17$\alpha$-ethynyl-19-nortestosterone (norethisterone)

19-Nortestosterone, prepared by reduction of the A ring in estradiol methyl ether, shows less androgenic activity than testosterone but has been used to prepare 17$\alpha$-ethynyl-19-nortestosterone (norethisterone) and its $C_5$ (to $C_{10}$) olefin.

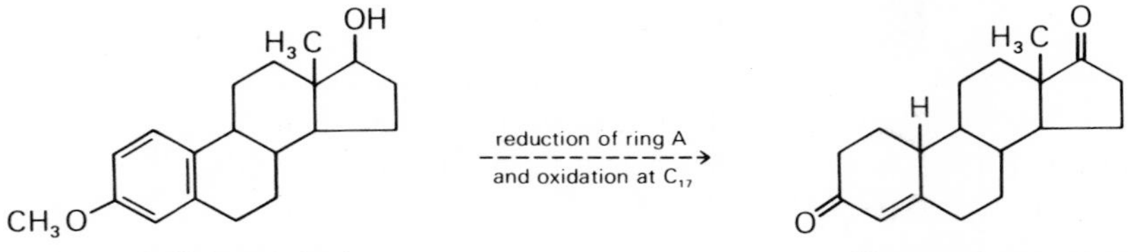

estradiol methyl ether — reduction of ring A and oxidation at $C_{17}$ → 19-nortestosterone

Male sex hormones, androgens, have been isolated from urine (of males, females, and eunuchs) and from testicular extracts. A bioassay has been developed based on measurement of the area of comb growth on a capon. Another method measures the increase of the seminal vesicles (in milligrams) in castrated rats.

One of the most powerful androgens is testosterone (from extraction of testicles), which is administered as the propionate because of its prolonged activity and effects on seminal vesicle growth. Three additional androgens are found in male urine: androsterone, dehydroisoandrosterone, and 3-chlorodehydroisoandrosterone.

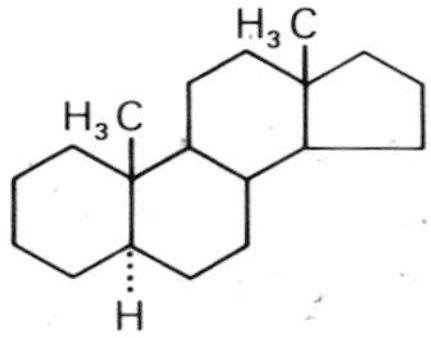

androstane (etio*allo*cholane)

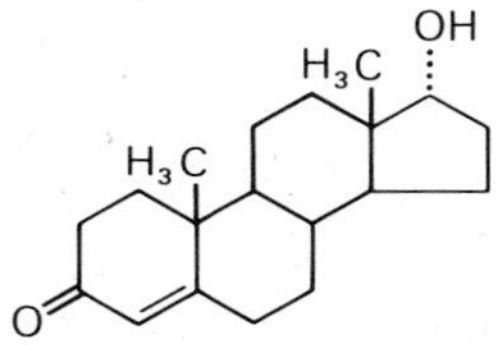

testosterone

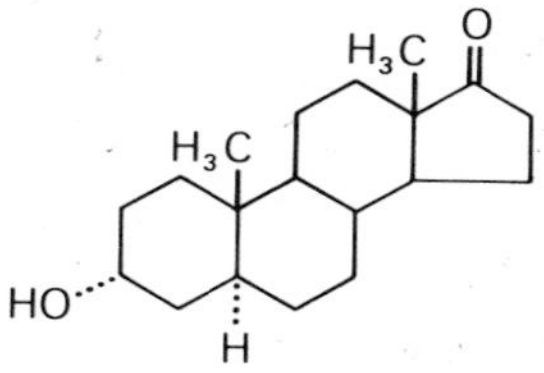

androsterone

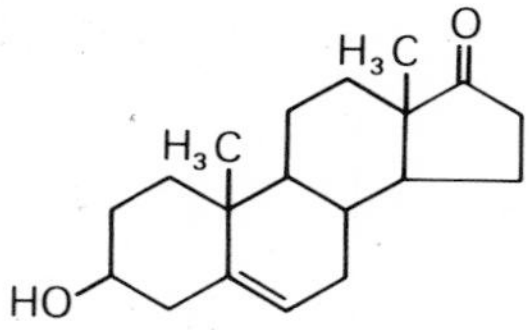

dehydroisoandrosterone

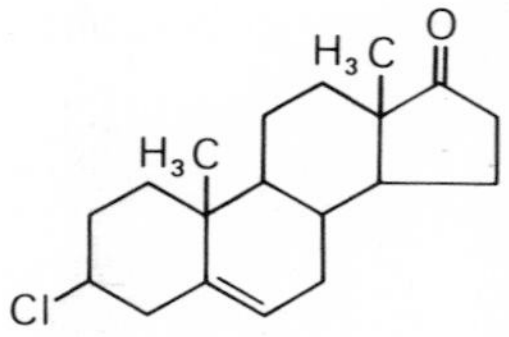

3-chlorodehydroisoandrosterone

An inactive compound has also been isolated and identified as $3\alpha$-etiocholanol-17-one. Note that the $C_{17}$ keto group is characteristic of the androgens.

Given the four androgens discussed above, how could you chemically distinguish between them? Show how you might establish the structural relationships with the group and with androstane.

## 19-5 OTHER STEROIDS

*Cardiac glycosides* are steroid sugar molecules, often isolated from plant sources, which on acid hydrolysis yield a sugar and a steroid. The steroid moiety is known as an *aglycone* or a *genin*. The best-known compounds of this group of aglycones are those obtained by hydrolysis of digitalis, a glycosidic mixture isolated from the purple foxglove, *Digitalis purpurea*. Digitalis is one of the most valuable substances known for increasing cardiac activity by increasing the intensity of the heart muscle contractions but diminishing the rate; these glycosides have a specific affinity for heart muscle when administered either orally or intravenously. Low doses (0.3 mg daily) are extremely effective.

Hydrolysis of digitalis produces three major aglycones, or genins, all of which contain an $\alpha,\beta$-unsaturated lactone ring (cyclic ester) in addition to other structural similarities. Both the $C_{14}(\beta)$ hydroxyl group and the unsaturated lactone are essential to activity.

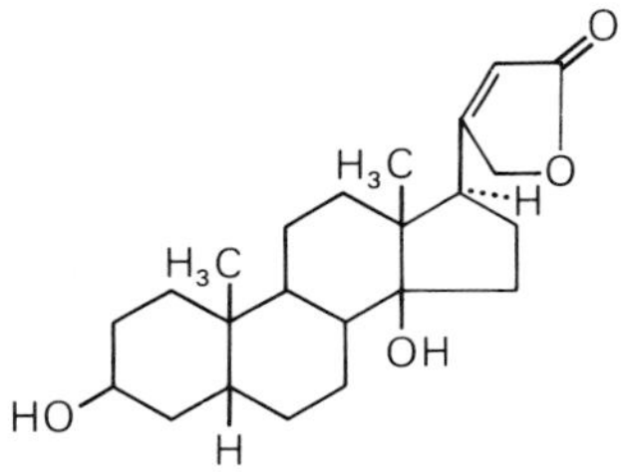

digitoxigenin

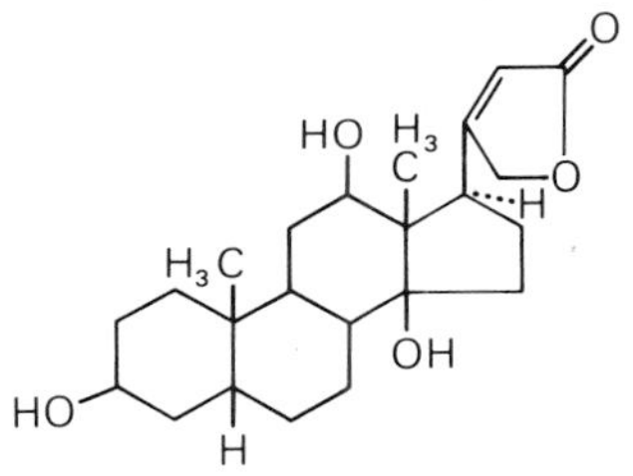

digoxigenin

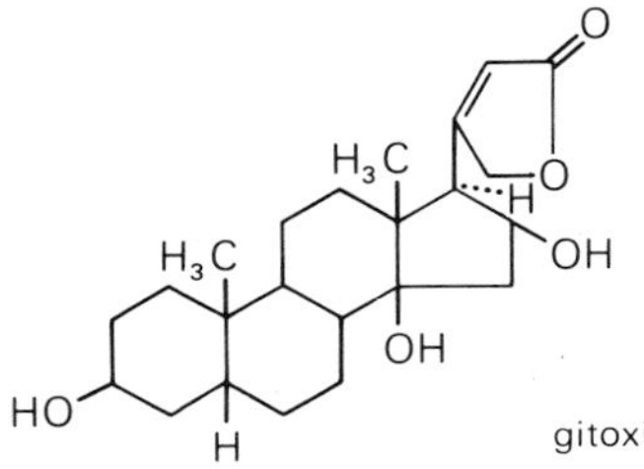

gitoxigenin

Poisons excreted by the common toad, *Bufo vulgaris*, produce physiological activity similar to that of digitalis. The genins derived by hydrolysis of the natural products are often called ***bufogenins***. The natural toad poisons are suberylarginine esters of the bufogenins. Bufotalin is but one of the many toad poisons which have been extensively studied.

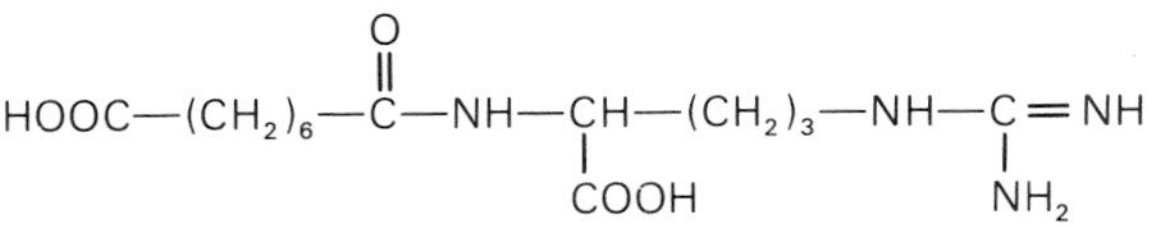

$$HOOC{-}(CH_2)_6{-}\overset{\overset{\displaystyle O}{\|}}{C}{-}NH{-}\underset{\underset{\displaystyle COOH}{|}}{CH}{-}(CH_2)_3{-}NH{-}\underset{\underset{\displaystyle NH_2}{|}}{C}{=}NH$$

suberylarginine

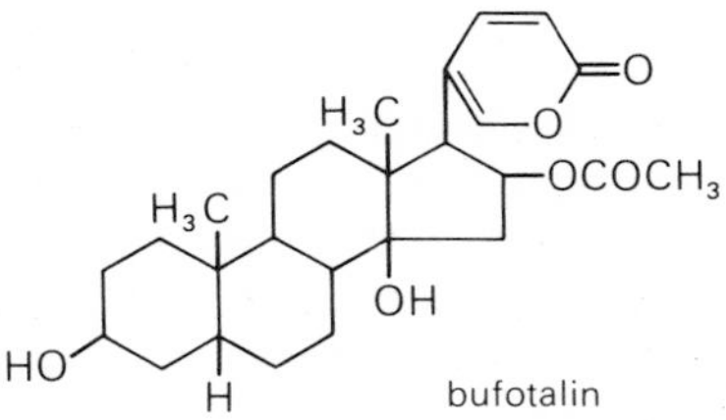

bufotalin

***Steroidal sapogenins*** are steroid glycosides able to produce stable foams in aqueous solution. The cardiac aglycones, or genins, are sapogenins, but they are placed in a special category (cardiac aglycones) because of their remarkable action on the heart. Other sapogenins have been used as poisons and also have the ability to form molecular compounds with alcohols and phenols. For example, digitonin, the glycoside of digitogenin, forms an insoluble molecular compound with equatorial 3-hydroxysterols but not the axial ones. This precipitation reaction has been important in establishing the stereochemistry at $C_3$ of many steroids.

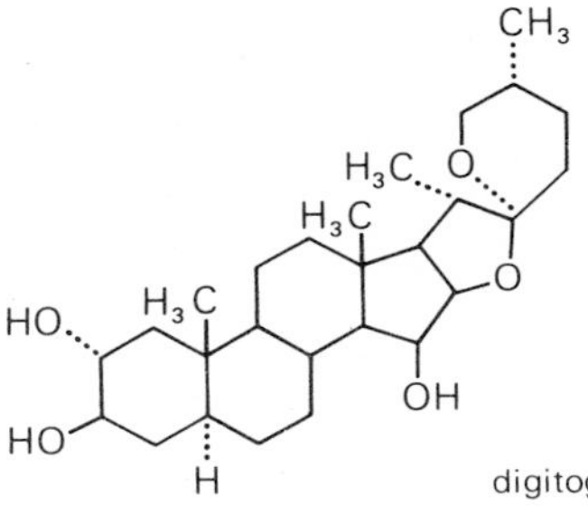

digitogenin

Steroids isolated from the outer structure or cortex of the adrenal glands of beef cattle are called ***adrenocortical steroids***. Of the 28 which have been isolated, only 6 are highly active in maintaining life in dogs whose adrenal glands have been surgically removed. One of the significant physiological properties of these adrenocortical hormones is the ability to promote the synthesis of carbohydrates, stored as glycogen (Sec. 18-16) in the liver. They also control the balance of electrolytes in body fluids. Cortisone, as the $C_{21}$ acetate, has many effective medical applications, including relief from rheumatoid arthritis. Cortisol has also been used extensively.

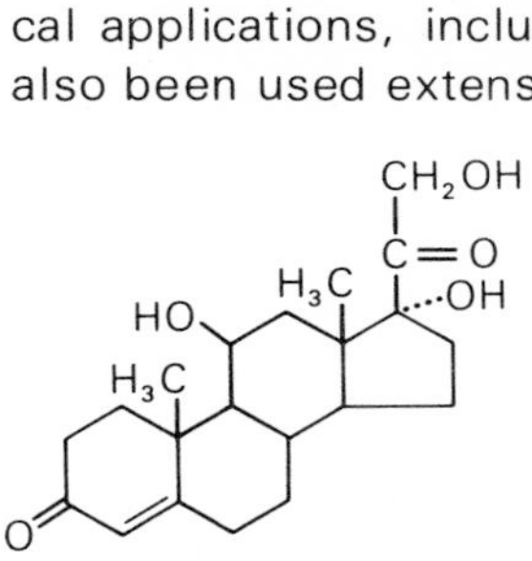

cortisol

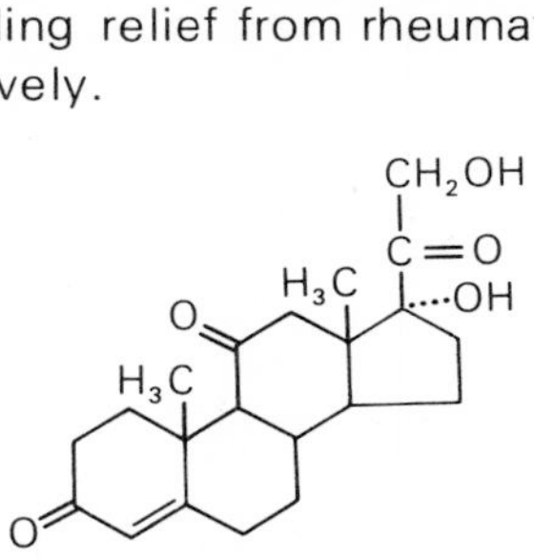

cortisone

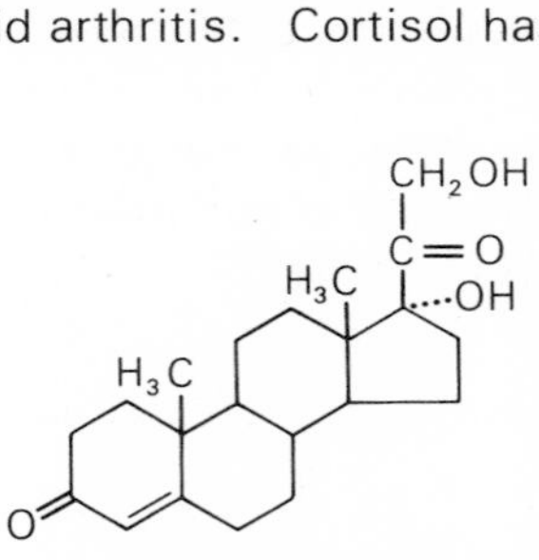

17$\alpha$-hydroxydesoxycorticosterone (cortexolone)

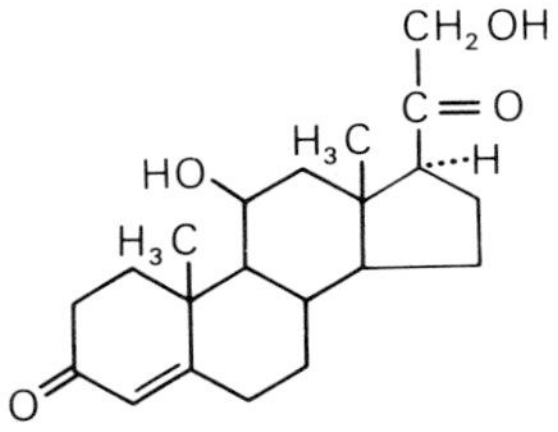

corticosterone

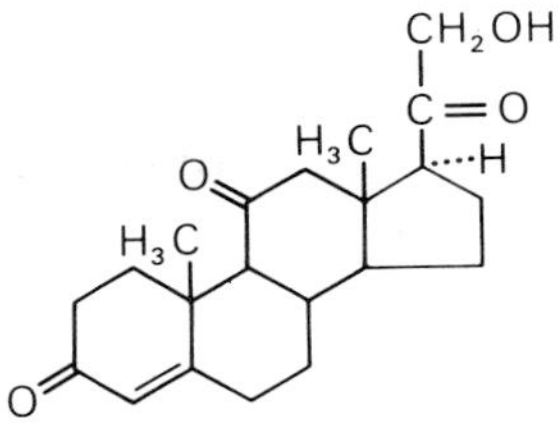

11-dehydrocorticosterone

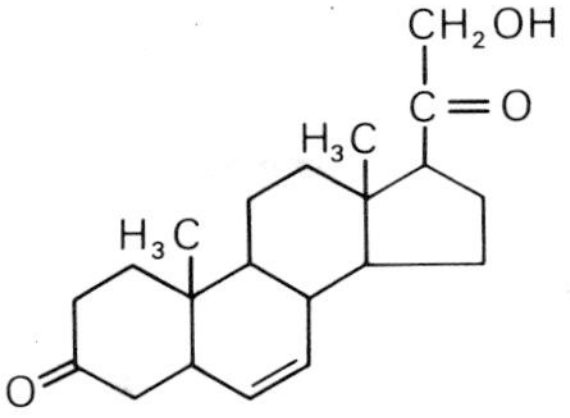

11-desoxycorticosterone
(cortexone)

Name each of the above six adrenalcortical steroids as derivatives of pregnane.

### 19-6 BIOSYNTHESIS OF CHOLESTEROL

One of the most fascinating series of chemical and biochemical studies led to the elucidation of the biosynthetic pathway for the *in vivo* construction of cholesterol from small organic molecules. In 1913 it was discovered that animals on a cholesterol-free diet are still capable of producing this compound. The chemical-biochemical studies started in the 1930s, when it was shown that cholesterol isolated from rats on a diet enriched in heavy water, $D_2O$, contained deuterium at about half the level of the body fluids. This indicated that about half the hydrogen (or deuterium) atoms came from the water, and hence cholesterol is probably synthesized from small chemical fragments. It was later found that labeled deuterioacetate, $CD_3COO^-$, fed to rats was incorporated into the cholesterol at such a high level that it was unlikely that the acetate was first decomposed to water and the steroid formed in its presence; more likely, the acetate was a direct precursor. Other low-molecular-weight compounds such as acetaldehyde, $CH_3CHO$, acetamide, $CH_3CONH_2$, acetone, $CH_3COCH_3$, and butyrate, $CH_3CH_2CH_2COO^-$ were also incorporated; however, the efficiency of incorporation appeared to depend on the ease with which they could be transformed to acetate, $CH_3COO^-$. At this point work was directed toward the biosynthesis of cholesterol using isotopically labeled acetate such as $^{14}CH_3COOH$, $CH_3{}^{14}COOH$, or $^{13}CH_3{}^{14}COOH$. Further, in the interests of the ease of handling and the efficiency of incorporation, the labeled cholesterol was prepared by incubating these compounds with rat-liver slices rather than feeding whole animals.

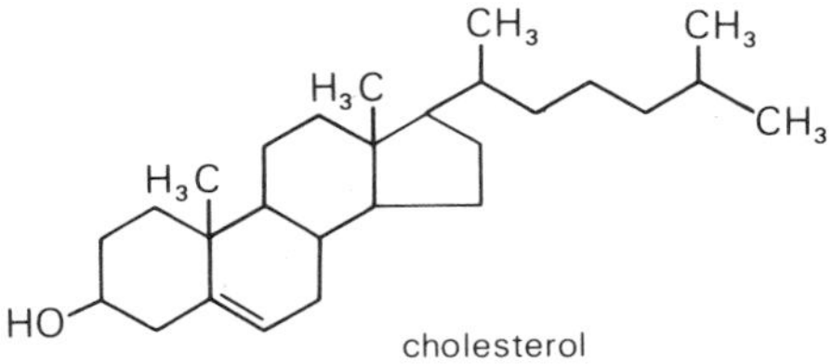

cholesterol

Degradation studies of the cholesterol side chain derived from $CH_3{}^{14}COOH$ and from $^{14}CH_3COOH$ both led to the same conclusion: the side chain is constituted as

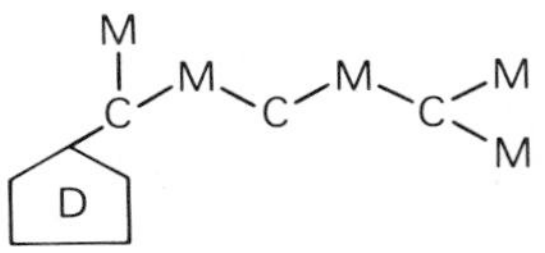

where C is a carboxyl carbon from acetate and M is a methyl carbon from acetate. The chemical details are shown in Table 19-3. By a

**Table 19-3**
**Degradation of cholesterol side chain**†

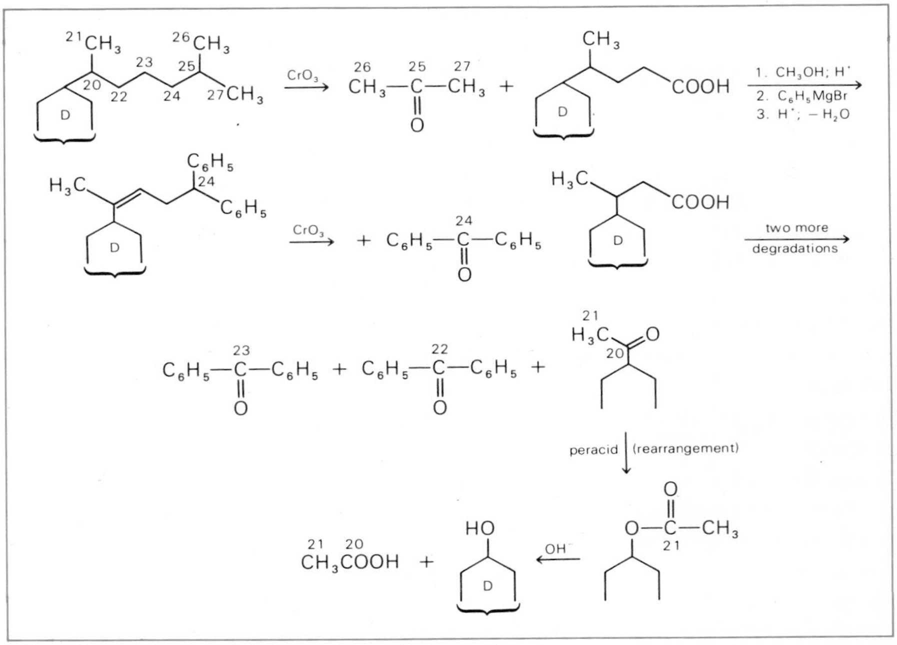

†The original carbons of cholesterol have been numbered.

series of oxidation reactions, rings A, B, C, and D were cleaved into smaller fragments, each was degraded by a scheme which allowed the activity of individual carbon atoms to be determined, and the source of each carbon was found to be

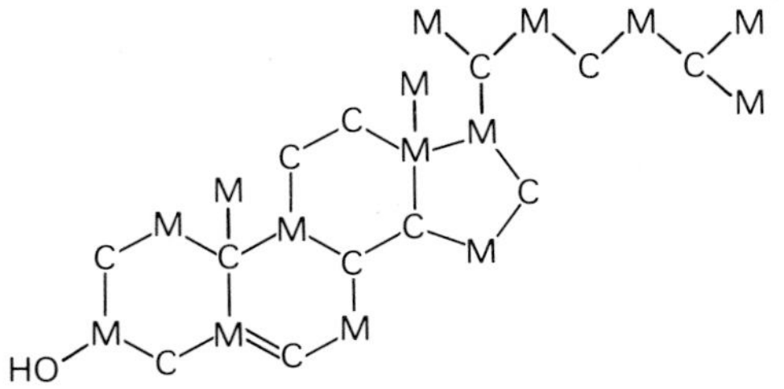

The questions of *how* the acetate fragments are joined and the specific intermediates involved were partially answered by the discovery that mevalonic acid, $HOCH_2CH_2$—$(HO)C(CH_3)CH_2COOH$, was capable of incorporation into cholesterol in very high yield. It was found that the carboxyl carbon is *not* incorporated, indicating an active *five*-carbon precursor. The formation of mevalonate from acetate (in liver tissue) has been demonstrated, and, further, only the dextrorotatory isomer exhibits biological activity.

## SUGGESTED READINGS


Beyler, R.E.: Some Recent Advances in the Field of Steroids, *J. Chem. Educ.*, **37**, 491 (1960).

Collier, H.O.J.: Kinins, *Sci. Am.*, **207** (2), 111 (1962). Discusses the group of protein hormones which dilate blood vessels and move smooth muscle.

Davidson, E.H.: Hormones and Genes, *Sci. Am.*, **212** (6), 36 (1965). Discussion of hormones, their source, chemical nature, and function.

Lerner, A.B.: Hormones and Skin Color, *Sci. Am.*, **205** (1), 99 (1961). Effect of hormones on melanin, a dark skin pigment.

Levey, R.H.: The Thymus Hormone, *Sci. Am.*, **211** (1), 66 (1964). The role of the thymus in blood manufacture and the origin of antibodies.

Papkoff, H., and C.H. Li: Hormone Structure and Biological Activity, *J. Chem. Educ.*, **43**, 41 (1966).

Sarrett, L.H.: The Hormones, *J. Chem. Educ.*, **37**, 185 (1960).

# Chapter Twenty

Alkaloids are nitrogen-containing optically active organic compounds usually isolated from plants; these bases show dramatic physiological activity. The name "vegetable alkalis" was first applied to these amines, which are now called ***alkaloids***. They occur in nearly all parts of certain plants and especially in the leaves, seeds, roots, and bark. The most actively growing parts of the plant usually contain the highest proportion of alkaloids. Seldom does a single alkaloid occur alone in a given plant; rather it is accompanied by others which are closely related in structure and biosynthetic origin. These complex mixtures of solid bases are obtained by ethanol extraction of the plant parts and can be separated by fractional crystallization and other methods. Alkaloids are not only of medicinal value and physiological interest but their structural determination and total synthesis have provided interesting challenges to the organic chemist.

Alkaloids range from simple monocyclic amines to very complex polycyclic tri- or tetramines. Their chemical and physical properties and physiological activities vary greatly. Compare coniine, colchicine, and emetine, shown in Table 20-1.

Although alkaloids can be named by the IUPAC system, the more complex ones are known simply by their trivial names, which often reflect their physiological activity or some circumstance surrounding the isolation or structural determination. This chapter will present representative alkaloids from major heterocyclic (nitrogen) groups: pyrrolidine, piperidine (and pyridine), quinoline (and isoquinoline), and indole alkaloids.

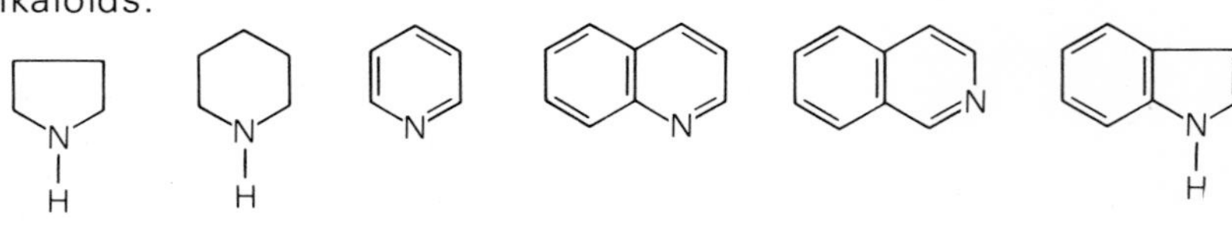

# Alkaloids

## PYRROLIDINE ALKALOIDS

### 20-1 HYGRINE

Hygrine, which is found in the coca leaf, is one of the most volatile alkaloids known.

$$\text{N-methylpyrrolidin-2-yl}-CH_2COCH_3$$

hygrine

Its simple structure has been synthesized by several routes. The synthesis of hygric acid, one of its degradation products, is presented below.

$$BrCH_2-CH_2-CH_2Br + NaCH(COOEt)_2 \longrightarrow BrCH_2-CH_2-CH_2-CH(COOEt)_2$$

$$\xrightarrow{Br_2} BrCH_2-CH_2-CH_2-CBr(COOEt)_2$$

$$\xrightarrow[\text{ring closure and amide formation}]{CH_3NH_2} \text{N-methylpyrrolidine-2,2-}(CONHCH_3)_2$$

$$\xrightarrow[\Delta]{H_2O} \text{N-methylpyrrolidin-2-yl}-COOH$$

**Table 20-1 Comparison of coniine, colchicine, and emetine**

| | *Coniine* | *Colchicine* | *Emetine dihydrochloride* |
|---|---|---|---|
| | 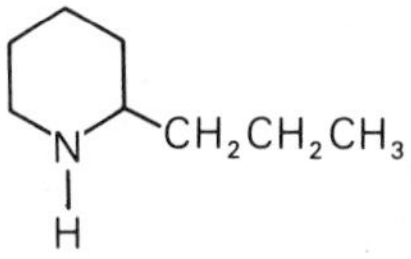 N, H, $CH_2CH_2CH_3$ | 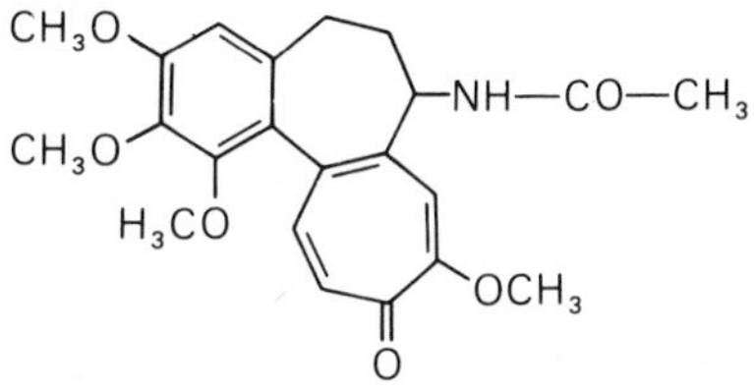 $CH_3O$, $CH_3O$, $H_3CO$, NH—CO—$CH_3$, $OCH_3$, O | 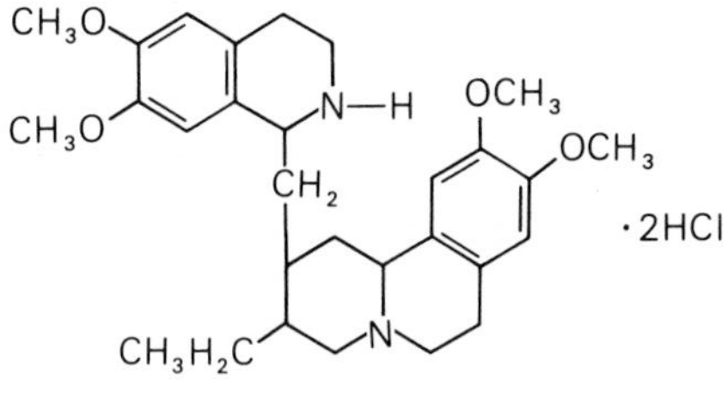 $CH_3O$, $CH_3O$, N—H, $CH_2$, $OCH_3$, $OCH_3$, N, $CH_3H_2C$, ·2HCl |
| molecular weight | 127 | 399 | 554 |
| m.p. (approx.) | −2° | 157° | 105° |
| solubility in $H_2O$ | 1 ml/90 ml | 1 g/22 ml | 1 g/7 ml |
| human fatal dose | 120 mg | 7 mg | > 60 mg |
| veterinary use | none | treatment of mammary tumors in dogs | treatment of lungworm infection in sheep and goats |
| medicinal use | none | acute gout (also used for doubling chromosomes in plant genetics) | acute amebiasis, amebic hepatitis, amebic abscesses |

## 20-2 HYOSCYAMINE, SCOPOLAMINE, AND COCAINE

These three alkaloids have the pyrrolidine ring incorporated into a bicyclic structure called the ***tropane ring***.

N—$CH_3$ H O—C(=O)—CH($CH_2OH$)—$C_6H_5$

atropine

N—$CH_3$ O H O—C(=O)—CH($CH_2OH$)—$C_6H_5$

scopolamine

N—$CH_3$ $COOCH_3$ H H O—C(=O)—$C_6H_5$

cocaine

Common derivatives are

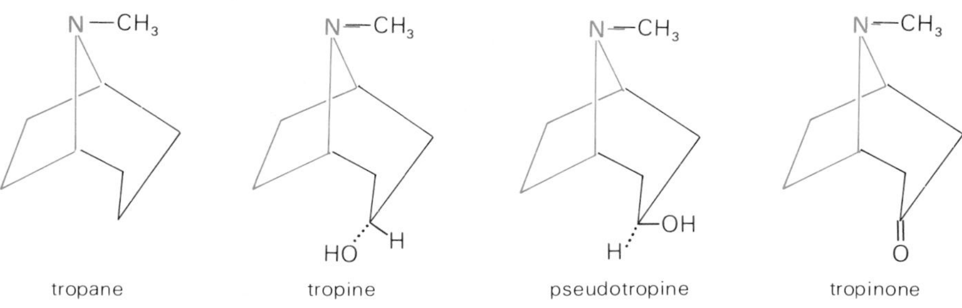


tropane tropine pseudotropine tropinone

Atropine is the racemate of hyoscyamine, which is the levorotatory isomer found in ***Atropa belladona***. The alkaloid is optically labile and is commonly used in the form of atropine sulfate to suppress salivary, gastric, and respiratory-tract secretions.

Scopolamine, also known as hyoscine, is a levorotatory alkaloid used medicinally (as the hydrobromide) as a sedative, to combat motion sickness, and to enhance the analgesic effect of narcotics. It has also been used to treat vertigo and certain psychoses.

Cocaine, isolated from the coca leaf, is a habit-forming narcotic used medicinally as a surface anesthetic in the form of the hydrochloride.

## 20-3 SYNTHESIS OF TROPANE ALKALOIDS

Tropinone and its derivatives have been synthesized under "physiological conditions" from chemical species (or their equivalents) which might occur naturally and be involved in the biosynthetic pathways of these compounds. It was found that incubation of a mixture of succindialdehyde, methylamine, and acetone at 25 to 30° in buffered solution at pH 5 gave small yields of tropinone.

$$OHC{-}CH_2{-}CH_2{-}CHO + H_2N{-}CH_3 + (H_3C)_2C{=}O \xrightarrow[\text{conditions}]{\text{physiological}} \text{tropinone}$$

succindialdehyde — methylamine — acetone — tropinone

Better yields can be obtained by the use of acetonedicarboxylic acid (as its calcium salt), which is prepared by the oxidation of citric acid. In a similar fashion, compounds in the cocaine series can be obtained by starting with the corresponding half ester.

$$HO{-}C(COOH)(CH_2COOH)(CH_2{-}COOH) \xrightarrow{\text{oleum}} HOOC{-}CH_2{-}C({=}O){-}CH_2{-}COOH \xrightarrow{Ca(OH)_2} {}^{-}OOC{-}CH_2{-}C({=}O){-}CH_2{-}COO^{-}\ Ca^{++}/2$$

citric acid — acetonedicarboxylic acid

$$OHC{-}CH_2{-}CH_2{-}CHO + H_2N{-}CH_3 + (Ca^{++}/2\ {}^{-}OOC{-}CH_2)_2C{=}O \xrightarrow[\text{conditions, pH 7}]{\text{physiological}} \text{tropinone } (N{-}CH_3) + 2CO_2$$

$$OHC{-}CH_2{-}CH_2{-}CHO + H_2N{-}CH_3 + CH_3OOC{-}CH_2{-}C({=}O){-}CH_2{-}COO^{-}\ Ca^{++}/2 \xrightarrow[\text{conditions, pH 5}]{\text{physiological}} \text{2-carbomethoxytropinone } (N{-}CH_3,\ COOCH_3) + CO_2$$

The fact that these syntheses can be accomplished *in vitro* under conditions which simulate those in growing plants must not be taken as *proof* that such reactions occur *in vivo* in an identical fashion. Nevertheless, these syntheses are a marked departure from the classical approaches to syntheses in the tropane series (see the problem below).

**1.** Pseudopelletierine was obtained in nearly quantitative yield by condensing glutaric aldehyde with methylamine and acetonedicarboxylic acid at pH 7 and 25°. Formulate this reaction.

**2.** Formulate the steps in the following classical chemical synthesis of pseudotropine, tropine, and tropinone.

Suberone (cycloheptanone) was converted to its oxime, which was reduced to the corresponding primary amine. Exhaustive methylation of the amine, followed by Hofmann degradation (Sec. 16-11) led to cycloheptene.

Conversion of cycloheptene to its dibromide (with $Br_2$) followed by treatment with dimethylamine gave an *unsaturated* amine, which was converted to a conjugated diene by exhaustive methylation and Hofmann degradation. This diene added 1 mole of bromine in the expected 1,4 addition. Heating the dibromide in quinoline afforded tropilidine, $C_7H_8$, which on treatment with HBr, followed by dimethylamine, gave a dimethylamine diene. This diene was treated first with sodium in alcohol (to reduce one of the double bonds) and then with one equivalent of bromine. The resulting compound, on heating, lost methyl bromide and hydrogen bromide, to give tropidine, $C_8H_{13}N$. The double bond in tropidine added 1 equiv of hydrogen bromide, and the bromide was hydrolyzed to pseudotropine in aqueous (acid) solution. Oxidation of the alcohol with $CrO_3$ gave tropinone, which was reduced with zinc and HI to tropine.

## PIPERIDINE AND PYRIDINE ALKALOIDS

### 20-4 PIPERINE, CONIINE, AND THE PELLETIERINES

The alkaloid piperine is so named because it occurs in the kernel of the ripe white pepper and in the unripe black pepper, or ***Piper nigrum***. It is optically inactive but is capable of exhibiting cis-trans isomerism; the acid derived from hydrolysis of the alkaloid has a trans, trans configuration. Piperic acid can be oxidized to piperonal and to piperonylic acid.

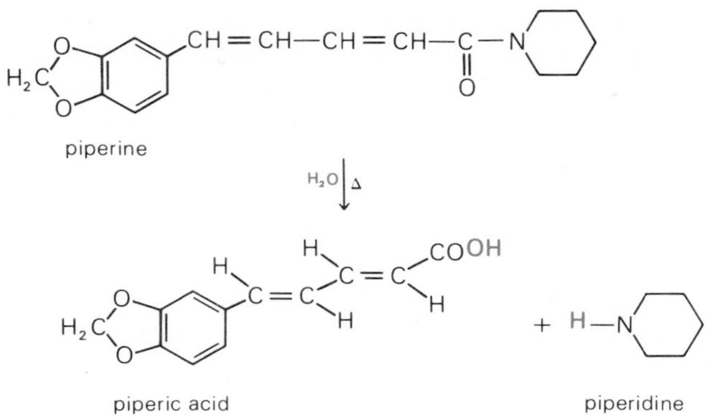

piperine

$H_2O$, $\Delta$

piperic acid + piperidine

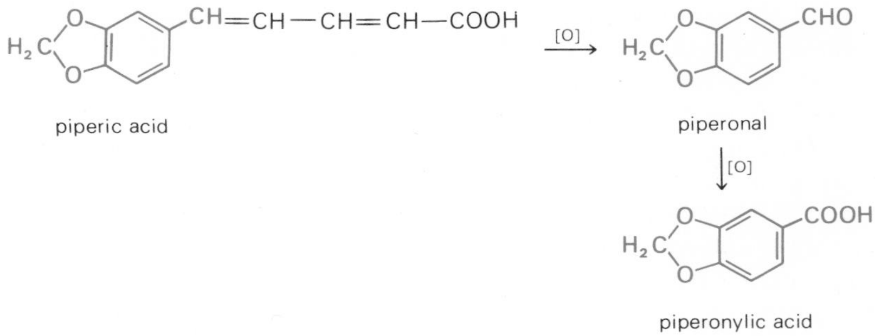

piperic acid $\xrightarrow{[O]}$ piperonal $\xrightarrow{[O]}$ piperonylic acid

Piperine has been used as a flavoring additive in brandy and as an insecticide for houseflies.

The properties of coniine, the principal toxic substance in hemlock, were shown in Table 20-1. One of the key steps in its structural determination was the zinc-dust dehydrogenation of coniine, which yielded 2-*n*-propylpyridine. D,L-Coniine has been synthesized by the high-temperature condensation of acetaldehyde with 2-methylpyridine ($\alpha$-picoline) followed by reduction with sodium in alcohol.

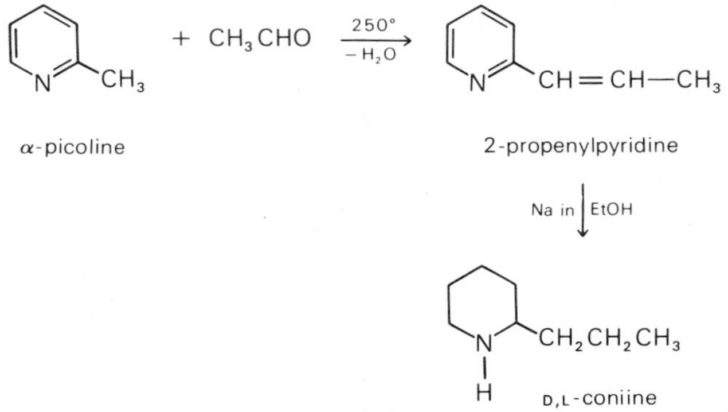

$\alpha$-picoline + $CH_3CHO$ $\xrightarrow[-H_2O]{250°}$ 2-propenylpyridine ($CH{=}CH{-}CH_3$)

Na in EtOH

D,L-coniine ($CH_2CH_2CH_3$)

Pelletierine is an unstable amine aldehyde which occurs in the root bark of the pomegranate tree. It has been used (as a mixture with other alkaloids extracted with it) in the treatment of tapeworm infections. Isopelletierine, methylisopelletierine, and pseudopelletierine are related alkaloids which are found in the root-bark extraction mixture.

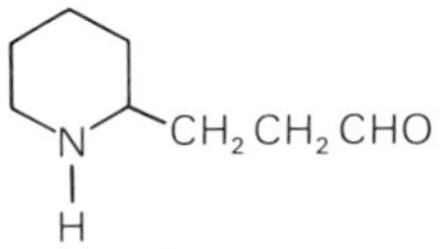

pelletierine

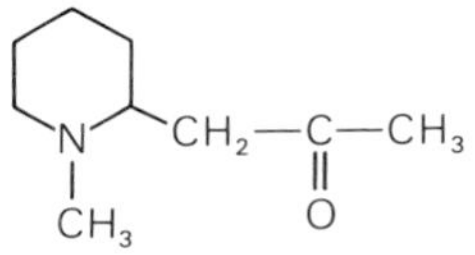

methylisopelletierine

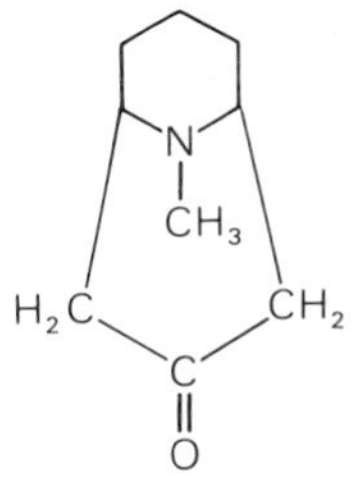

pseudopelletierine

Of these, pseudopelletierine (renamed *N*-methylgranatonine) is of special interest, since the first synthesis of cyclooctatetraene (COT) began with this natural product. The steps in this classical (1911) synthesis of COT from pseudopelletierine gave COT in 3% overall yield. This synthesis was repeated in 1947, confirming the earlier results, and the COT obtained was found to be identical with that obtained by the cyclic tetramerization of acetylene at 50° in the presence of $Ni(CN)_2$ (80 to 90% yield).

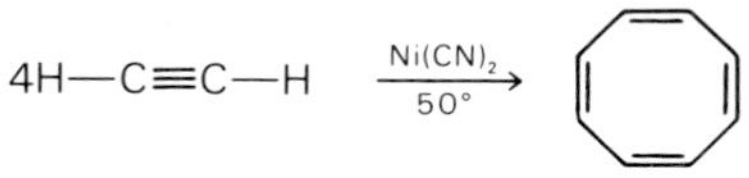

$$4H—C\equiv C—H \xrightarrow[50^\circ]{Ni(CN)_2}$$

cyclooctatetraene (COT)

## 20-5 NICOTINE AND OTHER TOBACCO ALKALOIDS

Although nicotine is the main alkaloid of tobacco (genus ***Nicotiana***), several related compounds occur in minor proportions: anabasine, anatabine, and their *N*-methyl derivatives.

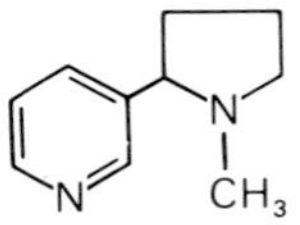

nicotine

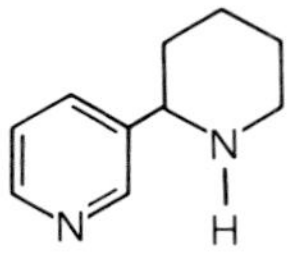

anabasine

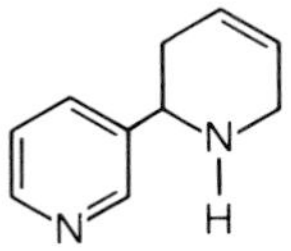

anatabine

Nicotine occurs to the extent of 2 to 8% in dried tobacco leaves. A 40% aqueous solution of nicotine sulfate is used as an insecticide and sold under various trade names such as Black Leaf 40. Over 500 tons of highly toxic nicotine are used annually in the United States for this purpose. Although the liquid free base is absorbed through the skin, the solid salts are not. As little as 40 mg (orally) of the liquid has been reported to be fatal to man.

The structure of nicotine, $C_{10}H_{14}N_2$, was established mainly by a study of its oxidation products. Strong oxidizing agents convert the side chain to an acid, and give nicotinic acid (pyridine-3-carboxylic acid), also known as *niacin*.

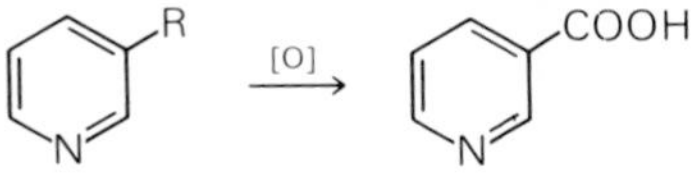

nicotine —[O]→ niacin

This establishes the position of side-chain attachment. Since nicotine behaves as a ditertiary amine, the side chain attached to the pyridine ring cannot be a simple piperidine ring (secondary amine). Oxidation with bromine gives a dibromodiketone which, on treatment with $Ba(OH)_2$, decomposes to nicotinic acid, malonic acid, and methylamine.

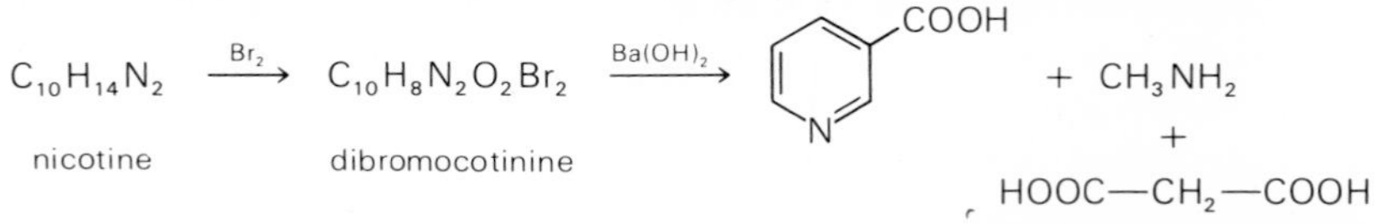

$$C_{10}H_{14}N_2 \xrightarrow{Br_2} C_{10}H_8N_2O_2Br_2 \xrightarrow{Ba(OH)_2} \text{nicotinic acid} + CH_3NH_2 + HOOC{-}CH_2{-}COOH$$

nicotine — dibromocotinine

The formation of the three-carbon fragment establishes the attachment of the *N*-methylpyrrolidine ring at its 2-position since a three-carbon acid is obtained.

Of the several syntheses of nicotine which have been carried out, only one will be shown here (see Table 20-2).

**Table 20-2 A synthesis of nicotine**

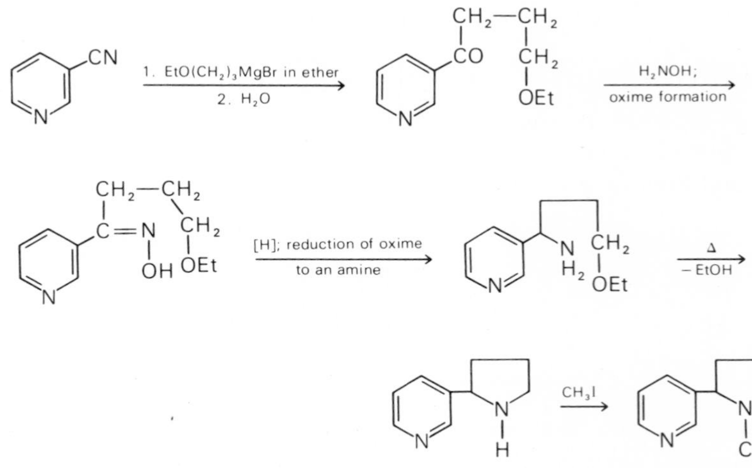

3-cyanopyridine —(1. $EtO(CH_2)_3MgBr$ in ether; 2. $H_2O$)→ 3-pyridyl ketone $CO{-}CH_2{-}CH_2{-}CH_2{-}OEt$ —($H_2NOH$; oxime formation)→ $C{=}N{-}OH$ with $CH_2{-}CH_2{-}CH_2{-}OEt$ —([H]; reduction of oxime to an amine)→ $NH_2$ amine with $CH_2{-}CH_2{-}CH_2{-}OEt$ —(Δ; − EtOH)→ D,L-nornicotine —($CH_3I$)→ D,L-nicotine

D,L-nornicotine

D,L-nicotine resolved via salt formation with D-tartaric acid

## QUINOLINE AND ISOQUINOLINE ALKALOIDS

### 20-6 CINCHONINE AND QUININE

Of the 40 or more alkaloids included in the quinoline group, cinchonine and quinine are two of the most important.

$CH_2=CH$ H

N

HO—CH

R

N

R = —H, cinchonine
R = —$OCH_3$, quinine

In addition to the quinoline ring, these alkaloids also contain the quinuclidine ring. Both of these bases have been used in the resolution of optically active acids via the formation of diastereomeric salts.

Both of these alkaloids occur, with others of similar structure, in the bark of species of *Cinchona*. For many years quinine was the most effective antimalarial agent and is still used for this purpose. The trees, native to the high Andes, are cultivated in Java. Although the bark of native trees contain about 8% quinine, several of the grafted varieties have produced more than 15% quinine (as the sulfate). It is often used medicinally as either the sulfate or dihydrochloride.

The total synthesis of quinine was achieved in 1945; only the general approach will be shown here. It consists of formation of the appropriate quinoline, partial synthesis of the quinuclidine ring (a substituted piperidine), and finally condensation of these two fragments to give the ketone, which on reduction yields quinine.

*General*:

COOR

$CH_3O$

N

+ EtOOC—$CH_2$ $CH_2$ $CH_2$ $CH_2$ $CH=CH_2$ N H →

$CH=CH_2$

CO

N

$CH_3O$

N

Synthesis of the quinoline:

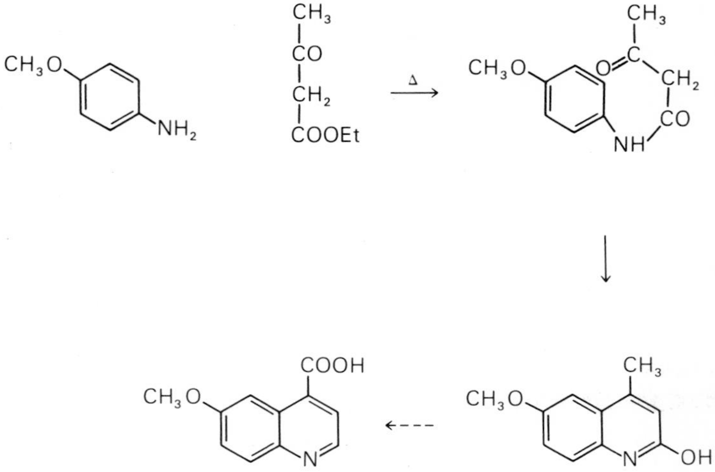

$CH_3O$ $NH_2$ $CH_3$ CO $CH_2$ COOEt Δ → $CH_3O$ $CH_3$ O=C $CH_2$ CO NH

↓

COOH $CH_3O$ N ←--- $CH_3$ $CH_3O$ N OH

Synthesis of the substituted piperidine:

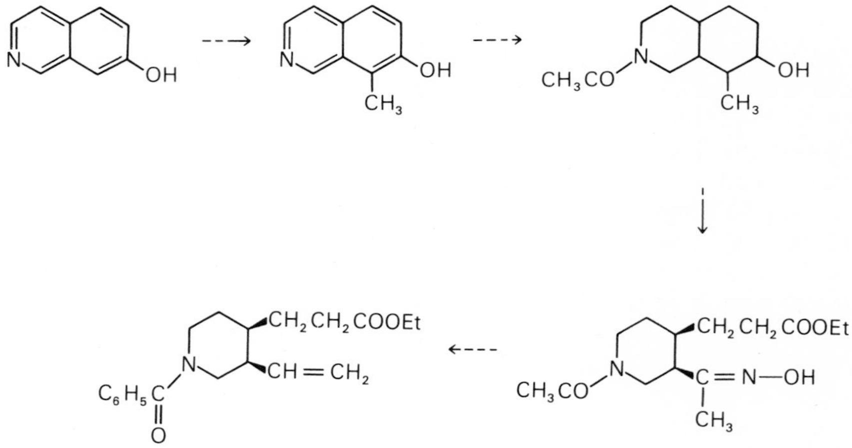

N OH ---→ N OH $CH_3$ ---→ $CH_3CO$ N OH $CH_3$

↓

$CH_2CH_2COOEt$ N $CH{=}CH_2$ $C_6H_5C$ O ←--- $CH_2CH_2COOEt$ $CH_3CO$ N C=N—OH $CH_3$

## 20-7 MESCALINE AND PAPAVARINE

Although mescaline does not contain the isoquinoline nucleus, it is included with this group of alkaloids, of which papavarine is an example, because of its structural relationship to alkaloids of this isoquinoline group.

Mescaline has a very simple chemical structure which can be readily synthesized in a few steps. Many syntheses have been devised.

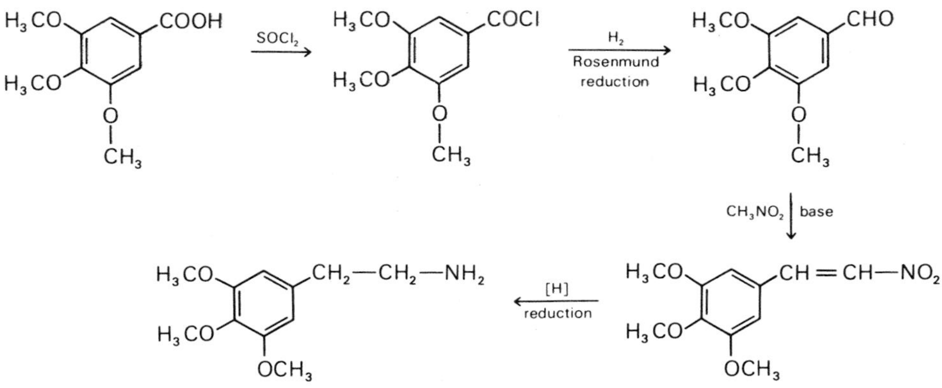

$H_3CO$, $H_3CO$, COOH, O, $CH_3$ $\xrightarrow{SOCl_2}$ $H_3CO$, $H_3CO$, COCl, O, $CH_3$ $\xrightarrow[\text{Rosenmund reduction}]{H_2}$ $H_3CO$, $H_3CO$, CHO, O, $CH_3$

$\downarrow$ $CH_3NO_2$ | base

$H_3CO$, $H_3CO$, $CH_2—CH_2—NH_2$, $OCH_3$ $\xleftarrow[\text{reduction}]{[H]}$ $H_3CO$, $H_3CO$, $CH{=}CH—NO_2$, $OCH_3$

Mescaline

Mescaline produces powerful hallucinatory effects. It is isolated from the flowering heads (Mescal buttons) of several species of cactus. Dried slices of these buttons are chewed or extracts are drunk as part of certain ceremonial rites of Indians of Mexico and the southwestern United States. The exhilarating effect and the color and sound hallucinations are due mainly to mescaline.

> Papavarine is an isoquinoline alkaloid found in opium. From the information given below, derived mainly from oxidation studies, deduce a structure for papavarine and its oxidation products. Papavarine, $C_{20}H_{21}O_4N$, is optically inactive. On gentle oxidation it gives papaverinol, $C_{20}H_{21}O_5N$, a secondary alcohol; more strenuous oxidation gives papaveraldine, $C_{20}H_{19}O_5N$, a ketone. Strenuous oxidation gives papaverinic acid, $C_{16}H_{13}O_7N$, a dibasic acid; oxidation of this diacid yields veratric acid (3,4-dimethyoxybenzoic acid), metahemipinic acid (4,5-dimethoxyphthalic acid), 2,3,4-pyridinetricarboxylic acid, and 6,7-dimethoxyisoquinoline-1-carboxylic acid.

## 20-8 OPIUM ALKALOID

Opium is prepared by drying the milky juice of unripe seed capsules of the opium poppy, ***Papaver somniferum***. About 25% of this dried material consists of a mixture of more than 20 alkaloids, of which morphine is the principal constituent. Morphine and related compounds (codeine and thebaine) are discussed in Sec. 20-9. Opium, which causes addiction, is used principally in the manufacture of morphine and related narcotics.

Papavarine and related benzylisoquinoline compounds have been isolated and find some use in medicine. Papavarine (as the hydrochloride) is used as an antispasmodic for smooth muscle; it is not habit-forming but is listed as a narcotic under the federal narcotic laws of the United States.

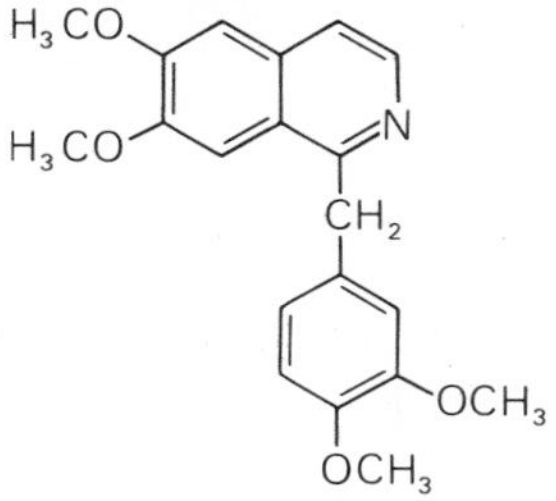

papavarine

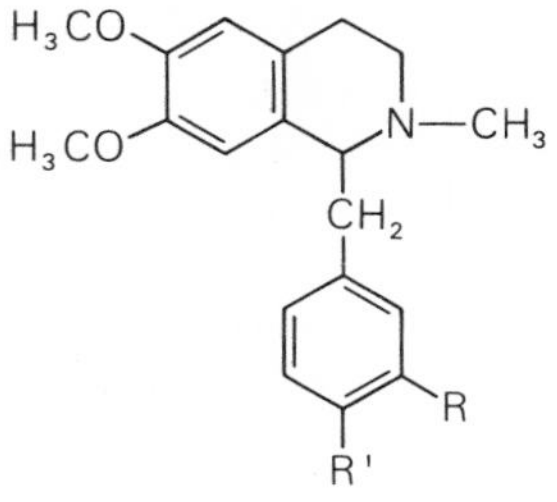

$R = R' = —OCH_3$, laudanosine
$R = —OH, R' = —OCH_3$, laudanine

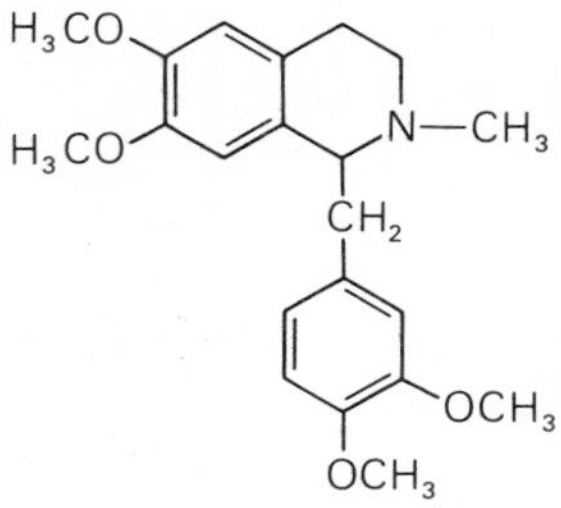

codamine

Narcotine (also called gnoscopine) occurs in large amounts in opium. It is not addicting and is a better antitussive than codeine, which is a constituent of several cough-syrup formulations.

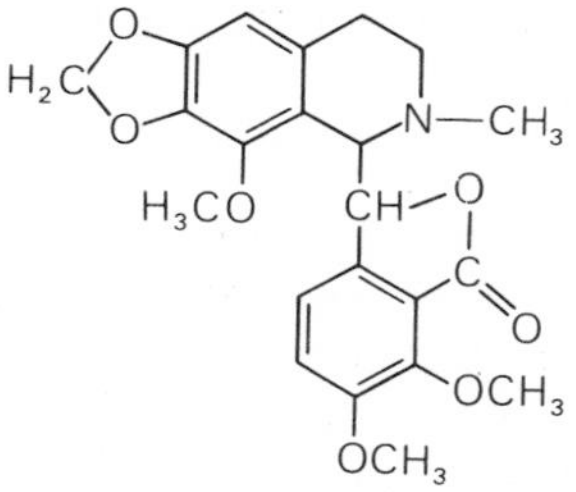

narcotine
(gnoscopine, racemic narcotine)

## 20-9 MORPHINE ALKALOIDS

The main alkaloids found in opium are shown in Table 20-3; of these, morphine, codeine, and thebaine are structurally related. They have been studied in greater detail than any others, not only because of their remarkable physiological properties, but also because of the various rearrangements these compounds undergo. In the period from 1889 to 1925 about 20 different structures were advanced for mor-

**Table 20-3 Major alkaloids from opium**

| *Compounds* | % |
|---|---|
| morphine | 10-16 |
| narcotine | 4-8 |
| codeine | 0.8-2.5 |
| papavarine | 0.5-2.5 |
| thebaine | 0.5-2.0 |

phine. Since the establishment of the morphine structure in 1925, it has been totally synthesized by several groups of chemists.

Morphine is an addicting narcotic which is used, as the sulfate, as an analgesic and sedative. It has a marked depressant action on various parts of the nervous system. Codeine (sulfate) although less effective, is also used as an analgesic and as an antitussive; codeine also causes addiction. Thebaine has little medicinal value and produces convulsions, similar to those observed with strychnine, rather than narcosis. These alkaloids are shown in Table 20-4.

**Table 20-4 Structures of morphine, codeine, and thebaine**

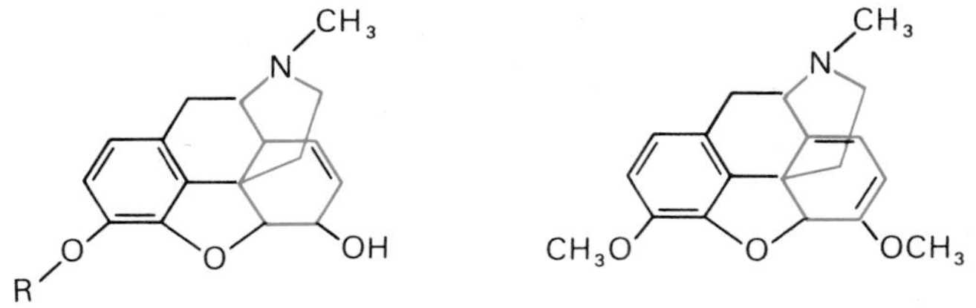

R = —H, morphine
R = $—CH_3$, codeine

thebaine

Note the reduced isoquinoline ring in these structures (colored).

## INDOLE ALKALOIDS

### 20-10 STRYCHNINE AND BRUCINE

Together with several other related alkaloids, strychnine and brucine are isolated from the seeds of ***Strychnos nux-vomica***. Both alkaloids occur in optically active form and have been employed in the resolution of racemic acids via the formation of diastereomeric salts. Strychnine is the more physiologically active of the two. It is extremely toxic to man and produces painful convulsions; 30 mg has been fatal. In very small quantities strychnine has been used as an antidote for overdosage of central-nervous-system depressants, and in turn, an antidote for strychnine is an intraveneous injection of a barbiturate. Strychnine is also used as a rat poison and for trapping fur-bearing animals.

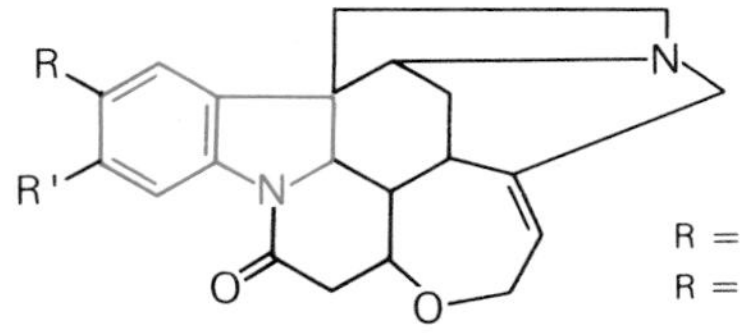

R = R' = —H, strychnine
R = R' = $—OCH_3$, brucine

Note the indole ring (colored lines).

## 20-11 ERGOT ALKALOIDS; LYSERGIC ACID

Ergot is a mixture of peptide alkaloids obtained from the fungus *Claviceps purpurea*. The drug acts on the uterus and vasomotor center and has been used in medicine for many years. Hydrolysis of the ergot alkaloids yields lysergic acid.

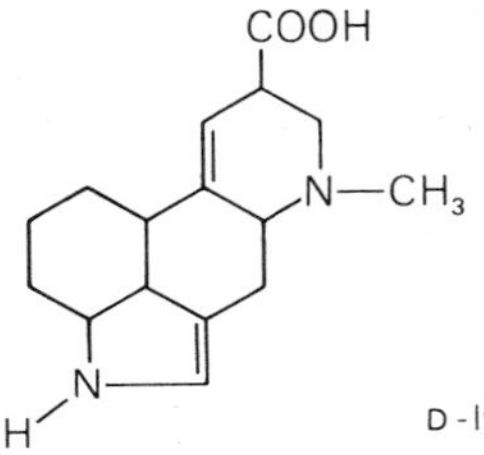

COOH

$N—CH_3$

H N

D-lysergic acid

The corresponding diethylamide, known as LSD-25, is a powerful hallucinogen which causes transient schizophrenia in normal individuals. Lysergic acid has been synthesized as shown in Table 20-5.

**Table 20-5**
**Synthesis of lysergic acid**

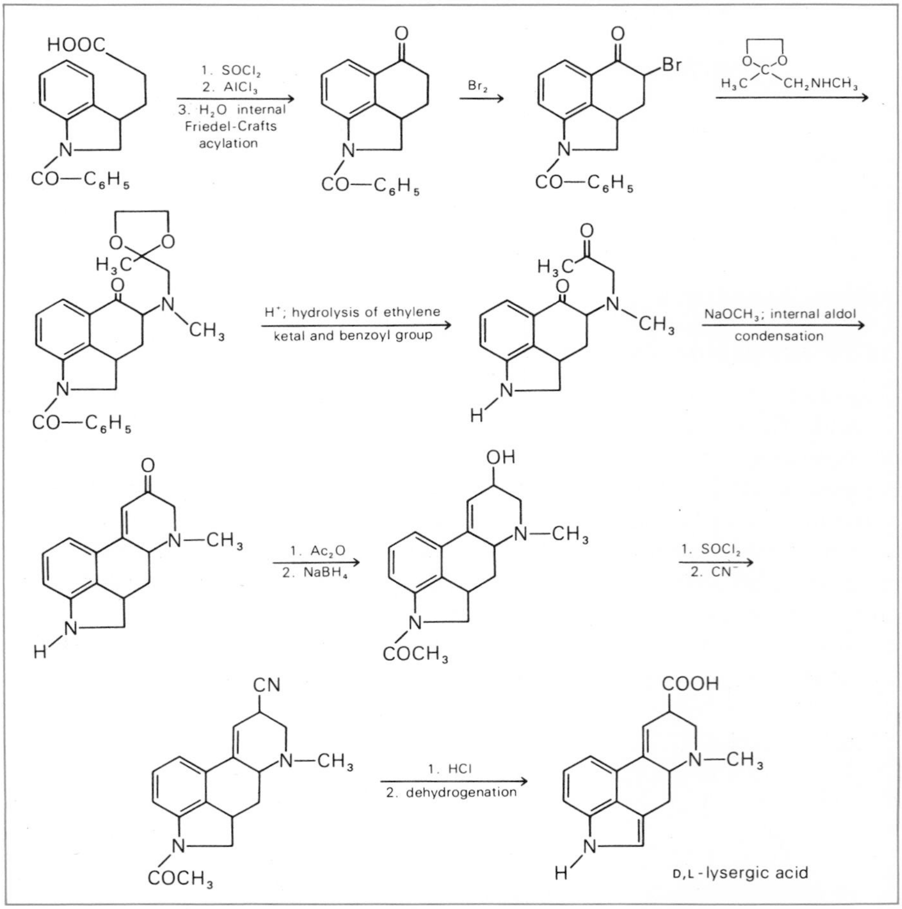

HOOC

$CO—C_6H_5$

1. $SOCl_2$
2. $AlCl_3$
3. $H_2O$ internal Friedel-Crafts acylation

O

$CO—C_6H_5$

$Br_2$

O Br

$CO—C_6H_5$

$H_3C$ $CH_2NHCH_3$

$H_3C$ O O N $CH_3$

$CO—C_6H_5$

$H^+$; hydrolysis of ethylene ketal and benzoyl group

$H_3C$ O N $CH_3$

H N

$NaOCH_3$; internal aldol condensation

O

$N—CH_3$

H N

1. $Ac_2O$
2. $NaBH_4$

OH

$N—CH_3$

$COCH_3$

1. $SOCl_2$
2. $CN^-$

CN

$N—CH_3$

$COCH_3$

1. HCl
2. dehydrogenation

COOH

$N—CH_3$

H N

D,L-lysergic acid

## SUGGESTED READINGS

Barron, F., M.E. Jarvik, and S. Bunnell, Jr.: The Hallucinogenic Drugs, *Sci. Am.*, **210** (4), 29 (1964). Discusses natural and synthetic drugs, particularly those containing an indole ring.

Freedman, L.Z.: Truth Drugs, *Sci. Am.*, **202** (3), 145 (1960). Discusses the uses of various truth serums containing alkaloids.

Huisgen, R.: Richard Willstätter, *J. Chem. Educ.*, **38**, 10 (1961). Describes, among others, the synthesis of tropine from cycloheptanone and of cyclooctatetraene from pseudopelletierine.

Ray, R.L.: Alkaloids: The World's Pain Killers, *J. Chem. Educ.*, **37**, 451 (1960).

Robinson, T.: Alkaloids, *Sci. Am.*, **201** (1), 113 (1959). Shows the natural source and structure of many alkaloids.

Sangster, A.W.: Determination of Alkaloid Structures, I. Isolation, Characterization, and Physical Methods; II. Chemical Methods, *J. Chem. Educ.*, **37**, 454, 518 (1960).

# Chapter Twenty-One

## COMPOSITION OF NUCLEIC ACIDS

Nucleic acids (Fig. 21-1) are high-molecular-weight polymers composed of a sugar phosphate ester backbone to which various heterocyclic bases are attached. They are so named because they were first isolated from nuclei of pus cells in the nineteenth century. It is now known that they are constituents of nearly all cells.

**Figure 21-1 Diagrammatic representation of nucleic acids**

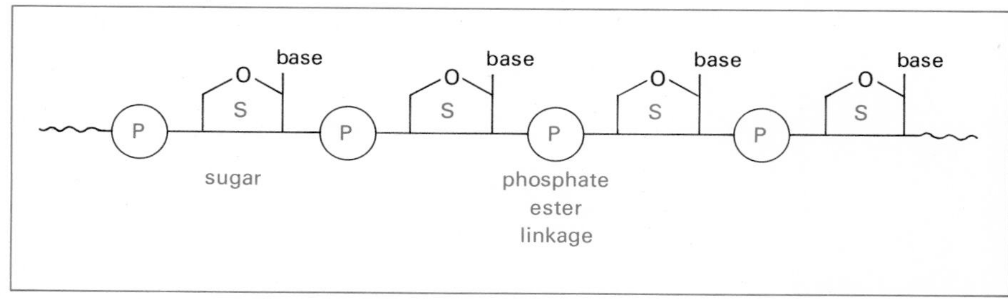


There are two principal types, those containing the sugar D-ribose, known as ***ribonucleic acids*** (RNA), and those containing D-deoxyribose, known as ***deoxyribonucleic acids*** (DNA).

$\beta$-D-ribofuranose

$\beta$-D-2-deoxyribofuranose

Both DNA and RNA are found in plant and animal cells. The details of the constituents of nucleic acids are discussed in the following sections. Figure 21-2 shows examples of synthetic DNA and RNA molecules.

# Nucleic Acids



**Figure 21-2 Examples of DNA and RNA**

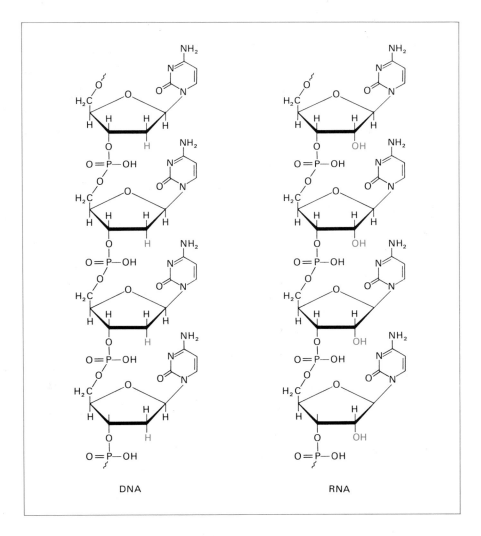

## 21-1 PYRIMIDINES AND PURINES

The heterocyclic bases of DNA and RNA are derivatives of pyrimidine or purine.

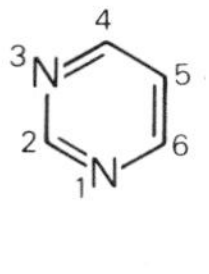

pyrimidine 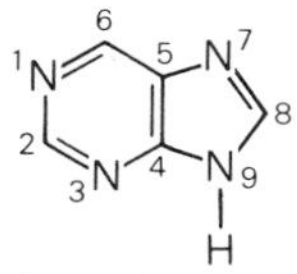　　purine

There are four principal pyrimidines found in nucleic acids: cytosine in DNA and RNA, uracil in RNA, thymine and 5-methylcytosine in DNA. The cytosine derivative, 5-hydroxymethylcytosine, is found in certain nucleic acids.

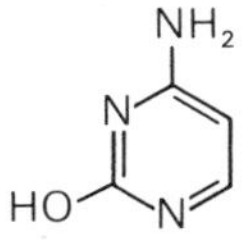

cytosine 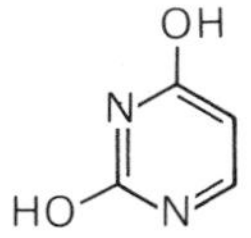　　uracil 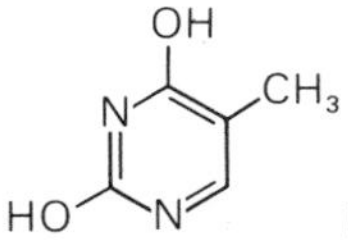　　thymine 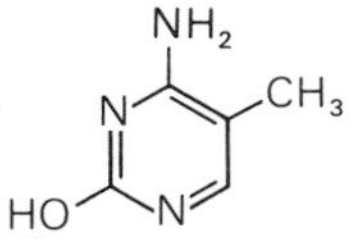　　5-methylcytosine

> **1.** Name each of the above compounds as derivatives of pyrimidine.
>
> **2.** The structures above are shown in the enol form. Show that each of these pyrimidines can exist in at least two different keto forms.

Although one pyrimidine can be synthesized from another by means of reactions previously discussed in the text, the formation of some pyrimidines from open-chain molecules is a one-step procedure. The synthesis of two substituted pyrimidines is shown below.

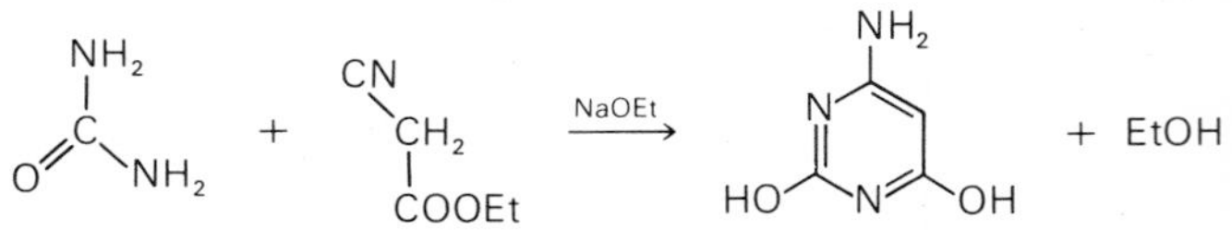

urea + ethyl cyanoacetate $\xrightarrow{\text{NaOEt}}$ 6-aminouracil + EtOH

guanidine + $EtO-C(=O)-CH_2-CN$ $\xrightarrow[\text{80\% yield}]{\text{NaOEt}}$ 2,4-diamino-6-hydroxypyrimidine + EtOH

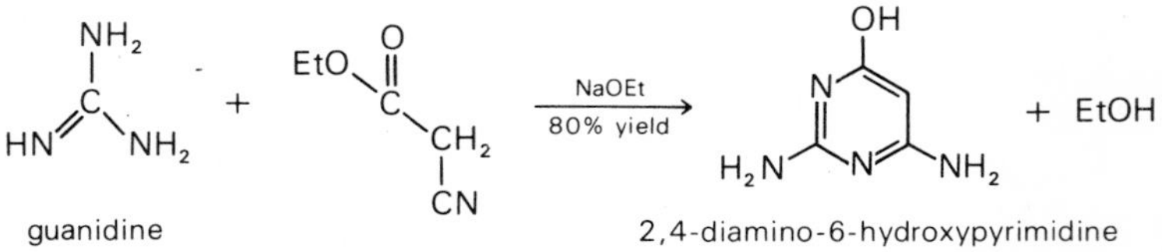

The other heterocyclic bases found in nucleic acids are purines, formally derived by the fusion of an imidazolo ring to a pyrimidine.

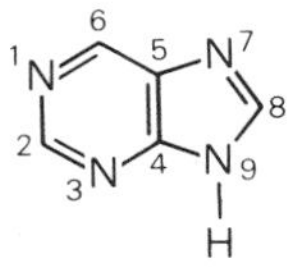

The most common purine bases found in DNA and RNA are adenine and guanine.

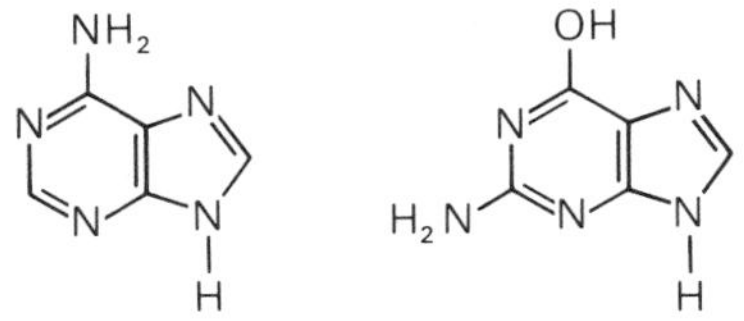

adenine (6-aminopurine) guanine (2-amino-6-hydroxypurine)

**1.** Some of the other purines obtained from the hydrolysis of nucleic acids are hypoxanthine (6-hydroxypurine), xanthine (2,6-dihydroxypurine), and uric acid (2,6,8-trihydroxypurine). Draw the enol and keto structures of these compounds.

**2.** One of the nucleic acids, soluble RNA, may contain as much as 5% ''methylated'' purine and pyrimidine bases such as 2-methyladenine, 6-methylaminopurine, 5-methylcytosine, 1-methylguanine, and 6-hydroxy-2-methylaminopurine. Draw the structures of these compounds.

Rather than synthesizing the purine ring system directly from open-chain compounds, schemes have been devised starting either with a pyrimidine, onto which the imidazole ring is built, or with an imidazole, which is elaborated to form the pyrimidine ring. Most schemes have started with substituted pyrimidines, and an example is shown in which uric acid, xanthine, and caffeine are synthesized via 5,6-diaminopyrimidine starting with 6-aminouracil.

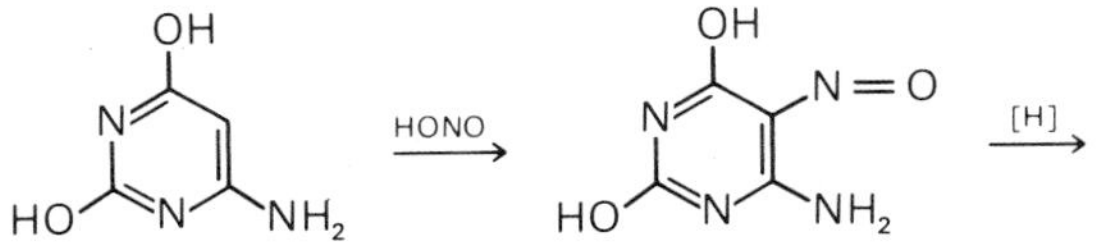

$\xrightarrow{\text{HONO}}$ $\xrightarrow{[H]}$

6-aminouracil 5-nitroso-6-aminouracil

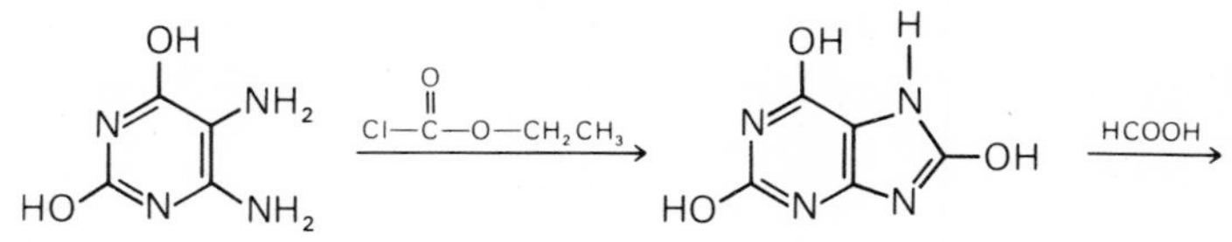

5,6-diaminouracil → ($Cl—C(=O)—O—CH_2CH_3$) → uric acid → (HCOOH) → xanthine → ($CH_3Cl$, base) → caffeine

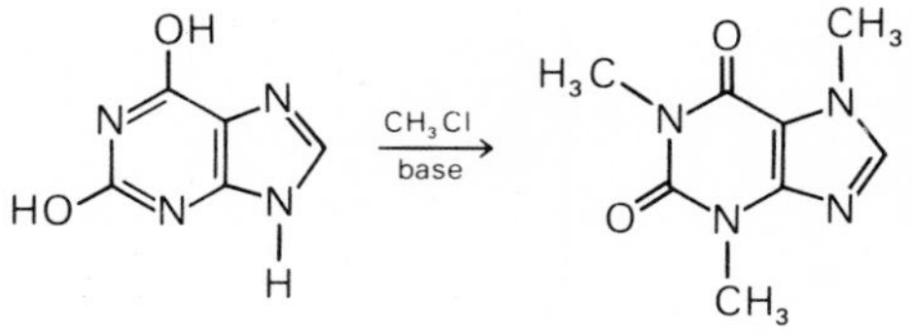

## 21-2 SUGARS IN NUCLEIC ACIDS

Both ribose and deoxyribose have been found in nucleic acids, and the presence of one of these sugars determines whether the compound is a DNA or an RNA. It is important to note that these sugars have been found to occur in the $\beta$-furanoside form, rather than as a pyranoside structure.

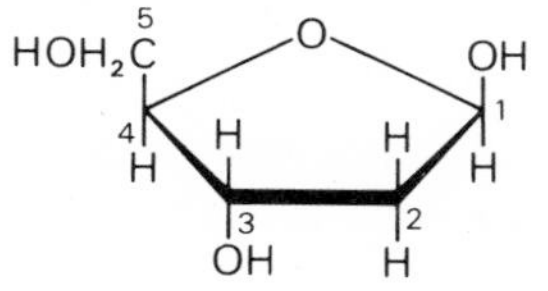

$\beta$-D-2-deoxyribofuranose

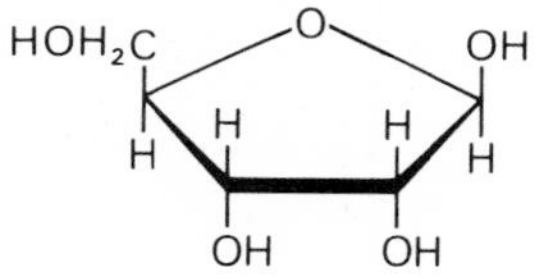

$\beta$-D-ribofuranose

The sugar units are linked to each other in nucleic acids by a phosphate ester bond from the 3-position of one sugar to the 5-position of the adjoining one.

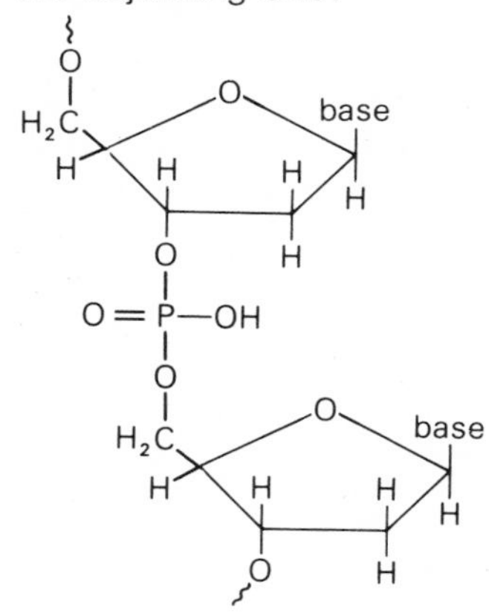

## 21-3 NUCLEOSIDES

A base joined to a sugar is called a *nucleoside*. These are such fundamental units in nucleic acids that each of the base-sugar molecules has been given a name which reflects the sugar and the base present. The attachment of the base, whether a pyrimidine or purine, is from $C_1$ of the sugar to the 1-position in pyrimidines or the 9-position in purines. Since there are several common bases and two sugars, two series of nucleosides are encountered as constituents of nucleic acids. The common ribose-base molecules are adenosine, guanosine, cytidine, and uridine; ribothymidine (ribose and thymine) is rarely found in RNA.

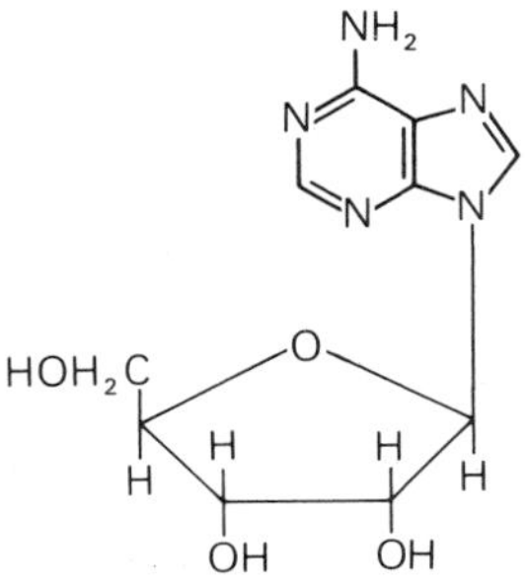

$NH_2$ N N N N $HOH_2C$ O H H H H OH OH

adenosine
ribose + adenine

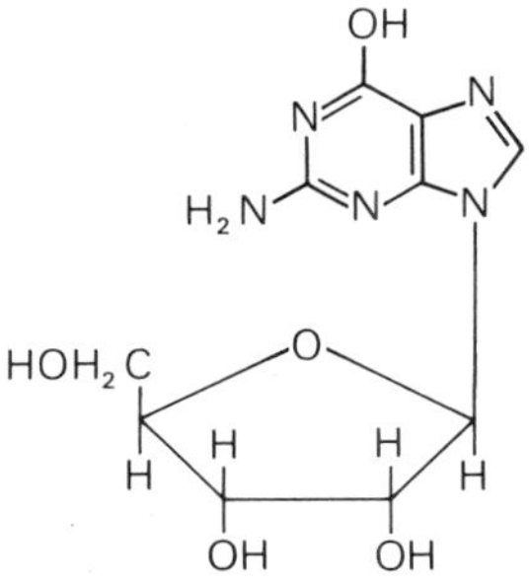

OH N N $H_2N$ N N $HOH_2C$ O H H H H OH OH

guanosine
ribose + guanine

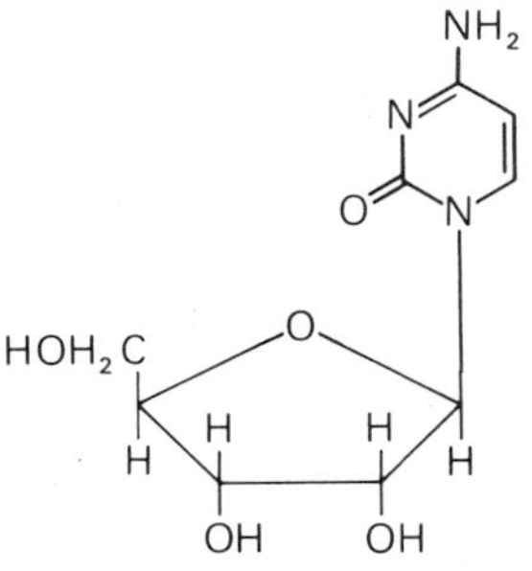

$NH_2$ N O N $HOH_2C$ O H H H H OH OH

cytidine
ribose + cytosine

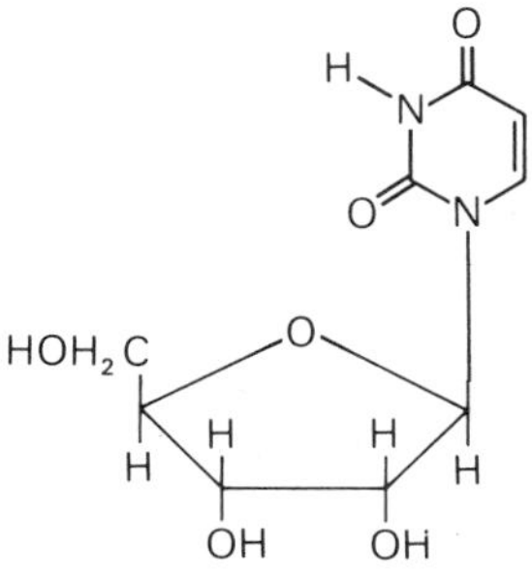

O H N O N $HOH_2C$ O H H H H OH OH

uridine
ribose + uracil

The four DNA nucleosides which correspond to those above are called deoxyadenosine, deoxyguanosine, and deoxycytidine. Deoxythymidine, simply called thymidine, is also found; deoxyuridine is not.

| Draw the structural formulas of the nucleosides found in DNA. |
|---|

## 21-4 NUCLEOSIDE PHOSPHATES

Of the various nucleoside phosphates, called ***nucleotides***, which may be prepared, the discussion here will be confined to the adenosine phosphates. Other nucleoside phosphates also occur in the cell and can be removed by extraction with acid. Of the three hydroxyl groups on the ribose portion, phosphorylation is notably important when it occurs at $C_5$, giving rise to adenosine 5'-phosphate (AMP), adenosine diphosphate (ADP), and adenosine triphosphate (ATP).

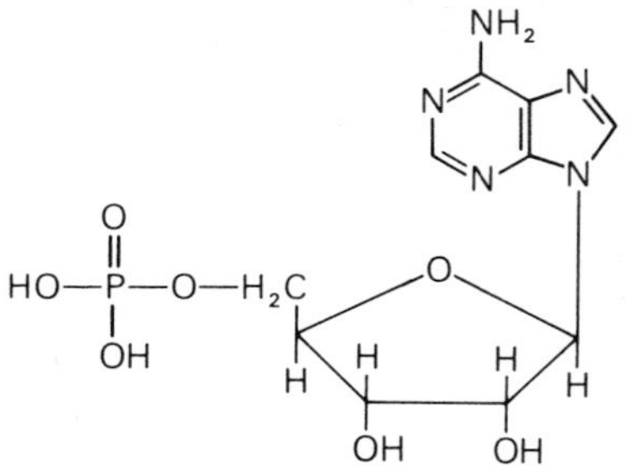

adenosine 5'-phosphate (AMP)

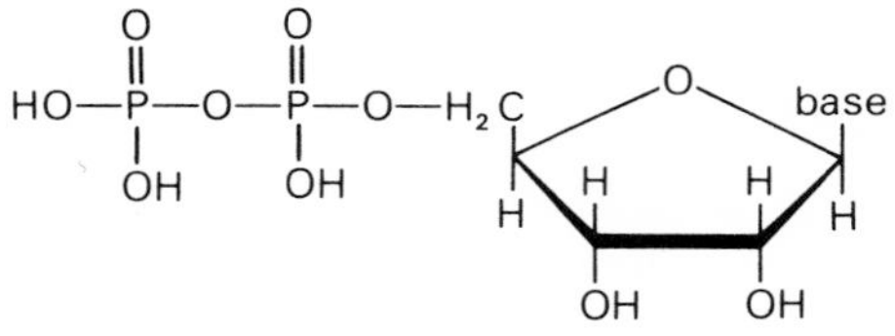

ADP

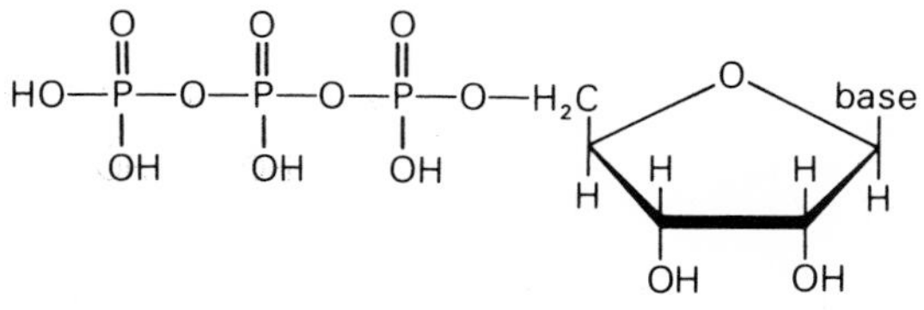

ATP

These —P—O—P— bonds are the high-energy phosphate bonds which are used to carry out certain chemical transformations in the cell. All the possible 5'-mono-, di-, and triphosphates of adenosine, guanosine, cytidine, and uridine occur in cells and have been removed and separated.

There is, of course, the possibility of forming phosphates at the 2'- and 3'-positions in ribonucleosides and at the 3'-position in deoxyribonucleosides. For example, adenosine 2',3'-cyclic monophosphate is an intermediate in the enzyme-catalyzed hydrolysis of RNA; the end product is a mixture of the 2'- and the 3'-monophosphates.

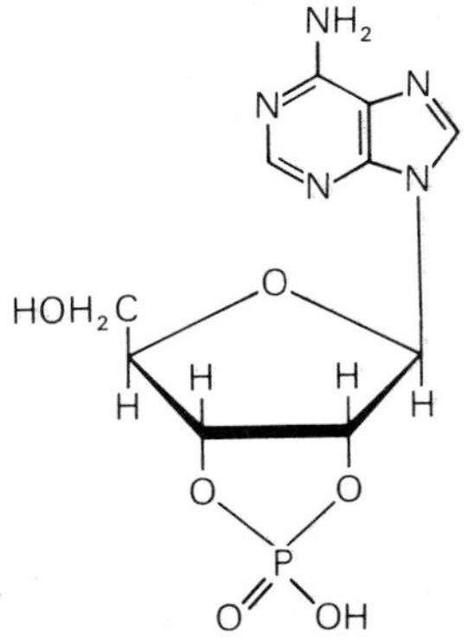

adenosine 2',3'-cyclic monophosphate

Molecules composed of nucleotides joined by means of phosphate ester linkages are known as ***polynucleotides*** or ***nucleic acids***. Ribonucleic acids are those composed of ribonucleosides; deoxyribonucleotides are made up of deoxyribonucleosides. The molecules shown in Fig. 21-2 are nucleic acids. Certain nucleic acids, described below, are important in the synthesis of proteins in cells and are often found together; these are known as ***nucleoproteins***.

## DEOXYRIBONUCLEIC ACIDS

Deoxyribonucleic acid is a polymer of deoxyribonucleotides. It must be emphasized that the term deoxyribonucleic acid (DNA) is a generic one and it cannot be assumed that DNA from different species or from different organs of one species will be identical. Even DNA from the same organ of two individuals may vary slightly in the order of nucleotide units. Often the source of the material is affixed to the name, e.g., calf thymus DNA.

### 21-5 STRUCTURE OF DNA

Chemical and physical evidence support the suggestion that the DNA molecule is a double right-handed helix composed of two polynucleotide chains wound around the same axis and held by hydrogen bonding of the bases. The biological activity of DNA is, in part, its ability to direct the synthesis of other DNA molecules, and this function depends on the helical structure of the two strands. If a solution of DNA is heated, the chains separate, because the hydrogen bonds are broken; quick cooling of the solution leaves the two strands separated, and there is a loss of biological activity. **If the warm solution is cooled slowly, the two strands reassociate in the form of the double helix and biological activity is restored.**

## 21-6 OCCURRENCE AND COMPOSITION

DNA occurs in the cell nucleus, where it is associated with protein from which it can be separated. It has a molecular weight of about $10^6$ to $10^9$ and occurs as a double-stranded helix. Solutions of DNA appear after purification to contain asbestoslike, fibrous solids, which are so delicate that even stirring or pipetting DNA solutions may break some of the chains. Thus, its molecular weight may be somewhat higher than the value found experimentally. It is a striking fact that the DNA in a single human germ cell contains $10^6$ base pairs and forms a chain that is 1 meter long!

Studies of the composition of DNA show that there is a large variation in the molar ratios of the bases present; however, the ratios are nearly constant in DNA from the same species. The number of purines, adenine (A) and guanine (G), is nearly equal to the number of pyrimidine bases, cystosine (C) and thymine (T), and the sum of adenine plus cytosine is equal to the sum of guanine plus thymine. Symbolically, then,

If $\quad A + G \cong C + T$

and $\quad A + C \cong G + T$

then $\quad A \cong T$

and $\quad C \cong G$

Because the ratio of A to T units and of C to G units is approximately 1, it was proposed that adenosine and thymine (and cytosine and quanine) are paired in a way that is responsible for the helical conformation of DNA. In particular, the molecular geometry of the bases in each pair favors the formation of hydrogen bonds between members of each pair.

The x-ray data corroborate the conclusions drawn from an examination of molecular models concerning the dimensions of those molecules which are hydrogen bonded. The overall dimension of both base pairs (G–C and A–T) is the same, 10.7 Å. Any attempt to construct models in which other base pairs are attracted by hydrogen bonds leads to a distortion of the observed, regular, helical structure of double-stranded DNA molecules.

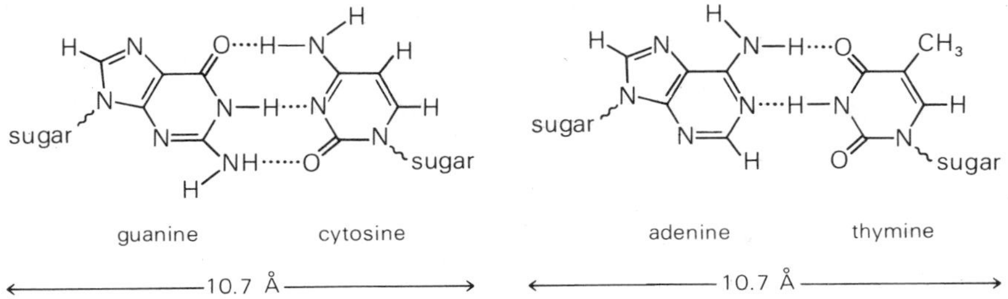

guanine cytosine adenine thymine

←— 10.7 Å —→ ←— 10.7 Å —→

The determination of the nucleotide sequence in DNA is carried out chemically in a manner similar to that described in Chap. 17 for the determination of amino acids in proteins **except that such studies are considerably more difficult to apply to nucleic acids.** First, it is nearly impossible to obtain a single molecular species of DNA from a natural source. Second, whereas there are about 20 amino acid constituents of proteins there are usually only four very similar nucleotides found in nucleic acids. Finally, refined chemical methods and techniques for the sequence determination of nucleotides in DNA are only now beginning to be fully developed and exploited.

### 21-7 BIOSYNTHESIS OF DNA

Although it is difficult to determine precisely the nature of DNA synthesis in the living cell, experiments have shown that the newly synthesized DNA is identical to that of the starting DNA. Thus, a self-replication process takes place with extreme accuracy. When DNA was produced in a normal cell to which $^{15}N$-labeled DNA had been added, the DNA produced after one generation was half $^{15}N$-labeled and half normal ($^{14}N$). After several generations, only normal ($^{14}N$) DNA and half-labeled DNA could be found. Further, the half-labeled DNA could be separated into one strand containing $^{14}N$ and one containing $^{15}N$. This indicates that the mode of synthesis is one in which the double strand becomes at least partially unwound and serves as a template for the new strand.

A natural enzyme has been found which aids the replication process by directing the specific base, capable of hydrogen bonding to the template, to the end of the growing polymer. At least a single strand of DNA is necessary as a "primer." It has been shown that when a mixture of the triphosphates of all four deoxyribonucleosides, $Mg^{++}$, and a primer (such as thymus DNA) is treated with this enzyme, the DNA obtained is identical with the primer. The absence of any of these species leads to much lower incorporation and rate of synthesis. This method of synthesis can be used to prepare synthetic DNA **if the deoxyribonucleoside triphosphate has the proper geometry to hydrogen-bond to the base in the primer.** This base pairing in both natural and "unnatural"

DNA is invariant and shows the equivalences mentioned earlier: A is equal to T, G is equal to C, and the ratio of A-T pairs to G-C pairs is constant for a given primer.

### 21-8 CELLULAR FUNCTION OF DNA

DNA carries genetic information and, as mentioned in Sec. 21-7, makes exact copies of itself. It also functions by passing this coded information to messenger RNA, which then translates the information in terms of the four bases (A, T, G, and C) into the language of the 20 amino acids so that proteins can be synthesized. The fascinating story of cellular protein synthesis will be briefly outlined in the following sections.

## RIBONUCLEIC ACIDS

### 21-9 OCCURRENCE, COMPOSITION, AND TYPES OF RNA

Three principal kinds of RNA are found in living cells: ribosomal RNA (rRNA), transfer, or soluble, RNA (sRNA), and transcript, or messenger, RNA (mRNA). A comparison of these types of RNA is shown in Table 21-1. RNA exists in various parts of cells, where it occurs with protein, from which it must be separated before further study. Although the molar composition of bases varies considerably depending on the RNA and its source, the sum of adenine (A) and cytosine, (C), in a given molecule is about equal to the sum of guanine (G) and uracil (U).

**Table 21-1 Comparison of ribonucleic acids (RNA)**

| | *Source* | *RNA proportion, %* | *Mol. wt.* | *Comments* |
|---|---|---|---|---|
| rRNA: | ribosomes | 80 | $100 \times 10^4$ | metabolically stable |
| sRNA: | soluble cytoplasm | 15 | $2.5 \times 10^4$ | important in amino acid transport |
| mRNA: | ribosomes, cytoplasm, and nucleus | 5 | $50 \times 10^4$ | Metabolically labile; similar to DNA in base composition; also called D-RNA |

## 21-10 STRUCTURE OF RNA

It is believed that RNA is a single-strand polynucleotide looped back on itself to form a helical structure (Fig. 21-3). Base pairing can occur in the helical portion of the molecule, but there are several bases along the loop which cannot be paired. Evidence indicates that this loop forms a site for the coding process. This loop is particularly rich in the methylated bases which occur to only a limited extent in the RNA molecules (see the problem in Sec. 21-1). RNA molecules vary in size, most having several loop-and-helix units within the entire molecule.

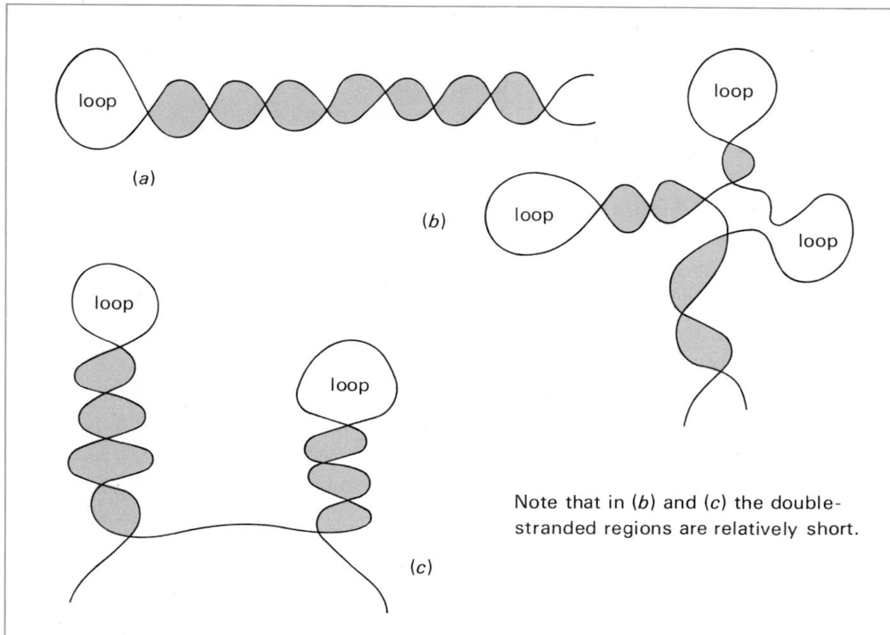
loop
(a)
loop
loop
loop
(b)
loop
loop
(c)
Note that in (b) and (c) the double-stranded regions are relatively short.

**Figure 21-3 Schematic representations of an RNA molecule showing possible loop and base pairing configurations.**

## 21-11 BIOSYNTHESIS OF RNA

The synthesis of RNA in the living cell is an exceedingly complex process; it is evident that both DNA and RNA can act as primers or templates for the synthesis of RNA. Although mRNA has been shown to have a base sequence which would be expected if DNA were acting as the template, the base composition of rRNA and sRNA corresponds to only a very small fraction of the complementary bases present in the DNA molecules.

As with the synthesis of DNA, an enzyme has been found which catalyzes the formation of mRNA when added to an incubated mixture of the four triphosphates, $Mn^{++}$, and a DNA primer. Since the mRNA produced is single-stranded, there remains the question of whether both strands or only one strand of the DNA is copied. This question is unsettled; investigations have shown that the nature of the synthesis depends on the DNA primer, its source, the cell system employed, and other variables.

### 21-12 BIOLOGICAL FUNCTION OF RNA

Whereas DNA duplicates genetic information, mRNA translates genetic information conveyed in 4-letter type (A, C, G, U) into that of the 20-letter amino acid language of proteins. There are indications that RNA may be associated with memory storage and learning.

Soluble RNA, consisting of about 75 nucleotides, is present as a loop-and-helical structure in which the loop, the coding area, contains methylated bases. It is on the loop portion of the molecule that the sRNA and mRNA link together. This transfer or soluble RNA ''recognizes'' the necessary enzyme (which, in turn, accepts the correct amino acid), and it ensures that the amino acid is incorporated at the proper position of the growing protein by coding with the mRNA. At least one kind of sRNA is specific for each amino acid, although more than one sRNA has been found for some of the amino acids.

Having attached the correct amino acid to the terminus of the sRNA, which always ends in an adenosine group, the complex is carried to the ribosomes, where the protein synthesis takes place under the coding influence of the mRNA. It is believed that one mRNA is associated with four to eight ribosomes.

### 21-13 THE GENETIC CODE

What is the nature of the mRNA genetic code? If the four bases were used singly, only four amino acids could be coded. Using all combinations of the four bases in pairs would permit the coding of only 16 amino acids. It is therefore apparent that the minimum number of bases in a given coding unit must be three, which allows the coding of 64 different units. Since there are about 20 amino acids, this group of three, or *codon*, is more than sufficient. Experimental evidence supports this idea, and at least one base triplet has been found for each of the common amino acids. In many cases more than one codon can be assigned to a given amino acid (see Table 21-2).

A mechanism for the transmission of genetic information must also include provision for the formation of mutants, which are products of a defective genetic code. One of the effects of this triplet coding is that removal of one base in the sequence renders the code unreadable for a large portion of the chain; however, removal of one *and* replacement by another base allows the code to be read in regions further down the chain. For example, given the code in which the three bases are different

AUG | AUG | AUG | AUG | AUG | AUG | AUG | AUG | AUG |

suppose a G is removed. The result may be

AUG | AUG | AUG | AUG | AUA | UGA | UGA | UGA | UGA |

Let us now insert a different base, C, at some point, which need *not* be the same one from which the G was removed. The result is

AUG | AUG | AUG | AUG | AUA | UGC | AUG | AUG | AUG |

which may be read again as AUG, although further down the chain. Thus, small changes close together in the sequence often do not alter a sizable portion of the chain.

**Table 21-2**
**Triplets for amino acids**

| *Amino acid* | *Codon* |
|---|---|
| alanine | CAG, CCG, CUG |
| arginine | GAA, GCC, CUG |
| asparagine | CAA, CUA, UAA |
| aspartic acid | GCA, GUA |
| cysteine | GUU |
| glutamic acid | AAG, AUG |
| glutamine | AAC, UAC |
| glycine | GAG, GCG, GUG |
| histidine | ACC, AUC |
| isoleucine | AAU, CAU, UUA |
| leucine | CCU, UAU, UGU, UUC |
| lysine | AAA, AUA |
| methionine | AGU |
| phenylalanine | UCU, UUU |
| proline | CAC, CCC, CUC |
| serine | ACG, CUU, UCC |
| threonine | ACA, CCA, UCA |
| tryptophane | UGG |
| tyrosine | ACU, AUU |
| valine | UUG |

Investigate the consequences of adding (or replacing) *two* bases and of adding (or replacing) *three* bases in this three-letter genetic code.

The coding of amino acids has been worked out by experiments of the following type, which rely heavily on synthetic polynucleotides. When a mixture of ATP, GTP, $Mg^{++}$, $K^+$, and amino acids is incubated with a cell-free extract of certain bacteria, amino acids are incorporated into an isolable protein. Use of radioactive ($^{14}C$) amino acids allows the amino acid which is incorporated to be determined. The DNA in the cell extract may be destroyed; the mRNA is depleted by enzyme deactivation, and in place of RNA, a synthetic polynucleotide may be added. From the nature of the polynucleotide and the amino acids incorporated into the protein it is possible to determine the amino acid code. For example, when poly U (UUUUUUUUU • • •) was added to such a system with mixtures of the 20 amino acids, **only phenylalanine was incorporated into the protein;** therefore, the triplet UUU is assigned to phenylalanine. A copolymer of A and U allows the incorporation of phenylalanine, isoleucine, leucine, and tyrosine. Since there are eight triplets of A and U, some of these sequences must be coding for the same amino acid. Experiments of this type have led to the information given in Table 21-2.

### 21-14 VIRUSES

A virus is essentially a polynucleotide, such as DNA or RNA, protected by a coat of protein. Plant viruses contain only RNA, but animal and bacterial viruses may contain either RNA or DNA. Viruses have been studied in great detail and some have even been obtained in crystalline form.

There are spherical plant viruses, e.g., turnip yellow mosaic virus, and rodlike ones, e.g., tobacco mosaic virus (TMV), which has received much attention. TMV is 5% RNA and 95% protein. The protein in TMV is composed of 2,100 polypeptide subunits, and the complete sequence of the 164 amino acids has been established. The protein is a protective coat for the viral RNA, and variations in the protein component are observed with different strains of TMV.

Among the animal viruses isolated, some have been found to contain only RNA (poliomyelitis, influenza, and encephalitis), and some contain only DNA (cowpox, rabies, and polyoma). The cancer-producing viruses, which contain DNA, have been extensively studied. It is found that they have base compositions resembling those of the DNA in the cell they infect.

Viruses which can infect bacterial cells are known as ***bacteriophages***. They have been studied in detail, since it is much more difficult to gain similar information from plant and animal cells. Bacteriophages may contain either RNA or DNA, and it is from these phages that much of the biochemical information about RNA and DNA has been obtained.

## SUGGESTED READINGS


### Photosynthesis

Bassham, J.A.: New Aspects of Photosynthesis, *J. Chem. Educ.*, **38**, 151 (1961).

Bassham, J.A.: The Path of Carbon in Photosynthesis, *Sci. Am.*, **206** (6), 88 (1962). Details the chemical transformations of $CO_2$ to carbohydrates, amino acids, and fats in the presence of light, showing the apparatus employed.

Park, R.B.: Advances in Photosynthesis, *J. Chem. Educ.*, **39**, 424 (1962).

Rabinowitch, E.I., and Govindjee: The Role of Chlorophyll in Photosynthesis, *Sci. Am.*, **213** (1), 74 (1965).

Wald, G.: Life and Light, *Sci. Am.*, **201** (4), 92 (1959). Role of light in photosynthesis and vision.

### RNA

Fraenkel-Conrat, H.: Ribonucleic Acid, the Simplest Information-transmitting Molecule, *J. Chem. Educ.*, **40**, 216 (1963).

Hoagland, M.B.: Nucleic Acids and Proteins, *Sci. Am.*, **201** (6), 55 (1959). Role of RNA in peptide synthesis.

Hurwitz, J., and J.J. Furth: Messenger RNA, *Sci. Am.*, **206** (2) 41 (1962).

Moore, W.J., and H.R. Mahler: Introduction to Molecular Psychology, *J. Chem. Educ.*, **42**, 49 (1965). Good discussion of the role of acetylcholine in neutral transmission of information and a description of the experiments indicating the role of RNA in memory storage and transfer.

Rich, A.: Polyribosomes, *Sci. Am.*, **209** (6), 44 (1963). Shows the function of ribosomes, particles on which cells synthesize proteins.

Roth, J.S.: Ribonucleic Acid and Protein Synthesis, *J. Chem. Educ.*, **38**, 217 (1961).

### DNA

Crick, F.H.C.: The Genetic Code, *Sci. Am.*, **207** (4), 66 (1962). See below under Nirenberg for comment.

Deering, R.A.: Ultraviolet Radiation and Nucleic Acid, *Sci. Am.*, **207** (6), 135 (1962). Discusses the fundamental changes in DNA on radiation with ultraviolet light.

McClellan, A.L.: The Significance of Hydrogen Bonds in Biological Structures, *J. Chem. Educ.*, **44**, 547 (1967). Discusses bonding DNA, proteins, lysozyme, and viruses.

Nirenberg, M.W.: The Genetic Code, II, *Sci. Am.*, **208** (3), 80 (1963). Examines in detail the triplet coding of bases for amino acid synthesis in the cell.

Sinsheimer, R.L.: Single-stranded DNA, *Sci. Am.*, **207** (1), 109 (1962). Discusses a particular virus, $\phi$X174, and the single-stranded DNA it contains.

### Viruses

Edgar, R.S., and R.H. Epstein: The Genetics of a Bacterial Virus, *Sci. Am.*, **212** (2), 70 (1965). Shows the gene mapping of the DNA of T4 virus.

Fraenkel-Conrat, H.: The Genetic Code of a Virus, *Sci. Am.*, **211** (4), 46 (1964). A discussion of the tobacco mosaic virus and how artificial chemical changes effect the synthesis of mutants.

Horne, R.W.: The Structure of Viruses, *Sci. Am.*, **208** (1), 48 (1963). Shows the three-dimensional structure of viruses, which possess a high degree of symmetry.

Jacob, F., and E.L. Wollman: Viruses and Genes, *Sci. Am.*, **204** (6), 93 (1961). Discusses effects of viral infection of bacteria on heredity.

Maramorosch, K.: Friendly Viruses, *Sci. Am.*, **203** (2), 138 (1960). Discusses viruses which cause variations, such as the color variation in flowers.

Melnick, J.L.: Enteroviruses, *Sci. Am.*, **200** (2), 88 (1959). Discusses the many viruses which are found in the human alimentary tract.

Rubin, H.: A Defective Cancer Virus, *Sci. Am.*, **210** (6), 46 (1964). A virus which cannot form a protein coat or reproduce without another virus present.

Schaffer, F.L.: Poliomyelitis Virus, *J. Chem. Educ.*, **36**, 469 (1959).

Stewart, S.E.: The Polyoma Virus, *Sci. Am.*, **203** (5), 63 (1960). Discusses production of tumors in laboratory animals and implicates a virus in causing human cancers.

### Enzymes

Baker, B.R.: Interactions of Enzymes and Inhibitors, *J. Chem. Educ.*, **44**, 610 (1967). Discusses binding forces, active sites, and hydrophobic bonding.

Changeux, J.: The Control of Biochemical Reactions, *Sci. Am.*, **212** (4), 36 (1965). Discusses the synthetic regulation mechanism and activity of enzymes.

Frieden, E.: The Enzyme-Substrate Complex, *Sci. Am.*, **201** (2), 119 (1959). Description of methods used to study short-lived enzyme-substrate interactions.

Neilands, J.B., and S. Rogers: Progress in Enzyme Chemistry, *J. Chem. Educ.*, **39**, 154 (1962).

Rubin, R.T.: Some Aspects of Anti-Acetylcholinestrase Chemistry, *J. Chem. Educ.*, **36**, 306 (1959).

### Others

Adams, E.: Poisons, *Sci. Am.*, **201** (5), 76 (1959). Shows how toxic materials are effective in blocking normal metabolic pathways.

Biochemistry Symposium, *J. Chem. Educ.*, **36**, 535-554 (1959). Discusses enzymes, vitamins, hormones, nucleic acids, genes, viruses, and photosynthesis.

"The Cell," *Sci. Am.*, **205** (3) (1961). An entire issue concerned with the cell and its biochemical functions.

Isaacs, A.: Interferon, *Sci. Am.*, **204** (5), 51 (1961). Describes the action of the protein, isolated from animal cells, which protects them from attack by viruses.

Isaacs, A.: Foreign Nucleic Acids, *Sci. Am.*, **209** (4), 46 (1963). Shows that interferon protects itself against all nucleic acids other than its own.

Ross, R.B.: Recent Advances in Chemotherapy of Cancer, *J. Chem. Educ.*, **36**, 368 (1959). Reviews the classes of organic compounds which are clinically useful in the treatment of cancer.

Spiegelman, S.: Hybrid Nucleic Acids, *Sci. Am.*, **210** (5), 48 (1964). Discusses the flow of information within the cell.

Woodward, J.D.: Biotin, *Sci. Am.*, **204** (6), 139 (1961). Outlines the role of biotin, a widely distributed vitamin, in purine synthesis.

# Answers to Selected Problems

## CHAPTER 1

**1.** (*a*) C ⟶ Br (*b*) I ⟶ Cl
(*c, d, g, h*) none

**2.** (*b*)

```
   H H
H:C:C:O:
   H H H
```

(*c*)

```
    :Cl:
:Cl:C:H
    :Cl:
```

(*f*)

```
  H
H:C:F:
  H
```

(*g*)

```
  H
H:C:N:H
  H H
```

(*h*) H:C:::C:H

(*j*)

```
  H
H:C:⁻  ⁺Mg:I:
  H
```

(*n*)

```
  :O:
   ::
 H:C:H
```

(*p*)

```
H:N:C:::N:
  H
```

**3.** (*a*) $H_2C{::}\overset{+}{N}{::}\overset{-}{N}$ ⟷ $H_2\overset{+}{C}{:}N{::}\overset{-}{N}$

(*b*) $H_2C{::}CH{-}CH{::}O$ ⟷ $H_2C{::}CH{-}\overset{+}{C}H{:}\overset{-}{O}{:}$ ⟷ $H_2\overset{+}{C}{:}CH{::}CH{:}O{:}^-$

(*d*) $(CH_3)_3\,\overset{+}{P}{:}\overset{-}{O}{:}$ ⟷ $(CH_3)_3\,P{::}O$ (*g*) $:\overset{-}{O}{:}\overset{+}{N}(::O){:}O{:}H$ ⟷ $O{::}\overset{+}{N}(:\overset{-}{O}{:}){:}O{:}H$

(*h*) H:C(:C::C:)...C:$\overset{+}{C}$:H $\longleftrightarrow$ H:C(::C:C::)...C:$\overset{+}{C}$:H $\longleftrightarrow$ (ring)=$CH_2$ (+ at C bearing H) $\updownarrow$ (ring)=$CH_2$ (+ at ortho C–H) $\longleftrightarrow$ H–(+ring)=$CH_2$

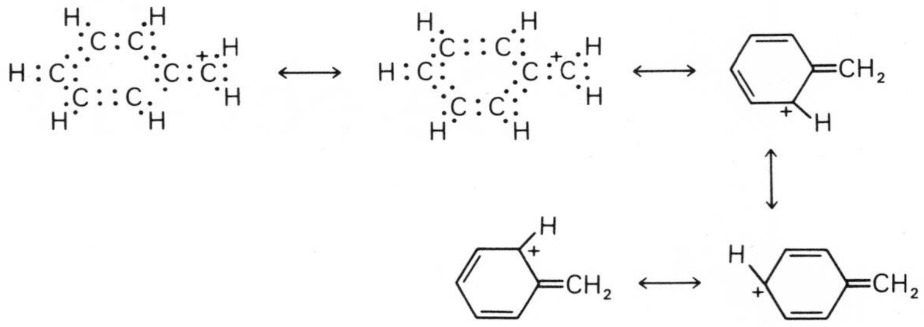

(*m*) H.:C::C:.H, :C:, ⊙.H $\longleftrightarrow$ H.⊙:C:C:.H, :C:, H

**4.** (*i*) $H\overset{\sigma}{—}C \overset{\sigma,\pi,\pi}{\equiv} C \overset{\sigma,(\pi),(\pi)}{—} C \overset{\sigma,\pi,\pi}{\equiv} N:$ all angles 180°

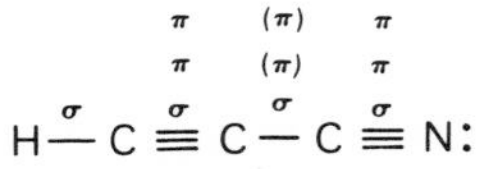

1*s* *sp* *sp* *sp* *sp*

(*ii*) $H_2C_1\overset{\sigma,\pi}{=}C_2H\overset{\sigma}{—}C_3H_3$

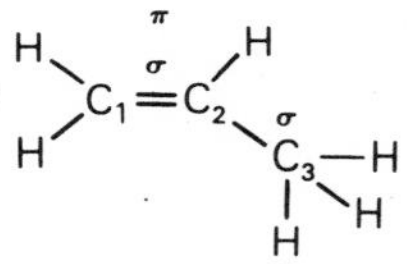

All H are 1*s*; $C_1$, $C_2$ are $sp^2$; $C_3$ is $sp^3$; all C—H bonds are $\sigma$, all angles are 120° except $H—C_3—C_2$ which are 109°28'.

(*v*) $H_2C_3\overset{\sigma,\pi}{=}C_2H\overset{\sigma\,(\pi)}{—}C_1H{=}O$

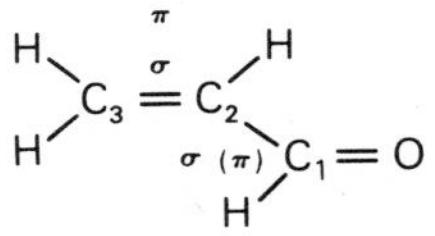

All H are 1*s*, all C and O are $sp^2$, C=O is $\sigma$ and $\pi$, all angles are 120°. Note $C_1—C_2$ $\pi$-bond overlap.

(*vii*) $H—C_4H_2\overset{\sigma}{—}C_3H\overset{\sigma,\pi}{=}C_2\overset{\sigma,\pi}{=}C_1H_2$

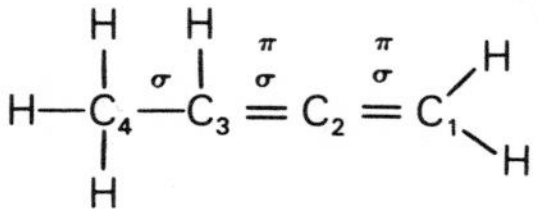

$sp^3$ $sp^2$ $sp$ $sp^2$

$\measuredangle H—C_1—C_2 = 120°$, $\measuredangle C_1—C_2—C_3 = 180°$, $\measuredangle H—C_3—C_2(C_4) = 120°$, $\measuredangle H—C_4—C_3 = 109°28'$.

(*x*) $C_6H_5—CH{=}CH_2$

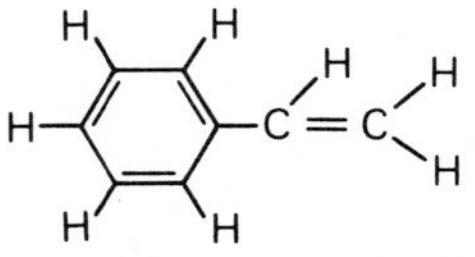

All C are $sp^2$, H are 1*s*, all angles are 120°, note overlap between the ring and the vinyl group.

5. (*a*) 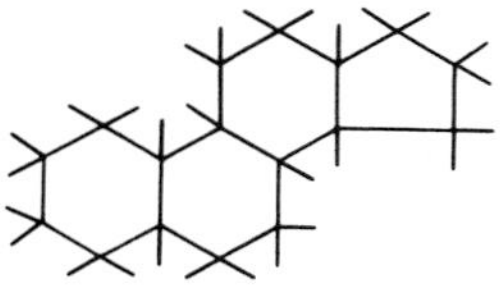 (*b*) secondary alcohol, double bond

total of 28 H atoms

(*c*) three secondary alcohols, acid (*d*) phenol, secondary alcohol
(*e*) ketone, double bond, secondary alcohol
(*f*) two ketones, double bond, primary and secondary alcohol, aldehyde
(*g*) three ketones, double bond, primary and tertiary alcohol

## CHAPTER 2

1. (*a*) $CH_3CH(CH_3)CH(CH_3)CH_3$
1° 3° 1° 3° 1° 1°

(*b*) $CH_3CH(CH_3)CH_2CH_2CH_3$
1° 3° 1° 2° 2° 1°

(*g*) $CH_3CH(CH_3)CH(CH_3)CH_2CH_2CH_2CH_3$
1° 3° 1° 3° 1° 2° 2° 2° 1°

(*k*) $CH_3C(CH_3)_2CH_2CH_2CH_3$
1° 4° 1° 2° 2° 1°

2. (*a*) 2,3,4-tribromopentane (*b*) 2,2,3,3,4,4-hexamethylpentane
(*c*) 2-bromo-1-chloropropane (*f*) 3-phenylpentane
(*g*) 2-phenylpropane or isopropylbenzene

4. A: 2,2,3,3,4,4,5,5-octamethylhexane; B: 2-iodo-2,3,3-trimethylbutane; C: 2,2,3-trimethylbutane; D, E: 1-bromo-2,2,3,3,4,4,5,5-octamethylhexane and 3-bromomethyl-2,2,3,4,4,5,5-heptamethylhexane; F: 2-bromo-2,3,3-trimethylbutane; G,H: 1-bromo-2,3,3-trimethylbutane and 1-bromo-2,2,3-trimethylbutane.

5. (*a*) ethyl iodide (iodoethane), cyclohexyl chloride (chlorocyclohexane) ⟶ butane, dicyclohexyl (cyclohexylcyclohexane), ethylcyclohexane
(*b*) propane, N.R.
(*c*) iodocyclopentane (cyclopentyl iodide) ⟶ cyclopentylmagnesium iodide
(*d*) ethanol (ethyl alcohol) ⟶ cyclopentane, ethoxymagnesium iodide
(*f*) cyclopentene ⟶ 1,2-didueterocyclopentane (cyclopentane-1,2-$d_2$)
(*h*) biphenyl ⟶ N.R.

7. (*a*) $(CH_3)_3C{-}Cl \xrightarrow{LiAlH_4}$ (*b*) $CH_3$––I $\xrightarrow[2.\ D_2O]{1.\ Mg\ in\ dry\ ether}$

(*c*) $CH_2{=}CH{-}CH_2Br \xrightarrow[2.\ D_2/Pt]{1.\ Na}$

(*d*) $CH_3$––I + $CH_2{=}CH{-}CH_2Br \xrightarrow{Na}$ $CH_3$–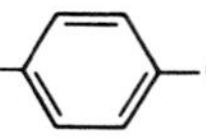–$CH_2{-}CH{=}CH_2$,

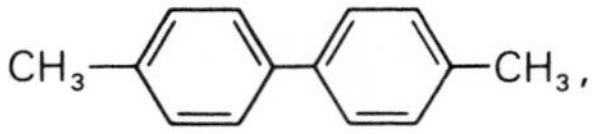, $CH_2=CH-CH_2-CH_2-CH=CH_2$;

$CH_3-C_6H_4-CH_2-CH=CH_2 \xrightarrow{H_2/Pt}$

(*e*) $(CH_3)_3C-Cl \xrightarrow[\text{2. } Cl_2/h\nu \text{ (limited amount)}]{\text{1. Na}}$

## CHAPTER 3

1. (*a*) cyclohexylbenzene (phenylcyclohexane)
   (*b*) 1-chloro-2,2-dimethylcyclopentane
   (*c*) *cis*-1,2-dimethylcyclopropane (*d*) *cis*-3-methylcyclopentanol
   (*f*) *cis*-1,4-dibromocyclohexane (*i*) *cis*-1,3-dibromocyclobutane

2. (*a*)

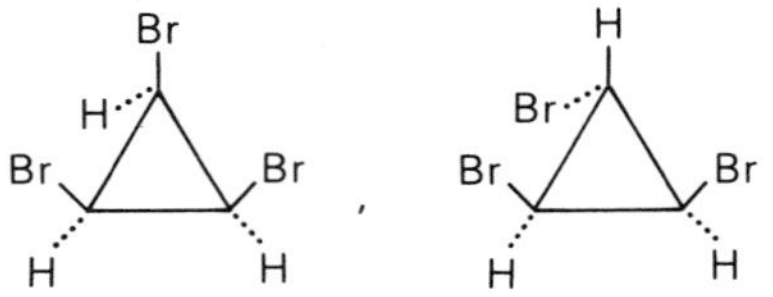

(*b*)

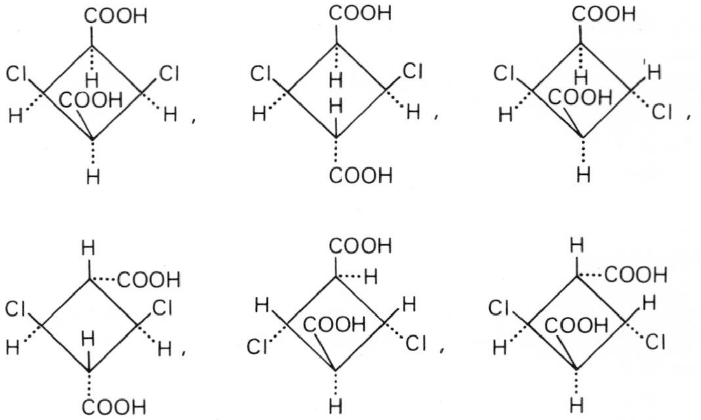

3. (*a*)

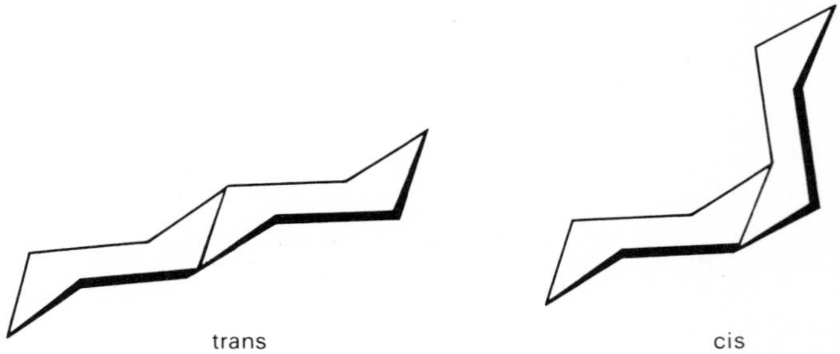

trans cis

(*b*) trans (diequatorial ring juncture) more stable

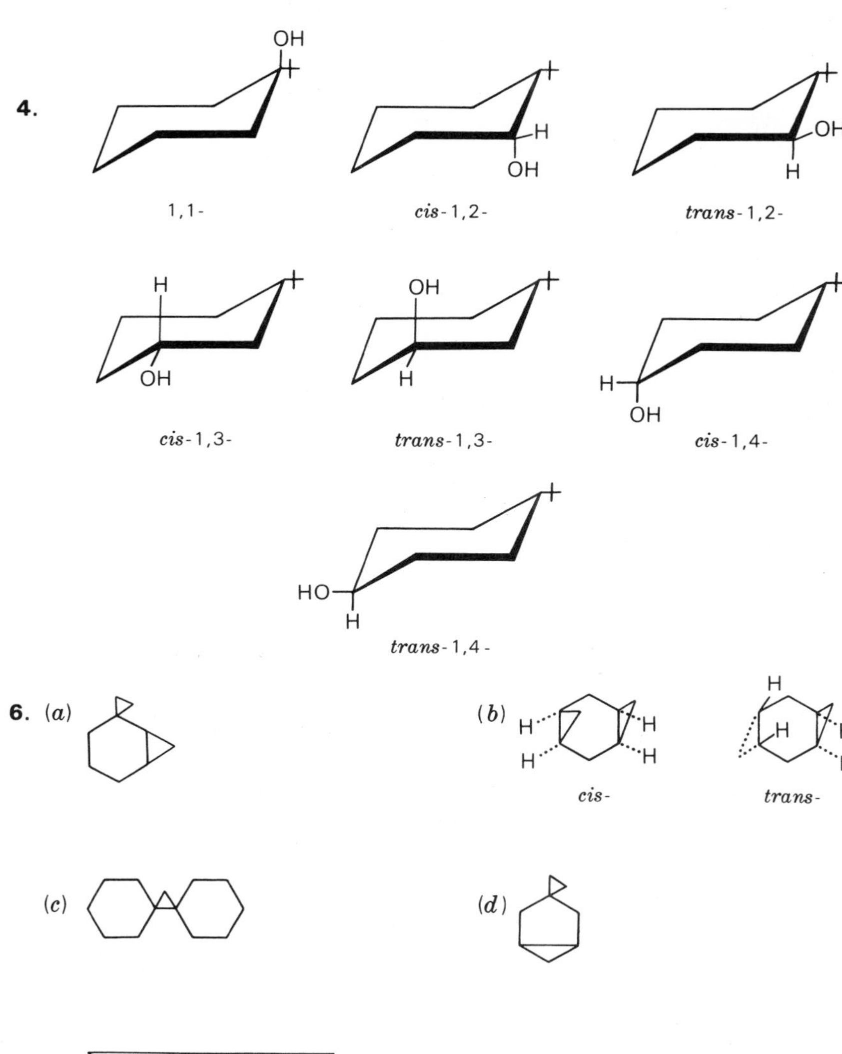


## CHAPTER 4

1. (*a*) 3-heptene, 2, cis and trans
   (*c*) 2,4-dimethyl-6-ethyl-1,6-heptadiene, no geometrical isomers
   (*e*) 1,1,2,3,4,5-hexaphenylcyclopentadiene, no geometrical isomers
   (*g*) 1,3-cyclohexadiene, no geometrical isomers
   (*h*) 1-chlorocyclooctatetraene
   (*i*) 1,2-divinylcyclohexane, 2, cis and trans

**2.** (*b*) $CH_2{=}CH{-}CH_2CH_2CH_2CH_2CH_2CH_2CH{=}CH_2$

(*c*)

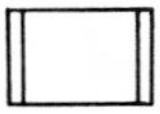

(*f*) $CH_2CH_3$ $CH_2CH_3$

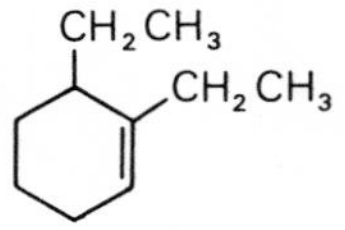

(*g*) $CH_2{=}CH{-}CH_2Br$

(*h*) $CH_2{=}CH{-}Cl$

(*j*)

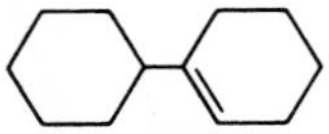

**3.** (*a*) Most highly substituted olefin should be expected

(*c*) Terminal olefins expected

(*ii*) 1-phenyl-2-propanol $\xrightarrow{Al_2O_3}$ 1-phenylpropene

1-phenyl-2-propanol $\xrightarrow{ThO_2}$ 3-phenylpropene

Statistical = 2:3

(*iv*) 4-penten-2-ol $\xrightarrow{Al_2O_3}$ 1,3-pentadiene

4-penten-2-ol $\xrightarrow{ThO_2}$ 1,4-pentadiene

Statistical = 2:3

(*vi*) 1-methylcyclohexanol $\xrightarrow{Al_2O_3}$ 1-methylcyclohexene

1-methylcyclohexanol $\xrightarrow{ThO_2}$ exomethylenecyclohexane

Statistical = 4:3

**5.** (*a*) cyclohexene,

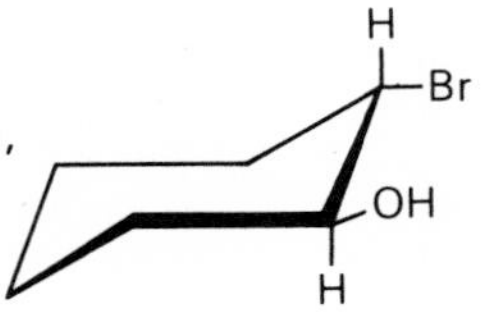

H Br OH H

(*b*) 1-methyl-2-isopropylcyclohexene,

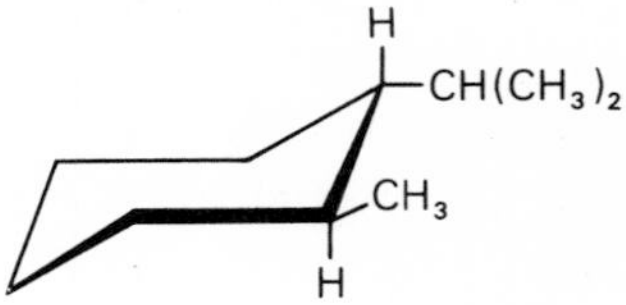

H $CH(CH_3)_2$ $CH_3$ H

(*c*) 1-methylcyclohexene,

$CH_3$ Cl Cl H

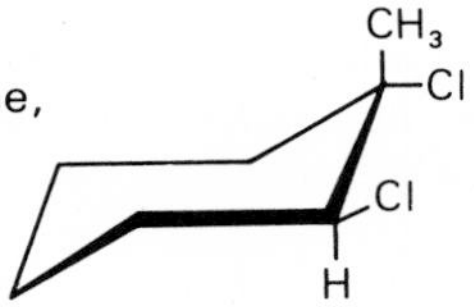

(*d*) 1-ethylcyclohexene,

$CH_2CH_3$ — OH — Cl — H

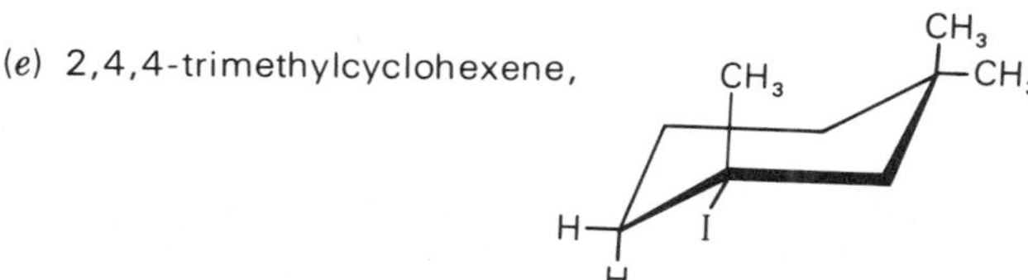


(*f*) 1,2-dimethylcyclohexene,

$CH_3$ — Br — Br — $CH_3$

7. *cis*- and *trans*-2-hexene

8. The $\pi$ bond of ethylene can coordinate with orbitals of metal atoms.

## CHAPTER 5

1. (*a*) methylcyclopropylacetylene (*b*) vinylacetylene
   (*d*) sodium phenylacetylide (*f*) 3-ethylpentyn-3-ol

3. (*a*) phenylacetylene $\longrightarrow$ 1,3-diphenylpropyne (phenylbenzylacetylene)
   (*b*) 1-butene $\longrightarrow$ 1-butyne
   (*c*) acetylene-$d_2$ $\longrightarrow$ acetaldehyde-$d_4$
   (*e*) cyclobutylcyclopentylacetylene $\longrightarrow$ 1-cyclobutyl-2-cyclopentylethane
   (*f*) ethyl bromide (bromoethane) $\longrightarrow$ phenylacetylene-1-$d_1$
   (*i*) 3,3-dibromo-2,2,5,5-tetramethylhexane $\longrightarrow$ di-*tert*-butylacetylene

4. (*a*)

$$CaCO_3 \xrightarrow{\Delta} CaO \xrightarrow[\Delta]{C} CaC_2 \xrightarrow{H_2O} H{-}C{\equiv}C{-}H \xrightarrow{CuCl_2}$$

$$H{-}C{\equiv}C{-}CH{=}CH_2 \xrightarrow[H_2SO_4]{H_2O,\,Hg^{++}} CH_3{-}\overset{\overset{\displaystyle O}{\|}}{C}{-}CH{=}CH_2$$

(*b*)

$$H{-}C{\equiv}C{-}CH{=}CH_2\text{ (from a)} \xrightarrow{HCl} H_2C{=}C(Cl){-}CH{=}CH_2 \xrightarrow{Br_2}$$

$$CH_2(Br){-}C(Cl){=}CH{-}CH_2(Br)$$

5. A = 2-bromo-4-phenyl-1-butene or 2-bromo-3-phenyl-1-butene, B = 1,1-dibromo-4-phenylbutane or 1,1-dibromo-3-phenylbutene, C = 4-phenylbutyne or 3-phenylbutyne.

**7.** X = (cyclohexylidene)$=C(C_6H_5)-C{\equiv}CH$

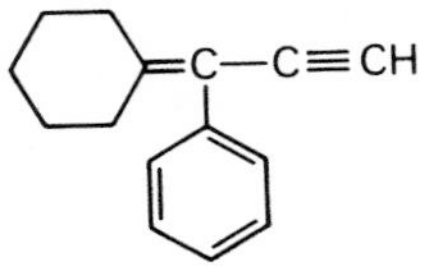

CHAPTER 6

**1.** The tar could be a product of 1,4-polymerization of the product, 1,3-cyclohexadiene, or of a 1,2-polymerization of the intermediate, 3-bromocyclohexene.

**2.** (*a*) [structure: 4-methyl-4-cyclohexene-1,2-dicarboxylic anhydride; $H_3C$, O, C, O, C, O] (*b*) [structure: octahydronaphthalene-1,2-dicarboxylic anhydride; O, C, O, C, O]

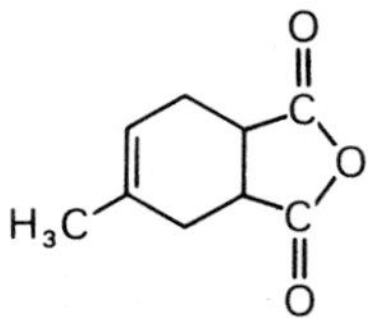

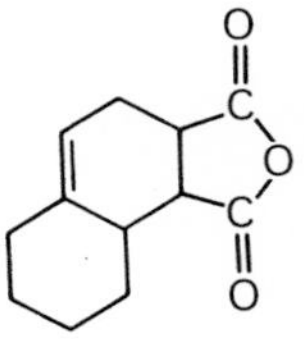

(*d*) [structure; $O{=}C$, O, $C{=}O$]

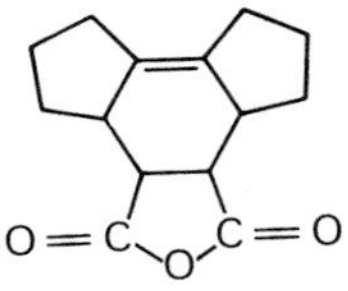

CHAPTER 7

**1.** expected = 32.8 + 48.9 = 81.7; found = 77.5, stabilization equals 81.7 − 77.5 = 4.2 kcal/mole

**3.** 9,10-dibromoanthracene

**5.** (*a*) (*i*) ⟶ ***meta***-sulfonic acid; (*ii*) ⟶ ortho, para isomers.
***Resonance***: (*i*) meta (electron withdrawing; deactivator, slower than benzene); (*ii*) *o*, *p*-(electron donation of unshared pair on nitrogen, activator, faster than benzene).
***Inductive***: (*i*) withdraws ( $>\overset{}{\underset{+}{C}}-\underline{O}$); (*ii*) nitrogen more electronegative than carbon. Write the aronium ion intermediate resonance structures for each.

(*c*) (*i*) 4-bromo-*o*-xylene; (*ii*) 4-bromo-*m*-xylene; (*iii*) 2-bromo-*p*-xylene (only possible ring monosubstitution product). Note steric effect at $C_3$ in (*i*) and at $C_2$ in (*ii*). All of these compounds react faster than benzene because $CH_3$— donates electrons.

(*f*) $CH_3-C_6H_4-CO-CH_2-CH_2-COOH$ faster than benzene, note steric effect at $C_2$ of starting material.

7. 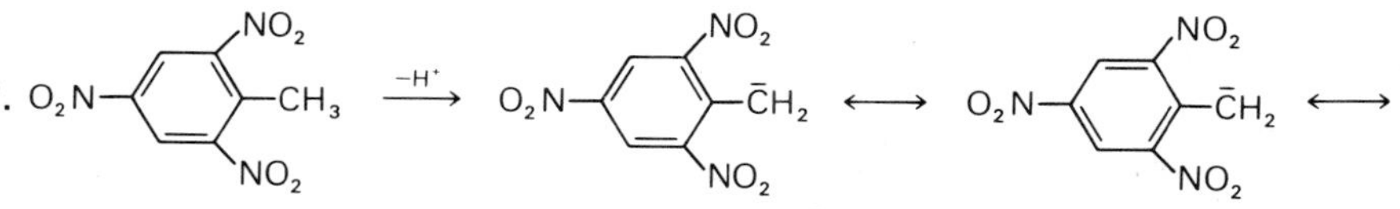 $O_2N$–(2,6-dinitro-4-... ring)–$CH_3$ $\xrightarrow{-H^+}$ $O_2N$–(ring, $NO_2$, $NO_2$)–$\bar{C}H_2$ $\longleftrightarrow$ $O_2N$–(ring, $NO_2$, $NO_2$)–$\bar{C}H_2$ $\longleftrightarrow$

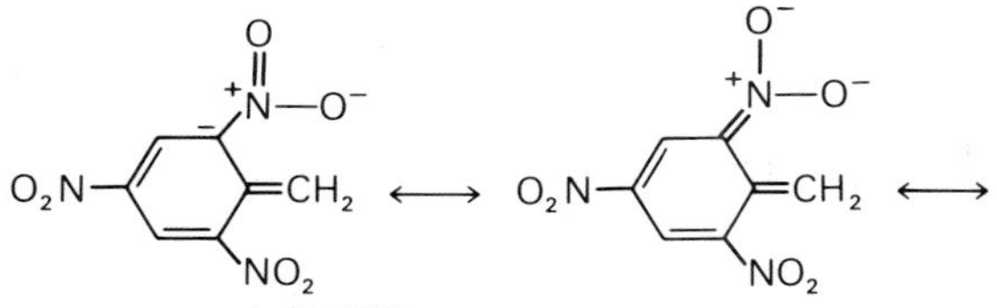

$O_2N$–(ring)$=CH_2$ with $^{+}N(=O)-O^-$ and $NO_2$ $\longleftrightarrow$ $O_2N$–(ring)$=CH_2$ with $^{+}N(-O^-)-O^-$ and $NO_2$ $\longleftrightarrow$ and other resonance structures involving the $-NO_2$ groups

8. (*a*) benzene $\xrightarrow[\text{1.1 equiv. } AlCl_3 \text{ in } CS_2\text{, then } H^+ \quad 2.\ Br_2/FeBr_3]{1.\ CH_3COCl}$

(*b*) benzene $\xrightarrow[2.\ CH_3COCl \quad \text{1.1 equiv. } AlCl_3 \text{ in } CS_2\text{, then } H_3O^+]{1.\ Br_2/FeBr_3}$

(*d*) *o*-xylene $\xrightarrow[2.\ HNO_3\text{-}H_2SO_4]{1.\ Br_2/FeBr_3}$

(*f*) benzene $\xrightarrow[3.\ \text{separate isomers} \quad 4.\ Sn/HCl]{1.\ Cl_2/FeCl_3 \quad 2.\ HNO_3\text{-}H_2SO_4}$

## CHAPTER 8

1. There is generally more than one correct answer to each part.

(*a*) $C_6H_4(CH_3)$–$CH_2F$, *o*-methylbenzyl fluoride

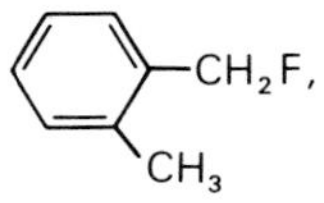

(*b*) $CH_3CH_2CH_2CH_2Cl$, *n*-butyl chloride (1-chlorobutane)

$(CH_3)_2CH-CH_2Cl$, isobutyl chloride (1-chloro-2-methylpropane)

(*c*) $C_6H_5$–Br, bromobenzene

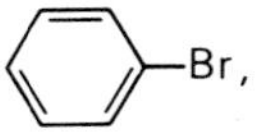

(*d*) ring with I, $H_3C$, $H_3C$, $CH_3$, $CH_2I$, 3,4,5-trimethyl-2-iodomethyliodobenzene

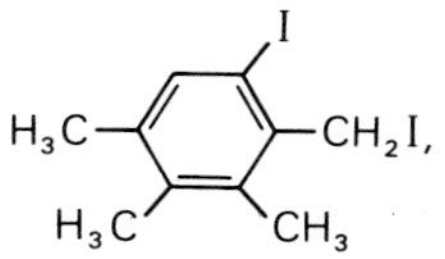

(*e*) $CH_3-CH(Br)-CH(Br)-CH_2CH_3$, 2,3-dibromopentane

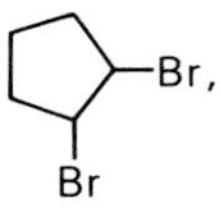

cyclopentane with Br, Br, 1,2-dibromocyclopentane

(*f*) $CH_3(CH_2)_8CF_3$, 1,1,1-trifluorodecane

(*g*) [cyclohexane ring with Cl and $CH_3$ on the same carbon], 1-chloro-1-methylcyclohexane

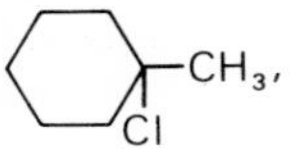

**2.** 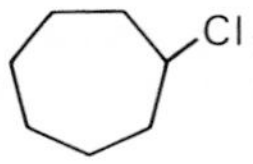 [cycloheptane ring with Cl], cycloheptyl chloride; [cyclohexane ring with $CH_3$ and adjacent Br], 2-bromo-1-methylcyclohexane;

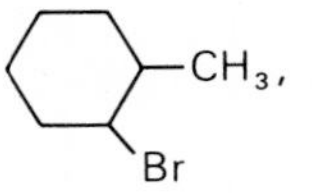

2-, 3-, or 4-haloheptane. The halide should be primary or secondary, but not vinylic, allylic, aromatic, or benzylic. Diagram should show a transition state as the point of highest energy.

**3.** $CH_2{=}CH{-}CH_2{-}Br$, allyl bromide. Diagram should show a small valley at the highest energy since a discrete intermediate, the allyl carbonium ion, is involved.

**4.** (*a*) $NH_3 + O_2N{-}C_6H_3(NO_2){-}F \longrightarrow O_2N{-}C_6H_3(NO_2){-}NH_2$

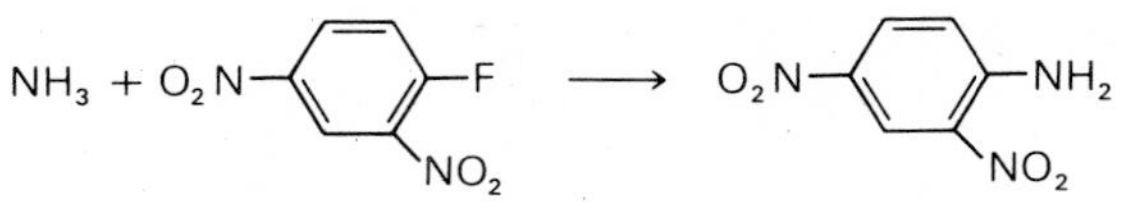

(*c*) Generally $S_N1$ reactions will show a greater solvent effect in their rate of solvolysis; thus, tertiary, allylic or a benzylic halide would react faster in acetone, since it is the more polar solvent.

(*g*) $Cl_2 + C_6H_5{-}CH_3 \xrightarrow{\text{light}} C_6H_5{-}CH_2Cl$, benzyl chloride

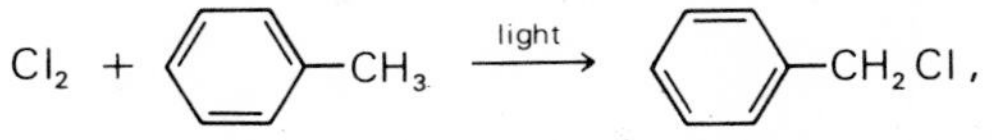

(*i*) $(CH_3)_3C{-}F$, *t*-butyl fluoride

(*k*) $CH_3O^- + CH_3CH_2I \longrightarrow CH_3OCH_2CH_3$, methyl ethyl ether

**5.** The low-temperature bromination in a polar solvent gives rise to $Br^+$, which then adds (with $Br^-$) to the double bond. The high temperature treatment, in the gas phase generates Br•, which abstracts a H• from the allylic position, giving rise to a substitution reaction.

**6.** (*a*) cyclohexene $\longrightarrow$ ***trans***-1,2-dibromocyclohexane (diequatorial), electrophilic addition of $Br_2$ to double bond

(*b*) bromocyclohexane $\longrightarrow$ cyclohexanol, $S_N2$

(*c*) bromocyclohexane $\longrightarrow$ cyclohexene, $E_2$

(*d*) ***Hint***: HOBr produced here, which adds to the double bond

(*e*) 1,2-dimethylcyclohexene $\longrightarrow$ 3-bromo-1,2-dimethylcyclohexene, free-radical substitution

(*k*) N.R.

(*n*) produces the benzyne intermediate which, in the absence of another acceptor, reacts with itself affording diphenylene

(*t*) N.R. (*u*) N.R.

## CHAPTER 9

**1.** Only a few examples are given. It is important to note that the starting materials given are more restrictive than those which are commercially available in order to provide practice in writing organic transformations. In fact, many of these heptanols are commercially available.

(*i*) $CH_3CH_2CH_2CH_2CH_2CH(OH){-}CH_3$; 2-heptanol; secondary alcohol

$$CH_3CH_2CHO \xrightarrow[\text{4. ethylene oxide; 5. } H_3O^+\text{; hydrolysis; 6. HBr; } H^+]{\text{1. } NaBH_4\text{; 2. HBr; } H^+\text{; 3. Mg in dry ether}} CH_3CH_2CH_2CH_2CH_2Br \xrightarrow[\text{3. } H_3O^+\text{; hydrolysis}]{\text{1. Mg in dry ether; 2. acetaldehyde}}$$

(*ii*) $(CH_3)_3C{-}CH_2CH_2CH_2OH$; 4,4-dimethyl-1-pentanol; primary

$$CH_2O \xrightarrow[\text{3. Mg in dry ether; 4. } CH_3CHO\text{; 5. } H_3O^+\text{, hydrolysis}]{\text{1. } NaBH_4\text{; 2. HI, } H^+} CH_3{-}CH(OH){-}CH_3 \xrightarrow[\text{or } CrO_3]{KMnO_4} CH_3{-}C(=O){-}CH_3 \xrightarrow[\text{2. } NH_4Cl\text{-}H_2O]{\text{1 } [CH_3MgI]}$$

$$(CH_3)_3C{-}OH \xrightarrow[\text{3. ethylene oxide; 4. } H_3O^+]{\text{1. HBr; 2. Mg in dry ether}} (CH_3)_3C{-}CH_2CH_2OH \xrightarrow[\text{3. formaldehyde; 4. } H_2O\text{, hydrolysis}]{\text{1. HBr, } H^+\text{; 2. Mg in dry ether}}$$

(*iii*) $CH_3CH_2CH_2{-}CH(OH){-}CH_2CH_2CH_3$; 4-heptanol; secondary

$$CH_3CH_2CHO \xrightarrow[\text{3. Mg in dry ether; 4. methyl formate}]{\text{1. } NaBH_4\text{; 2. } PBr_3}$$

$$CH_2O \xrightarrow{NaBH_4} CH_3OH \xrightarrow{HCOOH,\ H^+} \text{methyl formate}$$

$$CH_2O \xrightarrow{CrO_3} HCOOH \quad \text{(overoxidation possible)}$$

**2.** (*b*)

$$C_6H_5CH_3 \xrightarrow[h\nu]{Br_2} C_6H_5CH_2Br \xrightarrow[\text{very dilute conditions}]{\text{Mg in ether}}$$

$$[C_6H_5CH_2MgBr] \xrightarrow[\text{2. } H_2O]{\text{1. ethylene oxide}} C_6H_5CH_2CH_2CH_2OH \xrightarrow[\text{2. } D_2/Pt]{\text{1. } Al_2O_3,\ \Delta}$$

(*c*)

$$[C_6H_5CH_2MgBr] + C_6H_5CHO \xrightarrow[H_2O]{\text{then}} \text{product}$$

from part (*b*)

$C_6H_5CH_3 \xrightarrow{CrO_3}$ benzaldehyde (caution, overoxidation with $CrO_3$ possible)

$C_6H_5CH_3 \xrightarrow[h\nu]{2Cl_2} C_6H_5CHCl_2 \xrightarrow{H_2O}$ benzaldehyde

**3.** (*a*) N.R., aryl chlorides do not react readily in ether
(*b*) $(CH_3CH_2CH_2)_2C(OH)CH_2CH_3$ (*d*) $CH_3CH_2—CO—CH_3$
(*e*) benzaldehyde (*f*) $CH_3CH_2O^-Na^+$, sodium ethoxide
(*g*) $(CH_3)_2C{=}CH_2 + CH_3CH_2OH + NaBr$
(*i*) benzyl iodide (*m*) 1-pentanol

**4.** $C_{12}H_{16}$ is cyclohexylbenzene, $C_{12}H_{16}O$ is 1-phenylcyclohexanol, $C_{12}H_{12}$ is 2-phenyl-1,3-cyclohexadiene, $C_{12}H_{10}$ is diphenyl.

**5.** Compound A is 3,3-dimethyl-1,5-(or 1,4- or 2,4-) pentandiol.

**6.** (*a*) $CH_3CH(OH)CH_3 \xrightarrow{CrO_3} CH_3COCH_3$

$CH_3CH_2CH(OH)CH_3 \xrightarrow[\text{3. acetone; 4. } H_3O^+]{\text{1. } PBr_3\text{; 2. Mg in dry ether}}$

(*c*) $(CH_3)_2CHCH_2OH \xrightarrow[\text{3. acetone-see (a); 4. } H^+\text{; }\Delta\text{-dehydration; 5. } H_2/Pt]{\text{1. HBr, } H^+\text{; 2. Mg in dry ether}}$

## CHAPTER 10

**1.** (*a*) N.R., bicarbonate is not a sufficiently strong base to react with the phenolic hydrogen
(*c*) N.R., phenols are generally nitrosated (—N=O) under these conditions but the ortho and para positions are blocked here
(*d*) N.R., phenols, unlike alcohols, cannot be converted to esters by treatment with a carboxylic acid and a mineral acid
(*g*) 2-naphthol (*h*) 2,5-dimethylanisole

**2.** (*a*) The phenol will dissolve in NaOH (others will not), the phenol and styrene will decolorize $KMnO_4$ (anisole will not). Note that all 3 will react fairly readily with $Br_2/CCl_4$.
(*b*) Acid will dissolve in $NaHCO_3$, acid and phenol will dissolve in NaOH, benzyl alcohol is not acidic.

**3.** (*b*) toluene $\xrightarrow[\text{2. separate } p\text{-isomer; 3. KOH fusion}]{\text{1. } H_2SO_4}$

(*d*) benzene $\xrightarrow[\text{4. } H_3O^+\text{; }\Delta\text{; 5. NaOH; 6. } n\text{-butyl bromide}]{\text{1. } HNO_3\text{-}H_2SO_4\text{; 2. Sn/HCl; 3. HCl-}NaNO_2 \text{ at } 0°}$

$CH_3CH_2CH_2CHO \xrightarrow[\text{2. HBr; } H^+]{\text{1. } NaBH_4}$

## CHAPTER 11

**1.** (*a*) *para*-bromoanisole
(*c*) *tert*-butyl cyclohexyl ether, *tert*-butoxycyclohexane
(*d*) tetrahydropyran
(*f*) $\beta$-methoxynaphthalene, methyl 2-naphthyl ether

**3.** (*c*) $NBS + H_2O \longrightarrow HOBr \rightleftharpoons Br^+ HO^-$

Anisole undergoes electrophilic aromatic substitution by $Br^+$ in the para position.

**4.** $\left[ C_6H_5\text{—}\ddot{O}\text{—}CH_2\text{—}\bar{C}H_2\overset{+}{M}gBr \right] \longrightarrow C_6H_5\text{—}O^- \overset{+}{M}gBr + CH_2{=}CH_2 \xrightarrow{H_2O}$ products

## CHAPTER 12

**1.**

| Compound | Total possible number of stereoisomers | Number of optically active forms | Comment |
|---|---|---|---|
| (*a*) | 8 | 8 | 4 D,L pairs |
| | | | rings *cis*-OH up |
| | | | rings *cis*-OH down |
| | | | rings *trans*-OH down |
| | | | rings *trans*-OH up |
| (*c*) | 2 | 0 | *cis* and *trans* |
| (*d*) | none | 0 | |
| (*f*) | 2 | 2 | one D,L pair |
| (*g*) | 8 | 8 | D,L-*cis-cis* |
| | | | D,L-*cis-trans* |
| | | | D,L-*trans-trans* |
| | | | D,L-*trans-cis* |
| (*l*) | 2 | 2 | one D,L pair |
| (*m*) | $2^7$ | $2^7$ | 7 different asymmetric carbons |
| (*o*) | 2 | 2 | one D,L pair (restricted rotation) |
| (*p*) | none | | no restricted rotation |

**2.** (*a*) Same as (*o*) above (*b*) unsymmetrically substituted allene
(*d*) no ammonialike inversion possible at the nitrogen atom
(*e*) *cis*-cyclooctene is inactive, ***trans***-isomer exists as a D,L pair

**3.** (*a*) ammonialike inversion (*b*) no restricted rotation
(*c*) cis-trans isomers, but none optically active
(*d*) each isomer has an element of symmetry
(*e*) contains an element of symmetry

**4.** See Chap. 18.

## CHAPTER 13: PROBLEM SET II

**1.** (*a*) $\alpha$-naphthaldehyde $\longrightarrow$ $\alpha$-naphthoic acid + 1-hydroxymethylnaphthalene
(*b*) terephthaldehyde $\longrightarrow$ *p*-divinylbenzene
(*c*) phenyl $\beta$-naphthyl ketone $\longrightarrow$ phenyl $\beta$-naphthyl ketone phenylhydrazone $\longrightarrow$ 2-benzylnaphthalene
(*d*) $\alpha$-naphthaldehyde via HMTA
(*g*) methyl cyclohexyl ketone $\longrightarrow$ cyclohexylacetylene
(*i*) 1-(3-bromophenyl)-1-bromoethane

**2.** (*c*) *m*-methylbenzaldehyde $\longrightarrow$ formic acid + *m*-methylbenzyl alcohol
(*e*) 2,5-hexandione $\longrightarrow$ hexane
(*h*) mixture of four products
(*k*) N.R., —$NO_2$ groups deactivate toward Friedel-Crafts reactions
(*l*) *p*-bromophenylhydrazine + 3-cyclobutyl-6-phenyl-2,5,8-nonatrione $\longrightarrow$ gives the tri-(or tris-)*p*-bromophenylhydrazone

**3.** (*a*) $C + CaO \xrightarrow{\Delta} CaC_2 \xrightarrow{H_2O} H{-}C{\equiv}C{-}H \xrightarrow[\substack{3.\ H_2O,\ Hg^{++}\ H_2SO_4 \\ 4.\ Al(Hg) \\ 5.\ H_2O}]{\substack{1.\ NaNH_2 \\ 2.\ CH_3I}}$

$$(CH_3)_2CH(OH)CH(OH)(CH_3)_2 \xrightarrow{H^+} CH_3COC(CH_3)_3 \xrightarrow[\substack{3.\ SOCl_2 \\ 4.\ H_2/Pd\text{-}C \\ S\ poison}]{\substack{1.\ X_2,\ NaOH \\ 2.\ H^+}} \text{product}$$

$$H{-}C{\equiv}C{-}H \xrightarrow[\substack{3.\ NaBH_4 \\ 4.\ HI}]{\substack{1.\ O_3 \\ 2.\ \text{reductive work-up}}} CH_3I$$

(*b*) phenol $\xrightarrow[\text{temp.; pressure}]{H_2/\text{cat}}$ cyclohexanol (cyclohexane ring—OH) $\xrightarrow{K_2Cr_2O_7}$ adipic acid $\xrightarrow[2.\ \Delta]{1.\ Ca(OH)_2}$

$$\text{cyclopentanone} \xrightarrow[\substack{2.\ H_2O \\ 3.\ H^+;\ \Delta;\ -H_2O}]{1.\ [CH_3MgI]} \text{product}$$

$$CH_3OH \xrightarrow[2.\ \text{Mg in dry ether}]{1.\ HI}$$

(*c*) toluene $\xrightarrow[\text{5. LiAlH}_4\text{ 6. H}_3\text{O}^+\text{ 7. HBr 8. Mg in dry ether 9. dry CdCl}_2]{\text{1. Br}_2/\text{FeBr}_3\text{ 2. separate }p\text{-isomer 3. KCN-Cu}_2(\text{CN})_2\text{ 4. H}_3\text{O}^+\text{ (gives }p\text{-toluic acid)}}$ $[CH_3-C_6H_4-CH_2]_2Cd$

Use steps 1 to 4 to obtain *ortho*-toluic acid, convert to acid chloride with $SOCl_2$ and treat with Cd reagent.

(*d*) benzene $\xrightarrow[\text{2. }\Delta\text{; Cu}]{\text{1. Br}_2/\text{FeBr}_3}$ $C_6H_5-C_6H_5$ $\xrightarrow[\text{3. Zn(Hg)-HCl (to reduce ketone) 4. SOCl}_2\text{ 5. H}_2/\text{Pd-on-C, S poison 6. H}_2\text{N-NH}_2]{\text{1. succinic anhydride (from }\Delta\text{ acid) 2.1 equiv AlCl}_3\text{ in C}_6\text{H}_5\text{NO}_2\text{ 2. H}_3\text{O}^+}$

(*e*) $H-C\equiv C-H \xrightarrow[H_2SO_4]{H_2O,\ Hg^{++}} CH_3CHO \xrightarrow[\text{and a crossed Cannizzaro}]{H_2CO(xs),\ OH^-\text{ 3 aldol cond.}} C(CH_2OH)_4 \xrightarrow[\text{2. Zn}]{\text{1. HBr; H}^+}$

**4.** pinacolone formed by methyl rearrangement of $(CH_3)_2C(OH)-\overset{+}{C}(CH_3)_2$, followed by loss of a proton

**5.** $CH_3-\underset{\underset{O}{\|}}{C}-CH_2-CH_2-CH_2Cl \longrightarrow [CH_3-CO-\bar{C}H-CH_2-CH_2-Cl]$

↓

product

## CHAPTER 14

**2.** (*a*) Prepare methylmalonic ester from propionic acid (Sec. 14-12)

$$CH_3-CH(COOEt)_2 \xrightarrow[\text{3. NaOH 4. H}^+\text{ 5. }\Delta\text{; -CO}_2]{\text{1. NaOEt 2. CH}_3\text{CH}_2\text{CH}_2\text{Br}} CH_3CH_2CH_2CH(CH_3)COOH \xrightarrow[\text{2. NH}_3]{\text{1. SOCl}_2}$$

(*b*) $$CH_2(COOEt)_2 \xrightarrow[\text{3. NaOEt 4. CH}_3\text{CH}_2\text{Br}]{\text{1. NaOEt 2. CH}_3\text{CH}_2\text{CH}_2\text{Br}} CH_3CH_2CH_2(CH_3CH_2)C(COOEt)_2 \xrightarrow[\text{3. }\Delta\text{; -CO}_2\text{ 4. }\Delta\text{; Ac}_2\text{O}]{\text{1. NaOH 2. H}^+}$$

(*e*) $$CH_3COCH_2COOEt \xrightarrow[\text{3. NaOH 4. H}^+\text{ 5. }\Delta\text{; -CO}_2]{\text{1. NaOEt 2. CH}_3\text{CH}_2\text{Br}} CH_3COCH_2CH_2CH_3 \xrightarrow{C_6H_5NHNH_2}$$

(*g*) Prepare *para*-toluylmalonic ester from $p$-$CH_3-C_6H_4-CH_2COOEt$ (see Sec. 14-12), which can then be alkylated with $\alpha$-bromo-$p$-xylene (and the product subsequently hydrolyzed and decarboxylated).

**3.** (*a*) Carboxylic acids are stronger than phenols (the $CH_3O$— group donates electrons to the ring and increases the O—H bond strength), which are stronger than alcohols.
(*b*) Inductive effects fall off rapidly as —Cl is removed from —COOH.
(*c*) —CN groups withdraw electrons (double bond aids transmission), the unsubstituted compound is the reference, the —$CH_3$ groups donate electrons to the O—H bond.

**4.** (*d*) $CH_3(CH_2)_4CH(CONH_2)_2$, *n*-pentylmalonamide
(*f*) $C_6H_5(CH_2)_3C(CH_2CH_2CH_2CH_3)COOCH_3$, 3-cyano-3-carbomethoxy-1-
CN
phenyloctane or methyl 2-*n*-butyl-2-cyano-5-phenylpentanoate
(*h*) 2-*n*-butyl-5-phenylpentanoic acid
(*k*) N.R., steric hindrance
(*n*) phenylacetamide
(*q*) 2,6-dichlorobenzoic acid
(*r*) 4,5-dimethyl-1-naphthoic acid
(*s*) 3,5-dimethylbenzonitrile

## CHAPTER 15

**1.** (*b*) $CH_3(CH_2)_4COO(CH_2)_5CH_3$
(*d*) 2-phenylethyl *p*-toluate
(*f*) methyl pentamethylbenzoate
(*i*) toluyl chloride (*o*-, *m*-, or *p*-)
(*l*) $CH_3CH_2CH_2CH(CH_3)CH_2COCl$
(*n*) COBr, Br, Br

**2.** (*b*) 4-nitrophthalic anhydride
(*d*) $CH_3CH_2CH_2$— —CO—O—CO—$CH_2CH_3$
(*g*) *para*-chloroacetanilide
(*h*) *N*-chloroacetanilide
(*j*) 4,5-dichlorophthalamide
(*m*) $CH_3$, $H_3C$—C—$CONH_2$, $CONH_2$

**3.** (*a*) propanimide
(*c*) 4,*N*-dimethylphthalimide
(*e*) NC— —$CH_2CN$
(*g*) $CH_3(CH_2)_5CO$—NH—CO—$(CH_2)_5CH_3$

**4.** (*a*) *n*-butyl phenylacetate
(*d*) methyl cyclopentylcarboxylate
(*g*) methyl 1-methyl-7-chloro-2-naphthoate
(*k*) acetic benzoic anhydride
(*n*) *N*-methylisobutyramide

**5.** (*a*) —COOH sterically hindered
(*b*) Phenols do not undergo Fischer esterification
(*c*) Acids + $NH_3$ $\longrightarrow$ ammonium salts which, on ***heating***, give amides.
(*d*) Acid must be used to stop at the amide stage.
(*e*) Aryl halides do not undergo $S_N1$ or $S_N2$ reactions.

**6.** (*a*) Succinoylate naphthalene in the $\alpha$ position, reduce ketone, cyclize to $\beta$-, use $C_6H_5MgBr$, etc.
(*b*) Succinoylate naphthalene in $\alpha$ position, use xs$CH_3MgI$, close on $\beta$, etc.
(*c*) Succinoylate benzene, reduce ketone, close, treat with 1 equiv $CH_3MgI$, etc.
(*d*) Try double succinoylation of naphthalene in 1- and the 5- positions etc. For steric reasons, it is unlikely that the 1,8-positions will be succinoylated.

## CHAPTER 16

**1.** (*a*) Aryl halides without electron-withdrawing groups in the ortho or para position are not displaced by ammonia; reduction of nitrobenzene.
(*b*) A mixture of amines will result.

$C_6H_5$—$CH_2COCl$ + $C_6H_5$—$CH_2CH_2NH_2$, then reduction of the amide

(*d*) —$NH_2$ is ortho, para director. Brominate $C_6H_5NO_2$, then reduce.
(*f*) A mixture, containing some diamino compound, will result; use ammonium polysulfide
(*h*) A mixture will result; use $C_6H_5N_2^+$ + $C_6H_5CH_3$ $\xrightarrow[NaOH]{Cu}$

**2.** (*b*) *n*-propylamine, ammonia, *para*-toluidine triphenylamine, acetamide (neutral), acetimide (acidic)
(*c*) *ortho*-toluidine, *para*-methylbenzyl alcohol, *ortho*-cresol (a phenol), phthalimide, *ortho*-methylbenzoic acid

**3.** (*b*) *para*-methylbenzyl bromide $\longrightarrow$ *para*-methylbenzylamine, $S_N2$
(*d*) hexanamide $\longrightarrow$ 1-aminopentane (*n*-pentylamine), rearrangement involving an electron deficient nitrogen atom
(*e*) dimethylethyl-3-butenylammonium hydroxide $\longrightarrow$ $H_2O$ + 1,3-butadiene + dimethylethylamine; $E_2$
(*g*) benzenesulfonyl chloride + isobutylamine $\longrightarrow$ isobutylamine benzenesulfonamide; attack of the unshared pair of electrons of nitrogen on S atom.

# Index

# Periodic table of the elements

| I | II | | | | | | | |
|---|---|---|---|---|---|---|---|---|
| 1<br>H<br>1.00797 | | | | | | | | |
| 3<br>Li<br>6.939 | 4<br>Be<br>9.0122 | | | | | | | |
| 11<br>Na<br>22.9898 | 12<br>Mg<br>24.312 | | | | | | | |
| 19<br>K<br>39.102 | 20<br>Ca<br>40.08 | 21<br>Sc<br>44.956 | | 22<br>Ti<br>47.90 | 23<br>V<br>50.942 | 24<br>Cr<br>51.996 | 25<br>Mn<br>54.9380 | 26<br>Fe<br>55.847 |
| 37<br>Rb<br>85.47 | 38<br>Sr<br>87.62 | 39<br>Y<br>88.905 | | 40<br>Zr<br>91.22 | 41<br>Nb<br>92.906 | 42<br>Mo<br>95.94 | 43<br>Tc<br>(99) | 44<br>Ru<br>101.07 |
| 55<br>Cs<br>132.905 | 56<br>Ba<br>137.34 | 57<br>La<br>138.91 | 58<br>to<br>71 | 72<br>Hf<br>178.49 | 73<br>Ta<br>180.948 | 74<br>W<br>183.85 | 75<br>Re<br>186.2 | 76<br>Os<br>190.2 |
| 87<br>Fr<br>(223) | 88<br>Ra<br>(226) | 89<br>Ac<br>(227) | 90<br>to<br>103 | | | | | |

| | | | | |
|---|---|---|---|---|
| LANTHANIDES | 58<br>Ce<br>140.12 | 59<br>Pr<br>140.907 | 60<br>Nd<br>144.24 | 61<br>Pm<br>(147) |
| ACTINIDES | 90<br>Th<br>232.038 | 91<br>Pa<br>(231) | 92<br>U<br>238.03 | 93<br>Np<br>(237) |

Values in parentheses are atomic masses of longest-lived or best-known isotopes.